Selected Readings in the
History of Physiology

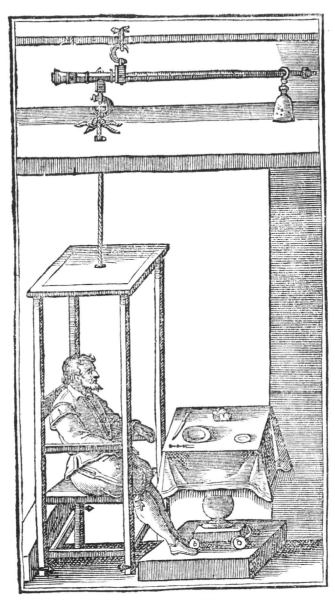

FRONTISPIECE. The weighing chair of Santorio Santorio, taken from his *Commentaria in primam fen primi libri canonis Avicennae*, Venice, 1625, col. 557.

Selected Readings in the History of Physiology

COMPILED BY

John F. Fulton, M.D., D.PHIL.

Late Sterling Professor of the History of Medicine
Formerly Sterling Professor of Physiology
Yale University

COMPLETED BY

Leonard G. Wilson, PH.D.

Associate Professor of the History of Medicine
Yale University

SECOND EDITION · REVISED, ENLARGED, AND RESET

CHARLES C THOMAS · PUBLISHER

SPRINGFIELD · ILLINOIS · U.S.A.

Published and Distributed Throughout the World by
CHARLES C THOMAS · PUBLISHER
BANNERSTONE HOUSE
301-327 East Lawrence Avenue, Springfield, Illinois, U.S.A.
NATCHEZ PLANTATION HOUSE
735 North Atlantic Boulevard, Fort Lauderdale, Florida, U.S.A.

First Edition, 1930
Second Edition, 1966

With THOMAS BOOKS careful attention is given to all details of manufacturing and design. It is the Publisher's desire to present books that are satisfactory as to their physical qualities and artistic possibilities and appropriate for their particular use. THOMAS BOOKS will be true to those laws of quality that assure a good name and good will.

Printed in the United States of America
B-7

To
Lucia Pickering Fulton

Table of Contents

· vii ·

List of Illustrations

Linecuts

Preface to Second Edition

During the long months of the particularly severe and snowy winter of 1957-58 John Fulton was in rural New Hampshire slowly making his way back to health after a severe illness. To take his mind away from the frustrations of this enforced rest he turned to the revision of his *Selected Readings in Physiology* which had long been out of print. He labored under circumstances far different from those to which he was accustomed, and the greatest handicap was the distance from his library and the difficulties involved in securing from New Haven the hundreds of books and journals needed.

Nevertheless, more than half of the manuscript was in an advanced state when Dr. Fulton resumed active work at Yale in the autumn of 1958. At the urging of friends he had written a brief account of his early experiences in collecting the books on which this volume is largely based. He had roughly blocked out the chapters being added to this edition, had written some of the head notes and chosen some of the selections, but the real work of completing these chapters he had left until he was back at the Library with the books close at hand.

Return to his desk, however, brought duties and demands which occupied much of his time. He was also most eager to bring out a second edition of his bibliography of Robert Boyle in time for the three hundredth anniversary of the founding of the Royal Society in 1960, so the manuscript of the *Readings* was laid aside. When Madeline Stanton and I, whom he had charged with the responsibility of his papers after he died, collected the material from his house, we found with it a copy of *Harper's Magazine* containing an article which had much interested him—a discourse partly on the duties and devotion of the vestal virgins[1]—and we read it anew, meditating meanwhile on the significance of its reappearance. But more than devotion was needed to complete the manuscript.

Dr. Fulton had been looking forward with keen anticipation to

[1] Bowen, Elizabeth. "The virgins and the empress." *Harper's Magazine*, 1959, **219**, 50-55.

association with Leonard G. Wilson, whose work in the history of physiology he had been following for several years and with whom he hoped to work on the *Readings* when Dr. Wilson joined the Department in July of 1960. But John Fulton died on 29 May 1960, and the task of completing the book has fallen to Leonard Wilson alone. He has followed as closely as possible Dr. Fulton's plan wherever it was clear, but in the later chapters has had to guess the intent in some areas and to make choices which seemed to fit into the general scheme. He has had the valuable help and advice in several chapters, particularly Chapter VIII, of one of Dr. Fulton's students, Robert J. T. Joy (Major, U.S. Army; M.D. Yale 1954). Dr. Joy has maintained an interest in the history of medicine fostered during his student years, and his generous contribution to the revision has been made not only out of his great admiration for Dr. Fulton, but from genuine enthusiasm for the subject. Dr. Gertrude van Wagenen kindly read certain chapters and made a number of valuable suggestions.

In the early stages of the revision Dr. Fulton had helpful letters from Drs. Paul MacLean, Harold Lamport, Hallowell Davis, and Sir John Eccles, and also advice, which he much appreciated, from a number of former Fellows and faculty of the Laboratory of Physiology, particularly Dr. William C. Gibson and Dr. Donald H. Barron who has also assisted the later editors. In the typing of the manuscript and checking selections against original texts, the following have assisted over the span of six years: in New Hampshire, Margaret Abbott, Barbara Long Simons, and Marlene Nelson; in New Haven, Prudence Fairbrother Meehan, Imogene C. Coleman, Elizabeth C. Sullivan, and Elizabeth C. Musgrave.

A most important contribution has been made by Madeline E. Stanton. Her intimate knowledge of the Library and her editorial reading of the manuscript have been very helpful, but her most substantial contribution has been the gathering together, sometimes from far afield, of the illustrative material, all of which has been redone.

The publication of the book has been in the hands of old friends, the house of Charles C Thomas. Mr. Thomas, whose association with Dr. Fulton began with the publication (by Williams and Wilkins) of his first book, *Muscular Contraction and the Reflex Control of Movement,* in 1926, and later his son Payne and associate, Mr. Warren Green, have given every encouragement during the long period the book has been under revision. The design and printing have been in the capable hands of the George Banta Company, Inc. whose designer, Mr. Reinhold F. Gehner, worked with Dr. Fulton on several publications over the years, notably the *Journal of Neurophysiology* and his biography of Harvey Cushing. The illustrations have been done by the Meriden Gravure Company, whose Director, Mr. Harold Hugo, and Manager, Mr. John F. Peckham, still give to their every production the personal attention, care, and artistry which so enhanced the work of the scholar-printers of times long past.

We also welcome this opportunity to acknowledge the great debt we all owe to Lucia Fulton who has shared in the work from first to last, physically, financially, and especially spiritually. The time-honored phrase "without whose help this book could not have been written" was never more apt.

We have done the utmost within our capacities to make this final book of John Fulton's meet his own exacting standards. We have no doubt that his learning and wide knowledge of the field would have reduced to a minimum the points which reviewers may notice. Such a book as this cannot be a history, or cover all the advances on every front of a rapidly expanding field. And even though undertaken with the advice of experts, it must in the last analysis be interpreted as one physiologist's view and judgment of the events which will withstand the test of time. If students can find in it some measure of inspiration and encouragement from the gropings toward truth of their peers and some knowledge of the richness of their heritage, then I believe John Fulton would feel he had achieved his purpose.

ELIZABETH H. THOMSON

In making selections for the second edition of these *Readings* Dr. Fulton was faced with the fact that the increase in the number of chapters from eight to twelve and the addition of selections to the original chapters make this a large instead of a moderate-sized book. Since it was Dr. Fulton's hope that it would be read by students of medicine and physiology, he tried to limit the length by keeping the selections brief while at the same time including those which would suggest the main developments in each area of physiology covered.

The source of each passage is given at the end of the selection.

We have retained only those footnotes from the original work which seemed essential, and they are indicated by asterisks. The numbered footnotes are our own.

At the suggestion of Dr. Robert Joy we included several selections on the physiology of temperature regulation. We have linked these with selections on the concept of the internal environment and homeostasis to make Chapter VIII which thus introduces the succeeding chapters on the kidney, sexual generation, and endocrinology, each of which reflects particular aspects of the maintenance of constant internal conditions.

Though we may have executed it imperfectly, the vision of physiology which Dr. Fulton had embodied in his plan for this book was singularly large-minded. It has been a privilege to carry his work to completion. I could not have done so without the fullest collaboration of Miss Elizabeth Thomson and Miss Madeline Stanton who had been Dr. Fulton's associates and co-workers. Whatever this book possesses of accuracy, consistency, and literary quality is largely owing to them. Where I have used the pronoun "we," I have had them in mind. On the other hand, I must take responsibility for whatever errors of judgment or failures of knowledge exist in the book. Miss Thomson has already mentioned those who have helped in different ways with its preparation. To all of them I wish to add my own grateful thanks.

LEONARD G. WILSON

Yale University School of Medicine
New Haven, Connecticut

Preface to First Edition

Long's attractive *Readings in Pathology*[1] which was published in 1929, suggested to me that a similar volume of physiological readings might prove acceptable. My qualifications for editing such a work are meagre enough, but the problem of selection was to some extent simplified by having at hand many of the necessary texts. For several years I have collected books relating to the history of physiology, and at odd times I have tried to follow Osler's practice of placing slips beside passages which have exerted a great influence upon the development of physiological thought. Such passages —especially those which describe an important discovery—have a peculiar fascination for many people, and they often prove a great stimulus to those who are entering upon the study of science. In many places where physiology is taught, contact with the original sources is necessarily infrequent, and a pupil's outlook tends to be confined to second-hand knowledge obtained from lectures and textbooks. For many reasons it is desirable that a medical student be conducted early in his career to the front-line trenches of medical and physiological discovery. Let him realize that men as young as himself have made important contributions: that de Graaf at 23 years of age devised the first pancreatic fistula: that Helmholtz at 24 measured for the first time the heat production of frog muscle; that Johannes Müller at 25 had enunciated the principle of specific nerve energies. Let him discover that simple facts were once hidden in a fog of faulty observation and faulty reasoning, and that it was sometimes the enquiring minds of students like himself that made matters clear.

In order to preserve the sequence of ideas in the several fields of physiological thought, the material in this volume has been grouped in subjects:—*e.g.*, circulation, respiration, digestion, etc., each group arranged in chronological order. It must not be supposed, however, that such a collection of annotated readings represents in any sense a history of physiology; it is intended rather to resemble the 'source

[1] Long, E. R. *Selected readings in pathology from Hippocrates to Virchow*. Springfield, Illinois, Baltimore, Maryland, Charles C Thomas, xiv, 301 pp., 4 leaves, 1929.

book' of the professional historian, and as such cannot be expected to tell the continuous story of a given subject or period.

I shall not attempt here to justify my choice of readings; the reason for the inclusion of Lavoisier's discovery of oxygen is self-evident; with others a personal bias may have determined the choice, but this, I suppose, is inevitable. Occasionally an author is 'represented' because he exerted a great influence on physiology, though his discoveries may have been of little importance (*e.g.*, Haller). In a few instances selections are included from writers who preached doctrines found later to be false. Fabricius and Alexander Walker, though wrong, are more interesting than many who have been right; and to anyone who concerns himself with the psychology of discovery, Fabricius' book on the valves in the veins is one of the most remarkable documents in scientific history,—deserving incidentally to be reprinted in facsimile with translation. It is interesting primarily because it was wrong: he had accurately assembled the essential facts, the circulation lay before him, and yet he did not see it. Why did he fail? Probably for much the same reason that we fail now to make the great discoveries of to-morrow: the scientific background was absent which would have given him the aptitude to see. It is a curious and important fact that though Fabricius did not himself grasp the circulation, he undoubtedly sowed in the mind of his young English pupil the seeds that came to such rich fruition.

In dealing with modern literature it is often difficult to assign credit for a given discovery, and still more difficult to choose the passage which contains the description of an important contribution. Teamwork, healthy interchange of ideas between investigators, and many other factors associated with modern scientific work combine to prevent final judgment of priority. Similar difficulty is evidently experienced by the Nobel Committee if we may judge from the frequency in recent awards that the prize has been divided between two individuals working in the same field. Who, for example, was responsible for the discovery of the true nature of mountain sickness, or of the volume output of the heart? Coming to the endocrines the uncertainty, except for the paper of Oliver and Schäfer, is even greater, and in consequence I have made but few selections in this and similar fields in which I did not feel competent to pass judgment.

After the material had been collected several facts of interest emerged. Of the 65 selections of which information was available concerning the age of the author when the work was done, 11 were written between 20 and 30 years of age,—Mayow and de Graaf being 23, Arrhenius 24, and Helmholtz (Conservation of Energy), Blagden, Cannon and Herbert Mayo 26; 23 were written between the ages of 30 and 40 years, and the remaining 42 were written when their authors were over 40. Réaumur, for example, was actually 69 when he carried out his memorable observations upon the digestive juice of his pet kite.

The frequency with which far-reaching conclusions have been drawn from experiments upon human beings deserves also to be mentioned. I was unaware of this when starting to make the selections, and if asked beforehand I should have replied that, with a few notable exceptions, such as Beaumont's observations, the chief advances in physiology had come from animal experimentation, where conditions can usually be more readily controlled than in man. However, I find that 14 of the 85 selections were based chiefly, if not entirely, upon human experimentation. One need only mention Sanctorius, Fabricius, Spallanzani, Blagden, Beaumont, Haldane and Priestley, Barcroft, Cushing, and Lewis, all of whom obtained evidence which would have been either impossible or far less convincing had the observations been carried out upon animals. This should prove a great stimulus to those who have at their disposal extensive clinical resources.

Some passages present a peculiar appeal from the light which they shed upon the personality of the writers.[2] Who has not smiled over Malpighi's confession that in studying the capillary circulation he had "destroyed nearly the whole race of frogs—which," he adds, "does not happen in that savage batrachomyomachia of Homer"; or, in reading Boyle's crucial experiment upon the volume and pressure of gases, who has not experienced the feeling of delight that Boyle himself displayed as he wrote. Such details make science vivid and real, and they give human interest to facts which might otherwise seem dull and irrelevant. And they serve to remind us that, no matter how much science may advance, personality will always be a living force in Medicine, not only at the bedside, but

[2] This is illustrated in another way in Sir William Osler's catalogue in which the great characters of medical history are made to live again by virtue of the personal detail which Osler skilfully included in his attractive annotations. *Bibliotheca Osleriana. A catalogue of books illustrating the history of medicine and science collected, arranged and annotated by Sir William Osler, Bt. and bequeathed to McGill University.* Oxford: at the Clarendon Press, xxxv, 786 pp., 1929 [Edited by W. W. Francis, R. H. Hill and Archibald Malloch with the assistance of L. L. Mackall, R. R. Trotman and others].

also in the laboratory. How well was this illustrated by the life and influence of William Osler! He had a touch of St. Francis about him and there will always be room in Medicine for men of his genius.

The transcriptions have been made from the earliest editions of a work and in the footnotes full bibliographical description is given of each book or journal cited, with the pagination of the quotation itself (in parenthesis). Care has been taken to preserve original spelling and punctuation of all English passages. Selections originally in French, German or Latin have been given, where possible, in contemporary English translation. When no translations exist or when those available have seemed inaccurate, the passage has been rendered into modern English. In translations from French, my labours have been considerably lightened by my secretary, Miss Holmes, who is an accomplished French scholar; in translating from Latin, I have had the invaluable assistance of my friend, Arnold Meadowcroft Muirhead, M.A., formerly of Brasenose College, who has given most generously of his time. For the final form of all translations, however, and for technical phraseology, I must hold myself personally responsible. Except in two instances I have avoided the use of Sir Michael Foster's excellent translations already available to physiologists in his *Lectures on the history of physiology.*

The illustrations have been selected without any special criterion of suitability except personal preference and the desire not to repeat the figures and portraits so often seen in other historical works on physiology. The frontispiece of Helmholtz, made from a daguerreotype taken at the age of 27 (1848), the year after the publication of his memoir on the conservation of energy will, it is hoped, not be deemed inappropriate; for I am in sympathy with those who feel that this gifted man possessed one of the most remarkable intellects that ever applied itself to physiological thought.

* * * * *

I should like to take this opportunity of expressing my sincere thanks to the publisher, whose resourcefulness and judgment will be evident to the reader of these pages. He has identified himself with physiology, ancient and modern, and one hopes that we shall long continue to have the benefit of this enthusiastic cooperation.

J. F. FULTON

Magdalen College,
Oxford, April 8, 1930.

On Gathering a Library of Physiology

In the autumn of 1921 I was invited to tea at Oxford by Dame Grace Revere Osler, widow of the beloved physician and book collector, Sir William Osler, *Bart.*, who had been Regius Professor of Medicine at the University. As a newly arrived Rhodes Scholar at Magdalen College, I was preparing for "Final Honour Schools" in Physiology under Professor Charles S. Sherrington. Sir William had died at the end of December 1919, but his remarkable library was still at 13 Norham Gardens where his nephew, Dr. W. W. Francis, was engaged in the formidable task of compiling a catalogue of the books in accordance with a special scheme of classification worked out by Sir William prior to his death. I became fascinated by his novel plan to have all the great books arranged chronologically in a special group to be known as *Bibliotheca prima,* so that from its titles and annotations one could see at a glance the outstanding landmarks in the history of medicine. Works of less original content, but of importance historically, were to be included alphabetically in other sections: Secunda, Biographica, Historica, Litteraria, etc.

The occasion proved to be one of great portent for me since it was then that the idea of bringing together a library of similar scope, but devoted to physiology rather than primarily to medicine, became my firm ambition. Although there are a number of general histories of physiology, there never had been available an anthology of selections from the writings of the masters of physiology. Inquiry revealed that few libraries in England, the Continent, the United States, or Canada possessed even a fraction of the texts essential for such a compilation, and since it was clearly desirable to have the important books and papers at one's elbow, there seemed no choice but to begin collecting such a library.

Fortunately, my youthful enthusiasm far exceeded my knowledge of the subject else, as Dr. Cushing once said of himself, "I should never have had the sand to begin." Although the plan seemed worthy at the outset, two difficulties soon became apparent, the first and most practical being that it would exceed by a wide margin the resources of a student living on the income of a Rhodes Scholarship (which at that time was £300, or approximately $1,500 per annum). But since I had worked for subsistence—survival is a better word—while at Harvard College, starvation was not an entirely new sensation. As it turned out, conditions for collecting were favorable at that time, since very few had begun to collect books on the history of physiology and many of the great texts could still be had for sums which now, almost forty years later, seem fantastically small.

The second difficulty was that Sir William's over-all scheme was too vast in scope to adopt for physiology, and it became clear after a year or two that the subject must be subdivided and that, to buy wisely, it was essential to select areas of physiology of which one had some personal knowledge, however incomplete this might be.

At first these considerations troubled me but little, and I plunged into the maelstrom of bookshops, auctions, and sale catalogues with all the fervor of a neophyte—enthusiasm undimmed by the Bank Manager, the Secretary of the Rhodes Trust, or friends who enjoined caution. Lady Osler passed along book catalogues to me, even stuffed my pocket full of them when, two years later, Lucia and I were starting off on our honeymoon. This might have wrecked a very happy marriage at the start had it not been that then and ever since I have had a most understanding, loving, and forgiving wife.

Dr. Francis gave me invaluable advice, and I also met a most helpful bookseller who heard of my interest in medical books through another Fulton (Marshall) from America. Eric Bligh has been a good friend since that time and did much, particularly in my early years of collecting, to foster my plan. In retrospect I only wish that I had kept a list of the innumerable books he added to my collections, some of them items which now only rarely appear for sale—items such as Richard Bright's *Reports on Medical Cases,* 1827 (Bright's disease) and Thomas Addison on . . . *Disease of the Suprarenal Capsules,* 1855 (Addison's disease), both of which are dramatic physiological entities as important to pure physiology as to scientific medicine; and of course there were many others. Mr. Bligh's letters were models of clarity and accuracy and sometimes, after our exchanges became less formal, they displayed a certain dry wit about topics relating more to the medicine of history than to the history of medicine—or physiology—Bligh's broad view of things never permitted him to distinguish one from the other. Here are two characteristic "E. B." letters.

75 Great Portland St., W.I.
25 Sept., 1930

My dear Fulton.

. . . I have a charming little book, which I rather feel ought to go to you, as its title-page declares it to be the first Latin translation of Aristotle on the Parts of Animals (Bk. 1.), a work of some physiological import! I enclose a copy of my cataloguing, from which you will see it is a very early child of Conrad Gesner's. And if you will look at Michael Ephesius in the Osler Catalogue you will see that Osler possessed only a *late* 16th century edition of this book [B.O. 232, 1573]. One thing & another, and the dedication to Cardinal Pole make this a very intriguing little book. A most pleasant copy in vellum. This I will keep till I hear from you.

I will look out for another copy of Macewen, but I *did* rather regret at the time that you gave that copy away, as the book has become not only rare but expensive! . . .

25 Great Portland St., W.I.
27 Oct., 1930

My dear Fulton,

Your letter of Oct. 4th *did* reach me several days after your letter of Oct. 9th, and with it your glorious present, your "Readings in the History of Physiology." This reached me at Midhurst (where I still am for a couple of days more) and caused me the greatest delight. The book shows all your enthusiasm etc. . . . who but you would have had the note about Walter Charleton on p. 236? Sometimes, too, I find a trace of myself: the reproduction of the Descartes on p. 237 which I found at Ealing. On p. 250 appears Alexander Walker, whose book I wrote to you about in a great hurry one afternoon. It is all most delightful to me. The portraits are magnificent: chosen with such familiarity with the best & least known sources. I feel most gratified & honoured by receiving this gift. Thanks so very much.

Miss Newman has posted you both the Hooper & the Gorter, and the Latin Aristotle. I have not seen what the binder has done with the first two, but I hope they are all right. I think the Hooper is most beautiful. You will like this. The Aristotle charmed me very much when I bought it. I felt it might be a good early text for your collection. Look at the end of Gesner's preface & see how he says he laid aside his more serious studies during the Dog Days & made this translation [Greek into Latin] as a relaxation. Probably what he did want to do it for was two guineas to spend! Cardinal Pole, to whom one of the treatises is dedicated, was sometime Rector of Harting, a village in Sussex a few miles from Midhurst, which I know very well.

This morning comes your letter of Oct. 15th about Wood Jones . . . curious that I should have written to you the other day about his copy of Tyson on Pigmies. . . . I think on the whole Wood Jones is the most magnificent man I've ever known. An absolutely glorious figure: such enthusiasm, such avidity for experience (that's why he's let the London world of professors & jobs go to the devil). Such sincerity, such enormous wit and humour, such trueness, & magnetic geniality of manner. His marriage of course was a vast romance. Mrs. Wood Jones was the daughter of George Clunies Ross. . . . If you do not happen to be familiar with the extraordinary story of the Clunies Ross family & the Cocos Islands, do get Wood Jones, "Coral and Atolls" & read the historical introduction.

Indeed Muirhead is becoming a great friend. The humanism of his collection of books delights me of course. I hope to go there again soon, & am so happy to find I can talk with comparative fluency to them both. . . .

I think this is all this time, but I am pretty sure to have something or other to write about in a few days. Yours ever, E.B.

Many early acquisitions were likewise found in Oxford's oldest bookshop, B. H. Blackwell's, situated on The Broad just opposite Christopher Wren's Sheldonian Theatre; and it was here that I came upon one of the best friends any young book collector could possibly have had—William King, who was known among his colleagues in the trade and to all his far-flung correspondents simply as *"Rex."* And *Rex* he certainly was, for although of soft voice and a gentle and most kindly man, he ruled Blackwell's Antiquarian Book Department as one well worthy of his name. He knew my special interests in Oxford medicine and science of the seventeenth century and whenever I dropped in on him (which was as often as two or three times a week during term), Mr. King nearly always had something put aside. His prices were moderate and in retrospect I have had the uncomfortable feeling that he may sometimes have made them so to fit my purse. Exchanges with Mr. King went on every week or two after I went back to Boston, and periodic visits to the old-book department were begun again in 1928 when I returned to Oxford as a Fellow at Magdalen and were continued each summer after 1930 during our annual trips from New Haven to England until the gentle Rex, whose health had never been good, in September 1950 joined that long succession of Oxford men of books with whom he felt kinship. An excerpt from a letter to Arnold Muirhead, my close friend at Oxford and fellow collector, reveals the man as few were privileged to know him.

As from
50/51 Broad Street
Oxford
Aug. 13.39

Dear Mr. Muirhead,

. . . I share your delight in the peace & solitude of Nature: & before my mother's death I spent many restorative holidays on the Cotswolds, sitting on a stile watching the rotation of the crops! A recluse by nature & disposition, the circumstances of my life have intensified this unsocial trait—& like Thoreau, few things give me greater enjoyment than a long walk on a *foggy winter's* day. The rise in temperature which usually accompanies a fog imparts a feeling of relative warmth and well-being; outside distractions are cut down to a minimum by the fog which wraps one round like a blanket; there is for the time no one to remark on the slovenliness of your bearing, or the saturnine cast of your countenance; one's sense of individuality is strengthened, and one's reveries—generally so tenuous, so broken, and intermittent—gradually glow into a vivid and satisfying consistency that deepens and enhances the feeling of self-hood; and in the absence of checks and comparisons, one becomes the uncrowned (or self-crowned) king of the universe; & one undergoes a species of transfiguration, when the elements of flesh and blood and nerves are submerged, and the spiritual & intellectual elements are in the ascendant. One is able for the time to slough off the skin of one's *trade,* & join the communion of the illustrious dead: Sir Thomas Browne, Elia, and other old cronies of mine. . . .

In addition to the items put in my way by Eric Bligh and Will King, I looked for books in London, and trips to the Continent were always possible during the long Oxford vacation. I acquired a copy of John Mayow's *Tractatus duo* (1669), a very rare little book, for a few shillings (at Christie's, 15 June 1925, lot 21), and my first copy of Richard Lower's *De corde* (1669) for 7/6. Although it was inevitable that I would be interested in Robert Boyle, it may be that a lucky purchase at Sotheby's was my final undoing and set me off on a search that has never ended. I bought a "package lot" for twelve guineas which seemed like a fortune to an impecunious student, but collectors of this day will gasp at the titles which are shown in the entry from Sotheby's catalogue.

1271 BOYLE (Hon. Robert). A Collection of 22 of his Scientific and Philosophical Works, as detailed below. *Bound in* 18 vols., sm. 4to. *and* sm. 8vo. *old calf*   1661-95   12 12   0

CONTENTS:

Certain Physiological Essays 1661	mental Naturall Philosophy 1664
The Sceptical Chymist 1661	Experiments and Considerations touching Colours 1664
A Defence of the Doctrine touching the Spring and Weight of the Air 1662	New Experiments and Observations touching Cold 1665
An Examen of Mr. T. Hobbes his Dialogus Physicus De Naturâ Aëris 1662	The Origine of Formes and Qualities 1667
New Experiments Physico-Mechanical 1662	A Continuation of New Experiments Physico-Mechanical. Parts I and 2 1669-1682
Some Considerations touching the usefulnesse of Experi-	Tracts 1671
	Three Tracts 1671

An Essay about the origine and
virtues of Gems   1672
Tracts   1673
The Excellency of Theology
1674
About the excellency and
grounds of the Mechanical
Hypothesis   1674
Experiments, Notes, etc., about
the mechanical Origine or
Production of divers particu-
lar Qualities   1676
New Experiments, and Observa-
tions, made upon the Icy
Noctiluca . . . to which is an-
nexed a Chymical Paradox
1681
Experiments and Considerations
about the Porosity of Bodies
1684
Short Memoirs of the Natural
Experimental History of Min-
eral Waters   1684
Of the Reconcileableness of
Specifick Medicines   1685
A Free Discourse against Cus-
tomary Swearing   1695

THE HON. ROBERT BOYLE (1627-1691) TOOK A LEADING PART IN
FOUNDING THE ROYAL SOCIETY.

I sold the copy of *The Sceptical Chymist,* of which I had a better copy, for eight pounds, which I thought then was a canny bit of business. A recent copy of this rare text fetched some two thousand dollars!*

While studying anatomy at Heidelberg in the spring "vac" in 1922 during the tragic inflation of the mark, I added more titles, since old books and some of the finest examples of modern German printing could be bought by those who had dollar or sterling exchange for as little as sixpence. In Paris that fine race of men who dealt in old medicine had also been hard hit during the war years, and their prices, even to a Rhodes Scholar, seemed exceedingly low.

By 1930, when I realized my ambition of making available to medical students selected passages from the principal contributors to the growth of physiology, I had gathered a library of some seven to eight thousand items.

JOHN F. FULTON

New London, New Hampshire
Spring 1958

* At a sale at Sotheby & Co. on 12 July 1965, a copy sold for $13,440. *Ed.*

Selected Readings in the

History of Physiology

I

Biophysical Forerunners

The first and second laws of thermodynamics were summarized in 1850 by Rudolf Clausius (1822-1888) as follows:

First law. For a cyclic process in any closed system, the net work is proportional to the net heat.

Second law. The effects of a direct heat interaction between two bodies cannot be completely undone.

In interpreting the past the better to foresee the future, certain outstanding trends in the ever-widening field of physiology become conspicuously clear. Perhaps the most significant of these is the unmistakable drift toward the broader use of biophysical and biochemical principles in the analysis and interpretation of biological phenomena. In the first edition of this book, the opening chapter bore the title "General Principles." The selections were taken largely at random with little or no logical sequence, i.e., the Helmholtz passage on "conservation of energy" was included without indication of what had led up to its enunciation and with little or no explanation of its usefulness to students of biology. In this edition, consideration will be given to the background and physiological implications of the Helmholtz tract and of other selections included.

The beginnings of thermodynamics can be traced to certain early scientists such as Jean Fernel (1497-1558) who some thirty years after Columbus' voyages published three fundamental treatises on the world as a sphere—*Monalosphaerium*, 1527, *Cosmotheoria*, 1528, and *De proportionibus*, 1528. In these celebrated tracts, Fernel elaborated upon the mathematical, astronomical, and geographical implications of a sphere whirling with the other planets about the sun, and he incidentally was the first to measure a degree of meridian, i.e., of longitude (*Cosmotheoria*).[1] This versatile mathematician-astrophysicist later became a physiologist of note as well as a practising physician. In 1600 another physician-astronomer, William Gilbert, concluded that our spherical planet is also a great magnet.

A half-century after Gilbert, Robert Boyle laid the foundation of the gas laws through experimental determination of the reciprocal volume-pressure relationship. Boyle's contention that the expansion of a gas, which takes place on heating, results from increased motion of its constituent corpuscles led him to give the first clear statement of the modern kinetic theory of the gases. Two centuries after Fernel, one of his countrymen, Jean Bernoulli (1667-1748), propounded the idea that if any system of forces is in equilibrium, a small displacement of one is quickly balanced by the others in accordance with simple and predictable algebraic laws.

The next step was taken early in 1793 by a precocious young physician named Thomas Young (1773-1829), who at the age of nineteen presented to the Royal Society a paper on diffraction of light (as by the lens of the eye)[2] which indicated that Newton's corpuscular theory of light required modification. As a result of this communication he was made a Fellow of the Royal Society in 1794 when just twenty-one. It was also Young who first insisted that force can no longer be expressed as a simple mathematical formula of mass $\times$ velocity[2] and suggested in its place the term "energy" for this arithmetical product, adding that some method must be discovered to define the proper relation between work and heat.[3] In 1798, Benjamin Thompson (Count Rumford) expressed his belief, as had Robert Boyle, that heat is a form of molecular motion. (In this connection, one is reminded of Humphry Davy's youthful experiment in which a pendulum made of ice melted without application of heat when merely swung through air.) It was only a few years later that the first in the nineteenth century family of thermodynamicists, N. L. Sadi Carnot (1796-1832), the young French engineer, put forth his brilliant analysis of the way in which heat-engines convert heat into work (1824); this is generally regarded as the earliest statement of the First Law of Thermodynamics and is often referred to as "Carnot's Cycle."

[1] Sherrington, Sir Charles. *The endeavour of Jean Fernel with a list of the editions of his writings.* Cambridge, At the University Press, 1946. x, 223 pp. [p. 15].
[2] Young, Thomas. "Observations on vision." *Phil. Trans.*, 1793, *83*, 169-181.
[3] Young, Thomas. *A course of lectures on natural philosophy and the mechanical arts.* London, J. Johnson, 1807. 2 vols., vol. I, pp. 44, 78-79.

The brief selections which follow in this chapter constitute one of the greatest records of sustained abstract thinking in the history of science.

William Gilbert

1540-1603

William Gilbert,[4] Elizabethan physician and experimenter on electricity and magnetism, was known in his native town of Colchester as "Gilberd." He received his M.D. in 1569 from Cambridge University where he had been made a fellow of St. Johns College in 1561; later he enjoyed the honor of being elected President of the Royal College of Physicians, London (1600).

It is generally agreed that William Gilbert wrote the first great scientific book by an Englishman—*De magnete, magneticisque corporibus.* . . . Possibly influenced to some slight extent by the writings of Francis Bacon (1561-1626), Gilbert and William Harvey between them were principally responsible for reintroducing the experimental method in the field of scientific endeavor; indeed, experimentation became the cornerstone of the so-called "New Philosophy." There was a new and refreshing force abroad in the world, which had first manifested itself in the renaissance of Italian painting. Leonardo da Vinci (1452-1519) had built bridges and designed "engines" to fly in the air as he simultaneously instilled the breath of life into his vibrant anatomical drawings and marvellous pictures. It was near the time when Michelangelo (1475-1564) was creating his divine "Pietà" and marking the advent of the new age through his incomparable figures in the Sistine Chapel. The renaissance in science was also at hand, having begun about the time of William Gilbert's birth with Copernicus' heliocentric concept of the Universe and Vesalius' great "anatomy" (both 1543).

Gilbert's exploring mind reflected the widening horizons of the Elizabethan era—when British navigators such as Sir Walter Raleigh (1552-1618) and John Frampton (fl. 1577-1596) fired the imagination of Britain's people, Raleigh with his romantic accounts of the "Isles of the Azores" (1591) and "Empyre of Guiana" (1596), and Frampton with his translation of Marco Polo's "Travels" (1579) and his similar rendering of the Seville physician Nicolás Monardes' (1493-1588) "Joyfull Newes out of the Newe Founde Worlde" (1577). Gilbert was stirred by this prevailing spirit of adventure, and he sought to explain the nature of magnetism as exemplified by the loadstone. It was on the basis of these studies that he concluded the world itself is a great magnet, a fact which explained the unpredicted behavior of Christopher Columbus' magnetic compass. Since, how-

[4] Thompson, S. P. *William Gilbert and terrestrial magnetism in the time of Queen Elizabeth.* London, C. Whittingham and Company, 1903; Hale-White, *Sir* William. *Bacon, Gilbert and Harvey, being the Harveian oration delivered before the Royal College of Physicians of London, October 18th, 1927.* London, J. Bale, Sons and Danielsson, Ltd., 1927. 54 pp.; and Dibner, Bern: *Doctor William Gilbert.* New York, Burndy Library, 1947. 14 pp.

ever, Gilbert was a physician, the following passage has been chosen because
it reflects one of his medical interests.

MEDICINAL POWER OF IRON

It will not be alien to our purpose to treat briefly of the medicinal
power of iron; for it is beneficial in many diseases of the human
system, and by its virtues, both natural and acquired through fit
and skilful preparation, it brings about wonderful changes in the
human body; so that we may more clearly describe its nature through
its medicinal power and by means of a few well-known experiments;
to the end that even those prentices of medicine who abuse this most
excellent medicinal agent may learn to prescribe it more judiciously,
for the curing of patients, not as is too often the case, to their
destruction. The best iron, i.e., *stomoma, chalybs, acies,* or *aciarium*
(steel), is reduced by filing to a fine powder; this powder has strongest
vinegar poured on it, is dried in the sun, again treated with vinegar,
and once more dried. Then it is washed in spring water or other
water at hand, and dried. It is again pulverized and pounded fine on
porphyry, sifted through a fine sieve, and kept for use. It is given
chiefly in cases of lax and overhumid liver, and in cases of tumid
spleen after suitable evacuations; hence young women of pale,
muddy, blotchy complexion are by it restored to soundness and
comeliness, for it is highly exsiccative and harmlessly astringent.
But some, who in every internal disorder always recognize obstructions of liver and spleen, think it beneficial in such cases, as removing
obstructions; and herein they accept the opinions chiefly of Arabic
writers. Hence in cases of dropsy, schirrus of the liver, of chronic
jaundice, and hypochondriac melancholia, or complaints of the
oesophagus, they prescribe it, or add it to electuaries, often to the
sure destruction of many a patient. Fallopius recommends a preparation of iron of his own for schirrus of the spleen; but he is much
mistaken, for though loadstone is exceedingly beneficial where the
spleen is lax and tumid on account of humors, so far is it from curing a spleen thickened to a schirrus, that it makes the mischief far
worse; for agents that are greatly siccative and that absorb humors,
transform viscera that have been thickened by schirrus, into the hardness almost of a stone. Some there are who dry it at a high temperature in an oven, burning it till its color is changed to red: it is then
called "saffron of Mars," and is a very powerful exsiccant and quickly

penetrates the intestines. Further, they prescribe violent exercise so that the remedy may enter the heated intestines and reach the part affected. Hence it is reduced to a very fine powder; else it would remain in the oesophagus and in the chyle and would not penetrate to the intestines. Therefore this dry, earthly medicament is proved by the most conclusive tests to be, after due evacuations, a remedy in diseases arising from humor (when the intestines are running and overflowing with morbid fluids). (Gilbert, William. *De magnete, magneticisque corporibus, et de magno magnete tellure; physiologia nova, plurimis & argumentis & experimentis demonstrata.* London, P. Short, 1600. 8 *ll.*, 240 pp., 1 pl. English translation by P. Fleury Mottelay. London, 1893. liv, 368 pp. Reissued in paperback in 1958 by Dover Publications, Inc., New York, New York [pp. 55-56].)

The Honourable Robert Boyle

1627-1691

Robert Boyle, physicist, physiologist, and natural philosopher, has been described as the "seventh son of the Earl of Cork and father of modern chemistry." However, though he must be given credit for defining an element in his oft-cited book, *The Sceptical Chymist* (1661), and though he did much to abolish the hocus-pocus of the alchemist, Boyle was not a great chemist. But he was a supremely great physicist. He not only established the reciprocal relation between the pressure of a gas and the volume which it occupies, as elucidated in the second edition (1662) of *The Spring and Weight of the Air* (Pls. 1 & 2), but he also promulgated the modern concept of the particulate kinetic theory of the gases, and came nearer to formulation of the laws governing the conservation of energy than anyone prior to Sadi Carnot (1824).

Boyle's scientific life began and ended with studies of the air (Pl. 3) and from the outset he was convinced of its particulate nature, as is abundantly clear in the 1660 edition of *Spring and Weight of the Air;* he corrected proof sheets of his final book, *The General History of the Air* (1692), when on his deathbed. Boyle tells us that the "*atmospherical* air may consist of three kinds of corpuscles": the first are the particles of vapours which ascend into the atmosphere from "Earth, Water, Minerals, Vegetables and Animals, etc." under the influence of heat; the second are particles which are emitted from the sun and stars and produce magnetism and light; the third kind of particles are those properly called the particles of air which produce its elasticity and pressure. This last class of particles may be like coiled watch springs, like hairs of wool, or like shavings of wood which when compressed try to extend themselves. But while the elas-

ticity of the air may thus depend partly on the structure of the particles themselves, it is also influenced by heat. At this point Boyle makes a prescient statement foreshadowing the kinetic theory of gases.

TWO NEW EXPERIMENTS TOUCHING THE MEASURE
OF THE FORCE OF THE SPRING OF AIR
COMPRESS'D AND DILATED

The other thing that I would have considered touching our Ad-
versaries *Hypothesis* is, That it is *needless.* For whereas he denies not
that the Air has some Weight and Spring, but affirms that it is very
insufficient to perform such great matters as the counterpoising of a
Mercurial Cylinder of 29. Inches, as we teach that it may: We shall
now endeavour to manifest by Experiments purposely made, that the
Spring of the Air is capable of doing far more than 'tis necessary for
us to ascribe to it, to solve the *Phænomena* of the *Torricellian* Experiment.

We took then a long Glass-Tube, which by a dexterous hand and
the help of Lamp was in such a manner crooked at the bottom, that
the part turned up was almost parallel to the rest of the Tube, and
the Orifice of this shorter leg of the Siphon (if I may so call the whole
Instrument) being Hermetically seal'd, the length of it was divided
into Inches, (each of which was subdivided into eight parts) by a
straight list of paper, which containing those Divisions was carefully
pasted all along it: then putting in as much Quicksilver as served to
fill the Arch or bended part of the Siphon, that the *Mercury* standing in a level might reach in the one leg to the bottom of the divided
paper, and just to the same height or horizontal line in the other;
we took care, by frequently inclining the Tube, so that the Air might
freely pass from one leg into the other by the sides of the Mercury,
(We took (I say) care) that the Air at last included in the shorter
Cylinder should be of the same laxity with the rest of the Air about
it. This done, we began to pour Quicksilver into the longer leg of
the Siphon, which by its weight pressing up that in the shorter leg,
did by degrees streighten the included Air: and continuing this pouring in of Quicksilver till the Air in the shorter leg was by condensation reduced to take up but half the space it possess'd (I say, *possess'd,* not *fill'd*) before; *we cast our eyes upon the longer leg of the
Glass, on which was likewise pasted a list of Paper carefully divided
into Inches and parts, and we observed, not without delight and satisfaction, that the Quicksilver in that longer part of the Tube was*

29. Inches higher then the other. [Italics mine, J. F. F.] Now that this Observation does both very well agree with and confirm our *Hypothesis,* will be easily discerned by him that takes notice that we teach, and Monsieur *Paschall* and our *English* friends Experiments prove, that the greater the weight is that leans upon the Air, the more forcible is its endeavour of Dilatation, and consequently its power of resistance (as other Springs are stronger when bent by greater weights). For this being considered it will appear to agree rarely-well with the *Hypothesis,* that as according to it the Air in that degree of density and correspondent measure of resistance to which the weight of the incumbent Atmosphere had brought it, was able to counterbalance and resist the pressure of a Mercurial Cylinder of about 29. Inches, as we are taught by the *Torricellian* Experiment; so here the same Air being brought to a degree of density about twice as great as that it had before, obtains a Spring twice as strong as formerly. As may appear by its being able to sustain or resist a Cylinder of 29. Inches in the longer Tube, together with the weight of the Atmospherical Cylinder, that lean'd upon those 29. Inches of *Mercury;* and, as we just now inferr'd from the *Torricellian* Experiment, was equivalent to them.

We were hindered from prosecuting the tryal at that time by the casual breaking of the Tube. But because an accurate Experiment of this nature would be of great importance to the Doctrine of the Spring of the Air, and has not yet been made (that I know) by any man; and because also it is more uneasie to be made then one would think, in regard of the difficulty as well of procuring crooked Tubes fit for the purpose, as of making a just estimate of the true place of the Protuberant *Mercury's* surface; I suppose it will not be unwelcome to the Reader, to be informed that after some other tryals, one of which we made in a Tube whose longer leg was perpendicular, and the other, that contained the air, parallel to the horizon, we at last procured a Tube of the Figure exprest in the scheme; which Tube, though of a pretty bigness, was so long, that the Cylinder whereof the shorter leg of it consisted admitted a list of Paper, which had before been divided into 12. Inches and their quarters, and the longer leg admitted another list of Paper of divers foot in length, and divided after the same manner: then Quicksilver being poured in to fill up the bended part of the Glass, that the surface of it in either leg might rest in the same Horizontal line, as we lately taught, there was more and more Quicksilver poured into the longer Tube;

and notice being watchfully taken how far the *Mercury* was risen in that longer Tube, when it appeared to have ascended to any of the divisions in the shorter Tube, the several Observations that were thus successively made, and as they were made set down, afforded us the ensuing Table. (Boyle, R. *A defence of the doctrine touching the spring and weight of the air.* . . . [Appended to the second edition of the *Spring and weight of the air.*] London, Thomas Robinson, 1662. 86 pp. [Chap. V, pp. 57-60].)

DEFINITION OF AIR AND KINETIC THEORY
OF ITS PARTICLES

By the *Air* I commonly understand that thin, fluid, diaphanous, compressible and dilatable Body in which we breath, and wherein we move, which envelops the Earth on all sides to a great height above the highest Mountains; but yet is so different from the *Æther* [or *Vacuum*] in the intermundane or interplanetary Spaces, that it refracts the Rays of the Moon and other remoter Luminaries. [p. 1]

. . . Only I shall here intimate, that though the Elastical Air seem to continue such, rather upon the score of its Structure, than any external Agitation; yet Heat, that is a kind of Motion, may make the agitated Particles strive to recede further and further from the Centers of their Motions, and to beat off those, that would hinder the freedom of their Gyrations, and so very much add to the endeavour of such Air to expand it self. And I will allow you to suspect, that there may be sometimes mingled with the Particles that are springy, upon the newly mentioned Account, some others, that owe their Elasticity, not so much to their Structure, as their Motion, which, variously brandishing them and whirling them about, may make them beat off the neighbouring particles, and thereby promote an expansive Endeavour in the Air, whereof they are Parts. [pp. 6-7] (Boyle, R. *The general history of the air, designed and begun by the Honble Robert Boyle, Esq.* London, Awnsham and John Churchill, 1692. xii, 260 pp. [pp. 1, 6-7].)[5]

⁵ For full description and collation of this book see J. F. Fulton's *A bibliography of the Honourable Robert Boyle,* 2d ed. Oxford, The Clarendon Press, 1961. xxvi, 217 pp. [pp. 133-135].

Humphry Davy
1778-1829

Sir Humphry Davy, F.R.S.,[6] natural philosopher, chemist, and man of letters, affords another striking example of a precocious young man of science who, like Lorenzo Bellini, the first Charles Darwin (1756-1778), Thomas Young, and John Richardson Young, began publishing at an early age. When fifteen, he was discovered by Davies Giddy (1767-1839) "carelessly swinging on the half-gate of Dr. Borlase's house," and it was Giddy (later Davies Gilbert) who was chiefly responsible for giving Davy his start and who was to succeed him, many years later, as President of the Royal Society. In 1795, Davy wrote a poem "The Sons of Genius" and three years later published his maiden scientific effort (on colors) from the Pneumatic Institution of Bristol. More important was his first separate monograph on nitrous oxide *(Researches, Chemical and Philosophical, Chiefly Concerning Nitrous Oxide and its Respiration,* London, 1800), in which he describes in clear language the anesthetic effect of the so-called 'laughing gas' on himself and his many articulate literary friends (Coleridge, Southey, Peter Roget, and sundry others).

On the heels of Alessandro Volta's celebrated letter of 26 June 1800 to Sir Joseph Banks, President of the Royal Society, describing the electric battery came Davy's classic eight-page paper, "An account of some galvanic combinations," published in the *Philosophical Transactions.* It was communicated to the Royal Society on 18 June 1801, when Davy was in his twenty-third year, and won for him his F.R.S. in 1803. Davy thus shares with Volta the credit for having first harnessed the vast reservoirs of electrical energy which transformed the modern world and a century later unleashed the infinite power of the atom.

GALVANIC COMBINATIONS OF METALLIC PLATES AND FLUIDS

I. All the GALVANIC combinations analogous to the new apparatus of Mr. VOLTA, which have been heretofore described by experimentalists, consist (as far as my knowledge extends) of series containing at least two metallic substances, or one metal and charcoal, and a stratum of fluid. And it has been generally supposed, that their agencies are, in some measure, connected with the different powers

---

[6] The only impartial life of Davy is that in *The dictionary of national biography.* Of the longer biographies, that by his younger brother John Davy, M.D. (2 vols. London, 1835) can be recommended even though it glosses over Sir Humphry's many human foibles and to an even greater extent those of his overbearing, self-centered wife, Lady Davy (née Jane Kerr) who was continually insulting to Sir Humphry's most important "discovery" in science, the loyal and ever modest Michael Faraday (1791-1867).

of the metals to conduct electricity. But I have found that an accumulation of GALVANIC influence, exactly similar to the accumulation in the common pile, may be produced by the arrangement of single metallic plates, or arcs, with different strata of fluids. . . .

A combination of fifty copper-plates, arranged in this manner, with weak solutions of nitrous acid, or nitrate of ammoniac, and sulphuret of potash, gives pretty strong shocks, rapidly evolves gas from water and affects the condensing electrometer.

It does not lose its power of action for many hours; and, when this power is lost, it may be restored by the addition of small quantities of concentrated solutions of the proper chemical agents to the fluids in the different cells.

From two experiments made on copper and silver, it would appear, that the single metallic batteries act equally well, when the metals made use of are slightly alloyed, and when they are in a state of purity. (Davy, H. "An account of some Galvanic combinations, formed by the arrangement of single metallic plates and fluids, analogous to the new Galvanic apparatus of Mr. Volta." *Phil. Trans.*, 1801, *91*, pt. II, 397-402 [pp. 397, 402].)

Nicolas Léonard Sadi Carnot
1796-1832

Nicolas L. Sadi Carnot, French physicist and mathematician, brilliant son of Lazare-Nicholas-Marguerite Carnot (1753-1823), the celebrated military engineer, inventor, and author of *Essais sur le Machine en Général* (1783) and *Homme d'Etat Français,* is best known for his enunciation, twenty years prior to the work of Julius Robert von Mayer and James Prescott Joule, of the first law of thermodynamics often referred to as "Carnot's Cycle." His high place in the annals of science is based upon his only book, *Réflexions sur la Puissance Motrice du Feu et sur les Machines Propres à Développer cette Puissance,* which is as important as it is rare. Its significance was not recognized by English-speaking scientists until Lord Kelvin drew attention to it in 1848,[7] nearly twenty-five years after its appearance, although the French engineer Émile Clapeyron (1799-1854) had given it a favorable review in 1834 in the *Journal de l'Ecole Polytechnique,* a periodical little read outside of engineering circles.[8] In his *Réflexions,*

[7] Kelvin, W. Thomson, *1st baron.* "An account of Carnot's theory of the motive power of heat. . . . *Roy. Soc. Edinburgh Trans.,* 1849, *16,* 541-574.

[8] Daumas, Maurice, Ed. *Encyclopédie de la pléiade.* Vol. 5, *Histoire de la science.* Bruges, Imprimerie Ste-Catherine, 1957. xlvii, 1,904 pp. [p. 901].

Carnot outlined a series of experiments almost identical with those subsequently made by Joule and Kelvin, i.e., he made an accurate estimate of the mechanical equivalent of heat, and it was this that gave him status as one of the greatest scientific men of the century, or, as Pledge says: ". . . it is no bad summing up of Carnot's work to say that, as the Greeks gave us the abstract ideas (point, line, etc.) with which to think of space, and the seventeenth century those (mass, acceleration, etc.) with which to think of mechanics, so Carnot gave us those needed in thinking of heat engines. In each case the ideas are so pervasive that we use them even to state that they never apply exactly to visible objects."[9]

CARNOT ON HEAT AND ENERGY

Heat is nothing else than motive power, or rather motion which has changed its form. It is a movement in the particles of bodies. Wherever there is destruction of motive power, there is at the same time production of heat in quantity precisely proportional to the quantity of motive power destroyed. Reciprocally, wherever there is destruction of heat, there is production of motive power.

One can therefore state as a general thesis that motive power is a constant quantity in nature, which, properly speaking, is never either produced or destroyed. In fact it changes form, that is to say it produces sometimes one kind of movement, sometimes another, but it is never destroyed.

From some ideas which I have developed on the theory of heat, the production of one unit of motive power requires the destruction of 2.70 units of heat.

A machine which would produce 20 units of motive power for every kilogram of coal ought to destroy $\dfrac{20 \times 2.70}{7000}$ of heat developed by the combustion; about $\dfrac{20 \times 2.7}{7000} = \dfrac{8}{1000}$, that is to say, less than 1 per cent. (Sarton, G. "The discovery of the law of conservation of energy." *Isis*, 1929, *13*, 18-[44]. On pages [35-44] Sarton reproduced facsimiles of Mayer's first published paper [with English translation, pp. 27-33], the summary of Joule's paper, and Sadi Carnot's manuscript note [transcription, pp. 33-34. Translation by L. G. W.].)

[9] Pledge, H. T. *Science since 1500. A short history of mathematics, physics, chemistry, biology.* New York, Philosophical Library, 1947. 357 pp. [p. 144].

Robert Brown of Montrose
1773-1858

Robert Brown, F.R.S., was a Scottish botanist born at Montrose where he received his early education in the local grammar school with Joseph Hume and James Mill as schoolfellows. Subsequently he attended Marischal College, Aberdeen, and two years later entered Edinburgh University. Through his conspicuous ability he attracted the immediate attention of his teachers, especially those in botany, and while still in his teens (1791), Brown became known as an authority on the flora of Scotland. Following graduation he secured an Army commission and served in Ireland in 1795 and London in 1798. He was able again to take up his botanical studies in 1801 when Sir Joseph Banks made him naturalist to Captain Matthew Flinders' five-year Australasian expedition. He returned (1805) with some four thousand botanical specimens, many of them rare and chiefly from the coastal flora of Australia, on which he based his greatest work, *Prodromus florae Novae Hollandiae et insulae Van Dieman,* published in 1810. In that year Banks made Brown his private secretary and librarian, and also librarian to the Linnean Society of London. When Banks died, both his botanical museum and library were left to Robert Brown for life. In 1827, however, Brown turned the Banks collections over to the British Museum, and he in turn was made Keeper of the Museum's Botanical Department, a post held until his death in 1858.

Professionally, Brown is given credit for having discovered the nucleus of plant cells (1831) and the significance of pollen in fecundation. That he was also the Brown of "Brownian movement" (agitation of small particles suspended in fluid) is not recognized in the official accounts of his life in the *Dictionary of National Biography* or *Encyclopaedia Britannica,* 1956 edition (but see *Everyman's Encyclopaedia,* 4th ed., 1958, 2, 588). His original description of the phenomenon, which I quote, was set forth quite casually in the midst of a paper on the pollen of plants. The active "molecules" mentioned in the title refer to pollen grains visible microscopically. Now, thanks to Albert Einstein (1905) and Jean Perrin (1909), the spontaneous movement of the pollen is recognized as due to "molecular" bombardment of individual grains by the constituent atoms of the fluid in which the pollen is suspended. The passages following that of Brown are taken from an English translation of Einstein's original paper (German) and from that of Perrin published five years later. Brownian movement illustrates in most dramatic fashion how a biological phenomenon came to be accounted for through application of the kinetic theory of heat and simple thermodynamic concepts by a man of genius such as Albert Einstein.

SPONTANEOUS MOVEMENTS OF SUSPENDED POLLEN PARTICLES

The observations, of which it is my object to give a summary in the following pages, have all been made with a simple microscope, and indeed with one and the same lens, the focal length of which is about 1/32nd of an inch. . . .

My inquiry on this point was commenced in June 1827, and the first plant examined proved in some respects remarkably well adapted to the object in view.

This plant was *Clarckia pulchella*, of which the grains of pollen, taken from antherae full grown, but before bursting, were filled with particles or granules of unusually large size, varying from nearly 1/4000th to about 1/5000th of an inch in length, and of a figure between cylindrical and oblong, perhaps slightly flattened, and having rounded and equal extremities. While examining the form of these particles immersed in water, I observed many of them very evidently in motion; their motion consisting not only of a change of place in the fluid, manifested by alterations in their relative positions, but also not unfrequently of a change of form in the particle itself; a contraction or curvature taking place repeatedly about the middle of one side, accompanied by a corresponding swelling or convexity on the opposite side of the particle. In a few instances the particle was seen to turn on its longer axis. These motions were such as to satisfy me, after frequently repeated observation, that they arose neither from currents in the fluid, nor from its gradual evaporation, but belonged to the particle itself.

Grains of pollen of the same plant taken from antherae immediately after bursting, contained similar subcylindrical particles, in reduced numbers however, and mixed with other particles, at least as numerous, of much smaller size, apparently spherical, and in rapid oscillatory motion.

These smaller particles, or molecules, as I shall term them, when first seen, I considered to be some of the cylindrical particles swimming vertically in the fluid. But frequent and careful examination lessened my confidence in this supposition; and on continuing to observe them until the water had entirely evaporated, both the cylindrical particles and the spherical molecules were found on the stage of the microscope. (Brown, R. "A brief account of the microscopical observations made in the months of June, July, and August, 1827, on the particles contained in the pollen of plants; and on the general existence of active molecules in organic and inorganic bodies." *Edin. new philos. J.*, 1828, *5*, 358-371; *Philos. Mag.* 1828, *4*, 160-182 [pp. 161-163].)

EINSTEIN'S THEORY OF BROWNIAN MOVEMENT

Soon after the appearance of my paper [*Ann. d. Phys.*, 1905, *17*, 549], on the movements of particles suspended in liquids demanded by the molecular theory of heat, Siedentopf (of Jena) informed me that he and other physicists—in the first instance, Prof. Gouy (of Lyons)—had been convinced by direct observation that the so-called Brownian motion is caused by the irregular thermal movements of the molecules of the liquid [*J. Phys.*, 1888, *7*, 561].

Not only the qualitative properties of the Brownian motion, but also the order of magnitude of the paths described by the particles correspond completely with the results of the theory. I will not attempt here a comparison of the slender experimental material at my disposal with the results of the theory, but will leave this comparison to those who may be handling the experimental side of the problem.

The following paper will amplify in some points the author's own paper mentioned above. We will derive here not only the translational movement, but also the rotational movement of suspended particles, for the simplest special case where the particles have a spherical form. We will show further, up to how short a time of observation the results given in that discussion hold true.

To derive these we will use here a more general method, partly in order to show how the Brownian motion is related to the fundamentals of the molecular theory of heat, partly to be able to develop the formula for the translational and the rotational movement in a single discussion. Suppose, accordingly, that α is a measurable parameter of a physical system in thermal equilibrium, and assume that the system is in the so-called neutral equilibrium for every (possible) value of α. According to classical thermodynamics, which differentiates in principle between heat and other kinds of energy, spontaneous alterations of α cannot occur; according to the molecular theory of heat, it is otherwise. In the following we will investigate according to what laws the alterations implied by the latter theory take place. We must then apply these laws to the following special cases:

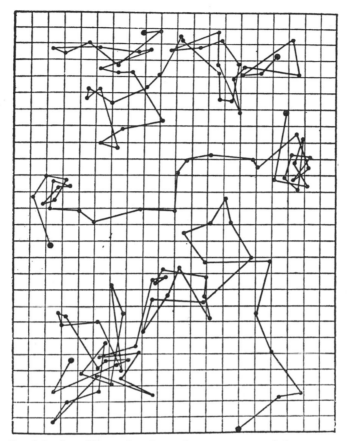

Figure 1. Perrin's chart illustrating Brownian movement of three suspended particles of mastic obtained by joining with straight lines their positions at intervals of 30 seconds.

1. α is the X-co-ordinate of the centre of gravity of a suspended particle of spherical form in a homogeneous liquid (not subject to gravitation).

2. α is the angle which determines the position of a particle, rotatable about a diameter, that is suspended in a liquid. (Einstein, Albert. *Investigations on the theory of the Brownian movement.* R. Furth, Ed., A. D. Cowper, Trans. New York, Dover Publications, Inc., 1956. 122 pp. [pp. 19-21].)

PERRIN ON BROWNIAN MOVEMENT AND MOLECULAR REALITY

The figure here reproduced [Fig. 1] shows three drawings obtained by tracing the segments which join the consecutive positions of the

same granules of mastic at intervals of 30 seconds. It is the half of
the mean square of such segments which verifies the formula of Einstein [1905]. One of these drawings shows 50 consecutive positions
of the same granule. They only give a very feeble idea of the prodigi-
ously entangled character of the real trajectory. If the positions were
indicated from second to second, each of these rectilinear segments
would be replaced by a polygonal contour of 30 sides, relatively as
complicated as the drawing here reproduced, and so on. One realises
from such examples how near the mathematicians are to the truth
in refusing, by logical instinct, to admit the pretended geometrical
demonstrations, which are regarded as experimental evidence for the
existence of a tangent at each point of a curve. . . .

44. Conclusion.—I think I have given in this Memoir the present
state of our knowledge of the Brownian movement and of molecular
magnitudes. The personal contributions which I have attempted to
bring to this knowledge, both by theory and experiment, will I hope
elucidate it, and will show that the observation of emulsions gives a
solid experimental basis to molecular theory. (Perrin, J. "Mouvement Brownien et réalité moléculaire." *Ann. Chim. Physique*, 1909,
8 sér. *18*, 5-114 [pp. 80-81; 113].)

Julius Robert von Mayer
1814-1878

J. Robert von Mayer, physician of Heilbronn (Germany), established at the age
of twenty-eight that the first law of thermodynamics is applicable to physiological processes. Four years earlier (in 1838) this precocious young man had correctly described the pharmacological action of the new drug "santonin" which
had been first synthesized by Kahler and Alms in 1830. In referring to the in-
difference with which English scientists received the epic work of James Prescott
Joule, the eminent historian of science, William P. D. Wightman, writes divert-
ingly: "Obtuse as were the British men of science, it is some comfort to know
that the Germans were even worse; for the first philosophical attempt to clarify
the confusion surrounding the various 'forces' was actually ignored by the editor
of *Poggendorf's Annalen*. Its subsequent publication by Liebig in 1842 evoked
so little interest that the author was requested not to send any more. The author
was Robert Mayer whose thoughts were turned to the subject by the fact that
blood of members of the ship's company, to whom he had been appointed surgeon, was brighter when drawn in the tropics than in cooler regions. Correlation
of 'animal' heat with the level of consumption of food and oxygen had been
demonstrated by Lavoisier and his associates. But Mayer, remembering that there

is also at least a rough correlation between food consumption and 'work', now faced the question "What do we understand by 'forces'?" And how are different forces related to each other? His answer, though not free from the metaphysical obscurity which D'Alembert had been at pains to remove, and vitiated by the retention of the word 'force' when [Thomas] Young's term 'energy' would have made the distinction clearer, at any rate pointed to the paramount necessity of *asking* the question and of the possibility of fruitfully applying the answer to the case of the relation between work and heat. His analogies were also most suggestive, as when he compares a train to a 'distilling apparatus; the heat applied under the boiler passes off as motion and this is deposited again as heat at the axles of the wheels.' Moreover he gave the first calculation of the ratio of work done to heat produced. . . ."[10]

REMARKS ON FORCES OF INORGANIC NATURE

The following pages are designed as an attempt to answer the questions, What are we to understand by "Forces"? and how are different forces related to each other? Whereas the term *matter* implies the possession, by the object to which it is applied, of very definite properties, such as weight and extension, the term *force* conveys for the most part the idea of something unknown, unsearchable, and hypothetical. An attempt to render the notion of force equally exact with that of matter, and so to denote by it only objects of actual investigation, is one which, with the consequences that flow from it, ought not to be unwelcome to those who desire that their views of nature may be clear and unencumbered by hypotheses.

Forces are causes: accordingly, we may in relation to them make full application of the principle—*causa aequat effectum*. If the cause c has the effect e, then $c = e$; if, in its turn, e is the cause of a second effect f, we have $e = f$, and so on: $c = e = f \ldots = c$.—In a chain of causes and effects, a term or a part of a term can never, as plainly appears from the nature of an equation, become equal to nothing. This first property of all causes we call their *indestructibility*.

If the given cause c has produced an effect e equal to itself, it has in that very act ceased to be: c has become e; if, after the production of e, c still remained in whole or in part, there must be still further effects corresponding to this remaining cause: the total effect of c would thus be e, which would be contrary to the supposition $c = e$. Accordingly, since c becomes e, and e becomes f, etc., we must regard these various magnitudes as different forms under which one and the same object makes its appearance. This capability of assuming

[10] Wightman, W. P. D. *The growth of scientific ideas.* Edinburgh, Oliver and Boyd, 1950. xii, 495 pp. [pp. 279-280]. Emended by author in letter dated 9 April 1964.

various forms is the second essential property of all causes. Taking
both properties together, we may say, causes are (quantitatively) *indestructible* and (qualitatively) *convertible* objects.

Two classes of causes occur in nature, which, so far as experience
goes, never pass one into another. The first class consists of such
causes as possess the properties of weight and impenetrability; these
are kinds of Matter: the other class is made up of causes which are
wanting in the properties just mentioned, namely Forces, called also
Imponderables, from the negative property that has been indicated.
Forces are therefore *indestructible, convertible, imponderable objects.* (Mayer, J. R. von. "Bemerkungen über die Kräfte der un-
belebten Natur." *Ann. Chem. Pharm. (Lemgo)*, 1842, *42*, 233-240.
English translation by G. C. Foster of Glasgow. From G. Sarton's
"The discovery of the law of conservation of energy." *Isis*, 1929,
13, 18-[44] [pp. 27-38].)

James Prescott Joule
1818-1889

Robert Mayer was neither mathematician nor experimental physicist, and, as
Sarton has pointed out, his great discovery was accomplished by purely abstract
means.[11] His brilliant generalization, made through a flash of genius, would have
remained unconvincing had it not been supported by experimental data. This was
provided by the English physicist, *James Prescott Joule.* He was chiefly concerned
with making exact measurements in qualitative experiments and he devised various methods for determining with increasing precision the mechanical equivalent
of heat (or the thermal equivalent of work). He published an account of these
experiments in the *Philosophical Magazine* (1843),[12] but a summary appeared in
the *Reports of the Cork Meeting* of the British Association for the Advancement
of Science (p. 33). The summary is reprinted here.

ELECTRICITY AND THE MECHANICAL
EQUIVALENT OF HEAT

Although it had been long known that fine platinum wire can be
ignited by magneto-electricity, it still remained a matter of doubt
whether heat was evolved by the coils in which the magneto-electricity was generated: and it seemed indeed not unreasonable to suppose

[11] Sarton, George. "The discovery of the law of conservation of energy." *Isis*, 1929, *13*,
18-[44].

[12] 1843, *23*, 263-276, 347-355, 435-443.

that cold was produced there, in order to make up for the heat evolved by the other parts of the circuit. The author had endeavoured therefore to clear up this uncertainty by experiment. His apparatus consisted of a small compound electro-magnet, immersed in water, revolving between the poles of a powerful stationary magnet. The magneto-electricity developed in the coils of the revolving electromagnet was measured by an accurate galvanometer; and the temperature of the water was taken before and after each experiment by a very delicate thermometer. The influence of the temperature of the surrounding atmospheric air was guarded against by covering the revolving tube with flannel, &c., and by the adoption of a system of interpolation. By an extensive series of experiments with the above apparatus the author succeeded in proving that heat is evolved by the coils of the magneto-electrical machine, as well as by any other part of the circuit, in proportion to the resistance to conduction of the wire and the square of the current; the magneto-, having, under comparable circumstances, the same calorific power as the voltaic electricity. Prof. Jacobi, of St. Petersburgh, had shown that the motion of an electro-magnetic engine generates magneto-electricity in opposition to the voltaic current of the battery. The author had observed the same phenomenon on arranging his apparatus as an electro-magnetic engine; but had found that no additional heat was evolved on account of the conflict of forces in the coil of the revolving electro-magnet, and that the heat evolved by the coil remained, as before, proportional to the square of the current. Again, by turning the machine contrary to the direction of the attractive forces, so as to *increase* the intensity of the voltaic current by the assistance of the magneto-electricity, he found that the evolution of heat was still proportional to the square of the current. The author discovered, therefore, that the heat evolved by the voltaic current is invariably proportional to the square of the current, however the intensity of the current may be varied by magnetic induction. But Dr. Faraday had shown that the chemical effects of the current are simply as its quantity. Therefore he concluded that in the electro-magnetic engine, a part of the heat due to the chemical actions of the battery is lost by the circuit, and converted into mechanical power; and that when the electro-magnetic engine is turned *contrary* to the direction of the attractive forces, a *greater* quantity of heat is evolved by the circuit than is due to the chemical reactions of the battery, the overplus quantity being

produced by the conversion of the mechanical force exerted in turning the machine. By a dynamometrical apparatus attached to his
machine, the author has ascertained that, in all the above cases, a
quantity of heat, capable of increasing the temperature of a pound
of water by one degree of Fahrenheit's scale, is equal to a mechanical force capable of raising a weight of about 838 pounds to the
height of one foot. (Sarton, G. *loc. cit.* [note 11], p. [43].)

Hermann von Helmholtz
1821-1894

Hermann von Helmholtz, one of the greatest thinkers of all time (Pl. 4), had
German, French, and English forebears, his mother being descended from William Penn. At the age of twenty-one he became a pupil of Johannes Müller and
soon after wrote a neuroanatomical thesis of unusual merit (nerve cells of
leeches); at twenty-four he measured the heat production of frog muscle, and at
twenty-six enunciated the principle of the conservation of energy. Starting his
professional life as a military physician, Helmholtz when twenty-eight was appointed to a professorship of physiology at Königsberg; it is often forgotten that
he continued to occupy chairs of physiology throughout the greater part of his
active life. "Medicine," he said in later years, "was once the intellectual home
in which I grew up; and even the emigrant best understands and is best understood by his native land" (Garrison).

One cannot enumerate all of Helmholtz's contributions to physiology; everything he touched, except psychology, was, as if by magic, turned to gold. His
paper on the conservation of energy, written early in 1847, was offered to *Pog-
gendorff's Annalen,* but the editor thought ill of it and turned it down. The importance of the essay was recognized by Du Bois-Reymond who advised Helmholtz to issue it as a separate tract. Reimer, the Berlin publisher, was accordingly
approached and on Du Bois-Reymond's recommendation this now historic paper
was not only immediately accepted, but Helmholtz, to his astonishment, received
a small honorarium. The following passage is taken from the philosophical introduction.

THE CONSERVATION OF ENERGY

The principal contents of the present memoir show it to be
addressed to physicists chiefly, and I have therefore thought it judicious to lay down its fundamental principles purely in the form of
a physical premise, and, independent of metaphysical considerations,
to develop the consequences of these principles, and to submit them
to a comparison with what experience has established in the various

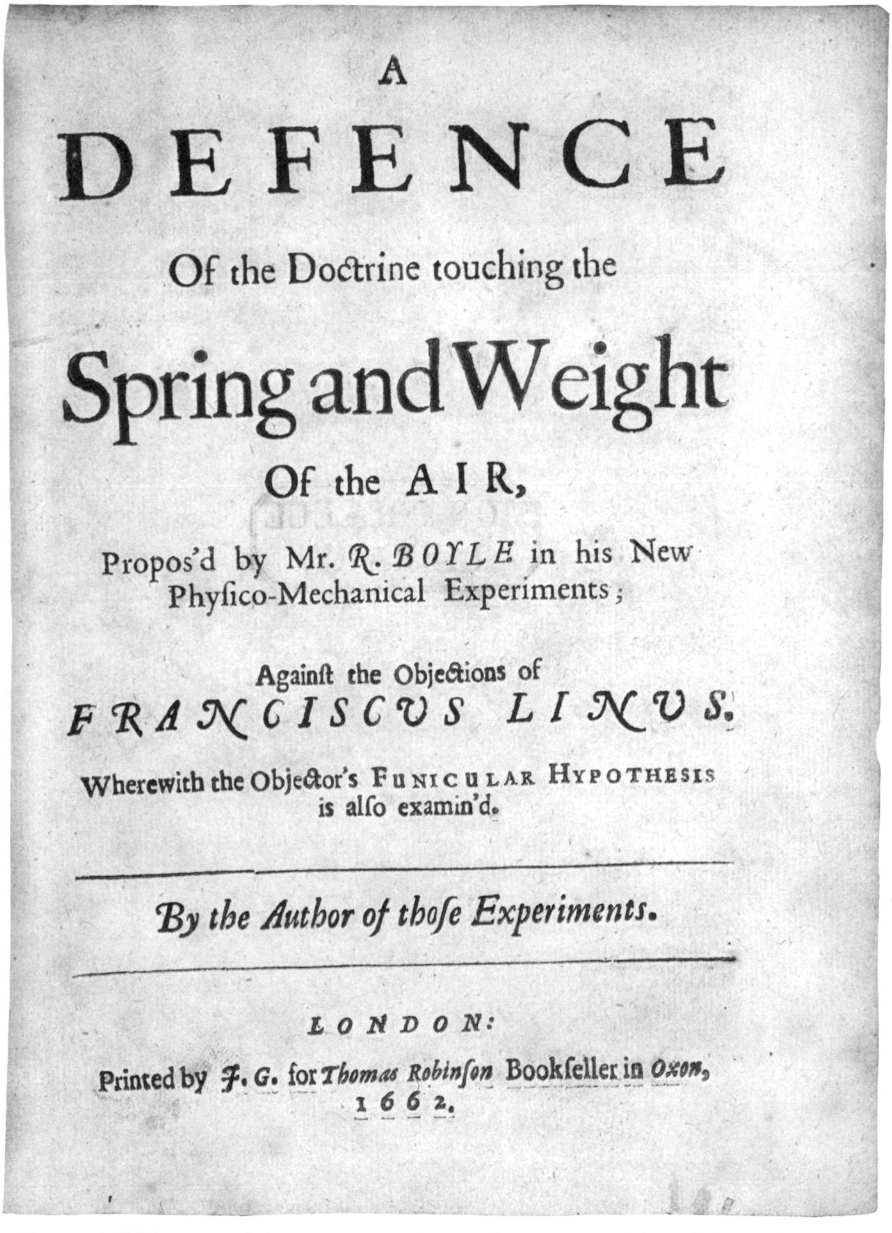

A
DEFENCE

Of the Doctrine touching the

Spring and Weight

Of the A I R,

Propos'd by Mr. *R. BOYLE* in his New
Physico-Mechanical Experiments;

Against the Objections of
F R A N C I S C V S   L I N V S.

Wherewith the Objector's FUNICULAR HYPOTHESIS
is also examin'd.

By the Author of those Experiments.

L O N D O N:

Printed by *J. G.* for *Thomas Robinson* Bookseller in *Oxon,*
1 6 6 2.

PLATE 1. Title-page of the tract appended to the second edition of the *Spring and Weight of the Air*, 1662, in which Boyle's law is set forth.

diviſions in the ſhorter Tube, the ſeveral Obſervations that were thus ſucceſſively made, and as they were made ſet down, afforded us the enſuing Table.

A Table of the Condenſation of the Air.

A	A	B	C	D	E
48	12	00		29 2/16	29 2/16
46	11½	01 7/16		30 9/16	30 6/16
44	11	02 13/16		31 6/16	31 12/16
42	10½	04 6/16		33 8/16	33 7
40	10	06 3/16		35 5/16	35 --
38	9½	07 14/16		37 --	36 15/19
36	9	10 2/16		39 5/16	38 7/8
34	8½	12 8/16		41 10/16	41 2/17
32	8	15 1/16		44 2/16	43 11/16
30	7½	17 15/16		47 1/16	46 3/5
28	7	21 3/16	Added to 29 9/16 makes	50 5/16	50 --
26	6½	25 3/16		54 2/16	53 10/13
24	6	29 11/16		58 13/16	58 2/8
23	5¾	32 3/16		61 5/16	60 18/23
22	5½	34 15/16		64 1/16	63 6/11
21	5¼	37 15/16		67 2/16	66 4/7
20	5	41 9/16		70 11/16	70 --
19	4¾	45 --		74 2/16	73 11/19
18	4½	48 12/16		77 2/16	77 2/3
17	4¼	53 11/16		82 12/16	82 2/17
16	4	58 2/16		87 14/16	87 3/8
15	3¾	63 15/16		93 1/16	93 3/5
14	3½	71 5/16		100 7/16	99 6/7
13	3¼	78 11/16		107 13/16	107 1/13
12	3	88 7/16		117 9/16	116 8/9

AA. The number of equal ſpaces in the ſhorter leg, that contained the ſame parcel of Air diverſly extended.

B. The height of the Mercurial Cylinder in the longer leg, that compreſs'd the Air into thoſe dimenſions.

C. The height of a Mercurial Cylinder that counterbalanc'd the preſſure of the Atmoſphere.

D. The Aggregate of the two laſt Columns B and C, exhibiting the preſſure ſuſtained by the included Air.

E. What that preſſure ſhould be according to the *Hypotheſis*, that ſuppoſes the preſſures and expanſions to be in reciprocal proportion.

For the better underſtanding of this Experiment it may not be amiſs to take notice of the following particulars:

1. That the Tube being ſo tall that we could not conveniently make uſe of it in a Chamber, we were fain to uſe it on a pair of Stairs, which yet were very lightſom, the Tube being for preſer-

vations

PLATE 2. Boyle's original table proving the reciprocal relation between the volume and pressure of a gas (page 60 in the *Defence*.)

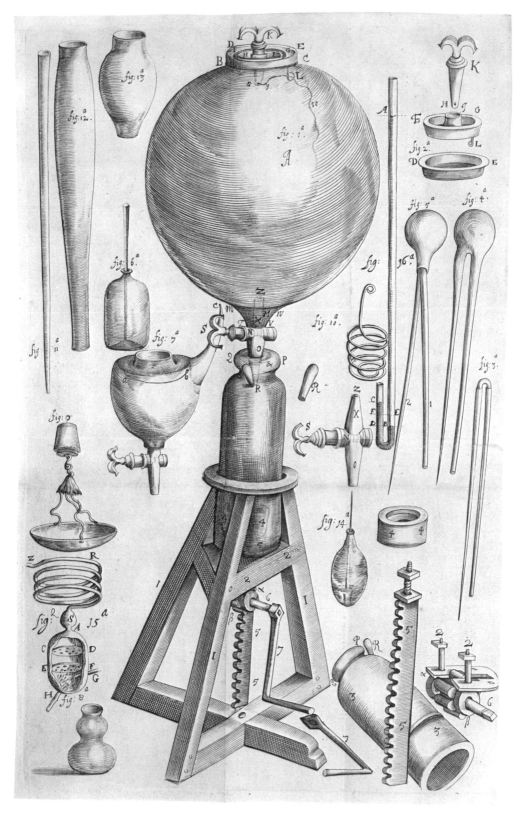

PLATE 3. Boyle's first air-pump. (From the first edition of the *Spring and Weight of the Air*, Oxford, 1660.)

PLATE 4. Helmholtz at the age of 27, the year after the publication of his memoir on the conservation of energy. (From a photograph of a daguerreotype donated by Dr. Joseph C. Aub.)

branches of physics. The deduction of the propositions contained in
the memoir may be based on either of two maxims; either on the
maxim that it is not possible by any combination whatever of natural
bodies to derive an unlimited amount of mechanical force, or on the
assumption that all actions in nature can be ultimately referred to
attractive or repulsive forces, the intensity of which depends solely
on the distances between the points at which the forces are exerted.
That both these propositions are identical is shown at the commencement of the memoir itself. Meanwhile the important bearing
which they have upon the final aim of the physical sciences may
with propriety be made the subject of a special introduction. . . .

To speak more particularly: the phenomena of nature are to be
referred back to motions of material particles possessing unchangeable moving forces, which are dependent upon conditions of space
alone. Motion is the alteration of the conditions of space. Motion, as
a matter of experience, can only appear as a change in the relative
position of at least two material bodies. Force, which originates
motion, can only be conceived of as referring to the relation of at
least two material bodies toward each other; it is therefore to be
defined as the endeavour of two masses to alter their relative position. But the force which two masses exert upon each other must be
resolved into those exerted by all their particles upon each other;
hence in mechanics we go back to forces exerted by material points.
The relation of one point to another, as regards space, has reference
solely to their distance apart: a moving force, therefore, exerted by
each upon the other, can only act so as to cause an alteration of their
distance, that is, it must be either attractive or repulsive.

Finally, therefore, we discover the problem of physical natural
science to be, to refer natural phenomena back to unchangeable
attractive and repulsive forces, whose intensity depends solely upon
distance. The solvability of this problem is the condition of the
complete comprehensibility of nature. In mechanical calculations
this limitation of the idea of moving force has not yet been assumed:
a great number, however, of general principles referring to the motion of compound systems of bodies are only valid for the case that
these bodies operate upon each other by unchangeable attractive or
repulsive forces; for example, the principle of virtual velocities; the
conservation of the motion of the centre of gravity; the conservation
of the principal plane of rotation; of the moment of rotation of free
systems; and the conservation of *vis viva*. In terrestrial matters appli-

cation is made chiefly of the first and last of these principles, inasmuch as the others refer to systems which are supposed to be completely free; we shall, however, show that the first is only a special case of the last, which therefore must be regarded as the most general and important consequence of the deduction which we have made.

Theoretical natural science therefore, if she does not rest contented with half-views of things, must bring her notions into harmony with the expressed requirements as to the nature of simple forces, and with the consequences which flow from them. Her vocation will be ended as soon as the reduction of natural phenomena to simple forces is complete, and the proof given that this is the only reduction of which the phenomena are capable. (Helmholtz, H. *Über die Erhaltung der Kraft*. Berlin, G. A. Reimer, 1847. 72 pp. The translation is that of J. Tyndall given by Frances A. Welby in her English edition of Koenigsberger's *Hermann von Helmholtz*. Oxford, Clarendon Press, 1906. xvii, 440 pp. [pp. 39, 41-42].)[13]

[13] Attention is directed to the letters of Anna von Helmholtz, which throw much light upon her husband's career. *Anna von Helmholtz. Ein Lebensbild in Briefen.* Herausgegeben von Ellen von Siemens-Helmholtz. Berlin, Verlag für Kulturpolitik, 1929. 2 vols.

II

Vascular System:
Discovery of the Circulation

Part 1. Forerunners of William Harvey

Before recorded history primitive man must have known that blood exists under pressure in the arteries, for, when cut, an artery spurted; the pulse was also recognized as occurring simultaneously with the heart beat. Some have thought it odd that with this knowledge and with the recognition of veins, the concept of the circulation was not grasped in antiquity. However, this is to fail to realize the bewildering nature of the anatomical and physiological evidence as it appeared to the ancients—and consequently, the true magnitude of Harvey's ultimate achievement.

The ancients saw three phenomena which indicated the presence of life in the body—the pulse, the heart beat, and breathing—and they realized that they were in some manner interconnected. Furthermore, they knew that loss of blood produced faintness and ultimately death. From very early times the customary method of slaughtering cattle, sheep, and pigs was, as it is still today, first to stun the animal with a blow on the head and then to bleed it to death by opening one of the jugular veins at the throat. They knew, too, that blood was present not only in the larger vessels but was to be found wherever the skin was broken. It was a fluid permeating the whole body.

Aristotle mentions that as a result of the method of slaughtering animals by bleeding, their blood vessels were left empty and were very difficult to trace. Consequently, the knowledge of the blood vessels before his time was imperfect. Aristotle made a radical innovation in anatomy by killing his animals for dissection by strangulation in order to retain blood within the vessels. This practice, however, had certain consequences, first brilliantly pointed out by T. H. Huxley,[1] which were to exert their effects on physiology through many centuries. Huxley showed that when an animal is strangled as described by Aristotle, the veins, the right side of the heart, and the pulmonary artery are left swollen and engorged with blood, whereas the left side of the heart and the arteries remain largely empty. Consequently, on the right side of the heart the right auricle and ventricle appear as one large single chamber continuous with the superior and inferior vena cava. For this reason the heart appeared to Aristotle to have only three chambers: a large right chamber (the right auricle and ventricle), a middle chamber (the left ventricle), and a smaller left chamber (the left auricle). Aristotle would probably not have persisted in this mistaken notion of the heart's structure if he had carefully examined the structure of an excised heart. His descriptions suggest instead that he limited his observations to study of the heart within the body of the dissected animal. Nevertheless, we are indebted to him for our first description of the blood vessels *as a connected system* arising from the heart and extending throughout the body.

Of more prolonged historical influence was the effect of Aristotle's method of preparing animals on the concept of the nature of the arteries. Since an artery has thick muscular walls, it does not collapse when emptied. Therefore, since in whatever manner an animal be killed for dissection the arteries are always left empty, whenever in dissection an artery was cut across, it would appear empty and hollow with much the appearance of a hollow pipe running through the flesh. For this reason an artery was early conceived to be not a blood vessel but an air tube. As a matter of fact, from the very moment that arteries were distinguished from veins they appear to have been distinguished as air tubes, whereas the veins were the true blood vessels. The term *"arteria"* means an air tube and the full name of the trachea, for instance, is the *trachea arteria,* or "rough artery," so called because of the ring-like cartilaginous thickenings which strengthen and roughen its walls. Aristotle himself does not appear to have distinguished arteries from veins but to have considered both together simply as blood vessels. The distinction appears to have been made first by Praxagoras of Cos (*c.* 320 B.C.) and it was given a more concrete anatomical definition by his

[1] Huxley, T. H. "On certain errors respecting the heart attributed to Aristotle." *Nature (Lond.),* 1880, *21,* 1-5.

great pupil Herophilus of Chalcedon (*c.* 300 B.C.). Herophilus based the distinction between arteries and veins on the thickness of their walls, for he estimated that on the average the walls of an artery were six times as thick as those of a vein. On this basis he became aware of an anomaly in the lungs. For he considered the pulmonary veins, by virtue of their connection with the left side of the heart and consequently with the arterial system, to be arteries, that is, air tubes. He considered them therefore to be connected also to the bronchioles, or branches of the rough artery, in the lungs and to transmit air from the lung to the left side of the heart. In this case he was defining a vessel as an artery on the basis of its connection with the left side of the heart, yet this "artery" had the thin coat characteristic of a vein. Therefore he called it the "vein-like artery" (*arteria venalis*). Similarly, he defined the pulmonary artery as a vein or blood vessel by virtue of its connection with the right side of the heart and the venous system, yet it had the thick coat characteristic of an artery. Therefore, he called it the artery-like vein (*vena arterialis*). These terms were to persist until the time of Harvey, who in fact still used them. Herophilus also noted that pulsation was peculiar to the arteries and did not occur in the veins.

That the structure of the heart was in the meantime subjected to further study is indicated by a short work on the heart included in the Hippocratic corpus. This work was probably written later than those of Aristotle because it describes the heart as four-chambered with two auricles and two ventricles and reveals a knowledge of the structure and action of the semilunar valves of the aorta and pulmonary artery.

The study of the structure and action of the heart was carried still further at Alexandria by Erasistratus of Julis who, though but dimly known today, ought probably to stand as one of the very greatest physiologists. Erasistratus studied the action not only of the semilunar valves but also of the tricuspid valve in the right ventricle and the mitral valve in the left. He saw that the valves in each case were so constructed as to allow the passage of materials in only one direction. He also realized that when the ventricles enlarged in diastole, they were filled so that the beating heart was acting as a unidirectional pump. However, he considered that the two sides of the heart were pumping different substances. On the right side the heart was receiving blood from the vena cava and was impelling it through the artery-like vein into the lungs where it was apparently consumed in the nourishment of the lungs. On the left side Erasistratus thought that the heart was receiving air from the arteries in the lung through the vein-like artery and was pumping this air or *pneuma* onward into the aorta whence it was distributed through the arterial system to the whole body. While Erasistratus greatly misjudged the quantity of the heart's output, it must be admitted that he correctly interpreted the action of both sets of heart valves in relation to the heart beat which no one after him was to do so fully until the time of Harvey.

Erasistratus' theory, ingenious though it was, nevertheless had the weakness of being fundamentally wrong. Even in his time he was confronted with the glaring fact that although according to his theory only air or pneuma was present in the arteries, yet whenever an artery was opened in a living animal, blood spurted forth from it. His explanation of this contradiction, though later severely ridiculed by Galen, was perhaps not implausible. Erasistratus said that when you open an artery, this by itself creates an abnormal and pathological situation. For instance, if you leave the artery open, bright red blood will issue forth in spurts which gradually grow more feeble until the animal faints and dies. If you then dissect the animal, you will find that all of the blood has been drained not only from the arteries but also from the veins. Since in ordinary dissections on strangled animals you have found most of the blood located in the veins and right side of the heart with very little, if any, present in the arteries, it looks as if, when the artery was opened, the blood had passed out *through* it, but had originated from its chief reservoir in the veins. Under natural conditions the blood was normally contained in the veins. In order that this passage of the blood from the veins to the arteries might occur there must be some anatomical connection between the two. Since there is no visible connection, Erasistratus postulated that there were many fine invisible passages existing between veins and arteries throughout the body. These he called *synanastomoses*. The sequence of events which occurred when an artery was opened in a living animal Erasistratus then suggested was as follows: 1) all of the pneuma in the artery escaped instantly from the opening; 2) this escape of pneuma created a vacuum in the artery; 3) to fill the vacuum, blood rushed from the adjacent veins through the synanastomoses into the artery and thence through the artery and out the opening.

This extraordinary theory to account for bleeding from an artery—

a vessel which was supposed to be an air tube and to contain no blood—was therefore no mere piece of casuistic reasoning but was carefully related to anatomical and physiological observation. That it satisfied the ancient mind rather well is suggested by the fact that athough first taught by Erasistratus near the beginning of the third century B.C., it was still being supported vigorously by a group of physicians, the Erasistrateans, in Galen's time in the second century A.D. over four hundred and fifty years later.

Although Galen's contributions to biology and medicine are numerous and many-sided, his most important contribution to the study of the circulatory system was to show that arteries are not simply air tubes, but that blood is normally contained in both the arteries and left ventricle of the heart. Therefore the blood which spurts from an opened artery is normally contained within that artery and has not merely flowed through the artery from the veins. Galen deals with this subject in a short essay entitled "Whether blood is contained in the arteries under natural conditions." In this work he subjects the arguments of Erasistratus and his followers to extremely destructive criticism and shows that when a length of artery has been dissected clear of other tissues and isolated by ligatures at either end, it is nonetheless found full of blood when opened. Galen also shows in another work, *On the Opinions of Hippocrates and Plato,* that whereas according to Erasistratus' theory the left ventricle of the heart should be an air chamber containing no blood, in fact it is always found full of blood when opened in a living animal.

Galen's own discoveries created serious theoretical difficulties for him because he still accepted the ancient assumption that it was necessary to life to distribute the breath or pneuma throughout the body. However, he had shown that the system of vessels which had been thought to distribute the pneuma, i.e., the arteries, was in fact full of blood. Galen was able to conceive that the pneuma might be mixed with the arterial blood, but he considered it impossible that the pneuma should be distributed through the blood in the arteries by passing from the lungs via the pulmonary veins and left ventricle of the heart into the arterial system. Instead, he accounted for the presence of pneuma in the arterial blood by saying that it had entered the arteries through minute pores in the skin under the influence of the pulse. Galen's concept of the pulse was that in pulsation a wave of dilation passed out from the left ventricle of the heart into all the arteries passing *through their walls.* He considered the pulse, there-

fore, solely as a movement of the arterial wall and not as a movement produced by the blood and pneuma in the arterial cavity. Instead, the dilatation of the arterial wall and consequent enlargement
of the cavity created a suction which on the one hand drew pneuma
from the surrounding air through minute pores in the skin and on
the other drew blood into the arteries from the veins through the
synanastomoses. In the contraction of the artery which follows pulsation, these movements are reversed. He considered the same kind of
movement to occur, with respect to blood, between the right and left
ventricles of the heart through the synanastomoses in the interventricular septum, for he considered the right ventricle as part of the
venous system and the left ventricle as part of the arterial system.

Galen still believed the heart to be the center of the innate heat
and its distribution throughout the body to be one of the principal
functions of the pulse in the arteries. His evidence for this was that
when a limb is bandaged so tightly as to destroy the pulse in it, the
limb soon becomes cold and pale. When the bandage is removed and
the pulse restored to the limb, it rapidly becomes warm again.

For the same reason that he considered the synanastomoses to exist
between the arteries and veins throughout the body and between the
left and right ventricles of the heart, Galen also considered that there
would be synanastomoses between artery and vein in the lung. Since
he also knew that the semilunar valves at the mouth of the "arterial
vein" (i.e., pulmonary artery) would prevent blood from returning
into the right ventricle, Galen thought that when the lungs were
compressed as a result of their collapse during expiration, the blood
in the "arterial vein" would be squeezed through the synanastomoses
in drops into the "venous artery." In that vessel it might pass onward to the left ventricle of the heart. Galen was therefore familiar
with the elements which go to make up the pathway for the circulation through the lungs and he was aware of the possibility that some
blood might pass along this pathway. However, he considered it at
best as far less important than the shorter and more direct pathway
to the left ventricle through the pores in the interventricular septum.
His speaking of the blood's being squeezed through the synanastomoses in drops suggests the passage of only a small quantity. The
blood in the venous artery or pulmonary vein would have to pass
inward at the same time as "smoky wastes" were passing outward
from the left ventricle of the heart to the lungs. For these reasons it
cannot be said that Galen understood the concept of the pulmonary

circulation. However, it is also clear that the passage in which Galen describes the distribution of blood to the lungs in his *De usu partium* (Book VI, Chapter 10) is the starting point from which other workers set out to discover the pulmonary circulation—Ibn Nafis, an Arab of the thirteenth century, Michael Servetus (1511-1553), a Spaniard, and Realdo Colombo (1515?-1559), an Italian. In each case they offer reasons why *all* of the blood must pass through the lungs in order to get from the right side of the heart to the left and in each case they are arguing within the context of Galenic physiology. Ibn an-Nafis says that the blood must pass through the lungs because the inter-ventricular septum is not porous. Servetus argues that the "arterial vein," or pulmonary artery, is too large and carries too much blood to serve merely for the nutrition of the lungs, while Colombo argues that according to Galen the "venous artery" or pulmonary vein should contain mainly air, but he has found it in both living and dead animals always full of blood.

Galen's description of the pulmonary pathway was likewise in the mind of William Harvey when he came to develop his argument for both the pulmonary and the systemic circulation of the blood. In the introduction to the *De motu cordis* Harvey subjects Galen's notions of the heart beat, the pulse, and the distribution of the blood to destructive criticism. Later, however, he invokes Galen's authority in support of his views when he presents his argument for the circulation of the blood through the lungs. He then quotes the passage from Book VI, Chapter 10 of Galen's *De usu partium* in which Galen describes the pulmonary pathway. Harvey's other arguments for the circulation are of course original with him.

The valves in the veins, structures vital for Harvey's argument, were recognized by Giovanni Battista Canano, for in 1541 he told Vesalius of his discovery of valves at the mouths of the azygos and renal veins. Canano published nothing on this subject, but in 1545 Charles Estienne described the valves in the hepatic veins. Jacobus Sylvius (1478-1555) in his *Isagoge* mentions the valves at the mouth of the azygos vein and the fact that valves are often present at the mouths of the larger veins but does not claim to be the discoverer of them. Salomon Alberti wrote on the valves in the veins in 1585 and gave drawings of them. He mentions the earlier work of Canano and ac-knowledges that he is indebted to Hieronymus Fabricius ab Aqua-pendente (1533?-1619), who had discovered these valves in 1574 and demonstrated them in his lectures as early as 1578 or 1579. Ultimately

Fabricius showed that the valves are structures which exist throughout the venous system and illustrated them fully with drawings of remarkable beauty in his *De venarum ostiolis* (Venice, 1603).

William Harvey first expounded his beliefs concerning the circulation in his Lumleian Lectures before the Royal College of Physicians in 1616, 1617, and 1618 but he waited another nine years before publishing his discovery in 1628. In this chapter attention will be directed in Part I to ideas concerning the vascular system prior to Harvey, and in Part II Harvey's work will be described on the basis of recent studies.

Aristotle of Stagira
384-322 B.C.

Aristotle, Greek philosopher, biologist, and polyhistor, was one of the commanding figures not only of the classical period, but of all time. Born the son of a court physician in the hamlet of Stagira in Thrace (modern Salonica), he lived near the ancient city of Pella,[2] the renowned cultural center of the kings of the Macedonian Empire. Aristotle's teachings spread to the far corners of the civilized world, and during the twenty-five centuries since his death the writings of the great Stagirite have exerted a profound and determining influence on the course of medical and biological thought. Many of his writings belong to medical literature, but his works also embrace logic, geometry, astronomy, as well as experimental studies in the fields of botany, zoology, comparative anatomy, and physiology. His interests likewise touched upon sex, growth, heredity, and nutrition, and he put forward a theory of evolution based on his own classification of the animal kingdom. Anyone touching upon such a wide range of subjects was inevitably destined to make some errors, as for example Aristotle's denial of sex in plants, his insistence that intelligence lay in the heart, and, in the sphere of more immediate interest, that arteries contain "air" as well as blood. The following passage from *De partibus animalium* (Bk. III, 4-5) illustrates his accuracy in anatomical description.

THE HEART

[666b] In animals of great size the heart has three cavities; in smaller animals it has two; and in all has at least one, for, as already stated, there must be some place in the heart to serve as a receptacle for the

---

[2] The site of the large ancient city of Pella was discovered in April 1957 and, as reported in *The Illustrated London News* for 2 August 1958, it has since been excavated. The Greek archeologist, Photios Petsas, director of excavation at Pella, states that Aristotle lived in Pella and it was there he served as tutor to twelve-year-old Prince Alexander who was to become Alexander the Great (356-323 B.C.).

first blood; which, as has been mentioned more than once, is formed in this organ. But inasmuch as the main blood-vessels are two in number, namely the so-called great vessel and the aorta, each of which is the origin of other vessels; inasmuch, moreover, as these two vessels present differences, hereafter to be discussed, when compared with each other, it is of advantage that they also shall themselves have distinct origins. This advantage will be obtained if each side have its own blood, and the blood of one side be kept separate from that of the other. For this reason the heart, whenever it is possible, has two receptacles. And this possibility exists in the case of large animals, for in them the heart, as the body generally, is of large size. Again it is still better that there shall be three cavities, so that the middle and odd one may serve as a centre common to both sides. But this requires the heart to be of greater magnitude, so that it is only in the largest hearts that there are three cavities.

Of these three cavities it is the right that has the most abundant and the hottest blood, and this explains why the limbs also on the right side of the body are warmer than those on the left. The left cavity has the least blood of all, and the coldest; while in the middle cavity the blood, as regards quantity and heat, is intermediate to the other two, being however of purer quality than either. . . .

[667a] What has been said of the heart as a whole is no less true of its cavities and of the blood-vessels; these also if of large size being cold. For just as a fire of equal size gives less heat in a large room than in a small one, so also does the heat in a large cavity or a large blood-vessel, that is in a large receptacle, have less effect than in a small one. Moreover, all hot bodies are cooled by motions external to themselves, and the more spacious the cavities and vessels are, the greater the amount of spirit they contain, and the more potent its action. Thus it is that no animal that has large cavities in its heart, or large blood-vessels, is ever fat, the vessels being indistinct and the cavities small in all or most fat animals. . . .

[668b] As the blood-vessels advance, they become gradually smaller and smaller, until at last their tubes are too fine to admit the blood. This fluid can therefore no longer find its way through them, though they still give passage to the humour which we call sweat; and especially so when the body is heated, and the mouths of the small vessels are dilated. Instances, indeed, are not unknown of persons

who in consequence of a cachectic state have secreted sweat that resembled blood, their body having become loose and flabby, and their blood watery, owing to the heat in the small vessels having been too scanty for its concoction. For, as was before said, every compound of earth and water—and both nutriment and blood are such—becomes thicker from concoction. The inability of the heat to effect concoction may be due either to its being absolutely small in amount, or to its being small in proportion to the quantity of food, when this has been taken in excess. This excess again may be of two kinds, either quantitative or qualitative; for all substances are not equally amenable to concoction. (From William Ogle's translation of the "De partibus" in *The works of Aristotle*. Oxford, Clarendon Press, 1912 [vol. 5, 666b, 667a, 668b].)[3]

Hippocratic Corpus, Peri Kardies

c. 320 B.C.

Although the works of the Hippocratic corpus have by tradition been ascribed to Hippocrates, they are a heterogeneous group of writings which, as Edelstein has pointed out,[4] cannot be the work of one man. Among these writings the short treatise on the heart stands peculiarly apart. It reflects the doctrines of the ancient Sicilian school of medicine which ascribed a central importance to the heart. Since it offers a description of the heart more accurate and more detailed than that of Aristotle, it probably dates from a period slightly later than his writings. It is particularly striking that the author understood the action of the aortic valve, as is clear from the following passage.

THE FIRST DESCRIPTION OF THE HEART VALVES

VIII. Near the outgrowth of the veins (aorta and pulmonary artery) there are, on either side of the hollow bellies, soft porous bodies which are called indeed, ears, but they have no holes of ears; for these do not take in noise, but are the instruments by which nature snatches up air, and indeed, I think it the creation of a good handicraftsman. For, perceiving that the organ would be solid in structure because of the compactness of its tissue, it being further-

[3] The reader may also consult with profit A. Platt's excellent paper, "Aristotle on the heart," in *Studies in the history and method of science*, edited by Charles Singer, 1921, vol. 2, pp. 521-532.

[4] Edelstein, Ludwig. "The genuine works of Hippocrates." *Bull. Hist. Med.*, 1939, 7, 236-248.

more entirely attractive, he placed bellows beside it, after the manner of the coppersmiths with their melting pots, and so it manages its breathing through these. And there is proof of this proposition, for one might observe the heart tossing about as a whole, but the ears independently inflating and collapsing.

IX. On this account I say that veins (pulmonary veins) effect the breathing into the left hollow, and a vein (pulmonary artery) does it for the other; for that which is soft is more attractive and yielding. It is suitable for us that the surrounding coverings (of the heart) should be less cooled than the heart. For there is no heat on the right side, so that, on account of this failing (lack), it does not work (too) easily, in order that it might not be entirely overcome by what comes in.

X. The remaining matter to treat of in the heart is hidden membranes, a thing very worthy of exposition. For membranes and other muscles resembling spiderwebs spread out, gird everywhere the outlets and send fibers into the solid parts of the heart. These seem to be the bands of the organ and the veins, beginnings of the veins. There is a pair of them at the entrances to which there have been constructed three membranes for each, rounded, at the extremity at least, to the extent of a half circle, and when they come together it is marvelous how they close the outlets, the end of the veins (aorta and pulmonary artery). And if some one who thoroughly understands the ancient method removes the heart of a dead man, and takes up one of these membranes and bends another up against it, water will not go through into the heart, nor even the breath when forced in. And even more (is this true) in the case of those of the left belly. Accordingly they have rightly been constructed more exactly, for the intelligence of man is innate in the left hollow and rules the rest of the soul.

XI. It (the soul) is nourished neither by the foods nor by the drinks which come from the body, but by a pure light excess, born out of the separation of the blood. And it gets plenty of this nourishment from the reservoir of blood right next to it, throwing its rays across and feeding, just as on the nourishment from stomach and intestines, and this is according to nature, but in order that the substance in the vein (aorta) may not inhibit this nourishment which is in a state of flux, it (left ventricle) closes the path to it (heart), for the large vein (aorta) feeds on the stomach and intestines, and is full of nourishment which is not of the highest type. That it is not nourished by visible blood is clear thus: when the animal was slaughtered, if the left hollow is split, it is seen to be quite empty, except for some watery liquid and yellow bile and the membranes about which I have already spoken; but the vein (aorta) is not lacking in blood, neither is the right hollow. Therefore, in my opinion, this is the reason for the membranes in this vein (aorta). (Hurlbutt, Frank R. "Peri Kardies: a treatise on the heart from the Hippocratic corpus: introduction and translation." *Bull. Hist. Med.,* 1939, 7, 1104-1113 [pp. 1111-1113].)

Erasistratus of Julis[5]

c. 330 B.C.-c. 250 B.C.

We know of Erasistratus only indirectly through the writings of Galen and a few other ancient writers, yet the outlines of the man loom large. He was trained by Metrodorus, a pupil of Chrysippus of Cnidos, and the son-in-law of Aristotle, so that we may safely assume that in his education Erasistratus partook both of the great scientific tradition of Athens and the medical tradition of Cos and Cnidos. However, like Herophilus, Erasistratus' name is associated with Alexandria where he may have been connected with the museum.

In his medical teaching Erasistratus emphasized the importance of anatomy and he seems to have considered that diseases had definite anatomical locations and were not merely the result of imbalance in the humors or fluids of the body. He studied the nervous system, which was then newly recognized as a *system* extending throughout the body, and attached great physiological importance to it. He also was evidently the first to describe the heart fully and to interpret correctly the action of all its valves. However, he considered that the left side of the heart transferred breath or pneuma from the arteries of the lungs (the bronchioles) to the arteries of the body.

ON THE DISTRIBUTION OF BLOOD AND PNEUMA

. . . According to him [Erasistratus], the artery is a vessel containing pneuma, the vein one containing blood. The vessels, as they are distributed through the body, continually divide, diminishing in size and increasing in number, so that there is no place without a vascular extremity. But these terminal ramifications are so small that the blood is retained within them by the coaptation of their walls. Consequently, although the mouths of the vein and the artery lie side by side, the blood nevertheless remains in its own vessels, and nowhere

[5] Julis was a town on the island of Ceos not far off the Attic Peninsula.

penetrates into those of the pneuma. So far, the system is in its normal condition. But when, from any disturbing cause, the blood is forced over from the veins into the arteries, a morbid action results. There may be several such causes, one of the most important of which is a *plethora of the blood.* By this, the blood-vessel is distended, and its extremities, previously closed, forced open; when the blood is transfused into the arteries, coming in conflict with the pneuma from the heart, and interfering with its motion. If this take place near the source of the pneuma, toward the heart, it produces fever; but if the blood be driven forward by the pneuma and impacted in the terminal arteries, it causes inflammation. It is in this way that inflammation arises from plethora. It may also result from *wounds;* but in that case the transfusion is due to the natural movement for filling a vacuum. For as the pneuma escapes from the divided arteries it tends to leave behind it a vacancy; and the blood consequently follows, through the vascular anastomoses, to occupy its place. (Galen, *De venae sectione adversus Erasistratum,* Ch. III [Kühn XI, 152-154] translated by John C. Dalton, *Doctrines of the circulation.* Philadelphia, Henry C. Lea's Son and Co., 1884, pp. 58-59.)

THE ACTION OF THE HEART VALVES

Erasistratus, in his treatise on fevers, has described how membranes are attached to the mouths of the vessels which serve the heart in the alternate reception and expulsion of materials. Some have ventured to deny the existence of these membranes, implying that they were made up by Erasistratus for the purpose of supporting his doctrine; but they have now come to be so well known to physicians generally, that one would seem very ill informed not to be acquainted with them. At the mouth of the vena cava there are three, shaped very much like spear points; whence, I suppose, they were called "tricuspids" (τριγλώχινας) by some of the Erasistrateans. Those at the arteria venalis, that is, the artery which has its ramification from the left ventricle of the heart into the lung, are of nearly the same form but not so many, for at this orifice the membranous appendages are two in number, while at each of the remaining mouths there are three, all of them sigmoid* in shape. Each of these

---

* The ancient Greek *sigma,* in the older monumental inscriptions, as well as in some existing manuscripts, has the form of C. The valves of the pulmonary artery and aorta were, therefore, properly named, from their semilunar or crescentic shape.

(last) mouths, as Erasistratus says, in his description, is a channel of exit, one of them for blood to the lung, the other for pneuma to the body at large. The use of the membranes, as he thinks, is to perform for the heart contrary functions, alternating at successive intervals. Those attached to the vessels which bring in materials, when pressed from without inward, yield to the influx of the materials, and, falling into the cavities of the heart, throw open its orifices and leave an unobstructed passage for what is drawn into it. For these matters, he says, do not come in of their own impulse, as into a passive receptacle; but the heart itself, expanding like a brazier's bellows, distends itself by its diastole. The membranes attached, on the other hand, to the vessels of exit, act in the contrary way. For, turning from within outward, they yield before the efflux, and open the orifices when the heart discharges its contents; while in the whole remaining interval they exactly close the orifices, preventing any return of what has been discharged. (Galen, *De placitis Hippocratis et Platonis,* Bk. VI, Ch. 6 [Kühn V, 548-550] translated by Dalton, *Doctrines,* pp. 250-251.)

Galen of Pergamon
130-200 A.D.

Galen of Pergamon, experimental physiologist and polyhistor, stands with Aristotle as a biologist, but as a philosopher he was limited and dogmatic and in no way resembled in breadth of outlook his incomparable Greek predecessor. Yet Galen is one of the most remarkable figures in the history of medicine.

Born in the thriving town of Pergamon in northern Asia Minor, this impetuous young Asiatic Greek went to Rome and through his industry and competence established himself as personal physician to the Emperor Marcus Aurelius and as one of the foremost physicians of the Roman Empire. He obtained his education partly in Asia Minor and partly in Greece. In the pursuit of knowledge he eventually worked his way to Egypt where he studied at the famous medical school at Alexandria prior to going to Rome, first in 162 and permanently in 169 A.D.

Galen was one of the earliest in the history of biology to appeal to planned experiment for an answer to questions confronting him, and in consequence he is often described as the founder of experimental physiology. There is scarcely a branch of the subject which, for better or for worse, he did not touch. He wrote prolifically and is said to have employed twelve scribes to record the details of his observations and experiments.

The first passage is of special interest because it indicates the acuteness of

Galen's powers of observation and his range and skill as an operator; the second gives his account of the relation of the pulmonary blood vessels to the heart. This passage was probably the point of departure from which later workers proceeded to the discovery of the pulmonary circulation.

VIVISECTION OF HEART AND LUNGS

. . . Use a young animal so that you do not need large knives. It must be on its back, on a board of the kind that you see I have quantities at hand, both large and small, so that one may always be found to fit the animal. This board should have holes bored in it through which a thin cord or even a rope will easily pass. An assistant should be instructed, when the animal is on its back on the board, to pass cords round it, one round each limb and the ends of the cords through the holes below and tied together there. If the animal has long hair about the breast-bone, that should be removed.

This is the way to prepare the subject for dissection. Make a straight incision with a large lancet along the sternum downwards to the ensiform cartilage. Thence turn the incision at right angles so as to bare the breast-bone—with or without the ensiform—of the overlying tissues.* Continue to apply the lancet in the same way, moving upwards over the sternum to where in the dead animal you have seen the pericardium attached under it.

In the living the procedure is the same, as far as the incision goes, but there is a complication on which there is no need for long explanations to those who have seen me operating. To those who have not, I would say that from the thorax arteries and veins [*internal mammary*] emerge beside the root of the ensiform cartilage, one of each on each side, and that when severed—as they must be in this operation—haemorrhage results, especially from the arteries.

Nothing upsets any operation like haemorrhage. Bearing this in mind, immediately you see blood spurt from the artery with the downward incision, turn the lancet as quickly as possible to the transverse incision. Then with the thumb and index of the left hand, grasp that part of the sternum where the artery is pouring forth blood, so that while the one finger acts as a stopper for the orifice, both grasp the bone.

Next try to do two things at the same time, viz. cut with the lancet as quickly as possible and connect with the end of the downward incision first the transverse cut and after it the upward, and also with

* Text reads "underlying."

your finger keep bending back the breast-bone. When it is bent back properly the cause of the haemorrhage no longer exists, for the incision at either orifice is thus controlled, and the attachment of the pericardium is visible. This guides you to the completion of the incision. For when the sternum is bent back, the lower end is raised and by this position the haemorrhage is stemmed and the position of the vessels is altered as they are kinked above at the sternum and do not run straight down. . . .

There is a third operation on the living animal which differs from the first-mentioned in that a similar incision is made in both the parts of the thorax. You will learn its usefulness a little later; that of the first you have already grasped sufficiently. But it is time for you to learn about the one which is our present subject. You will perform it most successfully if you expose the heart and keep the [pleural] cavities of the thorax unharmed. Sometimes in this operation the membrane round the heart is severed, but often it remains undamaged. In both those operations it is so far divided that the heart is exposed, but the membranes that partition the thorax are not damaged, for if one be wounded the animal necessarily develops these symptoms which, as will be explained later, arise when the thorax is perforated.

When the heart is exposed, your task is to preserve all its functions unimpaired, as in fact they are, so that you can see the animal breathing and uttering cries and, if loosed from its bonds, running as before. Further, if you continue to compress the wound with ligatures, you will see it taking food if hungry, and drinking if thirsty. And what is strange in that? The slave of Maryllus, the mime-writer, whose heart was once exposed, was cured and still lives. It is surely more likely that a non-rational brute, being less sensitive than a human being, will suffer nothing from such a wound. (*Galen on anatomical procedures.* Translation of the surviving books with introduction and notes by Charles Singer. London, Oxford University Press, 1956. xxvi, 289 pp. [pp. 190-192].)

THE PULMONARY PATIIWAY AND THE NUTRITION OF THE LUNGS

All over the body the arteries and veins communicate with one another by common openings and exchange blood and *pneuma* through certain invisible and extremely narrow passages. But if the

large orifice of the arterial vein [pulmonary artery] always lay uniformly open and if Nature had not found some device which could
close and open it again at the proper times, the blood would never be
taken over into the arteries through the little, invisible orifices when
the thorax contracts. For attraction and expulsion are not naturally
the same for every material and every place; on the contrary, just as
a light substance is attracted more easily by expanding instruments
than a heavier one and also expelled more easily when they contract,
so also attraction and expulsion too are accomplished through a
broad passage more readily than through a narrow one. When the
thorax contracts, the venous arteries [pulmonary veins], pushed inward and compressed from all sides, instantly force out the *pneuma*
they contain and receive in exchange a portion of blood through
those fine openings, an exchange that would never take place if the
blood were able to run back through a very large opening, such as
that of the vein [pulmonary artery] into the heart. As it is, however,
when the blood is compressed and cut off from returning through the
large orifice, some of it trickles through those fine openings, into the
arteries. Perhaps it is already clear to you what an excellent thing
this is for the lung, if you remember what I have said about its
nourishment. (Galen, *De usu partium*, Bk. VI, Ch. 10 [Kühn III,
455-457] translated by Mrs. Margaret T. May, Department of Zoology,
Cornell University.)

Ibn Nafis

1210-1288

[Ibn Nafis] presaged the very thoughts of Harvey when he wrote:
"The heart is the beginning of life; the sun of the microcosm
. . . it is the household divinity which, discharging its functions, nourishes, cherishes, quickens the whole body and is indeed the foundation of life, the source of all action . . . ."
(Bittar, Thesis, p. 70)

Ibn Nafis,[6] Arab physician and teacher who discovered the pulmonary circulation, was born at Damascus having been descended from a proud family long
resident in the near-by village of Qars ("beyond the river"). After finishing his

---

[6] Also known to Western medical historians as Ibn al-Nafis or Ibn an-Nafis; his full
Arabic name transliterated would be Ala' al-Din Ibn Abi al-Hazm al-Quarashie.

medical studies under Ad-Dakhwār at the Nuri School (Damascus), he proceeded to the Mansoury Medical School in Cairo where he became head physician.

Such biographical details as are known concerning this great thirteenth century physician are meagre; they have been summed up by E. Edward Bittar, in his medical school thesis: "Ibn Nafis' life was entirely devoted to medicine, to teaching, and writing, and like his master Ad-Dakhwār he gave up all personal happiness that a home and family can give and remained a bachelor, wrapped up in his profession of serving—day and night—all who needed his help. Like Dakhwār, he bequeathed his luxurious house and library to the medical school and hospital at which he taught the greatest part of his life. He continued working and writing almost up to his death, endeavoring to complete his 'All-Embracing.' Close upon his eightieth year, however, he suddenly fell ill, and took to bed. It is recorded that his fellow physicians asked him to take wine as a remedy, but, as a good Mohammedan, he refused to, saying 'I would not face my Creator with wine in my body.' He knew of impending death, and gradually his health declined till on the sixth day of his illness, Friday, December 18, 1288 A.D. he quietly passed away."[7]

Ibn Nafis' description of the pulmonary circuit is contained in his "Commentary on the Anatomy of the *Canon* of Avicenna" probably written sometime after 1245 A.D.[8] and is here quoted in the form of a posthumous dialogue between Avicenna and Ibn Nafis.

THE PULMONARY CIRCUIT

What we say (and God knows better) is that whereas one of the functions of the heart is the generation of the spirit, which consists of highly rarefied blood, extremely mixable with an airy substance,

[7] Bittar, E. E. "Ibn Nafis: A study with translations of two of his works." Thesis, Yale University School of Medicine, New Haven, 1955. 172 pp. [p. 46].

The thesis contains an informative section on Arab medicine, the fullest available account of the life of Ibn Nafis, and a new English translation from the original Arabic text of Ibn Nafis' "Commentary" on Avicenna's *Canon* from which is taken the passage on the lesser circulation here quoted. An essay based on this thesis won the William Osler Medal of 1955: "A Study of Ibn Nafis," *Bull. Hist. Med.*, 1955, *29*, 352-368; 429-447.

[8] The passage was discovered in Berlin and translated from Arabic into German by Dr. M. El-Tatawi in 1924 while preparing his doctoral dissertation for the medical faculty at Freiburg: "Der Lungenkreislauf nach el-Koraschi." The dissertation was subsequently reprinted by Max Meyerhof in *Mitt. Gesch. Med. Naturw.*, 1931, *30*, 55-57; see also Meyerhof's three papers: "Ibn an-Nafis und seine Theorie des Lungenkreislaufs," *Quellen Studien Gesch. Naturw. Med.*, 1933, *1*, 37-88 (the text in Arabic appended thereto includes selected passages from Ibn Nafis' Commentary on Avicenna's anatomy, 15 pp., and Safadi's biographical sketch, 5 pp.); "La découverte de la circulation pulmonaire par Ibn an-Nafis. Médecin Arabe du Caire," *Bull. Inst. Egypte*, 1934, *16*, 33-46; and "Ibn an-Nafis and his theory of the lesser circulation," *Isis*, 1935, *23*, 100-120. See also Joseph Schacht's "Ibn al-Nafis, Servetus and Colombo," *Al-Andalus*, 1957, *22*, 317-336.

it is essential that such highly rarefied blood and air meet in the heart to facilitate the evolution of the spirit from the compound formed of their mixture. This meeting takes place in the left cavity of the two cavities of the heart, where the animal spirit is generated.

It is also essential that there be in the heart of man, and other animals possessing lungs, another cavity in which the blood is rarefied to be fit for mixing with air. For if air were mixed with blood when thick, a homogenous compound could not result. This cavity is the right cavity of the two cavities of the heart.

After the blood has been rarefied in this cavity, it must of necessity pass to the left cavity, where the animal spirit is generated. But there is no opening, as some thought there was between these two cavities, for the septum of the heart there is watertight without any apparent fenestrations in it. Nor, as held by Galen, would an invisible opening be suitable for the passage of this blood, for the pores of the heart there are not patent and its septum is thick. The blood, therefore, after thinning, passes via the vena-arterialis to the lung for circulation and mixing with air in the pulmonary parenchyma. The aerated blood gets refined and passes through the arteria-venalis to reach the left cavity of the two cavities of the heart, after having mixed with the air and become suitable for the evolution of the animal spirit. (Bittar, Thesis [note 7], pp. 54-55.)

Michael Servetus of Villanueva

1511-1553

Michael Servetus, medical practitioner and religious heretic, was responsible for the first printed description of the lesser circulation.[9] The famous passage is buried on page 170 of a book that caused its author to be burned at the stake (27 October 1553). Servetus was born of well-to-do parents at Tudela in Navarre, it is thought, and reared at Villanueva de Sigena in Spain. He studied law at the University of Toulouse, but having no taste for it, turned to scriptural texts. With the publication of his *De trinitatis erroribus* in 1531 in his 20th year, he became naïvely involved in theological controversy. His retraction the following year in his *Diologorum de trinitate libri duo* did not absolve him from charges of heresy, and he was therefore obliged to go into hiding and to assume for the

---

[9] Fulton, J. F. *Michael Servetus, humanist and martyr.* New York, Herbert Reichner, 1953. 98 pp. See also: Bainton, R. H. *Hunted heretic. The life and death of Michael Servetus, 1511-1553.* Boston, Beacon Press. 1953. xii, 270 pp.

rest of his life the name of Michael Villanovanus. His movements are thus diffi-cult to follow with certainty but he spent some time between 1532 and 1538 in Paris studying medicine and working partly in the laboratory of Guenther von Andernach as prosector. As Guenther's assistant he followed Andreas Vesalius who was to startle the world of medicine in 1538 with his "Six Anatomical Tables" to be followed in 1543 by the immortal *Fabrica*. Servetus evidently im-pressed those with whom he worked in Paris since Guenther referred to him as "a man accomplished in all branches of literature and in the teachings of Galen scarcely second to anyone."

It is not known when Servetus arrived at his conclusions about the pulmonary circulation. The printed description occurs in the *Christianismi restitutio* of 1553 which was to prove his undoing (Pl. 5). Sometime before 1546 this book was already in manuscript and being circulated among his friends. This of itself established Servetus' priority over the claims of Realdo Colombo (1515?-1559) and Andrea Cesalpino (1519-1603), and likewise that of his fellow-Spaniard, Juan Valverde de Hamusco (*fl.* 1550). Servetus' passage describing the pulmonary circulation was rediscovered in 1695 by William Wotton and discussed in the second edition of his *Reflections upon ancient and modern learning* (London, 1694, p. 211).

THE LESSER (PULMONARY) CIRCULATION

In this matter there must first be understood the substantial gen-eration of the vital spirit which is composed of a very subtle blood nourished by the inspired air. The vital spirit has its origin in the left ventricle of the heart, and the lungs assist greatly in its genera-tion. It is a rarefied spirit, elaborated by the force of heat, reddish-yellow (*flavo*) and of fiery potency, so that it is a kind of clear vapor from very pure blood, containing in itself the substance of water, air and fire. It is generated in the lungs from a mixture of inspired air with elaborated, subtle blood which the right ventricle of the heart communicates to the left. *However, this communication is made not through the middle wall of the heart, as is commonly be-lieved, but by a very ingenious arrangement the subtle blood is urged forward by a long course through the lungs; it is elaborated by the lungs, becomes reddish-yellow and is poured from the pulmonary artery into the pulmonary vein. Then in the pulmonary vein it is mixed with inspired air and through expiration it is cleansed of its sooty vapors. Thus finally the whole mixture, suitably prepared for the production of the vital spirit, is drawn onward from the left ventricle of the heart by diastole.* [Italics mine. J. F. F.]

That the communication and elaboration are accomplished in this way through the lungs we are taught by the different conjunctions and the communication of the pulmonary artery with the pulmonary vein in the lungs. The notable size of the pulmonary artery confirms this; that is, it was not made of such sort or of such size, nor does it emit so great a force of pure blood from the heart itself into the lungs merely for their nourishment; nor would the heart be of such service to the lungs, since at an earlier stage, in the embryo, the lungs, as Galen teaches, are nourished from elsewhere because those little membranes or valvules of the heart are not opened until the time of birth. Therefore that the blood is poured from the heart into the lungs at the very time of birth, and so copiously, is for another purpose. Likewise, not merely air, but air mixed with blood, is sent from the lungs to the heart through the pulmonary vein; therefore the mixture occurs in the lungs. That reddish-yellow color is given to the spirituous blood by the lungs; it is not from the heart.

In the left ventricle of the heart there is no place large enough for so great and copious a mixture, nor for that elaboration imbuing the reddish-yellow color. Finally, that middle wall, since it is lacking in vessels and mechanisms, is not suitable for that communication and elaboration, although something may possibly sweat through. By the same arrangement by which a transfusion of the blood from the portal vein to the vena cava occurs in the liver, so a transfusion of the spirit from the pulmonary artery to the pulmonary vein occurs in the lung. If anyone compares these things with those which Galen wrote in books VI and VII, *De usu partium,* he will thoroughly understand a truth which was unknown to Galen. (O'Malley, C. D. *Michael Servetus. A translation of his geographical, medical and astrological writings with introductions and notes.* Philadelphia, American Philosophical Society, 1953. 208 pp. [pp. 204-205].)

Matteo Realdo Colombo

1515?-1559

Matteo Realdo Colombo, Italian anatomist, whose description of the pulmonary circuit appeared posthumously in 1559, occupied chairs successively at Padua (1544), Pisa (1545), and finally at Rome where he remained from 1548 until his premature death at the early age of forty-three. His views concerning the vascular system were set down in a substantial book, *De re anatomica* (Pl. 6), published at Rome a few months after his death, having been seen through the press by his Spanish pupil Juan Valverde. Vesalius, who saw in Realdo Colombo an able competitor, became jealous of him and of men such as Valverde whom he had trained, accusing them of having unblushingly plagiarized the work of others including his own.

Colombo deserves credit for having given a clear description of the mode of action of the pulmonary, cardiac, and aortic valves; and in a number of other respects his anatomical descriptions were actually more accurate than those of Vesalius. Colombo gives as his evidence for the passage of the blood through the lungs the fact that although according to Galen the pulmonary vein should contain air, he has always found it full of blood in both living and dead animals. That Colombo based his ideas on many experiments performed on living animals is confirmed by his friend Valverde. The following passage cited and translated by Coppola illustrates Colombo's beliefs.

THE PULMONARY TRANSIT OF THE BLOOD

Between these ventricles there is a septum through which almost everyone believes there opens a pathway for the blood from the right ventricle to the left, and that the blood is rendered thin so that this may be done more easily for the generation of vital spirits. *But they are in great error, for the blood is carried through the pulmonary artery to the lung and is there attenuated; then it is carried, along with air, through the pulmonary vein to the left ventricle of the heart. Hitherto no one has noticed this or left it in writing* [Coppola's italics], and it especially should be observed by all. . . .

But let us return to the aforesaid four vessels; two of them have been constructed so that they carry inwardly to the heart, that is, when the heart is dilated; but the other two carry outward when the heart is constricted. Therefore when it is dilated, and those membranes are loosened and yield ingress, the heart receives blood from the vena cava into the right ventricle, and also prepared blood from the pulmonary vein, as we said, along with air into the left ventricle. And when the heart is compressed, these valves are closed lest the vessels receive anything regressing along the same path; and at that same time the valves of both the aorta and the pulmonary artery are opened; they permit the passage of the outgoing spiritous blood which is diffused through the whole body and of the natural blood which is carried to the lungs; and it is always thus when the heart is dilated, as we noted before: [that the] other [valves] open and then shut. And so you will find that the blood which has entered the right ventricle is unable to return to the vena cava. (Coppola, E. D. "The discovery of the pulmonary circulation: a new approach." The William Osler Prize Essay for 1956. *Bull. Hist. Med.,* 1957, *31,* 44-77 [pp. 62, 65].)[10]

Hieronymus Fabricius ab Aquapendente
1537-1619

Hieronymus Fabricius of Aquapendente, anatomist of Padua, was the teacher of William Harvey and is best known for his monograph on the "valves in the veins" first published in 1603. Professor K. J. Franklin has made an excellent translation of this important landmark in physiology, and physiologists owe to him the first detailed study of the historical backgrounds of the venous valves, both as physical structures and as functional entities.[11] If one recalls the emphasis which Harvey placed on the fact that these valves are always so arranged as to promote flow of blood *toward* the heart (be it in the lower extremities or in the veins originating in the head), their historical importance becomes immediately obvious.

Although valves had been noted by Giovanni Battista Canano (1515-1579) as early as 1542 and had been mentioned in casual fashion by Amatus Lusitanus (1511-1568) in 1547, they had been missed or deliberately ignored by the great anatomists of the sixteenth century. The first author to give an accurate drawing of the valves was Salomon Alberti (*fl.* 1580), an obscure north Italian who, through his book and also by word of mouth, had passed on his knowledge to Fabricius. In the latter's monograph, *De venarum ostiolis* (Pl. 7), the valves are described in great detail, and a few fanciful speculations are offered concerning their probable function (Pl. 8). The following selection is taken from Franklin's rendering.

SHAPE AND FUNCTION OF VALVES

Valves of veins is the name I give to some extremely delicate little membranes in the lumen of veins. They occur at intervals, singly or in pairs, especially in the limb veins. They open upwards in the direction of the main venous trunk, and are closed below, while, viewed from the outside, they resemble the swellings in the stem and small branches of plants.

My theory is that Nature has formed them to delay the blood to

[10] Coppola's essay, offering a "new approach" to the history of pulmonary circulation, was based on his thesis entitled "Realdo Colombo of Cremona (1515?-1559) and the pulmonary circulation." Yale University School of Medicine, New Haven, 1955. 154 pp. Coppola believes that Colombo learned of Ibn Nafis' account of the lesser circulation through Andrea Alpago.

[11] Franklin, K. J. "Valves in veins. An historical survey." *Proc. roy. Soc. Med., Sect. Hist. Med.,* 1927, *21,* 1-33, 24 figs.

some extent, and to prevent the whole mass of it flooding into the feet, or hands and fingers, and collecting there. Two evils are thus avoided, namely, under-nutrition of the upper parts of the limbs, and a permanently swollen condition of the hands and feet. Valves were made, therefore, to ensure a really fair general distribution of the blood for the nutrition of the various parts.

A discussion of these valves must be preceded by an expression of wonder at the way in which they have hitherto escaped the notice of Anatomists, both of our own and of earlier generations; so much so that not only have they never been mentioned, but no one even set eye on them till 1574, when to my great delight I saw them in the course of my dissection. . . . (Fabricius ab Aquapendente, H. *De venarum ostiolis.* Padua, L. Pasquati, 1603. 23 pp. [10 tabulae with legends]. Facsimile with translation by K. J. Franklin. Springfield, Illinois, Charles C Thomas, Publisher, 1933. 98 pp. [p. 47].)

Part 2. William Harvey and His Followers
William Harvey
1578-1657

"But, damme, there are no pores" . . . I kept being reminded of the Harvey pictured by Aubrey— "short of stature, dark of skin, with shining black eyes and hair, alert and irritable, often fingering the handle of his dagger." Here, to illustrate the point, are the four translations of a certain sentence in the Introduction [*Sed mehercule porositates nullae sunt, neque demonstrari possunt*]. Harvey's contemporary wrote [1653], "But by my troth there are no such pores, nor can they be demonstrated." Ryan followed [1832] with, "But, in fact, there are not such porosities, nor can they be demonstrated," while Willis [1847] gave the rendering "But, in faith, no such pores can be demonstrated, neither in fact do any such exist." My own version [1957] was, "But, damme, there are no pores and it is not possible to show such." It took me two hours to think of "damme" as a sufficiently dramatic translation of "mehercule" [for] . . . getting the effect that Harvey had, to my mind, intended by his use of a particular Latin word. . . .
(K. J. Franklin)[12]

During the three centuries since William Harvey's death in 1657, historians of many nations have studied and restudied the man and his writings, his forerunners and those who followed him in the study of vascular physiology. One

[12] Franklin, K. J. "On translating Harvey." *J. Hist. Med.,* 1957, *12,* 114-119 [pp. 117-118].

therefore might think it difficult to add any further information to knowledge of the circulation in particular or to the vascular system in general. This would seem the more true since the Harveian Lectureship, established in 1656 shortly before Harvey's death, has provided some 253 Orations, 157 of which were published.

Despite this vast body of material, new knowledge about Harvey himself and the implications of his discovery was brought forward in connection with the many observances during the tercentenary of his death,[13] and a new rendering of his great treatise on the circulation (*De motu cordis*) by Kenneth J. Franklin was published.

Harvey, who first proved that the blood circulates, was born in the English coastal town of Folkestone on 1 April 1578, the eldest son of Thomas Harvey, a thrifty merchant-tradesman, and Joane Halke, a kindly, generous-hearted woman of unswerving loyalty to the Anglican faith. In 1586, young William entered near-by Canterbury Grammar School and thence went up to Caius College, Cambridge (31 May 1593), where he remained off and on till 30 October 1599.

Early in 1600 he proceeded to Padua, where he obtained his M.D. degree in 1602 while working under the eminent professor of anatomy, Fabricius of Aquapendente, who at that time was attracting students from every part of Europe. As already noted, Fabricius had observed the valves in the veins as early as 1574 and thereafter had frequently pointed them out to his pupils; many believed that it was through demonstration of these structures that Harvey became imbued with the idea which several years later was to make his name immortal. When Harvey put forward the celebrated argument that led to his triumphant conclusion concerning the circulation, the final and most telling step in his argument related to the existence of venous valves so placed as to promote the flow of blood towards the heart. It has therefore seemed fitting in making selections from Harvey's book to include a few paragraphs from Chapter 13 on the venous valves (Pl. 9).

Harvey had announced his discovery on 17 April 1616—a week prior to Shakespeare's death—at a Lumleian Lecture to the College of Physicians in London. His lecture notes used at that time are still in existence, and in 1886 were carefully reproduced in facsimile. The celebrated passage relating to the circulation has been translated as follows: "From the structure of the heart it is clear that the blood is constantly carried through the lungs into the aorta *as by two clacks of a water bellows to rayse water.* By [application of] a bandage [to the arm] it is clear that there is a transit of the blood from arteries into veins, wherefore the beat of the heart produces a perpetual circular motion of the blood. Is this for the purpose of nourishment, or more for the conservation of the blood and the parts by the distribution of heat; and, in turn, is the blood

[13] For a most useful list of recent studies of Harvey, see *Current Work in the History of Medicine* (London, The Wellcome Historical Medical Library), especially No. 12, October-December 1956 (3 refs.); No. 14, April-June 1957 (55 refs.); No. 15, July-September 1957 (25 refs.); No. 16, October-December 1957 (27 refs.); No. 17, January-March 1958 (12 refs.); No. 18, April-June 1958 (11 refs.) Also some 13 books are listed under New Books in these issues. An earlier issue (No. 9, January-March 1956) contained "A select bibliography of writings on William Harvey (1578-1657)," on pp. 57-62.

cooled by warming the parts made warm [again] by the heart?"[14] Harvey was not prevailed upon to publish his evidence and conclusions until 1628 (at the age of 50), when there appeared from the press of a second-rate publisher of Frankfort in Germany a miserably printed little book of 72 pages which described the greatest discovery in the annals of medicine.[15] His brilliant demonstration of the effectiveness of the experimental method in physiology was as significant as the discovery of the circulation itself.

VALVES IN VEINS—'CONFIRMATION OF BLOOD CIRCUIT'

[Chap. 13]. Thus far I have discussed the amount of blood which passes through the heart and lungs in the centre of the body, and which similarly passes from the arteries to the veins in the peripheral system of the same body. It remains for me to explain how the blood returns through the veins from the extremities to the heart, and how the veins are vessels whose sole function is such carriage of blood back from the extremities to the centre. When I have done that, I think that the three bases for argument which I put forward in favour of the existence of a circuit of the blood will all be evident, true, and irrefutable, and hence will secure adequate credence for my views. The third of my suppositions will be sufficiently evident from the finding of valves in the very lumina of the veins, from the function of these valves, and from ocular demonstrations.

The celebrated Girolamo Fabrizzi d'Acquapendente . . . the dis-

---

[14] Harvey, W. *Lectures on the whole of anatomy.* An annotated translation of *Prelectiones anatomiae universalis* by C. D. O'Malley, F. N. L. Poynter, and K. F. Russell. Berkeley and Los Angeles, University of California Press, 1961. 239 pp. [pp. 191-192].

[15] Harvey, W. *Exercitatio anatomica de motu cordis et sanguinis in animalibus.* Frankfurt, William Fitzer, 1628. 72 pp. English translations appeared in 1653 and 1673 (translators unknown) and new but scarcely adequate translations were issued by Ryan in 1832 and Robert Willis in 1857 (Sydenham Society, London), the latter being many times reprinted (1889, 1894, 1903, etc.). In 1928 in observance of the tercentenary of *De motu cordis* another edition based in part on Willis, but including relevant information derived from modern studies on the vascular system was published by C. D. Leake (Springfield, Ill., Charles C Thomas, Publisher, 74, 153 pp.). In 1957 when a congress was held in London to commemorate the 300th anniversary of Harvey's death, Kenneth J. Franklin, Professor of Physiology at St. Bartholomew's Hospital where Harvey 'qualified' in medicine, published a completely new translation, made without reference to any previous rendering. (See *Movement of the heart and blood in animals. An anatomical essay by William Harvey.* Oxford, Blackwell Scientific Publications, 1957, xii, 210 pp.) For bibliographical information of unfailing accuracy concerning Harvey and the discovery of the circulation, one is referred to the *Bibliotheca Osleriana*, Nos. 692-918 (Oxford, Clarendon Press, 1929) and G. L. Keynes's *A bibliography of the writings of William Harvey*, 2d ed. (Cambridge, At the University Press, 1953, xiii, 79 pp.).

coverer of the valves did not understand their real function, and others went no farther. This function is not to prevent the blood as a whole from rushing down, through its weight, into the parts below. *For in the jugular veins the valves face downwards, and here they prevent the blood from moving upwards. In other words, the direction in which the valves as a whole face is not upwards so much as towards the root of the veins and the region of the heart.* [J. F. F. italics]. . . . The sole purpose for which the valves were created was so that the blood should not move from the large veins into the smaller ones (thus rupturing the latter or making them varicose), or from the centre of the body to its extremities, but rather from those extremities to that centre. Hence the delicate valves readily open to allow this latter movement of the blood, but completely suppress the opposite one. They are also so regularly arranged that, if anything is insufficiently held up in its [would-be backward] passage through the horns of the valves above and would, so to speak, slip through the chinks between them, it would be caught up by the transversely placed sinuses of the succeeding valves and be prevented from travelling any farther.

This I very often found in my dissection of veins. If I started from the root of these vessels and tried with all the skill that I could muster to pass a probe in the direction of the small vessels, I was unable to do so over any great distance because of the obstacles provided by the valves; on the other hand, it was very easy to pass a probe from without inwards, that is, from the small branches towards the root of the veins. In the majority of places paired valves are so sited and arranged with relation one to the other that, as they rise away from the vein wall, they come together and meet exactly in the centre of the vein lumen, their free borders being so closely apposed that you could not discern by eye, or adequately trace out, the minute cleft or line of union between them. On the other hand, when the stylet is passed from without inwards, the valves give way even if (like the sluice gates which check the flow of streams) they are very easily turned back again in the opposite direction to check a movement of blood setting out from the heart and the vena cava, and (by their rising away from the vein wall and their mutual apposition in their closure) to bring it to a full stop. . . .

But so that this truth may be more openly manifest, let an arm be ligated above the elbow in a living human subject as if for a bloodletting [A A]. At intervals there will appear, especially in country folk and those with varicosis, certain so to speak nodes and swellings [B, C, D, D, E, F], not only where there is a point of division [E F], but even where none such exists [C D]; and those nodes are produced by valves, which show up in this way in the outer part of the hand or of the elbow. If by milking the vein downwards with the thumb or a finger [Fig. 2, O to H] you try to draw blood away from the node or valve [Fig. 2, O], you will see that none can follow your lead because of the complete obstacle provided by the valve; you will also see that the portion of vein [Fig. 2, O H] between the swelling and the drawn-back finger has been blotted out, though the portion above the swelling or valve is fairly distended [Fig. 2, O G]. If you keep the blood thus withdrawn [back to H] and the vein thus emptied, and with your other hand exert a pressure downwards towards the distended upper part of the valves [Fig. 3, K], you will see the blood completely resistant to being forcibly driven beyond the valve [Fig. 3, O]. And the greater the effort you put into your performance, the greater will be the swelling and distension of the vein which you will see at the valve or swelling [Fig. 3, O], though below that the vessel is empty [Fig. 3, H O]. . . .

Still another experiment should be noted. In a living human subject, with the arm ligated as before, the veins swelling up and nodes or valves coming into view, select a place where a second valve follows a first, and apply a thumb to occlude the vein and prevent any bloodflow up from the hand. Then with a finger, as detailed above, force the blood up out of that portion of vein [L N] into the stretch above the valve. Now take the finger [L] away and let the vein fill up again from below [as in D C]. Re-apply the thumb and again force the blood up out of the vein [Fig. 4 L N, and Fig. 2 or 3, H O], and do this quickly a thousand times. If after that you make a calculation (by multiplying by a thousand your estimate of the amount which is raised above the valve at each upward stroking of the vein), you will find that so much blood passes in a relatively short time through the one portion of vein that, I believe, you will be completely convinced, by the speed of the blood's movement, of the fact that it circulates.

In case, however, you feel like saying that this experiment is unnaturally rigorous, may I suggest that you try it on a vein with widely separated valves, and see how quickly and rapidly, once the thumb is removed, the blood flows upwards and fills the vein from below.

I have no doubt that making this test will carry conviction to you. (Franklin translation [note 15], pp. 81, 82, 83-85, 86.)

'CONCLUSION OF MY DESCRIPTION OF THE BLOOD CIRCUIT'

[Chap. 14] May I now be permitted to summarize my view about the circuit of the blood, and to make it generally known!

Since calculations and visual demonstrations have confirmed all my suppositions, to wit, that the blood is passed through the lungs and the heart by the pulsation of the ventricles, is forcibly ejected to all part of the body, therein steals into the veins and the porosities of the flesh, flows back everywhere through those very veins from the circumference to the centre, from small veins into larger ones, and thence comes at last into the vena cava and to the auricle of the heart; all this, too, in such amount and with so large a flux and reflux—from the heart out to the periphery, and back from the periphery to the heart—that it cannot be supplied from the ingesta, and is also in much greater bulk than would suffice for nutrition.

I am obliged to conclude that in animals the blood is driven round a circuit with an unceasing, circular sort of movement, that this is an activity or function of the heart which it carries out by virtue of its pulsation, and that in sum it constitutes the sole reason for that heart's pulsatile movement. (Franklin translation [note 15], p. 87.)

Richard Lower
1631-1691

Richard Lower,[16] a native of St. Tudy near Bodmin in Cornwall, where his family had lived for many generations, was one of the group of Oxford physiologists who shortly after the Restoration made some of the fundamental observations in physiology on which all subsequent work in the field was based. Lower is recognized for his classic observation that arterial blood changes in color from a dark purple to crimson red as it passes from the right heart through the lungs to the left, and also after brief exposure to atmospheric air outside the

---

[16] Fulton, J. F. "A bibliography of two Oxford physiologists: Richard Lower 1631-1691 and John Mayow 1643-1679." *Proc. Oxford bibliogr. Soc.*, 1935, *4*, 1-62 (Lower, pp. 1-38).

body (see Ch. IV). He is less well known for his anatomical studies of heart muscle in which he demonstrated that individual contractile fibers of the cardiac ventricle are disposed in a "figure-of-eight" fashion such that when they contract, the fibers tend to obliterate the ventricular cavity completely on both sides of the heart. He was also aware that this occlusion of the two ventricular cavities occurs virtually simultaneously during ventricular systole.

Lower's studies are noteworthy for his clear vision into the functional significance of the facts of anatomical structure. Like Charles Sherrington, another Oxford physiologist of over two centuries and a half later, Lower "turned anatomical facts into physiological language." Professor Kenneth Franklin has pointed out that he gave definite proof of the myogenic nature of the heart beat, and an estimation of the heart's output and of the rapidity of blood flow, that he missed by a narrow margin anticipating the Webers' discovery of vagal inhibition, and that he was the real inventor of transfusion, having first demonstrated the technique in February of 1665.

STRUCTURE OF THE HEART

[P. 30 of original Latin ed.] But in this ventricle also the whole of the fibres do not reach from the base to the apex, and, only after a number have been removed, can the others be separated that far; for several are deflected from the general course and path in the middle of their passage across the Heart, and disappear under the next preceding fibres to ascend obliquely to the tendon of the opposite side, and so describe by their passage a shorter circle. As was seen above in Fig. 5 [Fig. 2].

The inner fibres, on the other hand, all ascend obliquely upwards and to the left, in exactly the opposite direction to the outer fibres, to reach the base of the heart. They are inserted into the tendon at the base and form the inner wall of the ventricle.

The longer fibres of the opposite set run together to the apex of the Heart, and pass round it to form a whorl, in such a way, however, that the space which is left in the centre becomes the thinnest part of the Heart. The fashion of this whorl, and the meeting in it, at the apex of the Heart, of the fibres of the outer wall of the left ventricle with those [p. 31] of the inner wall, are quite well shown in Fig. 7 [Fig. 3]. In this figure

a is the tendon of the right side.
b is the tendon of the left side.
c are some fibres of the outer wall.
d are fibres of the inner wall, together with the whorl formed
    by fibres of both sets near the apex.

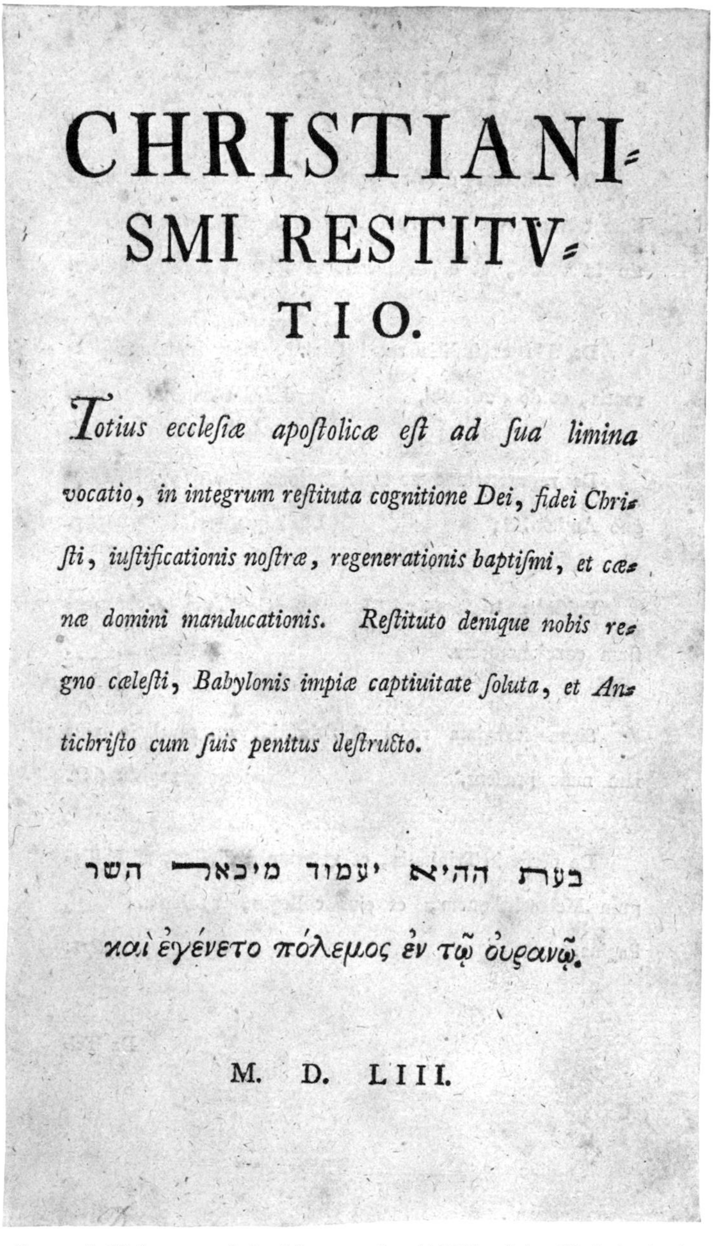

CHRISTIANI=
SMI RESTITV=
TIO.

Totius ecclesiæ apostolicæ est ad sua limina vocatio, in integrum restituta cognitione Dei, fidei Christi, iustificationis nostræ, regenerationis baptismi, et cænæ domini manducationis. Restituto denique nobis regno cælesti, Babylonis impiæ captiuitate soluta, et Antichristo cum suis penitus destructo.

בעת ההיא יעמוד מיכאל השר

καὶ ἐγένετο πόλεμος ἐν τῷ οὐρανῷ.

M. D. LIII.

PLATE 5. Title-page of the Murr reprint (1790) of the *Christianismi restitutio* of Servetus, 1553. The reprint is now almost as scarce as the original.

PLATE 6. Title-page of Colombo's *De re anatomica* (Venice, 1559.) Colombo (center) is shown in the performance of a dissection while another man on the far left reads from an anatomical book which, since it is illustrated, must be that of Vesalius.

HIERONYMI FABRICI
A B
AQVAPENDENTE
ANATOMICI
PATAVINI.
DE
VENARVM
OSTIOLIS.

PATAVII,
Ex Typographia Laurentij Pasquati.
M. D C. I I I.

PLATE 7. Title-page of Fabricius' tract on the valves in the veins, 1603. (Courtesy of the New York Academy of Medicine.)

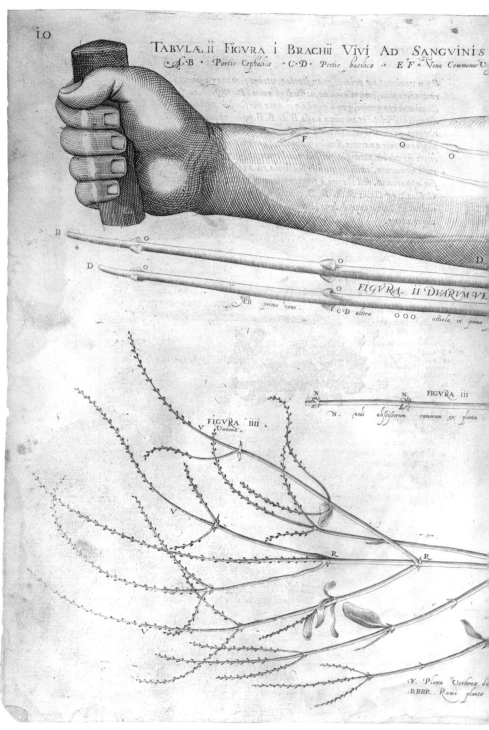

PLATE 8. Fabricius' drawings to show the valves in the veins, both in dissection

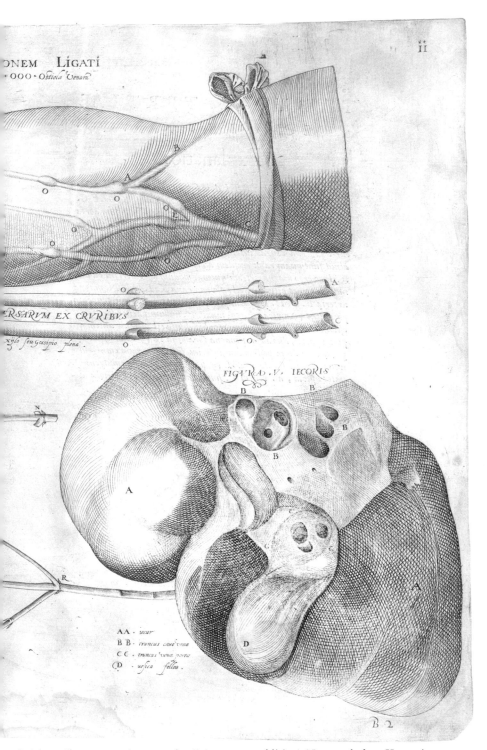

ONEM LIGATI
·OOO·Osticia Venarum

RSARVM EX CRVRIBVS

Xylo seu Gossipio plena

FIGVRA·V· IECORIS

AA . iecur
B B . truncus caue vena
C C . truncus vena porta
D . vesica fellea .

B 2

vealed by a ligature on the arm of a living man, published 25 years before Harvey's tract.

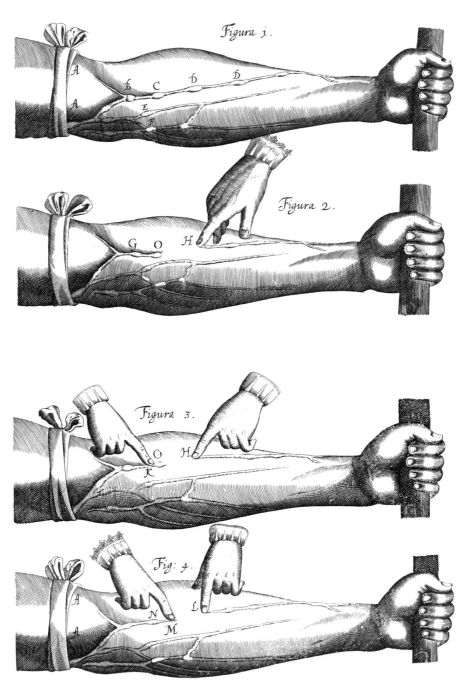

PLATE 9. The two illustrations of the valves in the veins, as revealed by a ligature, from Harvey's *De motu cordis*, 1628. [opp. p. 56]

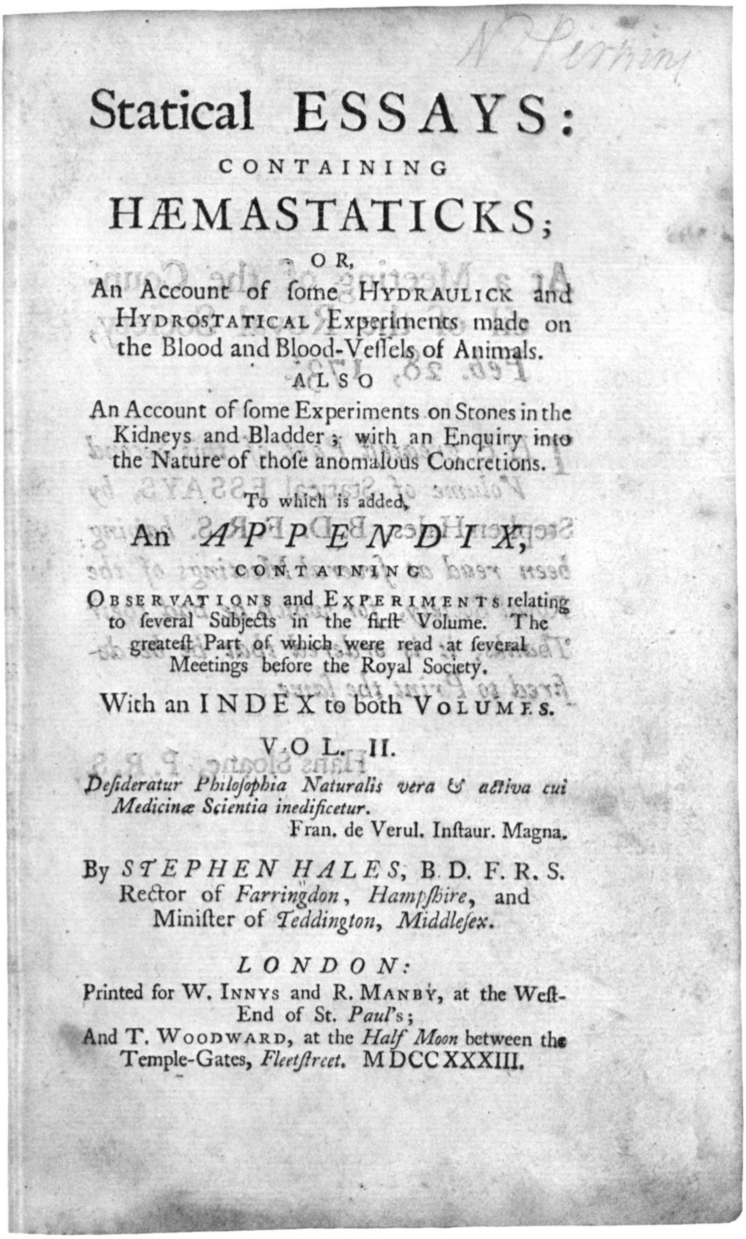

Statical ESSAYS:

CONTAINING

HÆMASTATICKS;

OR,

An Account of fome HYDRAULICK and HYDROSTATICAL Experiments made on the Blood and Blood-Veffels of Animals.

ALSO

An Account of fome Experiments on Stones in the Kidneys and Bladder; with an Enquiry into the Nature of thofe anomalous Concretions.

To which is added,

An *APPENDIX*,

CONTAINING

OBSERVATIONS and EXPERIMENTS relating to feveral Subjects in the firft Volume. The greateft Part of which were read at feveral Meetings before the Royal Society.

With an INDEX to both VOLUMES.

VOL. II.

Defideratur Philofophia Naturalis vera & activa cui Medicinæ Scientia inedificetur.

Fran. de Verul. Inftaur. Magna.

By *STEPHEN HALES*, B. D. F. R. S.
Rector of *Farringdon*, *Hampfhire*, and Minifter of *Teddington*, *Middlefex*.

LONDON:

Printed for W. INNYS and R. MANBY, at the Weft-End of St. *Paul*'s;
And T. WOODWARD, at the *Half Moon* between the Temple-Gates, *Fleetftreet*. MDCCXXXIII.

PLATE 10. Title-page of Hales's *Statical Essays,* vol. 2, 1733.

The ſeveral Trials.	The Quantities of Blood let out in Wine Meaſure.		The ſeveral Heights of the Blood after theſe evacuations	
	Quarts	Pints	Feet	Inches
1	0	*5 Ounces	8	3/4
2	1	0	7	8
3	2		7	2
4	3		6	6 1/2
5	4		6	10 1/2
6	5		6	5
7	6		5	5 1/4
8	7		4	8
9	8		3	3
10	8	1	3	7 1/4
11	9	0	3	10
12	9	1	3	6 1/2
13	10	0	3	9 1/2
14	10	1	4	3 1/2
15	11	0	3	8
16	11	1	3	10 1/4
17	12	0	3	9
18	12	1	3	7 1/2
19	13	0	3	2
20	13	1	4	1/2
21	14	0	3	9
22	14	1	3	3
23	15	0	3	4 1/2
24	15	1	3	1
25	16	0	2	4

*These 5 Ounces loſt in preparing the Artery.

By this time there is a Pint loſt in making the ſeveral Trials, which is not allowed for in this Table.

The ſeveral Trials.	Cubick Inches let out.	Perpendicular Height after each Evacuation.	
		Feet.	Inches.
1	70	9	6
2	130	7	10
3	190	7	6
4	250	7	3
5	310	6	5
6	370	4	9
7	430	3	9
8	490	3	4 1/2
9	550	2	9 1/2
10	610	3	2 1/2
11	670	{ *4	5
		2	9 1/2 }
12	730	3	6
13	790	3	5
14	820	2	0
15	833	2	5

* Deep Sighing raiſed the Blood.

When the Force of the Blood was thus ſmall, then faint Sweats came on. Very faint.

Now expired:

PLATE 11. Two charts from Hales's *Statical Essays* (vol. 2, 1733, pp. 4, 16.) showing the effect of bleeding upon the arterial blood pressure.

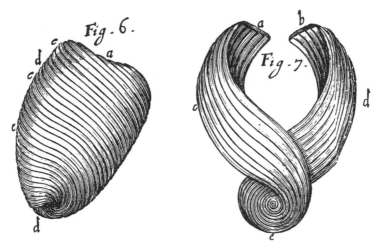

Figures 2, 3. Drawings from Lower's *De corde*.

From this it is obvious enough that the fibres of the outer and inner walls have contrary courses and also perform antagonistic movements, but that they do this in such a way that, while they cause the walls of the heart to shorten in opposite directions, they make both walls contract into a closer and more confined space. This will be shown more clearly later. . . .

The movement of any two-bellied muscle is effected in general by the fleshy fibres drawing the opposed tendons [p. 79] together towards a central point, and the Heart is also essentially composed, on the plan of the other muscles, of a double row of fibres facing in opposite directions—the outer ones stretching across from left to right and encircling the whole of the parenchyma in their folds, and the deeper ones being carried in the directly opposite direction—and so, since they draw the walls of the Heart more closely together on all sides, the intraventricular spaces must necessarily be greatly diminished and constricted. The process can, therefore, not unfittingly be compared with the wringing of a linen cloth to squeeze out the water, or with the closing of a purse by the traction of a double string in opposite directions. The fibres act in exactly the same way in constricting the Heart, and it is they principally which effect its movement.

Moreover, some of the fibres of the Heart are straight, but all the others twist round the apex and the whole of its surface in an oblique and contrary direction to end in spiral lines in its base. Hence these fibres not only compress and [p. 80] diminish the intraventricular cavity, whenever they contract on both sides, but they also bring the apex nearer the base. . . . (Lower, Richard. *A treatise on the heart, on the movement & colour of the blood.* . . . London, James Allestry, 1669. xvi, 220, 20 pp. Facsimile edition with introduction and translation by K. J. Franklin in R. T. Gunther's *Early science in Oxford,* Oxford, 1932. [Vol. IX, C3, D7].)

Stephen Hales

1677-1761

Stephen Hales, whose life is described in Chapter III, took the next important step after Harvey and Malpighi in elucidating the physiology of the circulation. The determination of blood pressure made it possible to calculate the work done by the heart and to estimate for the first time the magnitude of the peripheral resistance. The following selection is taken from his *Hæmastaticks* published in 1733 (Pls. 10 & 11).

EXPERIMENT III

1. In *December* I laid a common Field Gate on the Ground, with some Straw upon it, on which a white Mare was cast on her right Side, and in that Posture bound fast to the Gate; she was fourteen Hands and three Inches high; lean, tho' not to a great Degree, and about ten or twelve Years old. This and the above-mentioned Horse and Mare were to have been killed, as being unfit for Service.

2. Then laying open the left Jugular Vein, I fixed to that part of it which comes from the Head, a Glass Tube, which was four Feet, and two Inches long.

3. The Blood rose in it, in three or four Seconds of Time, about a Foot, and then was stationary for two or three Seconds; then in three or four Seconds more, it rose sometimes gradually, and sometimes with an unequally accelerated Motion nine Inches more, on small Strainings of the Mare: Then upon greater Strainings it rose about a Yard, and would subside five or six Inches: Then upon a larger Strain or Struggle of the Mare, it rose so high, as to flow a little out at the Top of the Tube; so that had the Tube been a few Inches higher, it would have risen probably to that Height.

4. When the Mare ceased to strain and struggle, the Blood subsided about eighteen or twenty Inches; so the Return of the Blood into the Vein was not hindered by the Valves; which I have also

observed in other Parts where there are Valves, tho' sometimes they absolutely hinder the Return of any Fluid.

5. The Diameter of the Brass Pipe and Tube which were fixed to the Vein, were nearly one seventh of an Inch: The Diameter of the Jugular Vein about half an Inch.

6. Then laying bare the left Carotid Artery, I fixed to it towards the Heart the Brass Pipe, and to that the Wind-Pipe of a Goose; to the other End of which a Glass Tube was fixed, which was twelve Feet nine Inches long. The Design of using the Wind-Pipe was by its Pliancy to prevent the Inconveniencies that might happen when the Mare struggled; if the Tube had been immediately fixed to the Artery, without the Intervention of this pliant Pipe.

7. There had been lost before the Tube was fixed to the Artery, about seventy cubick Inches of Blood. The Blood rose in the Tube in the same manner as in the Case of the two former Horses, till it reached to nine Feet six Inches Height. I then took away the Tube from the Artery, and let out by Measure sixty cubick Inches of Blood, and then immediately replaced the Tube to see how high the Blood would rise in it after each Evacuation; this was repeated several times, till the Mare expired, as follows, *viz.*

8. We may observe, that these three Horses all expired, when the perpendicular Height of the Blood in the Tube was about two Feet.

9. These 833 cubick Inches of Blood weight 28.89 Pounds, and are equal to fourteen Wine Quarts, the large Veins in the Body of the Mare were full of Blood, there was some also in the descending *Aorta,* and in both Ventricles and Auricles. (Hales, S. *Statical essays* [vol. 2]: *containing hæmastaticks; or, an account of some hydraulick and hydrostatical experiments made on the blood and blood-vessels of animals. . . .* London, W. Innys and R. Manby and T. Woodward, 1733. xxii, 361 pp. [pp. 13-17].)

Friedrich Hermann Stannius

1808-1883

Hermann Stannius was born at Hamburg and studied first at Breslau and later at Berlin where he formed one of that brilliant group of students including Du Bois-Reymond and Helmholtz who studied with Johannes Müller. Stannius became a lecturer under Müller at Berlin and later moved to Rostock as professor.

The experiments quoted here were performed, Stannius tells us, in the late summer of 1851 and repeated before his colleagues who included Jakob Henle, Emil Ludwig, and Karl von Siebold. They are especially striking because they illustrate vagal inhibition of the heart beat and indicate the existence of the pacemaker in the heart.

TWO SERIES OF PHYSIOLOGICAL EXPERIMENTS

1. EXPERIMENTS ON FROG HEARTS

The experiments described in the following series have been carried out with a view to discovering more precisely the influence of the nerves upon the heart beat. To this end I placed strong ligatures of silk thread first around the vagus nerves, later around those regions of the heart in which occur aggregations of ganglion cells, but excluding the nerves to those vascular trunks conducting blood to the heart and also to those trunks conducting blood away from the heart. In this way I obtain results both surprising and difficult to interpret. . . .

7. *If we ligate exactly at that point where the sinus of the vena cava opens into the right auricle, then the whole heart comes to a standstill in a state of diastole.* Only the three, the venae cavae and the sinus contract independently.

Only once did I succeed in producing the same result by excision at the named place, yet I was able to observe this result only twice. The contusion resulting from excision must have had the same effect as ligating. . . .

11. When one has brought the whole heart to a standstill in the way described above in 7, then by mechanical or galvanic stimulation it may be brought again into a longer or shorter sustained contraction. If one sticks the point of a needle into the ventricle, the auricles ordinarily contract first, next the ventricles and bulbus contract together. Thereupon there follows usually one or two contractions of the auricles without any participation of the ventricle. Occasionally, the contraction of the auricle precedes that of the ventricle and the bulbus.

Weak stimulation of the ventricle with the point of a needle or by stroking its surface with a feather or a thin scalpel has often resulted in no contraction of any portion of the heart at all, while an exactly similar stimulation of the auricles evokes a steady contraction propagating itself outward from the auricle on to the ventricle.

The difference in susceptibility to external stimulation of the two portions of the heart is thus very great. . . .

21. When the auricles were separated incompletely from the ventricle by section at the sulcus so that the latter still remained attached to it by a bridge, then both auricles and ventricle remained in a state of rhythmic contraction for a still longer time.

22. When, after the aforesaid application of a ligature around the venous sinus, one removes the right auricle by excision from the ventricle, then it remains in a state of rhythmic contraction. If now with scissors one cuts off a ring-like segment from the ventricular mouth, then the latter no longer contracts while the segment of the auricle remaining attached to the sinus venosus pulsates with a strong rhythmic contraction.

23. If the right auricle itself is attached in the neighborhood of the opening of the sinus venosus so that a portion of it remains in uninterrupted connection with the disconnected sinus venosus, then one sees that the said portion contracts rhythmically as well as the root of the vena cava. If the frog has not already lost too much blood, then one sometimes, but not always, sees the whole venous system in pulsation. For instance, these pulsations extend even to the renal veins and their branches in the kidneys. The touching of the vagus nerves with the electrode of the rotation apparatus produces a cessation of all these pulsations.

24. As soon as the trunks of the vena cava are distended with blood after the commencement of experiment 7, they stimulate themselves to contract, become emptied of blood, and thus begin their rhythmic contraction anew.

The most noteworthy feature of these experiments is therefore that:

any contraction of a point on the auricles produces a contraction of the adjacent ventricle, thus a portion of an auricle excised permanently hampers the ventricle; on the other hand, the contraction of the ventricular wall of a stimulated ventricle previously at rest again induces a continuing contraction. (Hermann Stannius. "Zwei Reihen physiologischer Versuche." *Arch. Anat. Physiol. wiss. Med.*, 1852, 85-100. [pp. 85, 87, 88-89, 91-92. Translated by L.G.W.])

Wilhelm His, Junior

1863-1934

Wilhelm His, Jr., anatomist and cardiologist, was the son of Wilhelm His (1831-1904), professor of anatomy and physiology at Leipzig.[17]

A precocious student, His did important work on the metabolism of pyridine while studying medicine at Strasbourg. In 1889, he received his medical degree at Leipzig and became assistant to Curschmann at the clinic there where he also worked with his father. His research on the embryonic heart led to discovery of the auriculo-ventricular bundle. Recognition of this special conducting tissue between auricle and ventricle, first announced in 1893, is undoubtedly one of the outstanding disclosures in the history of cardiology.[18] His spent a year at Dresden and five at Basel before being called in 1907 to Berlin as professor of internal medicine and director of the First Clinic at the Charité. He became rector of the University of Berlin in 1928.

It is interesting that A. F. S. Kent (1863-1958), who was born in the same year as His, had also come upon the auriculo-ventricular bundle,[19] which is now sometimes referred to as the His-Kent bundle. Almost immediately after the announcement of his discovery, His showed that following section of the A-V bundle, the auricular and ventricular beats became dissociated.[20] Einthoven (1860-1927) had meanwhile described his string galvanometer[21] which enabled clinicians to recognize cardiac lesions affecting the His-Kent bundle. A complete heart block had been described by Robert Adams (1791-1875) in 1827[22] and some twenty years later by William Stokes (1804-1878),[23] accounting for the designation

---

[17] Bast, T. H. and Gardner, W. D. "Wilhelm His, Jr. and the bundle of His." *J. Hist. Med.,* 1949, *4,* 170-187.

[18] His, Wilhelm, Jr. "Die Thätigkeit des embryonalen Herzens und deren Bedeutung für die Lehre von der Herzbewegung beim Erwachsenen. *Arb. med. Klin. Leipzig,* 1893, 14-49. English translation by T. H. Bast and W. D. Gardner. "The activity of the embryonic human heart and its significance for the understanding of the heart movement in the adult." *J. Hist. Med.,* 1949, *4,* 289-318. See also Bast and Gardner's translation of His's story of his discovery (*Klin. Wsch.,* 1933, *12,* 569-574), *J. Hist. Med.,* 1949, *4,* 319-333.

[19] Kent, A. F. S. "Researches on the structure and function of the mammalian heart." *J. Physiol. (Lond.),* 1893, *14,* 233-254.

[20] His, Wilhelm, Jr. "Herzmuskel und Herzganglien; Bemerkungen zu dem Vortrag des Herrn Geheimrath A. v. Kölliker: Ueber die feinere Anatomie und physiologische Bedeutung des sympathischen Nervensystems." *Wien med. Bl.,* 1894, *17,* 653-665.

[21] Einthoven, Willem. "Un nouveau galvanomètre." *Arch. néerl. Sci. exactes nat.,* 1901, 2 sér. *6,* 625-633.

[22] Adams, Robert. "Cases of diseases of the heart, accompanied with pathological observations." *Dublin Hosp. Rep.,* 1827, *4,* 353-453 [p. 396 ff.].

[23] Stokes, William. "Observations on some cases of permanently slow pulse." *Dublin quart. J. med. Sci.,* 1846, 2, 73-85.

of the Adams-Stokes syndrome. It was not long before this syndrome became recognized as due to interruption of the bundle.

DISCOVERY OF AURICULO-VENTRICULAR BUNDLE

In the meantime, I investigated the development of the cardiac nervous system in all classes of vertebrates and showed that in all of them the heart beat in an adult manner before it contained cerebrospinal nerves or ganglia.

One thing remained unexplained: the conduction of the stimulus from one heart segment to another. In the embryo the heart consisted of a continuous muscular tube; in the adult warm-blooded animals and, in part, in cold-blooded animals, a connective tissue sheet, which in general forms a complete ring, pushes in between the auricle and the ventricle. It is true that on the upper and under surface of the atrioventricular valves thin sheets of smooth muscle were known. However, their union had not been shown (except by Paladino). Gaskell had shown that in the frog and turtle the conduction passes through muscle substance. I looked for a muscle bridge in following the serial sections through increasing age stages, finally finding it in adult mammals and also in man. I described it in 1893 [His, Wilhelm, Jr. "The story of the atrioventricular bundle with remarks concerning embryonic heat activity." Bast, T. H. and Gardner, W. D., Translators. *J. Hist. Med.*, 1949, *4*, 319-333 (p. 320).] [as follows]:

After long search I have succeeded in finding a muscle bundle which unites the auricular and ventricular septal walls, and which, up to now, has escaped observation because of incomplete exposure, for it is visible in its entire extent only when the septa are cut exactly in their longitudinal direction. From such cuts, as well as in serial sections, I was able to recognize the course of the bundle and have demonstrated it in a grown mouse, a newborn dog, two newborn and one adult (30-year-old) human. The bundle arises from the posterior wall of the right auricle, near the auricular septum, in the atrioventricular groove; attaches itself along the upper margin of the ventricular septal muscle by means of numerous fiber exchanges; proceeds on top of this toward the front until near the aorta it forks itself into a right and left limb which latter ends in the base of the aortic cusp of the mitral valve.

Whether this bundle really transmits the impulse from the auricle to the ventricle I am unable to say with certainty since, up to now,

I have not attempted any transection experiments of it. Very likely its presence is an argument against the belief of those who, because of the lack of muscular continuity between auricle and ventricle, seek to prove the necessity of nervous conduction. (Bast and Gardner [note 17], p. 174; p. 23 in original paper.)

Arthur Keith and Martin W. Flack
1866-1956   *1882-1931*

While *Sir Arthur Keith,* F.R.S. (knighted 1921) is known principally for his writings on anthropology and human evolution, he did much of his early work in anatomy. Among the most important of these contributions is his joint paper with Flack of 1907 in which they reveal the form and structure of the pacemaker of the heart. In an earlier paper they had confirmed and extended the discovery of the A-V system by Tawara.[24] They now show that the A-V system is but part of a system of fibres which extend to the whole heart and determine its rhythm.

DISCOVERY OF THE CARDIAC PACEMAKER

Our search for a well-differentiated system of fibres within the sinus, which might serve as a basis for the inception of the cardiac rhythm, has led us to attach importance to this peculiar musculature surrounding the artery at the sino-auricular junction. . . . In the human heart the fibres are striated, fusiform, with well-marked elongated nuclei, plexiform in arrangement, and embedded in densely packed connective tissue—in fact, of closely similar structure to the Knoten. The amount of this musculature varies, depending upon how much of the sinus has remained of the primitive type; but in the neighbourhood of the tænia terminalis there is always some of this primitive tissue found. Macroscopically, the fibres resemble those of the a.-v. bundle in being paler than the surrounding musculature, *i.e.,* in being of the white variety. . . .

The nature of this remnant is perhaps best exemplified in the heart of the mole. . . . Here it is seen that at the sino-auricular junction . . . there is a mass of remarkable tissue. It appears to the eye as a very intimate network of palely stained undifferentiated fibres with a large number of well-stained nuclei. It is totally different

[24] Tawara, S. *Das Reizleitungssystem des Säugethierherzens.* Jena, Gustav Fischer, 1906.

from the surrounding musculature, and contains but little fibrous tissue. Although the mass by its connections is undoubtedly muscular, the nerves in the neighbourhood of the superior vena cava appear to come into very intimate connection with it, so much so that we feel justified in stating that a highly differentiated neuro-muscular junction occurs at this point. In this heart also the bundle . . . is of absolutely identical structure. . . .

. . . Physiological experiments have clearly demonstrated that normally the heart's rhythm begins in the neighbourhood of the great veins, and that here nervous influence has a most potent effect (MacWilliam, Engelmann, Hering, and others). The fact, therefore, that there is a constant differentiation of certain fibres in this region, which, moreover, are in close connection with the nerves affecting the heart's rhythm, leads us to attach great importance to these fibres, and we feel justified in expressing the opinion that it is in them that the dominating rhythm of the heart normally begins. . . . (Keith, Arthur and Flack, Martin. "The form and nature of the muscular connections between the primary divisions of the vertebrate heart." *J. Anat. Physiol.*, 1907, *41*, 172-189 [pp. 182-185].)

Ernest Henry Starling
1866-1927

In his Linacre lecture of 1915 *Starling* stated for the first time the law which governs force and magnitude of the heart beat and therefore regulates the whole circulation. His conclusions, though in part based on the work of others, were largely drawn from his own studies of a heart-lung preparation.

THE LAW OF THE HEART

Two important facts are rendered evident by these results. In the first place, provided the inflow remains constant, it seems to be immaterial to the heart whether it has to contract against a resistance of 44 mm. Hg, or 208 mm. Hg. In each case it puts out as much blood as it receives, so that the total outflow remains constant whatever the arterial pressure. Of course there is a limit which must not be exceeded. . . . The second fact which results from this experiment is that the fraction of the total output of blood which passes through the coronary vessels rises steadily with the height of the arterial pressure. This means that the more work the heart has to do, the better it is supplied with blood, i.e., with the oxygen and nutriment necessary to furnish it with energy.

Although altering the arterial pressure has no influence on the output of the heart, a great effect is at once produced by altering the venous inflow. . . . We then find that as we increase the inflow, the outflow is *pari passu* increased, so that there is no damming up of the blood on the venous side nor failure of the heart to send the blood on from the venous to the arterial side. In this case also there may be some increase of coronary flow, which is not however so marked as when we throw more work on the heart by increasing the arterial resistance. . . .

In the heart-lung preparation the respiratory metabolism of the heart can be investigated by measuring the oxygen taken up from the lungs, and the carbonic acid given out by the lungs. When we do this we find that any increase in the work of the heart, however caused, whether by a rise in the arterial pressure or by a more rapid venous inflow, is attended by a corresponding augmentation of the total chemical changes. . . .

Now here are two conditions in which the work of the heart is increased and in which this organ adapts itself by increasing the chemical changes in its muscle at each contraction to the increased demands made upon it. It is evident that there is one factor which is common to both cases, and that is the increased volume of the heart when it begins to contract. So that we may make the following general statement. *Within physiological limits the larger the volume of the heart, the greater are the energy of its contraction and the amount of chemical change at each contraction. . . .*

During the last few years a series of admirable experiments have been carried out by A. V. Hill on the influence of changes in length on the total energy, measured as heat, set free by a contracting muscle. With Evans he has investigated the influence of initial length of a skeletal muscle on the amount of mechanical energy and total energy in the form of heat set free at each contraction. They find that for moderate increments of length both tension and heat increase proportionately with the length, and we may therefore conclude that increased length of muscle fibre, whether heart muscle or skeletal muscle, causes corresponding increases both in the chemical changes and in the mechanical energy developed in the muscle at its contraction. The law of the heart is thus the same as the law of muscular tissue generally, that *the energy of contraction, however measured, is a function of the length of the muscle fibre.* (Starling, E. H. *The Linacre lecture on the law of the heart given at Cambridge, 1915.* London, Longmans Green and Co., 1918, 27 pp. [pp. 9-10, 17-18, 22].)

III

Blood Capillaries

The historical continuity of ideas in a relatively limited field of thought is nowhere more strikingly illustrated than in the development of knowledge of the blood capillaries. Their great importance lies in the fact that through the walls of these minute channels there occurs the exchange of substances between blood and tissues which makes possible the nutrition of the body as a whole. Before the blood capillaries were discovered, proof that circulation occurred within a closed hydraulic system was lacking, and knowledge of how the body is nourished was as much a mystery as in the time of Galen. Harvey knew of the presence of small vessels connecting arteries with veins, traditionally known as synanastomoses, but being a cautious scientist, he did not commit himself and referred merely to an indefinite soakage through "porosities of tissue." Malpighi was the first to see and to describe the capillary channels and in so doing demonstrated that the vascular circuit is part of an anatomically closed system.

Antony van Leeuwenhoek added to knowledge of capillary structure in tissues other than the lungs, and Stephen Hales observed that "the small capillary vessels" may become constricted or dilated when exposed to certain specific chemical substances. Those, therefore, who believe that the problem of independent capillary contractility has been under discussion only since 1917-1918, when the memorable papers of Thomas Lewis and August Krogh first appeared, will turn with interest to the acrimonious controversies which were waged over this very question by Robert Whytt, Albrecht von Haller, and their contemporaries in the eighteenth century, and by James Black, Johannes Müller, and Marshall Hall in the nineteenth century. The following passages from the writers just mentioned illustrate forcibly that advances of knowledge in this singularly fascinating field have come about slowly and through participation of open-minded men of many nations, for physiology, like its sister sciences, is international in time and scope and also in its belief in the high destiny of science in future generations.

The resolution of the question of the contractility of the capillaries has resulted from the discovery of the a-v. bridge and direct arterial-venous anastomoses. The presence of these structures shows that the capillaries constitute a system of parallel passageways rather than direct connections between the terminal endings of the fine arteries and veins. Whatever slight contractility the capillaries themselves may possess, the flow of blood through them is controlled by the contractility of the arterioles which determines the general distribution of the blood.

At the end of the nineteenth century Ernest H. Starling produced his brilliant hypothesis for the dynamics of the interchange between the capillary circulation and the interstitial fluid. In 1926, this hypothesis was first confirmed experimentally in frog capillaries by Eugene M. Landis and in 1947 it was further confirmed and subjected to dynamic study in the elegant experiments of John R. Pappenheimer and Armando Soto-Rivera. These experiments thus provide a tribute both to Starling's prescience and to the ingenuity of modern investigators.

Marcello Malpighi
1628-1694

Marcello Malpighi, anatomist and professor of medicine at Bologna (Pl. 12a), carried out pioneer investigations in many fields of biological thought. He is often referred to as the first general histologist; and it was through his microscope that he contributed fundamentally to botany, embryology, zoology, and pathology, taking full advantage of the endless vistas created by the introduction of optical lenses. While a student at Bologna, he came under the influence of a great but little-known man, Bartolommeo Massari, an ardent follower of the new learning whom Malpighi eventually succeeded at the University of Bologna in the chair of medicine. It is recorded that Massari gathered some of his older pupils into a small society (bearing some resemblance to the Accademia dei Lincei of Rome) which met at his house to carry out dissections. Malpighi soon joined their number and participated in wide-ranging discussions of many current scientific developments such as Harvey's discovery of the circulation and other physiological disclosures—the functions of the lacteals, the kidneys, the nature of muscular contraction—all timely topics of great mutual interest.

In 1656, when he was only twenty-eight, Malpighi was nominated public lecturer in medicine at Bologna (like Andreas Vesalius in anatomy at Padua); in

1658 he was offered the chair of medicine but went instead to Pisa where he formed a close friendship with Giovanni Borelli (1608-1679), twenty years his senior, who taught him the investigative philosophy of Galileo. In 1660, Malpighi returned to Bologna and began work on respiration, especially on the structure of the lung. After Harvey's discovery of the circulation it was thought that the blood on passing into the lungs became diffusely distributed within their porous parenchyma, since the existence of microscopic channels between the two sides of the circulation had not yet been demonstrated. Malpighi studied the lung of a living frog microscopically and in 1661 wrote two now memorable letters to his friend Borelli describing his observations. In his first letter he offered proof that the windpipe terminates in many small, dilated air vessels. As Michael Foster pointed out, he thus supplied the correct anatomical basis of respiratory exchange in the lungs. In the second letter, from which quotation is made below, Malpighi records his findings in the lungs of frogs and also in the mesentery, stating that he beheld within them small channels connecting arteries with veins—structures now known as the blood capillaries. If he had also sought to find out whether these vessels existed in other tissues, he makes no mention thereof; and so it remained for the picturesque Dutchman, Antony van Leeuwenhoek, to establish the existence of capillaries in the tissues and organs of the body as a whole.

EPISTLE II TO BORELLI—ABOUT THE LUNGS

So now, most distinguished Sir, I shall deal more closely with two matters which in my letter containing observations on the lungs I left in doubt as requiring more exact study. The first was what might be that network I have described by which the single vesicles and spaces are somehow bound together in the lungs. The second was whether the vessels of the lungs are joined together by mutual anastomosis or whether on the other hand they open into the common substance and spaces of the lungs. The solution of any problem prepares the way for solving greater ones and places the operations of nature more clearly before the eyes. Toward the disentangling of these matters I have sacrificed nearly the whole genus of frogs which did not occur even in that wild *batrachomyomachia* of Homer. For in the anatomy of frogs which I have studied through the courtesy of my excellent colleague Master Carolo Fracassati in order that I might determine with greater certainty the nature of the membranous substance of the lungs it occurred to me that I might not improperly better apply to the present problem that saying of Homer—"With my eyes I see a great and true work. . . ."

Microscopic observation detects in these terminal vessels something more wonderful than mere structure and connection, for, with the heart still beating, there may be observed in the vessels, although with difficulty, an opposite movement of the blood [i.e., in opposite directions in arteries and veins] so that here is clearly revealed the circulation of the blood which may also be observed more satisfactorily in the mesentery and in the other larger veins contained in the abdomen. Therefore, the blood is impelled by this force into each cellule through the arteries and thereby distributes its current in very small amounts through branches either passing through the cellule or ending therein. When the blood is thus much divided, its red color disappears and winding sinuously it is distributed everywhere, even to the walls and corners and to the branches of the veins one calls the resorbing ones.

The power of the eye could not be extended further in the opened living animal, hence I had believed that the mass of the blood broke out into empty spaces and was re-collected by an open-mouthed vessel and by the structure of its walls. To this problem the diverse, tortuous, and diffuse movements of the blood and its reunion at a fixed place offered a clue. However, my doubts were resolved by the dried lung of a frog which accidentally preserved its blood redness even in the smallest portions (as it had been de-tached later from its vessels). There, with a more perfect glass the points forming the skin which is called *Sagrino* no longer were seen to occur but rather interwoven looped vessels. So great is the branch-ing of these vessels as they extend out hither and thither from the vein and artery that no further order is maintained by the vessels, but a network appears formed from the offshoots of the two vessels and this network occupies not only the whole floor [of the vesicle] but extends also to the walls and afterwards connects with the out-going vessel as I was able to observe more abundantly, though with greater difficulty, in the oblong lung of a tortoise which is likewise membranous and translucent. Hence, it lay revealed to observation that the blood passes out through these twisting divided vessels and is not poured out into spaces but is always conveyed through tubules and is distributed by the many windings of the vessels. Nor is it a new caprice of Nature that the ultimate openings of the vessels join together since the same thing occurs in the intestines and other parts. Nay it will certainly seem more marvellous that the upper ends of the veins connect to the lower by visible anas-tomoses as the very learned Fallopio has so well observed.

But in order that you may be able to grasp more easily what I have proposed and follow it with your own sight, tie off, by the

thread with which it is joined to the heart, the bulging and swollen
lung of a dissected frog while it is abundantly nourished with blood
in every part, for this when dried will keep the vessels swollen with
blood which you will then see very well if you examine it with a
microscope, consisting of one flea lens, exposed against the horizontal sun. Or you can use another method in seeing these things.
You may place the lung on a plate of crystal illuminated from below
by the light of a lamp through a tube and bring to it a microscope
of two lenses. The vessels, proliferated in loops, will then be revealed to you. By the same arrangement of instruments and light
you will observe the movement of the blood through the vessels
mentioned and you will yourself be able, with different degrees
of light, to contrive to see other things which escape description by
the pen. In fact one matter concerning the movement of the blood
promises to be worthy of your speculation for when both auricle
and heart have been tied off so that the movement and impulse
which might have been transmitted from the heart into the attached vessels has been removed, the blood is still moved through
the veins to the heart. Thus it distends the vessels with its own
force and abundant flow, and this continues for several hours. Yet
in the end, especially if it be exposed to the rays of the sun, it is
not excited with the same continued movement but advances and
recedes, fluctuating at the same time as if impelled by alternating
forces. This also occurs when the heart and auricle have been excised.

Therefore, to resolve the primary problems, from these facts
and from the analogy and simplicity which Nature uses in her works,
it can be concluded that the network, which elsewhere I thought
consisted of nerves mixed in among vesicles and spaces, is a vessel
carrying away the mass of blood or conducting it out, and although
in the lungs of perfect animals a vessel may sometimes seem to end
and open in the middle of the loops of the network, it is nevertheless probable that just as occurs in the *cellulae* of frogs and tortoises
that very small vessel has further vessels arising from it in the form
of a network, which on account of its exquisite smallness also escapes observation.

The problem of the mutual junctions and anastomoses of the
vessels can in all likelihood also be solved from these facts. For if
in one case Nature turns about the blood within vessels and joins
the ends of the vessels together in a network, it is also probable
that in other cases they are joined by anastomosis. This may be

clearly perceived in a frog's bladder swollen with urine in which may be observed the rapid movement of the blood through transparent vessels joined together by mutual anastomosis. Nay rather those vessels receive that connection and order which the veins or fibres in the leaves of nearly all trees invariably display.

But to what end are these things made—beyond that which in my preceding letter I touched upon concerning pulmonary mixture—you yourself seem particularly to have perceived; nor is it my intention to defraud you of this your discovery which in your kindness you have committed to me in your elegant letters in which you philosophized subtly in observing the wonderful manifestations of nature in vegetables. We marvel that an apple hangs from a trunk not its own and that the grafting of plants has produced a happy mixture of bastard and legitimate parts. For we see that one and the same tree has taken on different habits in its branches; while on one the hanging fruits gratify the taste of some with their pleasant sharpness, all desire the nectar-like sweetness of those on another. You give confidence to truth when at Rome you marvelled that both the vine and the jasmine were produced from the trunk of a Massilian apple. He who made these ingenious things nurtured his plantations with a small scion grafted on larger branches and trained the not unwilling trees to bring forth a variety of things. In this connection Virgil in the Georgics aptly sang:

> *From an alien tree the sprout they ingraft*
> *And teach it to shoot from the moist inner bark. . . .*

I have included these few trifles in a letter in order that I might now add to the things discovered concerning the lungs. If I have brought forward any new point I owe the whole of my observations to the frog. By your authority and ingenuity you may gain value and dignity for these matters. In the meantime, may you philosophize felicitously and continue to make me perfectly happy in the knowledge that these very trifling thoughts of mine may contribute in some small way to your writings on the movement of animals. Farewell. (Malpighi, M. *De pulmonibus. Observationes anatomicae.* Bologna, Baptista Ferronius, 1661. 14, 9 pp., 2 pl. [Epistola altera, pp. 1-9. Translated by L.G.W.])[1]

[1] No copy of this exceedingly rare tract has been traced outside of Italy. Thanks to Dr. Dorothy M. Schullian of the History of Science Collections, Cornell University Libraries, Ithaca, New York, two copies have been located in Italy. Copy one is in Florence at Biblioteca Nazionale Centrale (Call no. M. 1062-17). Copy two was found

Antony van Leeuwenhoek
1632-1723

Antony van Leeuwenhoek, Dutch lens-grinder, naturalist, and one of the earliest and greatest microbiologists (Pl. 12b), was born at Delft in 1632 of humble parentage, his father a basket-maker, and his mother the daughter of a Delft brewer. After attending a rural primary school near Leiden, he became apprenticed for six years at the age of sixteen to an Amsterdam linen-draper. In 1654, when twenty-two, Antony married, purchased a Delft house of the type painted by his great contemporary Jan Vermeer, and set himself up in business as a draper. Six years later he found himself playing a part in the political life of his native town through appointment as Chamberlain of Delft's Worshipful Sheriffs.

In 1673, Leeuwenhoek wrote the first of 308 letters to the Royal Society of London describing his microscopical observations, the majority of which were published, as were many of Malpighi's communications, in the *Philosophical Transactions.* Nearly all the original manuscripts of these letters, whether published or not, are preserved in the Society's archives. In 1932, during the tercentenary celebrations of Leeuwenhoek's birth, many new studies of his life and work were published, the most important being an excellent full-length biography by the British protozoologist, Clifford Dobell.[2] G. H. Parker, in a paper on Leeuwenhoek and his microscopes, bids us recall that "without a vestige of university training and utterly devoid of academic associations he contributed to the scientific advance of his day as did scarcely another." Parker then gives an excellent brief summary of the many scientific advances for which this humble man was responsible. First and above all was his detailed study of the capillary vessels as seen in the tails of tadpoles, eels, frog's feet, and bat's wings, in the course of which studies he depicted the different blood corpuscles of various animals and many other microscopic structures such as the spermatozoa. He was the first to observe and delineate bacteria and protozoa, and A. W. Meyer stresses the fact that each new observation of Leeuwenhoek was almost invariably followed by further elucidation through experiment.[3] His celebrated communica-

---

in Bologna at Biblioteca Universitaria (Call no. A. IV. H.I. 222). The second edition of *De pulmonibus* published by Thomas Bartholin in Copenhagen in 1663 is also rare; the Malpighi letters appear as an appendix to Bartholin's harsh diatribe against the gentle Malpighi, and the figures as reproduced are decidedly inferior. An English rendering was published by James Young in *Proc. roy. Soc. Med.,* 1929, *23* [Sect. Hist. Med.], 1-10.

[2] Dobell, Clifford. *Antony van Leeuwenhoek and his little animals.* London, John Bale, Sons and Danielson, Ltd., 1932 (Paperbound edition: New York, Dover Publications, 1960); see also Parker, G. H. "Anthony van Leeuwenhoek and his microscopes." *Sci. Monthly,* 1933, *37,* 434-441; and Schierbeek, Abraham. *Measuring the invisible world; the life and works of Antoni van Leeuwenhoek, F.R.S.* London, Abelard-Schuman, 1959.

[3] Meyer, A. W. "Leeuwenhoek as experimental biologist." *Osiris,* 1938, *3,* 103-122.

tion on the capillaries, no doubt because of its great length and the fact that it was in Dutch, did not find its way into the *Philosophical Transactions* but appeared later in a collected edition of his works.

ANTONY VAN LEEUWENHOEK'S 65TH MISSIVE
TREATING OF

[p. 41] *Two kinds of frogs. Of what parts their eggs consist. That worms [tadpoles] come out of these eggs. How these worms [tadpoles] are composed. The circulation of the blood in six different places in the head of these worms [tadpoles]. Continual sudden impulses given by the heart to the blood. Circulation of the blood in many places in the tail of the worm [tadpole]. What are called arteries and veins are continued blood-vessels. Arteries and veins crossing each other. The circulation takes place in the thinnest blood-vessels. The circulation of the blood in small and large frogs. How in an artery the blood came running back, and what was the cause of it. The circulation of the blood in a little fish, and thirty-four particular circulations in its tail, it also being shown very distinctly that arteries and veins are continued blood-vessels. In a part of our skin, the size of a nail, as many as a thousand circulations of the blood take place. The bodies that make the blood of fish red, are flat and oval. What gentlemen, amongst others, have seen the true circulation of the blood. . . .*

[p. 61] When I looked along the length of the tail and at the thickest part of it, I could clearly see that on either side of the bone there was a large artery, through which the blood was carried to the extremity of the tail, and which on its way sent out several small branches.

When I looked at the part of the tail beside these arteries on the outside, I discovered there two large veins, which carried the blood back again to the heart, and moreover I saw that blood was driven into this large vein from several small veins. In short, I saw here the circulation of the blood to my perfect satisfaction, because there was nothing, though ever so slight, that caused me any doubt. . . .

[p. 63] Also I observed the young frogs when they had changed from worms [tadpoles] into frogs and I also discovered in them a very large number of small blood-vessels which, continually running in curves, formed the vessels called arteries and veins, from which it was perfectly clear to me that the arteries and veins are one and the same continuous blood-vessels. But I saw them clearest of all and most of all at the end of the projecting parts of the legs, which we may call fingers, and of which the frog has four on each fore-leg and five on each hind-leg.

These blood-vessels [i.e., capillaries], called arteries and veins (being nevertheless identical) were exceedingly numerous at the ends of these fingers, and each ran in a curve, which made it impossible to follow the particular course of each vessel. All these vessels were so small or thin that no more than one corpuscle could pass through it at a time. But when I examined these fingers about the first or second joint, I found the blood-vessels there, which we call arteries and veins, bigger, so big even that the blood in these vessels had a red colour. (Leeuwenhoek, A. "65th missive." English translation in *Opuscula selecta Neerlandicorum de arte medica*, 1907, *I*, 37-81 [pp. 41, 61, 63].)[4]

Stephen Hales

1677-1761

Stephen Hales, eminent physiologist and 'perpetual curate' of the parish of Teddington (originally "Tiding Town," i.e., the upper limit of the tide on the Thames) in the county of Middlesex, England, for many years occupied himself between sermons with a series of experiments on the hydraulics of the vascular system which rank as the most significant and original work on the circulation after the discoveries of William Harvey.

Hales (Pl. 13) had been well grounded at Cambridge in Newtonian physics and astronomy and in the laws of mechanics. The experiments described below were carried out after he left Cambridge in 1709, alone and unassisted in a country parsonage; they remained unpublished for a period of nearly twenty years and were eventually issued as the second volume of his *Statical Essays* in 1733. Hales meanwhile had become a Fellow of the Royal Society (1717) before which body he frequently read papers. The life of Hales by Professor A. E. Clark-Kennedy may be recommended as a model biography of a scientific man, for it is a truly inspiring record for any student of medicine, young or old.[5]

---

[4] Leeuwenhoek's letter on the capillary circulation is dated 7 September 1688, and the original manuscript is at the Royal Society. It first appeared in the collected edition of his works which was issued in Dutch in five volumes between 1685 and 1718. It occurs in volume 2 as the 65th "Missive" and bears the title "Den Waaragtigen Omloop des Bloeds, Als mede dat de Arterien en Venae gecontinueerde Bloed-Vaten zijn, Klaar voor de oogen gestelt."

[5] Clark-Kennedy, A. E. *Stephen Hales, D.D., F.R.S. An eighteenth century biography.* Cambridge, At the University Press, 1929. xii, 256 pp.

Hales's account of determining the systolic blood pressure by inserting a tube into the femoral artery of a mare, which he had "caused to be tied down on a field gate," is well known. The experiments from which he inferred that changes occur in the diameter of the capillaries as a result of perfusion with certain chemical agents are less widely known. Hales was not content to infer that capillary vessels existed but actually made critical microscopic observations on them in the living state.

EXPERIMENT IX

1. I Slit open with a Pair of Scissors, from end to end, the Guts of a Dog on that side which was opposite to the Insertion of the mesenterick Arteries and Veins; and having fixed a Tube 4½ Feet high to the descending *Aorta* a little below the Heart I poured blood warm Water thro' a Funnel into the Tube, which descended thence into the *Aorta,* with a Force equal to that, with which the Blood is there impelled by the Heart: This Water passed off thro' the Orifices of innumerable small capillary Vessels, which were cut asunder thro' the whole Length of the slit Gut. But notwithstanding it was impelled with a Force equal to that of the arterial Blood in a live Dog, yet it did not spout out in little distinct Streams, but only seemed to ouze out at the very fine Orifices of the Arteries, in the same manner as the Blood does from the capillary Arteries of a Muscle cut transversely.

2. Having provided a Pendulum which beat Seconds, and pouring in thro' the Tube known Quantities of warm Water, I found that 342 cubic Inches of Water passed off in 400 Seconds or 6.6 minutes. . . .

21. But the Resistance which the Blood meets with in those capillary Passages, may be greatly varied, either by the different Degrees of the Viscidity or Fluidity of the Blood, or by the several Degrees of Constriction or Relaxation of those fine Vessels; Instances of which may be seen in Experiments XV, XVI, XVII, XVIII.

22. And as the State of the Blood or Bloodvessels are in these Respects continually varying from divers Causes, as Motion, Rest, Food, Evacuations, Heat, Cold, &c. so as probably never to be exactly the same, any two Minutes, during the whole Life of an Animal; so nature has wisely provided, that a considerable Variation in these, shall not greatly disturb the healthy State of the Animal.

23. We may make a pretty near Estimate of the Force of the Blood in the capillary Vessels in the following manner, *viz.* taking the Diameter of a Blood Globule to be as above 1/3240th part of an Inch;

which *Leewenhoek* has observed to be of the same Size both in small and great Animals; and allowing these capillary Vessels to be a small Size larger than the Globules, which swim in and are carried along by *Serum* which surrounds them on all sides, we may therefore well suppose one of these Vessels to be double the Diameter of such a Globule, *viz.* 1/1620th part of an Inch or 0.00617, the Periphery therefore of this Vessel will be 0.0194, and its Area 0.0000298, which multiplied by 80, the Number of Inches to which the Blood rose in the Tube when fixed to the Artery of the Dog Numb. 1, gives 0.0000298 parts of eighty cubic Inches of Blood or of 21416 Grains, equal to 1.997 Grains. But the Resistance of the Blood in the Veins of the same Dog being found equal to six Inches Height or 1/12.5th part of eighty Inches, this 1/12.5th part being deducted out of 1.997 Grain, the Remainder 1.838 Grain is the Force with which the Blood would be impelled into such a Capillary by a Column of Blood of eighty Inches Height, supposing it were in a stagnant State; to which also must be added the Velocity which the Blood has acquired at its first Entrance in the capillary Vessel, which can be but small as appears by the great Resistance it meets with in the capillary Vessels, in this IXth Experiment, Numb. 18. whence we see both from Experiment and Calculation, that the Force of the Blood in these fine Capillaries can be but very little, and the longer such Capillaries are, the slower will the Motion of the Blood be in them. . . .

EXPERIMENT XV

3. I took a young Spaniel Dog which weighed twenty one Pounds, and as soon as he had bled to Death by having his jugular Veins cut, I immediately opened his *Thorax* and *Abdomen;* and having fixed a glass Tube, which was 4½ Feet high, to the descending *Aorta,* I then slit open his Guts from end to end the same manner as in *Experiment* IX; then having poured blood warm Water on them, and covered them with a folded Cloth dipped in the same Water, warm Water was poured into the Tunnel, which when it had subsided to a Mark on the lower Part of the glass Tunnel, eighteen cubic Inches of warm Water were immediately poured in, out of a Pot which held just that Quantity: The Time that it was running thro' the fine capillary Arteries was measured by a Pendulum that beat Seconds.

4. I first poured in seven Pots full of warm Water, the first of which passed off in fifty two Seconds, and the remaining six, gradually in less time, to the last which passed in forty six Seconds.

5. Then I poured in five Pots of common Brandy, or unrectify'd Spirit of Malt, the first of which was 68″ in passing, the last 72″.

6. Then I poured in a pot of warm Water which was 54″ in passing.

7. Hence we see that Brandy contracts the fine capillary Arteries of the Guts, and that Water soon relaxes them again, by diluting and carrying off the spirituous Part of Brandy, which as it is well known, not only contracts the Coats of the Blood-vessels, but also thickens the Blood and Humours, both which Effects contribute to the sudden Heating of the Blood, by much increasing thereby its Friction in the contracted capillary vessels; ....

EXPERIMENT XVI

5. I tried in like manner a strong Decoction of Oak Bark on another Dog, in which the preceding Pot of warm Water was 38″ in passing, but the following six pots of Decoction so contracted the Vessels that the last of them was 136″ in passing. ...

EXPERIMENT X

8. When we view in a strong Light the Blood circulating in the Lungs of a Frog, we see the Arteries as they pass on, sending Branches, which spread like a fine Net-work over the Surface of each Vesicle; and on some of these Vesicles we may very plainly see, the Blood when it has pass'd over little more than half their Surfaces, to enter corresponding capillary Veins, which thence unite in large Trunks; but on the greatest part of the Vesicles, the extream capillary Arteries, reach to the Verges of the Vesicles, and there enter at right Angles the Veins, which run along the Limits of those Vesicles; which Veins laying on the inner Sides of those Vesicles they are not visible like the Arteries: But when in here and there a Place I have clearly seen those Veins, I have then also seen the extream capillary Arteries, pour at right Angles their single Globules, into those much larger Veins; agreeable to what I saw in the injected Vessels in *Exper.* XXI. *Numb.* 8.

9. Now by this means the Blood has a much freer Passage thro' the Lungs, where it is requisite for it to move with much greater Velocity than in other parts of the Body. Whereas in some if not all the Muscles, by entering the finer capillary Vessels at right Angles its Velocity is much retarded. I have observed that where a long capil-

lary Artery branches off at an acute Angle, that there the Velocity of the Blood is many times greater, than where it branches off at right Angles, which plainly shews the great Degree of Retardation which the Blood suffers by its passing off at right Angles. . . .

15. I shall hence take occasion to attempt an Estimate, tho' a very inaccurate one, of the Number of extream capillary Arteries in a Man's Body, in the following manner, *viz.* Supposing as is mentioned in *Exper.* VIII *Numb.* 8. that the Area of the transverse Section of the *Aorta* in Man, is 0.4187 Inch, and that the Length of the Cylinder of Blood, which is thrown out at each *Systole* of the left Ventricle, is 3.96 Inches; and the Area of a transverse Section of a fine extream capillary Artery being there set at 0.0000298 Inch: Then since equal Cylinders are as their Bases and Heights, the fine capillary Cylinder thrown out in each *Systole* of the Heart, will be 55639.98 Inches long: This Number multiplied by ten gives the Sum of that Column in 1/10 Inches, *viz.* 55639.98 each of which was the Space the Blood flowed in nine Seconds. But this Length being to pass the extream capillary Arteries of a Man, in 1/75th part of a Minute, that is in 1/8.88 of nine Seconds (the Time in which the Blood moved 1/10th Inch in the Frog) tho' not with greater Velocity than in the Frog; therefore the Number of those extream Arteries in Man, must be proportionably increased by multiplying 556399.8 by 8.88, the Product is 494083, the astonishing Number of extream capillary Arteries. And if according to Dr. *Harvey* and Dr. *Lower,* double that Quantity of Blood be thrown out at each *Systole,* then the Number of extream capillary Arteries will also be double that Number, *viz.* 988166. And if the Velocity in the Lungs be 27.9 times greater as was found in *Exper.* IX. *Numb.* 6. then the Number of extream capillary Arteries there will be 3541713.

16. And how vastly more numerous are the many Branchings, Windings and Turnings of the Arteries and Veins, how innumerable the lymphatic Vessels and secretory Ducts? and these all adjusted and ranged, in the most exact Symetry and Order, to serve the several Purposes of the animal Oeconomy; *So curiously are we wrought, so fearfully and wonderfully are we made!* (Hales, Stephen. *Statical essays: Containing haemastaticks; or, an account of some hydraulick and hydrostatical experiments made on the blood and blood-vessels of animals.* London, 1733, vol. 2, xxii, 361 pp. [pp. 48-49; 56-58; 127-129; 133; 66-67; 70-72].)

Robert Whytt

1714-1766

The details of Whytt's life are mentioned in Chapter VII. Here we wish to direct attention to his little-known book, *Physiological Essays,* which appeared in Edinburgh in 1755 and passed through several editions. The work is chiefly controversial and is divided into two parts, the first entitled "An inquiry into the causes which promote the circulation of the fluids in the very small vessels of animals." Writers on the circulation in the eighteenth century fancied that peristaltic waves of contraction swept along the arterioles and capillaries, in this way assisting the heart. Whytt's consideration of this abandoned doctrine is critical and deserves to be recorded.

SECT. I

Of the force of the heart, contraction of the arteries, gravity and attraction of capillary tubes, considered as causes of the circulation of the fluids in the small vessels of animals.

The principal cause which propels the blood thro' the body, is, without doubt, the contraction of the heart: let us, then, first, inquire how far this may be supposed sufficient to account for the motion of the fluids in the very small vessels of animals.

If the force with which the blood is thrown, by the left ventricle of the heart, into the *aorta,* be supposed equal to the pressure of a column of blood 90 inches high*; the *momentum* of this fluid in any artery will be found, by multiplying the *area* of the transverse section of that artery into 90, the height of that column of blood, whose pressure is supposed equal to the protrusive force of the heart: for the product gives the number of cubic inches or parts of a cubic inch of blood, whose weight is equal to the pressing power with which the blood is driven by the force of the heart into that artery.

The diameter of a circulating red globule of blood, has been generally reckoned something less than 1/3000 part of an inch; but Dr. *Martine* has, from *Lewenhoeck's* and *Jurin's* later observations,

* Dr. *Hales,* from a variety of experiments made on horses, dogs, sheep, and other animals, thinks it probable that the blood would rise seven feet and an half, or 90 inches, in a tube fixed into the carotid artery of a middle-sized man. Statical Essays, vol. 2. p. 40.

shewn it to be 1/1933.5 part of an inch,* and *Lewenhoeck* has observed, that one of these globules is sometimes obliged, in passing thro' a very small capillary artery, to change its figure into an oblong spheroid, so that the diameter of such an artery may be supposed nearly equal to that of a red globule. If then, for the sake of more easy computation, we suppose the diameter of a red capillary artery to be equal to 1/2000 part of an inch, the *area* of its transverse section will be 0.000 000 196, and this multiplied by 90 gives 0.0000176 parts of a cubic inch of blood, which amounts to 0.00466 or 1/214 part of a grain; and is equal to the moment of the blood, arising from the force of the heart, in a capillary artery, whose diameter is 1/2000 part of an inch, upon the supposition that there were no loss of motion from friction, and that the areas of the transverse sections of all the capillary arteries in the human body were equal to that of the *aorta:* but since this is not the case, and the areas of the former greatly exceed that of the latter; the moment of the blood in a capillary red artery, will fall very much short of our computation. . . .

SECT. II

That the vibratory motion of the small vessels of animals is the principal cause promoting the circulation of the fluids.

Having shewn the insufficiency of the powers already mentioned to account for the circulation of the fluids in the very small vessels of animals, we shall now proceed to explain what we imagine to be the principal cause of this circulation.

Altho', as has been observed above, the regular alternate pulsation of the arteries does not extend beyond the capillaries of the first order, except, perhaps, in places very near the heart; yet we are not to consider the serous, lymphatic, and other still smaller vessels, as unactive canals no ways contributing to promote the circulation of their different fluids: on the contrary, it seems highly probable, that these vessels are continually agitated with very small alternate contractions, to which the circulation in them is, in a great measure, owing. . . . (Whytt, R. *Physiological essays.* Edinburgh, Hamilton, Balfour, and Neill, 1755. vii, 223 pp. [pp. 5-8 and 38-39].)

* Medical Essays, vol. 2, art. vii.

Albrecht von Haller

1708-1777

Albrecht von Haller, poet, bibliographer, and physiologist (Pl. 14), exerted a profound influence on physiological thought during the eighteenth century, perhaps greater than that of any other individual. His *Elementa physiologiae corporis humani* in nine volumes is a vast and well-systematized storehouse of physiological knowledge, replete with citation and an incredible number of accurate references to literature. His little book on the circulation (Pl. 15) is divided into two parts, the first containing 174 pages of deductions which are based upon the protocols of the observations collected in Part 2 (pp. 175-343). Haller's conclusion that the capillaries are without contractility was not seriously questioned again until 1917. Such men as Black, Philip, and Rouget, who recorded observations at variance with Haller, did not change opinion. The following paragraph contains Haller's statement of his conclusions.

ON THE MOVEMENT OF THE BLOOD AND THE EFFECTS OF BLEEDING

The contractile force of the arteries is generally considered to be the second cause of the circulation of the blood. Many writers thought that this force was equal to that of the heart and others thought it was even greater. It is quite commonly believed that the power of the heart is enough to send the blood to the smallest arteries and that the force of the arteries then sends it back through the veins. This is also the commonest explanation of the fact that veins do not pulsate. It is thought that venous blood maintains an even movement because it is impelled by the force of the heart and the arteries alternately. Indeed, in warm-blooded animals and in man, one finds that even the smallest arteries of the brain have red fibres capable of contraction and of causing constriction. Experiments have been made which prove this force. If an artery is tied, the part below the ligature still goes on sending the blood which it contains into the veins; if two ligatures are made the blood between them continues to flow into the contiguous veins. When the aorta is ossified the vena cava is filled with coagulated stagnant blood. These are but a few of the many experiments of this sort.

Although I have no intention of refuting these facts, I think it is my duty to relate what the study of anatomy and my own experi-

ments have taught me on this subject. In the first place, frogs' arteries appear to me to lack contractility at all times, either when
studying the perfect equality of their diameter in a state of inanition
and repletion, or the fact that the bitterest poison does not cause
them to contract in the smallest degree; or when examining their
composition, which is very much akin to that of cellular tissue, and
contains no fleshy fibres; or finally, considering that they have no
pulse, since it appears to follow that vessels which do not dilate do
not contract either. Frogs' arteries and veins when touched with
spirit of nitre undergo no change, nor do they contract even when
the poison alters the blood in the vessels, giving it an earthy colour
and muddy consistency. It is almost impossible to conclude anything
from the inanition of the blood-vessels. In frogs the arteries are often
quite empty and after bleeding, below ligatures and in various other
circumstances, corpuscles of blood can be seen gradually leaving
the artery until it is quite white and empty. These vessels can even
become so empty that there is not a single drop of blood left in them.
But I have satisfied myself by several experiments that the blood-
corpuscles move about in the arteries even though the arteries do
not contract, and independently of the heart's force. In an artery
which is nearly empty numbers of corpuscles can be seen to advance
into the artery, hesitate there and retreat and finally disappear,
without the slightest movement of the vessels, or diminution in the
diameter of the artery after the blood has left it, being detectable
through the most powerful microscope. (Haller, Albrecht von. *Deux
mémoires sur le mouvement du sang, et sur les effets de la saignée;
fondés sur des expériences faites sur des animaux.* Lausanne, Marc-
Mic. Bousquet and Comp., 1756. viii, 343 pp. [pp. 136-139].)

Alexander Philips Wilson Philip

1770-1847

Alexander Philips Wilson Philip, physician and physiologist, was an erratic
Scottish genius who, despite a lucrative practice in London, carried out a series
of important observations upon the physiology of the nervous system and the
capillary circulation. He was elected a Fellow of the Royal Society on 11 May
1826 and published 13 papers in the *Transactions* as well as a number of other
papers and books. Around 1843 or 1844 he disappeared from London, having

supposedly lost his fortune through injudicious investments, and is believed to have died abroad in 1847.[6]

The following passage indicates the character of his scientific observations. It should be noted that he had observed "central" acceleration and inhibition of the heart as a result of stimuli applied directly to tissue of the nervous system.

EXP. 30

A frog was rendered nearly insensible by having its back immersed in laudanum. A ligature was then thrown round the neck to prevent loss of blood, part of the cranium removed, the web of one of the hind legs brought before the microscope, and the circulation in it, which was rapid, observed. A strong infusion of tobacco was then applied to the brain, with the effect of at first rendering the circulation more rapid. In about half a minute it became more languid, and soon stopped altogether. On the infusion of tobacco being washed off, the circulation returned and regained considerable vigour. The tobacco was several times applied to the brain and washed off, with the same effects. It may be observed, that when the circulation in the web had almost ceased after the tobacco had been washed off, its velocity was immediately increased on applying spirit of wine to the brain.

The power of the blood-vessels, like that of the heart, is capable of being directly destroyed through the medium of the nervous system. . . .

EXP. 33

The author has often watched the capillaries from the commencement of inflammation to its greatest height, when the part is about wholly to lose its vital power, in the mesentery of a rabbit, the web of a frog's foot, and the fins of fishes, without perceiving the least tendency to this irregular motion when the part viewed was so applied to the microscope as not to compress any of its vessels.* When the circulation fails without any morbid distension of the vessels, the motion of the blood becomes irregular before it stops

[6] McMenemey, W. H. "Alexander Philips Wilson Philip (1770-1847). Physiologist and physician." *J. Hist. Med.*, 1958, *13*, 289-328.

* An account of these experiments is published in the introduction to the author's Treatise on Symptomatic Fevers, and a plate given representing the state of the vessels in the different stages of inflammation. See also the last part of this Inquiry.

altogether; when it fails from morbid distension of the vessels, which gives rise to the phenomena of inflammation, this irregularity is not perceived, the motion of the blood gradually becomes slower, till it ceases altogether.

What are the simple results of the experiments related in this and the preceding chapter? The first set prove, that the power of the heart and vessels of circulation is independent of the brain and spinal marrow, for we find that the functions of the former organs continue after the latter are destroyed or removed, and that their removal is not attended with any immediate effect on the motions of the heart and vessels. The second set prove, that the action of the heart and vessels of circulation may be influenced by agents applied either to the brain or spinal marrow. It is as readily influenced by agents applied to the anterior part of the brain, as by those applied to the cervical part of the spinal marrow. This is what we should expect when we trace the origins of their nerves. . . .

EXP. 47

The cervical part of the spine of a newly-dead rabbit was laid open, and a wire was repeatedly passed transversely through the spinal marrow, without being able at all to affect the motion of the heart; but on the wire being passed longitudinally, so as to bring it into contact with a larger portion of the spinal marrow, the motion of the heart was immediately accelerated. On the same principle, when the wire was made to wound many minute portions of the brain and spinal marrow in quick succession, the action of the heart was increased. . . .

EXP. 19

The reader has seen that if the head and spinal marrow of a frog be removed, the heart continues to perform its function perfectly for many hours, nor does it seem at all immediately affected by their removal. But we find the effect very different when the most sudden and powerful agent is applied to them. If either the brain or spinal marrow be instantly crushed, the heart immediately feels it. The brain of a large frog was crushed by the blow of a hammer. The heart immediately performed a few quick and weak contractions. It then lay quite still for about half a minute. After this its beating returned, but it supported the circulation very imperfectly. In ten minutes its vigour was so far restored, that it again supported the circulation with freedom, but with less force than before the destruction of the brain. An instrument was then introduced under the heart, and after ascertaining that this had produced no change on its action, the spinal marrow was crushed by one blow, as the brain had been. The heart again beat quickly and feebly for a few seconds, and then remained still, and seemed wholly to have lost its power. In about half a minute it again began to beat, and in a few minutes acquired considerable power, and again supported the circulation. It beat more feebly, however, than before the spinal marrow was destroyed. It ceased to beat in about an hour and a half after the brain had been destroyed. In another frog, after the brain and spinal marrow had been wholly removed without any further injury being done to them, the heart beat for nine hours, gradually becoming more languid. (Philip, A. P. W. *An experimental inquiry into the laws of the vital functions.* 3d ed. London, T. and G. Underwood, 1826. lv, 339 pp. [pp. 80-81; 83-84; 100; 72-73].)

James Black
1788-1867

James Black, a Scottish physician who had studied at Glasgow and Edinburgh, conducted a series of experiments of extraordinary interest upon the reactions of the capillaries and published his results in 1825. Black considered the question of peripheral hearts, i.e., waves of peristalsis passing along the capillary vessels, as of possible assistance in the maintenance of the circulation in its terminal ramifications. He points out, however, that the constriction of a capillary vessel necessary for such peristalsis would in reality serve to impede rather than to assist the work of the heart. As the following paragraph will show, Black observed contractility of the minute vessels in the webs of frogs' and ducks' feet, but Marshall Hall a few years later published a book in which he denied the existence of capillary contractility.[7]

CAPILLARY CIRCULATION OF THE BLOOD

Exp. 4. On a frog.—The natural circulation of the arteries in the web almost invisible, and without any red colour; but as soon as it

[7] Hall, M. *A critical and experimental essay on the circulation of the blood; especially as observed in the minute and capillary vessels of the batrachia and of fishes.* London, R. B. Seeley and W. Burnside, 1831. xviii, 187 pp., 10 plates.

was discovered, it was observed to circulate with considerable velocity, and the globules were not easily to be traced. Extension and gentle fastening of the foot even by the fingers, increased the flow of blood, and soon filled many of the colourless vessels with red globules. The application of Aq. Ammon., and more particularly of the salt solution, soon rendered the whole capillaries visible, and of double their former diameters; the circulation becoming slower, and congestion following in the veins, and lastly in the arteries.—The brain was crushed, and the circulation observed in the foot previously unexperimented upon. The vessels sooner than before became more visible, the circulation also became retarded, and congestion took place in the order of vessels as before remarked; but the circulation continued 20 minutes after the injury of the brain, and lastly the blood slowly retired from the smaller vessels of all descriptions, and left the web pale and flaccid.

Exp. 5. The web of a young duck's foot was made the subject of this experiment.—The veins in beautiful branches were easily seen by a common magnifying glass, but the arteries were only visible after some stimulation. The web could not be rendered transparent enough to see the red globules by the microscope. Aq. Ammon. was applied to both sides of one of the divisions of the foot; in two to four minutes great contraction took place in the large vessels; so much so, that many branches were rendered invisible, and others appeared like the finest hairs, which, before in their natural state, seemed three times the diameter. It was not a mere recession of the blood, for the line of the larger vessels was very distinctly contracted and well defined. After the space of about four minutes, all the vessels acquired their former natural diameters, and still further enlarged to complete phlogosis of the part, or to what may be termed inflammation. A fresh application of Aq. Ammon. produced a fresh contraction, but it was not near so complete as the former. The other foot was treated with a saturated solution of Mur. Sodæ, which application was soon followed by great enlargement of the vessels, especially of the larger veins in the web, which seemed much congested, until bathed on both sides with Aq. Ammon. when after five minutes, general contraction was produced, and many of the small vessels were rendered invisible.—During the above experiment, the animal scarcely struggled.

[On the basis of these and other observations Black draws 12 carefully worded conclusions, several of which may be given.]

Third.—The healthy and natural circulation in the capillaries depends, directly, on a tonic or *tensive* state of their delicate tubes; and mediately, on some power inherent in the part, a degree of which power seems to reside in the blood equally with the vessels, and its energy depends more on the integrity or vitality of the part or parts of this system, than upon any impulse derived from the heart. . . .

Fifth.—A strong stimulus suddenly applied, in a short time, produces a contraction of all the fibres of the part, and a diminution of the diameters of the whole classes of vessels, but more particularly of the arteries, which is followed, at a greater or less distance of time, by a corresponding dilatation—according to the extent of which, the phenomena of inflammation will be more or less observable; and more so, if the *vis a tergo* be powerful or stimulated.

Sixth.—A gentle or lesser stimulus produces an evanescent contraction, followed by relaxation, increased redness, and a slight acceleration of blood in the *leading* capillary arteries and veins; owing, it seems, to the increased capacity of the distended reticular vessels, while the former are yet relatively contracted.

Seventh.—The circulation in the capillary system is independent of the controul [sic] of the heart, except so far as this organ affords a constant pressure and a ready supply of blood, upon which the capillary vessels may act; and it is still more independent of the brain. . . .

Tenth.—The condition of a part, in what is termed inflammation, is essentially seated in the capillary vessels, and primarily and chiefly in those of the veins. (Black, J. *A short inquiry into the capillary circulation of the blood.* . . . London, Printed for Longman, Hurst, Rees, Orme, Brown, and Green, 1825. viii, 118 pp. [pp. 54-55, 62-63, 64].)[8]

Marshall Hall

1790-1857

Better known for his contributions to the physiology of the nervous system, *Marshall Hall* also carried out a remarkable series of observations of the capillary circulation in such membranous structures as the web of a frog's foot (Pl. 16), a

[8] See also Fulton, J. F. "James Black's description of the independent contractility of capillaries." *The Lancet*, 1929, *217*, 1010.

fish's tail and mesentery. He clearly distinguished the true capillaries from the arterioles.

THE TRANSITION FROM ARTERIAL INTO
CAPILLARY VESSELS—1831

The larger arteries first divide into branches. These subdivide into still smaller branches, which are also successively smaller than the trunk from which they proceed. At length the singular fact is observed, of each of the two branches being as large, or even larger, than the vessel from which they originate. At this point there is an obvious and remarkable change in the appearance of the circulation: the course of the blood becomes of only half its former velocity, and the globules, consequently, instead of moving too rapidly to be seen, become distinctly visible. If the vessel be traced, it is next observed, not to subdivide, but to unite with other branches, and to pass into that distinct system and net-work of vessels to which I would restrict and appropriate the term capillary. The object of this peculiar distinction and character of the capillary vessels is very obvious: a more diffused and slower circulation is required for administering to the nutrient vessels or functions, than that of the arteries; this peculiar character of the circulation is conferred at once, by the subdivision of the minute artery into branches of equal size with itself. (Hall, Marshall. *A critical and experimental essay on the circulation of the blood.* London, R. B. Seeley and W. Burnside, 1831. xviii, 187 pp., 10 plates [pp. 28-29].)

Johannes Müller

1801-1858

Johannes Müller, whose life is described in Chapter VII (Pl. 17), was deeply interested in almost every phase of physiology, and his celebrated *Handbuch der Physiologie der Menschen* is, like Haller's *Elementa physiologiæ*, a vast compendium of physiological knowledge of his day. The critical attitude which he adopts in the following passage on the capillaries is highly characteristic of his logical habits of thought.

CONTRACTILITY OF THE CAPILLARIES

Many substances, such as those called astringents,—for example, alum,—seem to have the property of producing an approximation of the molecules of living animal matter—a condensation of the matter,—and thus a contraction of the tissues which it forms. It is to this effect on the capillaries and small arteries that we must attribute the action of such astringents, and of cold, in arresting hemorrhage from wounds.

There can be little doubt but that the effect of cold and astringents on the animal textures is much greater during life, for it is only during life that the peculiar state of the skin, called "cutis anserina," can be produced. If the "cutis anserina" arose simply from the blood being repelled from the surface, so as to leave the capillaries less turgid, the skin collapsed, and the follicles consequently more prominent, it would be produced by the same cause after death. It must, therefore, be dependent on a vital contractility of the skin; the follicles becoming more evident in consequence of the contraction of the surrounding skin. A similar contraction is produced in the prepuce by the action of cold, and in a still greater degree in the dartos. The vital insensible contractility here referred to is distinguishable from muscular contractility by the contraction of the part in which it is excited being gradual and feeble; moreover, muscular contractions are excited by the nervous stimulus under all circumstances, while this insensible contraction of the skin is not excited by its specific causes, such as cold and nervous affections, unless under such circumstances as at the same time determine a diminished flow of blood to the skin, which is probably dependent on some sympathetic influence on the heart's action; while all stimulants which induce a greater afflux of blood to the surface produce vascular turgescence, but not the phenomenon of cutis anserina. The insensible contractility displayed by the skin is probably possessed, in a greater or less degree, by all the soft parts which are organised; and there is no reason to suppose that the minute arteries and capillaries are not endued with it. Every stimulant, however, does not excite it. Thus the contraction of the small arteries and capillaries, which causes the arrest of hemorrhage in operations, is produced by the sudden action of specific influences,—such as cold; while other stimuli,—heat, for example,—might, by increasing the turgescence of the part, have quite the contrary effect. Wedemeyer states that no contraction is produced in the capillaries by the agency of galvanism, but that the blood becomes stagnated in them from coagulation taking place. In the small arteries, however, he perceived a distinct permanent contraction, which did not arise, he says, from the action

of the acid developed at the positive pole, for it took place even
when he applied the negative pole to the vessel. It might, however,
in this case, be dependent on the action of the alkali developed at
the negative pole.

Action of different substances on the capillaries.—Direct experiments to determine the action of different substances on the capillary vessels, by watching the changes produced by the application of
these substances to the vessels of transparent parts, promised at first
to increase considerably our knowledge of the action of the capillaries. But these experiments have left our knowledge of the subject
in the greatest confusion. The most interesting observations are
those of Thomson, Wilson, Hastings, Kaltenbrunner, Wedemeyer,
and Koch. Two orders of changes are observed on the application
of chemical agents to the small arteries, capillaries, and veins. In
many instances,—for example, whenever common salt was applied,—
dilatation of the capillaries ensued after a few minutes. In Wedemeyer's experiments, however, on the application of salt to the small
arteries of the mesentery of the frog, contraction to the extent of
1/5th of their diameter was the first effect, and this was followed by
great dilation. The application of ammonia was observed by
Thomson to be followed by contraction of the vessels, with diminished rapidity of the circulation; while Wedemeyer and Hastings
found it produced dilation of the vessels with stagnation of the
blood. Oesterreicher also observed dilatation follow the application of a weak solution of ammonia, while he found that concentrated matters produce contraction of the vessels, and at last stagnation of the blood. Alcohol, according to Hastings, produced contraction of the capillaries: hot water had the same effect in frogs; the
application of ice was also followed by contraction. Hastings remarked that these substances frequently caused contraction first, and
afterwards dilatation. From the application of tincture of opium,
tartaric acid, very dilute muriatic acid and alcohol, Wedemeyer obtained no constant result. In two instances only did alcohol cause
retardation of the circulation, without, however, having excited distinct contraction in the small arteries. When dilatation of the vessels is produced, the circulation is generally at the same time retarded. Thomson is the only physiologist who has observed acceleration as well as retardation of the circulation accompanying dilatation of the vessels; and this was after the application of common

salt. In vessels in which the substance applied has produced contractions, the rate of the circulation also varies, being sometimes retarded, sometimes accelerated. (Müller, J. *Elements of physiology*. Translated by William Baly. London, Printed for Taylor and Walton, 1838-1842. 2 vols. xxxviii, 1715, 22 pp. [continuously paged]. [I, pp. 226-229].)

Charles-Marie-Benjamin Rouget
1824-1904

Charles-Marie-Benjamin Rouget, the son of a distinguished military surgeon of the army of the first Empire (Pl. 18), was born at Gisors and obtained his education at the Collège Sainte Barbé. He studied medicine at Paris and became an interne at the Hôtel Dieu, after which he accepted in 1860 the chair of physiology at the faculty of medicine at Montpellier. Following the death of Claude Bernard in 1878, a new chair of general physiology was created for Rouget at the Museum of Natural History in Paris; he went to occupy this post in 1879 and continued to hold it until 1893.[9] Rouget was a man of great energy and enthusiasm with a powerful yet kindly face and military bearing. He was an outstanding success as a teacher, lecturing always to crowded benches, and he counted among his pupils Mathias Duval and many well-known French clinicians. He was also an ardent histologist, and in 1867 (*Comptes rendus*) he propounded a theory of muscular contraction based upon the belief that the contractile elements in a muscle are arranged between the successive planes of a closed helicoid.

Rouget's observations upon the contractile cells of the capillaries of amphibia were important because they led to prolonged investigation of the control of capillary circulation. In 1917, Krogh revived the idea that the capillaries are contractile, and in 1928 Bensley and Vimtrup demonstrated the presence of myofibrils in the Rouget cells of amphibian capillaries.[10] Rouget cells have not been found, however, in mammalian capillaries, and after Zweifach distinguished a-v bridges from true capillaries in 1937 it has generally been concluded that in mammals the capillary proper is not contractile or that such contractility as it may possess exerts no effective control over the capillary circulation.

[9] The details of Rouget's life are little known, and the chief source of information seems to be the obituary notice by his successor, Nestor Gréhant, in the *Nouvelles Archives du Muséum d'Histoire Naturelle de Paris* (1904, 4 sér. vol. 6, pp. iii-xii), the last seven pages of which give a list of his papers. Professor Louis Lapicque, who was a pupil of Rouget, has put down recollections of his master and has given the history of the chair which he occupied ("La chaire de physiologie du Muséum." *Rev. sci.,* Paris, 1912, *50*, 769-779).

[10] Bensley, R. R. and Vimtrup, B. J. "On the nature of the Rouget cells of capillaries." *Anat. Rec.,* 1928, *39*, 37-53.

NOTE ON THE DEVELOPMENT OF THE
CONTRACTILE WALLS OF
BLOOD VESSELS

Further research into the development of blood vessels, conducted since the early spring on the larvae of amphibians, proves beyond doubt the contractility of cells with ramified protoplasmic elongations which I observed last year in the blood vessels of the hyaloid membrane of an adult frog.

Indeed, identical cells in larvae constitute a so-called "adventitial" wall in arterial, venous and true capillaries. This wall being merely a continuation of the muscular walls of the arteries and veins, it follows that the whole blood vascular system, from the heart to the capillaries inclusive, is surrounded by a contractile wall.

The blood vessels of the dorsal fin of amphibian larvae—which, according to a commonly accepted error which I shared myself till last year, have the complete structure of primitive capillaries, *i.e.* one membrane only of parietal (endothelial) cells—should be, according to my most recent observations, classed not only from a functional but also from a structural point of view, into arteries, veins and a network of capillary vessels.

On living vessels thus contracted, one can see refracting annular constrictions projecting at the edges of the vessels to which they give a crenated appearance. Their surface on cross section partially reproduces that of the fibre cells of the arteries, and here and there widely separated nuclei are visible. The ramifications of the arterioles which gradually become more widely separated and even the capillary arches nearest the free edge of the tail and those of the intermediate capillary network, present the same appearance, but with a gradual diminution in the diameter of the constrictions and an increasingly marked scarcity of nuclei. The refracting annular constrictions and the nuclei belong to cells with ramified protoplasmic elongations absolutely identical with those which I previously observed on the vessels of the hyaloid membrane in an adult frog. Under the successive action of alcoholized water and of iodine solution, an anhistious membraneous tube, constricted at regular intervals by twisted contractile cellular filaments, dilated by inhibition of the primitive vascular tube and retracted in the centre of the membraneous sheath, was also visible on the blood vessels of the dorsal fin. All the vessels of the dorsal fin in the final stages of development have this fundamental structure, but for this one difference, in the capillaries the nuclei are very scarce and very widely separated from each other, the contractile filaments are very fine, their division appearing merely as a point, in the venules the nuclei are farther apart than in arterioles of the same order, while the cellular ramifications are finer, more irregular and distant from each other. In addition, the contractility of the veins is much less obvious on account of the distension of their walls by the blood driven back from the arteries and capillaries.

The first contractile cells which make their appearance in a recently-formed blood vessel, do not proceed either from the primitive vascular cells (endothelial), from which they are separated by a membraneous cuticle, or from the cells of the surrounding connective tissue with which they have no connexion at any stage in their development. On the contrary I have often observed that in young vessels, as yet lacking a contractile tunic, the ameboid cells spread their elongations over their walls, as do later the ramified ameboid pigmentary cells, which are properly speaking the first constituent elements of the wall of connective or adventitial tissue. Comparing these observations with those which I made previously on the rôle of ameboid cells (leucocytes) in the formation of the secondary wall of the blood vessels of the hyaloid in the embryos of mammals, it follows that not only are the walls of connective tissue, the adventitial walls of the arteries, veins and neurilemma, made up of migratory cellular elements which attach themselves to the nerve vessels and cords, but also contractile tissue of a higher order may have the same origin. (Rouget, Ch.-M.-B. "Mémoire sur le développement de la tunique contractile de vaisseaux." *C.R. Acad. Sci. [Paris]*, 1873, 79, 559-562.)

THE CONTRACTILITY OF BLOOD CAPILLARIES [1879]

Five years ago I communicated to the Academy the first results of my observations on the contractility of the blood vessels of the dorsal fin of tadpoles. All these vessels are contractile and they do not owe this property to the endothelium—which, as I have shown, is entirely made up of cells of naked vacuolar protoplasm—but rather to a network of ramified contractile cells, whose existence I previously established for the first time in the capillaries of the hyaloid membrane of adult frogs.

If tadpoles are submitted to the action of an anaesthetic so as to produce the beginnings of syncope, one can see the distributing arteries which emerge from the caudal arterial trunk contract and shrink till the lumen of the vessel disappears at the numerous annular constrictions, especially near the point of branching. Local stimulation, whether mechanical, chemical or electrical, causes annular constrictions at the point excited; but, in addition, following similar stimulation of a cut surface of the tail on a living animal—*i.e.* on the nerve and vascular trunks from which the ramifications of the dorsal fin arise—the blood immediately flows back; this is entirely due to the contraction of the vessels themselves, chiefly that of the arterioles and their bifurcating branches in the capillary network; these, contracting slowly but strongly, cause a centripetal movement of the blood in all vessels; this movement may last 5 or 10 minutes after stimulation has ceased and drives all the blood from the capillaries into the veins. Even during contraction crenations are visible on the edge of the capillaries, which correspond to refracted annular strictures bearing here and there globular projecting nuclei, fairly far apart from each other. These constricting bands and nuclei are part of the contractile cells and their ramified protoplasmic elongations, the earliest embryonic form of the fusiform muscle cells of the vessels, developing from them in successive divisions.

Recent observations on the blood vessels of the nictitating membrane of mammals, either newly-born or in embryos of various ages, show that the same phenomenon of contractility observed in the larvae of batrachians is also present accompanied in the same way by a return of circulation in vessels isolated from the heart, whether provoked by mechanical stimulation or appearing at the onset of rigor. This contractility also belongs properly to the ramified protoplasmic cells which surround the endothelial wall in a network. I have found the same structure in the capillaries of the epiploon (omentum) of young mammals and in those of the electric organ of the eel.

Without contractility the capillaries would not be able to rid themselves of the blood which they contain. Even in animals bled to death I have found the capillaries swollen with blood immediately after death when they had not previously contracted in the death-agony and before rigor had set in. However complete may be the contraction of the small arteries it could not—as has been believed up till now—empty the capillaries of their contents; it could only act like a tap placed on the course of a tube through which a liquid flows. When the flow is interrupted, even if the tube were elastic, that part of it which is above the tap and therefore escapes its pressure, would not be emptied. Not only would a network of capillaries, which escapes pressure of the heart owing to the closing of the small arteries, not empty itself, but blood from the veins would flow into it; the absolutely bloodless condition of a living part, such as the skin of the face under the influence of emotion, or the extremities when exposed to long continued cold, can only be explained by actual contraction of the capillaries.

While studying, in 1874, the development of the capillaries of the nictitating membrane in the embryos of mammals, I described and depicted the adventitial wall of these vessels as made up of migratory cellular elements, which come and attach themselves to the outside of the endothelium—as occurs in the case of batrachian tadpoles. I have since realised that this adventitial wall is nothing more or less than the contractile wall itself. However strange this origin of muscular elements may seem, it has been recently confirmed (in 1878) by Professor Selenka of Erlangen, who has seen and described in embryos of holothuria tubulosa the muscular bed of the intestines, which is made up of migratory ameboid cells which come and attach themselves to the exterior of the intestinal mucosa. I consider, therefore, that I am justified in concluding that, in all vertebrates, a similar contractile tunic, modified only in the form of its elements, surrounds the whole system of the blood vascular channels, from the heart to the capillaries inclusive, and that its contractility—the character of whose manifestations is also modified according to its situation—is an essential property of every part of the vascular system. (Rouget, Ch.-M.-B. "Sur la contractilité des capillaires sanguins." *C.R. Acad. Sci. [Paris]*, 1879, *88*, 916-918.)

Ernest Henry Starling
1866-1927

E. H. Starling, British physiologist and eminent teacher, who for many years held the Jodrell Chair of Physiology at University College, London, made pioneer studies on the physiology of the circulation, the nature of lymph, and, in collaboration with W. M. Bayliss, a series of classical investigations upon the hormone control of the pancreas. Undoubtedly his most important discovery, however, was the functional significance of the osmotic pressure of the proteins of the blood. It was he who first pointed out that since the capillaries were permeable to the blood crystalloids, the effective osmotic pressure is exerted by the serum proteins and that this is responsible for the absorption of fluid from the tissues, a point of particular significance to the physiology of the kidney. The following selection is taken from his original paper.

OSMOTIC PRESSURE OF SERUM PROTEIDS

In the limbs and connective tissues generally of the peripheral parts of the body, we have capillaries which are more or less impervious to proteids. As the blood passes under pressure through these capillaries, a certain amount of lymph is filtered through their walls, but in the process it loses the greater part of its proteids. We have therefore on one side of the capillary wall blood-plasma with 8% proteids, on the other side lymph containing 2 to 3% proteids. In this separation of proteid a certain amount of work must have been done, and if the proteids of serum are really analogous to the substance X of my illustration and possess an osmotic pressure, there must be a difference of osmotic pressure between intra- and extra-vascular fluids tending to a reabsorption of the latter. It becomes desirable to inquire whether the proteids of serum have any osmotic pressure and if so, what is the extent of this pressure.

To decide these points I have attempted to measure the osmotic pressure of the proteids in the serum directly. . . .

In all my experiments the fluid in the osmometer began to rise in the tube within two or three hours after the commencement of the experiment, and rose steadily for 3 or 4 days, the final height varying from 30 to 41 mm. Hg. . . .

The importance of these measurements lies in the fact that, although the osmotic pressure of the proteids of the plasma is so insignificant, it is of an order of magnitude comparable to that of the capillary pressures; and whereas capillary pressure determines transudation, the osmotic pressure of the proteids of the serum determines absorption. Moreover, if we leave the frictional resistance of the capillary wall to the passage of fluid through it out of account, the osmotic attraction of the serum for the extravascular fluid will be proportional to the force expended in the production of this latter, so that, at any given time, there must be a balance between the hydrostatic pressure of the blood in the capillaries and the osmotic attraction of the blood for the surrounding fluids. With increased capillary pressure there must be increased transudation, until equilibrium is established at a somewhat higher point, when there is a more dilute fluid in the tissue-spaces and therefore a higher absorbing force to balance the increased capillary pressure. With diminished capillary pressure there will be an osmotic absorption of salt solution from the extravascular fluid, until this becomes richer in proteids; and the difference between its (proteid) osmotic pressure and that of the intravascular plasma is equal to the diminished capillary pressure. (Starling, E. H. "Absorption by blood vessels." *J. Physiol. (Lond.)*, 1895, *19*, 312-326 [pp. 322-325].)

August Krogh
1874-1949

Schack August Steenberg Krogh, formerly professor of zoö-physiology at the University of Copenhagen (Pl. 19a), was well known to physiologists prior to 1918 for his investigations on metabolism, the volume output of the heart, and respiration. In that year there began to appear a series of notable papers on the physiology of capillaries, which culminated in his Silliman Lectures at Yale in 1922. Krogh and Lewis together almost literally rediscovered the capillaries and made this field peculiarly their own. Krogh's observations upon the shifting of open capillaries in resting tissue, which is described in the following paragraphs, may well be regarded as one of the great contributions to modern physiology.

CAPILLARY BED DURING ACTIVITY

My own first contribution to the problem of capillary contractility was published in Danish in 1918, about a month after Dale and Richards' paper, and somewhat later appeared in the British *Journal of Physiology* (1919). It was undertaken to test the hypothesis of a regulation of the supply of blood to muscles through the opening and closing of individual capillaries. I found it possible to observe at least the superficial capillaries of muscles both in the frog and in mammals through a binocular microscope, using strong reflected light as a source of illumination. Resting muscles observed in this way are usually quite pale, and the microscope reveals only a few capillaries at fairly regular intervals. These capillaries are so narrow that red corpuscles can pass through only at a slow rate and with a change of form from the ordinary flat discs to elongated sausages. When the muscle under observation is stimulated to contractions a large number of capillaries become visible and dilated, and the rate of circulation through them is greatly increased. When the stimulus has lasted only a few seconds the circulation returns in some minutes to the resting state; the capillaries become narrower and most of them are emptied completely, while a small number remain open. Since capillaries, even in a group fed by the same arteriole, do not all behave in the same way, the changes obviously cannot be due to arterial pressure changes.

In resting muscles of the frog the average distance between open capillaries, observed simultaneously through the microscope, was estimated at 200 to 800μ, but after contractions this could be reduced to 70 or 60μ. In the guinea pig average distances of about 200μ could be observed during rest. The exposure to the air and the strong light always increased the circulation, and it was often possible to see the circulation begin in one capillary after another.

It might be argued that the observations here recorded could be explained as the results of dilatation of arterioles alone, on the assumption that the capillary paths offer various degrees of resistance, that a few are opened by a low pressure, while the majority of capillaries belonging to an arteriole require a higher pressure and are opened only when that arteriole is dilated. Such an assumption would involve as a consequence that a reduction of the pressure to zero by cutting the artery must produce an elastic contraction and emptying of the postulated high-pressure capillaries. Numerous observations have shown that all the capillaries may remain open when a piece of muscle is cut out after stimulation.

THE SHIFTING OF OPEN CAPILLARIES IN THE SKIN AND OTHER TISSUES

On the back of the hand it is usually possible to see only the tips of the capillaries, but occasionally the venous branch may be traced all the way to the richly anastomosing network of venules below, and we can see this horizontal plexus receive the blood from the capillary loops at regular intervals.

When a single small field is watched over a period of several minutes, it is found that here, unlike the conditions at the base of the nail, all the capillaries are not open at a given moment. They are opening and closing continuously, as seen in the figure, where drawings made every three minutes have been reproduced, together with a representation of all the capillaries present in this field, and opened up by the stimulus of a light pressure. Similar shifting of the open capillaries over the field has been observed again and again in the human skin when in a completely unstimulated condition. Hagen has seen corresponding changes in a flat capillary network in the rabbit's ear and given a diagrammatic representation of a number of changes taking place during a few minutes. They also regularly occur, though they are not so conspicuous, in the web of frogs, as I have described (1921), and I have seen them repeatedly in frogs' muscles. Quite recently a shifting of the blood flow from one capillary to another and from one glomerulus to another has been described by Richards (1922) for the frog's kidney.

I intend to apply cinematographic methods to make a closer and more extended study of these shiftings of open capillaries than is practicable by visual methods, because I believe them to represent the very essence of capillary circulation regulation.

A very small number of open capillaries (compared with the total number existing) is sufficient, as we have seen, to supply the wants of a resting tissue, but if the open capillaries were always the same the distribution of the substances supplied by them would be very unequal. The tissue elements nearest to the open capillaries would get more than they required, and the more distant would be starved. When the position of the open capillaries is continuously changing, a cell, starving at one moment, will get all it wants when the capillary nearest to it is opencd up. In this way an adequate, though intermittent, supply can be secured at every single point, while, at the same time, the blood is utilized with the utmost economy, the necessary minimum only being present at any one time in any tissue.

A regulation of this kind may possibly be brought about by metabolic products accumulating at points where the distance through which they have to diffuse in order to reach an open capillary is too great, and by their action causing the opening of a nearer vessel. It may be conceived as simply due to oxygen lack—in some tissues at least—and it may be due, perhaps, to the pituitary hormone, which gradually disappears from a capillary when it is closed to the passage of blood. It is at present impossible to make a choice between these and other possibilities. Several factors may work together, and all I can say is that the problem requires and will undoubtedly repay the most careful experimental investigation.

In the skin of man and, very noticeably, in the palm of the hands, there is a further shifting of open capillaries (and venules), in so far as fields of a few millimeters diameter in which there are only a few open capillaries, while the underlying vessels are indistinct, alternate with others in which a large number of capillaries are open and the underlying vessels are prominent. The difference is often quite distinct when seen with the naked eye (Ebbecke, 1917, p. 51), and it can be observed how the white and red spots may be continually changing in form and location. (Krogh, S. A. S. *The anatomy and physiology of capillaries* [Silliman Memorial Lectures]. New Haven, Yale University Press, 1922. xvii, 276 pp. [pp. 37-39 and 172-174]; second edition 1929.)

Thomas Lewis

1881-1945

Sir Thomas Lewis, cardiologist and authority on the circulation in the human skin (Pl. 19b), did as much as any other individual in modern times to introduce scientific methods of thought and investigation into clinical medicine. His contribution to pure physiology was also prodigious; in his work and teaching he effectively bridged the chasm between the laboratory and clinic—to the lasting benefit of both—and he taught an enthusiastic body of pupils how best to adapt the experimental method to the needs of clinical medicine. The influence which he exerted can be judged by the rich fruition of his own labours and of those of his followers in various parts of the world. His simple and well-conceived experiments, his painstaking observations and carefully worded conclusions are nowhere, it seems to me, better illustrated than in the following passage from his monograph on the human capillaries.

THE WHITE REACTION

Pallor of the skin can be produced, as will be seen, in one or other of several ways; but first we may consider the white reaction to a mechanical stimulus. If a blunt point is drawn with light pressure across the warm skin of the forearm or back, the skin pressed upon blanches as the point travels over it. This blanching results from a simple and temporary displacement of blood from the superficial vessels of the skin; the natural skin colour returns and the white track in the wake of the travelling point is obliterated almost as soon as it is formed. The skin over which the point has passed is now uniform in colour but, within a period varying usually from 15 to 20 seconds, the line of stroke again becomes visibly paler than its surroundings. After usually a half or a whole minute, this narrow band of pallor is of full intensity. . . .

Reduction in the size of the vessels that are responsible for skin colour has manifestly happened in the white reaction; and it might be natural to attribute this change to contraction of the arterioles supplying the corresponding area of skin; for such arteriolar constriction could be said to lower the distending pressure in the minute vessels and these would tend to become emptier as a consequence. But we were reluctant to accept such an explanation for the reason stated, namely, the sharpness with which the area stimulated is subsequently marked out by the reaction; there is the additional argument that obliteration of the brachial artery does not empty the minute vessels nor produce pallor of nearly the intensity that is seen in the white reaction. There remained the possibility that the reaction is due, not to a passive effect of arteriolar constriction, but to an active change in the minute vessels themselves.

The following experiment was devised finally to differentiate between the two last causes. An armlet is placed on the upper arm of a subject, the skin of whose forearm is known to yield a conspicuous white reaction to a stroke, and a pressure of 250 to 300 mm. Hg. is thrown abruptly into the armlet from a large pressure reservoir. The flow in the brachial artery and veins is instantly obstructed by this procedure and the onward flow in the capillaries of the lower arm rapidly ceases. Since, at the moment of compression, the pressure within the arteries is higher than in the veins, flow does not cease at once; but it does cease, as direct observation of the capillaries of the nail bed shows, within a very short time, namely within ½ to 1 minute (Neumann 1920, and personal observations). Kendrew (1926), working in my laboratory, found that the pressure in the veins rises for about these periods after the pressure is applied. The pressures in the vessels of the arm as a whole enter a state of general equilibrium and this state is subsequently maintained. If the two arms are now stroked simultaneously, the white reaction appears on both. Within observational error, it appears simultaneously on the two arms, is equally vivid on the two, and fades away in much the same time. Briefly, the reaction is not affected when the circulation in the limb is stopped. A white reaction may be obtained in the skin of such a limb when its main vessels have been firmly compressed for periods of 5, 10, or sometimes even 15 minutes. . . .

The appearance of a white reaction to stroking, when the circulation has been brought to rest, is an event of prime importance, for it is incompatible with a belief that the reaction is due to stimulation of the arterioles. It proves that the walls of the minute vessels contract and expel their contents. When the circulation has been stopped, an arteriolar contraction, if it affects the minute vessels at all, can only increase their contents. The reaction occurs in the walls of those vessels that are responsible for skin colour, and not in the walls of vessels conveying blood to these. It is an active and not a passive effect in the vessels that are under examination. This observation, made 11 years ago,[11] and the conclusion then based on it that "we are forced to regard the tissue elements immediately surrounding the capillary blood and forming an essential layer of the capillary wall as the source of the reaction," is to be emphasized. . . .

The reasons for placing these crucial observations in the foreground are several. The first will be apparent at once; the observations are undertaken upon the human subject and the conclusion applies to *human* capillaries and venules, thereby adding to its value. Secondly, the actual observations are of the simplest character, easy to repeat and demonstrate; for this reason and because the appearances are manifest they are the more convincing; likewise their interpretation is freed from many minor sources of error; for there is in this case minimal disturbance of the living structures concerned in what is evidently a delicate reaction. Thirdly, because they serve to illustrate the truth that a conclusion is suggested or may be reached from every distinct phenomenon observed, however simple or trivial such observations may at first sight seem, and that sometimes, as here, the conclusion may possess a far reaching application, if based on observations properly controlled. Fourthly, because the conclusion has proved unassailable; it formed the first of those demonstrations that during the last decade have converted physiologists to their recent and now almost universal belief in the important part played by the capillaries in controlling the circulation. (Lewis, T. *The blood vessels of the human skin and their responses.* London, Shaw and Sons, 1927. xv, 322 pp. [pp. 23, 25-29, 30].)

[11] That is, in 1917. Cotton, T. F., Slade, J. G., and Lewis, T. "Observations upon dermatographism with special reference to the contractile power of capillaries." *Heart,* 1915-17, *6,* 227-247.

PLATE 12B. Antony van Leeuwenhoek (1632-1723) from his *Epistolae ad Societatem Regiam Anglicam*, 1719.

PLATE 12A. Marcello Malpighi (1628-1694.). Photograph of the portrait by A. M. de Tobar which hangs in the Royal Society. (Courtesy of the Society.)

PLATE 13. Stephen Hales (1677-1761). (From the portrait by Thomas Hudson in
the National Portrait Gallery, London.)

PLATE 14. Albrecht von Haller (1708-1777). From Sigmund Freudenberger's portrait of 1773, considered by Artur Weese, his iconographer, to be the best of all Haller's portraits. (Weese, *Die Bildnisse Albrecht von Hallers*, Bern, 1909.)

Parquier in.   chez MARC-MICHEL BOUSQUET   Soubre sc.

D E U X
MEMOIRES
SUR LE
MOUVEMENT DU SANG,
ET SUR
LES EFFETS DE LA SAIGNÉE,
FONDÉS SUR DES EXPERIENCES
Faites ſur des Animaux :
PAR MONSIEUR
ALB. DE HALLER,
Préſident de la Societé Royale des Sciences de
GÖTTINGUE, Membre de l'Acadé-
mie Royale des Sciences de PARIS, LON-
DRES, BERLIN, STOKHOLM, &c.

A LAUSANNE,
Chez MARC-MIC. BOUSQUET & Comp.
Et ſe vend à PARIS,
Chez DAVID, Ruë & vis-à-vis la Grille des
Mathurins.

MDCCLVI.

PLATE 15. Engraved frontispiece and title-page of Haller's *Deux memoires sur le mouvement du sang,*
1756, in which are recorded his observations on the capillaries.

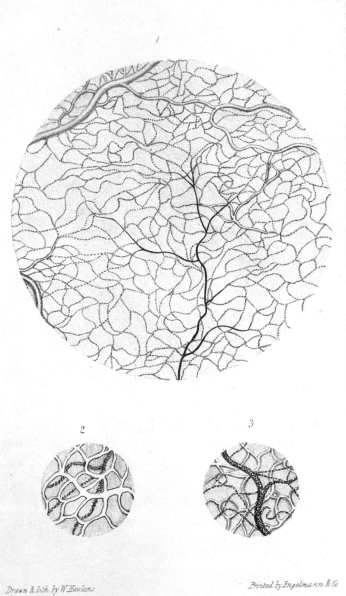

Drawn & lith. by W.Hawkins   Printed by Engelmann & Co

PLATE 16. Marshall Hall's drawing of the small blood vessels and capillaries in the web of the foot of a frog (1). The beaded appearance of the capillaries arises from the fact that the blood cells are individually distinguishable in them. Hall says: "The capillaries continually unite and redivide, retaining a uniform size and a uniform velocity of circulation; the various roots unite successively, forming larger and larger veins, and anastomose occasionally, still preserving the velocity of the capillary circulation." (2 and 3). The two layers of capillaries in the frog's web.

PLATE 17. Johannes Müller (1801-1858). (Courtesy of the National Library of Medicine.)

PLATE 18. Charles Rouget (1824-1904). (From the *Nouvelles Archives du Muséum d'Histoire Naturelle*, Paris, 1904, vol. 6.)

PLATE 19B. Sir Thomas Lewis (1881-1945), about 1928.

PLATE 19A. August Krogh (1874-1949).

Eugene Markley Landis

1901-

The Starling hypothesis concerning the interchange between the capillary blood and interstitial fluid was obliged to remain only an hypothesis until the blood-pressure changes within the capillaries could be measured. Only then could the hydrostatic pressure within the capillaries be compared with the osmotic pressure of the plasma proteins. It was not until 1926 that the direct measurement of the blood pressure within the capillaries was achieved by *Eugene Markley Landis,* then still a medical student.

A native of Pennsylvania, Landis was educated at the University of Pennsylvania where he received four different degrees in rapid succession (B.S. 1922, M.S. 1924, M.D. 1926, Ph.D. 1927). From 1931 until 1939 he taught at the University of Pennsylvania Medical School. In the latter year he became professor of internal medicine at the University of Virginia where he remained until 1943 when he succeeded Walter Cannon as George Higginson Professor of Physiology at Harvard University.

CAPILLARY PRESSURE IN FROG MESENTERY

Apparently only indirect methods have so far been applied to the measurement of capillary pressure in the frog. . . .

The direct method here described has been used to measure the pressure in certain portions of the vessels in frog mesentery, in an effort to determine the average gradient of pressure fall through this particular portion of the peripheral circulation, and the possible relations of capillary pressure to certain factors such as flow, venous obstruction, and perhaps constriction. The pipettes used are 4 to 8 micra in diameter at the tip, and after being introduced into the capillary, can be held firmly in position over relatively long periods of time to measure the fluctuation of pressure in relation to other factors. . . .

Two methods have been used in the determination of pressure in individual capillaries. The first is the more difficult but under proper conditions will measure both diastolic and systolic pressures in the vessel pierced. A very fine pipette, filled with a dye such as methylene blue, may be introduced into a dilated capillary or venous capillary and the flow not be hindered if the tip is brought as close as possible to the endothelial wall. When flow has continued for some minutes and is to all appearances normal the measurement may be made. As the pressure on the dye in the micro-pipette is gradually raised by increasing the height of the column of water in the upright tube, a point is reached where there is a barely visible spurt of dye during diastole. This would indicate the lowest pressure in the circulatory cycle—diastolic pressure. As the height of the water column is further increased another point is reached at which the dye flows into the passing plasma continuously, though the amount is larger during diastole, and just perceptible during systole. This gives some indication of systolic pressure. . . .

The second method has been the more generally useful and is entirely accurate for measurement of mean pressure but permits only a rough estimation of pulse pressure. It requires the insertion of the pipette into some collateral of the capillary, the pressure changes of which are to be measured. The pressure in this occluded collateral will be equal to the lateral pressure in the straight vessel at the point opposite the opening. Flow proceeds uninterruptedly throughout the entire period in the capillary observed. After the pipette is introduced into the collateral a few corpuscles may be drawn out of the main stream back into the vessel functioning as a side tube. Intermittent movement toward or away from the pipette occurs synchronously with the heartbeat when the pressure of the water column is below or above mean pressure respectively. When the proper height is reached the dye-plasma junction, or the corpuscles, whichever is used to determine the point of equilibrium, will oscillate back and forth about a single point, thus giving the mean pressure in the capillary at the moment. With lowering of pressure, the corpuscles will move toward the pipette only in systole, remaining stationary in diastole. At a higher pressure the converse will be true; the movement is away from the pipette in diastole but ceases in systole. The difference between these two levels gives a general idea of the magnitude of pulse pressure, but in all probability not so accurately as the first method. . . .

To determine the average fall of pressure [from artery to vein through the capillary bed] 189 determinations were made at various points in the peripheral vessels, 22 in the larger arteries near the attachment of the mesentery, 5 in the first bifurcations of these arteries near the intestine, 11 in the small arterioles, 111 in the capillaries, 17 in the venous capillaries, and 23 in venules and veins. . . . [Fig. 4].

Direct measurement in a single capillary shows that pressure as

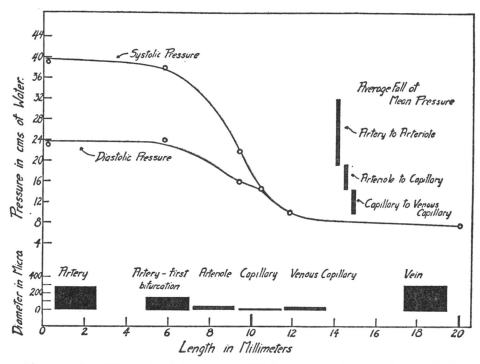

Figure 4. Landis' graph of the average fall in pressure through the vessels in the mesentery. Pressure is charted in centimeters of water againt the length of the respective vessels. Below, the relative diameters of the vessels are shown in micra.

well as flow is constantly varying and that the two apparently change in the same direction providing the pressure in the vein remains approximately the same. Within the limits mentioned above high capillary pressures are nearly always found to occur in regions showing more rapid flow, and low pressures where flow is very slow or absent.

The relation between pressure and velocity may be measured by inserting the pipette into the side capillary, taking pressure as usual, then immediately afterward determining the time it requires for a corpuscle or group of corpuscles to pass from a certain point to the opening of the side capillary. It is possible to measure the pressure in the venule or vein only at the beginning and the end of the experiment, but this pressure has been found to remain quite constant if capillary flow is increased over a small area only, as is usually the case. . . .

The relationship between the pressure in the capillary field and the osmotic pressure of blood colloids for the frog is of interest with reference to the interchange of fluid. White (1924) has found the osmotic pressure of plasma proteins of three frogs ranging between 9.6 and 11.5 cm. of serum, or 10.0 to 11.9 cm. water. Thus the average pressure in the arteriolar end of the capillary is above, and that in the venous capillary is slightly below, the average osmotic pressure of the colloids as reported by White. Moreover, capillary pressure changes continually, at some moments above, at others below, the reported colloid osmotic pressure, and flow is rapid or slow in the same relation. It is conceivable that in any capillary the flow of water through the wall might be outward at one moment, and inward at another, throughout the whole length of the capillary. (Landis, E. M. "The capillary pressure in frog mesentery as determined by micro-injection methods." *Amer. J. Physiol.,* 1926, 75, 548-570 [pp. 549, 551-553, 555, 561-562, 568].)

Benjamin William Zweifach

1910-

The controversy over the contractility of capillaries, which had persisted for a very long time, was clarified, if not finally settled, when *Benjamin William Zweifach* in 1937 demonstrated the existence of a-v bridges, which were contractile, as distinct from the capillaries which were not.

A native of New York City, Zweifach was educated at the City College (B.S. 1931) and at New York University where he took his Ph.D. in anatomy in 1936. He has been principally connected with the New York University Medical Center and has been professor of physiology there since 1958.

THE STRUCTURE OF SMALL BLOOD VESSELS

Muscular or a-v vessels. In examining the vascular pattern of a complete capillary bed, the blood is seen to flow most rapidly through those channels that pursue the most nearly direct route from the arterial to the venous side of the circulation and offer the least resistance to the moving blood cells. Many of the small vessels are often in a "collapsed" or "contracted" state and, for long periods, contain no flowing blood. The more direct channels, however, have a patent lumen at all times and permit an uninterrupted flow of blood. The latter vessels exhibit but slight variations in caliber, deviating only 2 to 3μ from the normal diameter. There is thus a continuous central trunk wherein the easily recognized arteriole and venule are connected by a thin-walled sinuous vessel (9 to 12μ wide). These connecting vessels are direct continuations of the arterioles and may be termed "a-v bridges" since they carry blood directly from the arterial to the venous side without an essential diversion of the blood flow. . . .

The muscle cells of a-v bridges are very plastic and follow the general contour of the vessel wall. The cell shape varies, in different regions, with irregularities in the underlying surface. Where the vessel divides the muscle cells frequently branch. In bent and twisted vessels, the muscle elements also branch. The muscle cell nuclei undergo similar alterations. . . .

It is true that the vessels I have designated a-v bridges function as capillaries, but instead of distinguishing between muscular capillaries and those which contain no smooth muscle cells, I have preferred to place these a-v bridges in a group with the arterioles and venules. Similar short vessels bridge between two small arterioles or venules and form arterial or venous arches.

A-v bridges differ from capillaries proper in the following respects: 1) The vessels are always open. 2) They exhibit but slight variations in caliber. 3) Their walls possess thin smooth muscle cells which are only partially effective as contractile elements. 4) The vessels do not collapse after extreme variations in blood flow.

Because of their small caliber, thin wall and poorly defined muscular tunic, the a-v bridges have been confused with true capillaries and placed in a common category with them. This has led to false generalizations concerning the reactions and anatomical features of capillaries. Claims have been made both for and against the presence of capillary muscle cells, depending upon the type of small vessel which was under consideration.

Another feature of the small blood vessel pattern which has not been sufficiently emphasized is the presence of extremely short arteriolar-venular anastomoses between vessels only slightly larger than capillaries. These short channels can effectively divert arterial blood directly into the venous circulation. The changes in caliber of the small arteriolar-venular anastomoses apparently are related to the capillary circulation. When a majority of the capillary vessels are open and contain an active blood flow, the arteriolar-venular anastomoses remain closed. In contrast, when the capillary circulation is diminished, the arteriolar-venular anastomoses are open to their widest extent. In this way they differ from a-v bridges which maintain a relatively fixed diameter.

STRUCTURE OF CAPILLARIES

The needs of most tissues vary with their degree of activity. This necessitates some means of expanding the blood flow to supply added tissue requirements, and is accomplished through a series of fine capillary vessels which arise as side branches of arterioles (10 to 12μ wide) and their terminal continuations (a-v bridges). It is to be noted that the capillary vessels are not terminal arteriolar continuations which spread out and then coalesce to form the venous vessels. They are side branches of the smaller arterioles and do not lie in the most nearly direct path of blood flow from arterioles to venules. (Zweifach, B. W. "The structure and reactions of the small blood vessels in amphibia." *Amer. J. Anat.,* 1936-1937, *60,* 473-514 [pp. 478-479, 501-502].)

John Richard Pappenheimer
1915-
and
Armando Soto-Rivera
1920-

The adequacy of the Starling hypothesis for the interpretation of the dynamics of capillary interchange was further confirmed in 1947 by the precise experiments of *John Richard Pappenheimer* and *Armando Soto-Rivera.*

A native of New York City, Pappenheimer was educated at Harvard University (B.S. 1936) and at Cambridge University, England, where he received his Ph.D. in zoology in 1940. In the same year he returned to the United States and after periods of teaching and research elsewhere he joined in 1945 the Department of Physiology of the Harvard Medical School. Not long after his arrival at Harvard he carried out the decisive and classic research described here. His collaborator, Armando Soto-Rivera, was born in Caracas and worked at Harvard in 1946-1948 as a Fellow of the Rockefeller Foundation. He is now professor of physiology at the Central University of Venezuela in Caracas where he had obtained his M.D. in 1943.

PROTEIN OSMOTIC PRESSURE IN
MAMMALIAN CAPILLARIES

Convincing quantitative evidence in support of the Starling theory was obtained by Landis* from direct measurements of the hydrostatic pressure and rates of fluid movement in individual capillaries of the frog's mesentery. In this preparation the rate of fluid movement across the capillary membrane is, on the average, proportional to the difference between the mean hydrostatic pressure in the capillary and the protein osmotic pressure of the plasma as measured in vitro. This behavior represents a special case of the Starling theory in which tissue pressure opposing filtration is negligible and the capillary membranes are almost completely impermeable to the plasma proteins; it implies that the protein concentration in tissue fluid immediately outside the capillary wall is too low to play a significant role in determining the osmotic balance.

No such direct measurements have been made in mammalian capillaries. Circumstantial evidence, reviewed by Landis,** has in general lent support to the Starling theory, but the quantitative relations between capillary pressure, effective protein osmotic pressure and rate of fluid exchange have never been clearly demonstrated in the mammalian circulation. In the present paper we shall describe methods for measuring these variables in the isolated perfused hindlimbs of cats and dogs. Quantitative evidence will be given that the Starling theory is in fact applicable to the perfused hindlimb and with a precision rarely encountered in biological preparations. . . .

. . . . The arterial pressure was initially set to maintain the limb at constant weight. A sudden rise from 91 to 110 mm. Hg produced an initial increment of weight followed by a slow steady gain in weight. Presumably the initial rise is a result of an increased vascular volume beyond the arterial system, for it is abolished if the arterioles are constricted with adrenaline. Nor is it present if the capillary pressure is maintained constant by simultaneous lowering of the venous pressure. . . . The slow steady gain in weight (+ 0.26 grams/min.) is presumably a result of filtration of fluid from blood to tissues. When the arterial pressure was restored to its initial

* Landis, E. M. This Journal *82*:217, 1927.
** Landis, E. M. Physiol. Revs. *14*:404, 1934.

value, the vascular volume was also restored, following which the leg weight remained constant at a new level corresponding to the amount of fluid which had been filtered. The arterial pressure was then lowered below the value necessary to maintain constant weight. Exactly analogous changes of weight resulted except that they were of opposite sign. The slow steady loss of weight (-0.28 grams/min.) is presumably a measure of the rate of absorption of fluid from tissues to blood.

In the intact animal changes of arterial pressure are generally associated with complex changes in mean capillary pressure owing to simultaneous alterations in vascular tone. It is therefore not surprising that in the whole animal a rise of arterial pressure may cause filtration,[*] absorption[**] or no detectable change in fluid balance.[†] . . .

The "isogravimetric state." It will be clear . . . that there exist an infinite number of pairs of values of arterial and venous pressures at which the leg will remain at constant weight. Thus the tendency to absorb, caused by a given reduction in arterial pressure, can be counter-balanced by raising the venous pressure until no net transfer of fluid occurs between blood and tissue (constant weight). . . . It is evident that if the arterial pressure is progressively lowered and the venous pressure raised to maintain constant weight there will come a point at which the venous pressure will equal the arterial pressure. Under these conditions there will be no pressure drop along the vascular tree and both the arterial and venous pressures will equal the capillary pressure. Since, by the terms of the experiment, there is no net transfer of fluid, this value of capillary pressure (isogravimetric capillary pressure) is equal and opposite to the sum of all pressures opposing filtration. . . .

The isogravimetric capillary pressure cannot be obtained directly by equalizing arterial and venous pressures without disturbing the physiological properties of the capillaries because, when the arterial and venous pressures are equal, there is no blood flow. However, its value may be estimated by plotting the difference between isogravimetric arterial and venous pressures (abscissa) against the iso-

[*] Adolph, E. F. and M. J. Leport. Proc. Soc. Exp. Biol. and Med. *28*:963, 1931.
[**] Scott, F. H., M. Rabinowitz and A. Rupp, Proc. Soc. Exp. Biol. and Med. *20*:227, 1923.
[†] Tani, I. Biochem. Z. *45*:189, 1924.

gravimetric arterial or venous pressures (ordinates) and extrapolating to zero pressure difference. The intercept on the ordinate is then the isogravimetric capillary pressure. (Pappenheimer, J. R. and Soto-Rivera, Armando. "Effective osmotic pressure of the plasma proteins and other quantities associated with the capillary circulation in the hindlimbs of dogs and cats." *Amer. J. Physiol.*, 1948, *152*, 471-491 [pp. 471-472, 476-478, 480].)

IV

Respiration:
Neurophysiology and Chemistry

"No animal can live in an atmosphere where a flame does not burn." LEONARDO DA VINCI, 1500.

From the beginning of time respiratory movements were looked upon casually as one of the "facts of life," and among early writers little attention was given to their nature or their basic significance, since this could not be understood prior to the discovery of the circulation. Aristotle in several places commented upon respiration, but he gave less profound thought to the phenomenon than he did to many other great areas of human knowledge (Ch. II). For him the air which passed into the lungs served merely to cool the heart, since he believed that this organ, the seat of all life, tended to be destroyed by the heat which it generated; but he had also grasped the idea that "poisonous vapours" are by-products of the "burning" which occurred in the tissues and are removed in the expired air.

In his valuable Clio Medica book on *Greek Medicine*[1] Fred B. Lund makes note of the fact that Galen of Pergamon approached the problem of respiration experimentally; thus Lund says: (p. 109) . . . "In regard to respiration, he [Galen] concluded as the result of experiments, such as cutting the intercostal nerves, excising a rib, or transverse section of the spinal cord above the origin of the phrenic nerve, that ordinary respiration was performed chiefly by the diaphragm itself, and that the intercostal muscles were called into play only on forced respiration. He believed with the Pneumatic sect, that respiration was carried out in part by the entire arterial system, through the pores in the skin and the fine terminations of the blood vessels beneath it. In contrast to the erroneous

[1] Lund, Fred B. *Greek medicine.* (Clio Medica Series.) New York, Paul B. Hoeber, Inc., 1936. x, 161 pp. [p. 109].

beliefs into which his logical mind led him with regard to the circulation, his researches on the nervous system were epoch-making. Division of nerves and of the spinal cord at different levels gave him definite information as to the source and seat of various paralyses [of the muscles involved in the movements of respiration]."

Fabricius in his little book on respiration (1615)[2] re-echoed Galenical doctrine. Vesalius (1543), however, had carried out artificial respiration on animals, observing that the heart-beat became weak and the arteries pulseless after he ceased to work the bellows, reviving again when the ventilation was renewed. With the discovery of the circulation various speculations were entertained concerning the exchange of substances between blood and air. Some postulated the existence of pores connecting the air spaces with the blood. Malpighi established that the bronchi terminated in minute air spaces in close proximity to the capillary vessels which he also discovered (Ch. III). Boyle, in 1660, performed the fundamental experiment of proving that a partial vacuum extinguished life at the same time that it abolished the burning of a candle.[3] Robert Hooke studied artificial respiration in dogs, proving that the lungs expanded by virtue of movements of the chest wall and that even this was unnecessary for life provided that adequate aeration obtained by a constant flow of air was through a uniformly expanded lung. Lower observed venous blood to become bright red on passing through the lungs and on being exposed to pure air. Mayow proved conclusively that a portion of the air, the *spiritus nitro-aereus*, as he called it, sufficed for life; and he added with singular appropriateness that "nitre has made as much noise in philosophy as in war." Mayow also gave a detailed description of the mechanics of the respiratory movements. These were the important contributions in the early history of respiration, and it remained only for Joseph Priestley and Antoine-Laurent Lavoisier to discover oxygen and for John Scott Haldane and John Gillies Priestley to define the activity of carbon dioxide as a normal stimulus to the respiratory centre of the brain, a centre which Legallois and Flourens had established anatomically in the early nineteenth century.

Recent developments have turned upon the study of the various

[2] Fabricius, H. *De respiratione et eius instrumentis, libri duo.* Padua, P. Megliettus, 1615. 4 *ll.*, 118, [2] pp.

[3] Boyle, R. *New experiments physico-mechanicall, touching the spring of the air, and its effects (made, for the most part, in a new pneumatical engine).* Oxford, H. Hall, 1660, 399 pp. [pp. 355-366].

physiological changes which come into play to adapt the individual to the low oxygen tensions occurring at high altitudes—and on the related study of the dissociation curve of haemoglobin to which Barcroft and his pupils have made notable contributions. Finally, the respiration of cells and tissues has come to the fore through the enormous development of biochemistry and the study of respiratory enzyme systems, but that is too large a story to launch upon here.

Jean Rey
1583-1645

Jean Rey, a native of Le Bugue in the present Department of Dordogne in France, was a physician-physiologist who occupied himself with investigations in chemistry and physics in an area which might now be termed "physical chemistry." Rey, a country doctor working in almost complete isolation in his native village, took advantage of his brother's forge and bellows to study the effect on the weight of metals (such as lead) of exposure to great heat, a problem put to him by Master-Apothecary Jean Brun of Bergerac, twenty miles away. He published his *Essays* on the subject in 1630,[4] his learned friend the physician Deschamps, also of Bergerac, contributing a verse on the subject of the book (p. 11). Brun gave a copy to the great bibliophile Pierre Trichet (*c.* 1586-1644) who in turn showed it to Père Marin Mersenne (1588-1648), the influential physician-philosopher-cleric of Paris who later corresponded with Rey and who referred to his theory with considerable approval in his *Les questions theologiques, morales, et mathématiques* (Paris, 1634), thus bringing Rey's work to the attention of scholars.

Rey was the first to prove that metals increase in weight on "calcination." He attributed these gains in weight to the union of metals with the air, thus anticipating to some extent the work of Lavoisier, whose detractors reprinted Rey's *Essays* at Paris in 1777. His inference might well have led him to the modern theory of combustion.

Rey also gave the thermometer its modern form, though in crude state. This thermometer or thermoscope, which represented a great advance in the construction of the instrument, he described in his first letter to Mersenne. Their correspondence is included with the facsimile reprint of the 1630 edition of the *Essays* to which Dr. Douglas McKie contributed an introduction. Rey wrote in a fresh and lively style, for example, he titled Essay XXV, "By a single experiment all opinions contrary to mine are entirely destroyed." The following passage indicates the nature of his argument and his manner of writing.

[4] Rey, J. *Essays de Jean Rey, docteur en medecine. Sur la rec[h]erche de la cause pour laquelle l'estain & le plomb augmentent de poids quand on les calcine.* Bazas, Guillaume Millanges, 1630. 144 pp. See also *The essays of Jean Rey,* a facsimile reprint of the original edition of 1630 with introduction and notes by Douglas McKie. London, Edward Arnold, 1951. xliv, 144, xlv-lxxxiii pp.

ESSAY XVI

*Formal response to the question, why Tin and Lead
increase in weight when they are calcined.*

Now I have made the preparations, nay, laid the foundations
for my answer to the question of the sieur Brun, which is, that having placed two pounds six ounces of fine English tin in an iron
vessel and heated it strongly on an open furnace for the space of
six hours with continual agitation and without adding anything to
it, he recovered two pounds thirteen ounces of a white calx; which
filled him at first with amazement, and with a desire to know whence
the seven ounces of surplus had come. And to increase the difficulty,
I say that it is necessary to enquire not only whence these seven
ounces have come, but besides them what has replaced the loss of
weight which occurred necessarily from the increase of volume of
the tin on its conversion into calx, and from the loss of the vapours
and exhalations which were given off. To this question, then, I respond and sustain proudly, resting on the foundations already laid,
"That this increase in weight comes from the air, which in the
vessel has been rendered denser, heavier, and in some measure ad-
hesive, by the vehement and long-continued heat of the furnace:
which air mixes with the calx (frequent agitation aiding) and becomes attached to its most minute particles: not otherwise than
water makes heavier sand which you throw into it and agitate, by
moistening it and adhering to the smallest of its grains." I fancy
there are many who would have been alarmed by the sole mention
of this response if I had given it at the beginning, who will now
willingly receive it, being as it were tamed and rendered tractable
by the evident truth of the preceding Essays. For those without
doubt whose minds were preoccupied with the opinion that air
was light, would have rushed to oppose it. Why (they would have
said) does not one extract cold from heat, white from black, light
from darkness, since so much heaviness is extracted from air, a thing
inherently light? And those who chanced to have bestowed their
credence on the heaviness of air, would not have been able to per-
suade themselves that it can ever increase weight, being balanced in
itself. On this account I was constrained to show that air had weight;
which was recognisable by other means than the balance: and that
even with the latter, a portion previously changed and made denser
could manifest its weight. . . . (Rey, J. *Essays of Jean Rey, Doctor
of Medicine. On an enquiry into the cause wherefore tin and lead*

increase in weight on calcination. [Alembic Club Reprints No. 11.]
Edinburgh, The Alembic Club, 1904. 54 pp. [pp. 36-37].)

Robert Boyle

1627-1691

Robert Boyle, whose life and scientific contributions have been described in
Chapter I, added notably to knowledge of respiration through study of the effect
of states of low and high pressures upon the activity of animals. It is interesting
that with the invention of the air pump, he was led almost at once to compare
the burning of a candle with vital activities, noting that both ceased to occur in
an exhausted vessel. Boyle began his observations as early as 1659 and continued
them at odd times throughout a period of more than twenty years.

NECESSITY OF AIR FOR RESPIRATION AND COMBUSTION

Another Opinion there is touching Respiration, which makes the
genuine use of it to be Ventilation (not of the Heart, but) of the
Blood, in its passage thorow the Lungs; in which passage, it is dis-
burthened of those Excrementitious Steams, proceeding, for the
most part, from the superfluous Serosities of the Blood, (we may
adde) and of the *Chyle* too, which (by those new Conduits of late
very happily detected by the famous *Pecquet*) hath been newly mix'd
with it in the Heart). And this Opinion is that of the Industrious
Moebius, and is said to have been that of that excellent Philosopher
Gassendus; and hath been in part an Opinion almost vulgar: But
this *Hypothesis* may be explicated two ways: For first, The necessity
of the Air in Respiration, may be suppos'd to proceed from hence;
That as a Flame cannot long burn in a narrow and close place,
because the Fuliginous Steams it uncessantly throws out, cannot be
long receiv'd into the ambient Body; which after a while growing
too full of them, to admit any more, stifles the flame, so that the
vital Fire in the Heart requires an ambient Body, of a yielding nature, to receive into it the superfluous Serosities and other Recre-
ments of the Blood, whose seasonable Expulsion is requisite to
depure the Mass of Blood, and make it fit both to Circulate, and
to maintain the vital heat residing in the Heart. The other way of
explicating the above-mentioned *Hypothesis,* is, by supposing, that
the Air does not onely, as a Receptacle, admit into its Pores the Excrementitious vapors of the Blood, when they are expell'd through

the Wind-Pipe, but does also convey them out of the Lungs, in regard that the inspired Air, reaching to all the ends of the *Aspera Arteria,* does there associate it self with the Exhalations of the circulating Blood, and when 'tis exploded, carrys them away with it self, as we see that winds speedily dry up the surfaces of wet Bodies, not to say any thing of what we formerly observ'd touching our Liquor, whose fumes were strangely elevated upon the Ingress of the Air.

Now of these two ways of explicating the use of Respiration, our Engine affords us this Objection against the first; That upon the Exsuction of the Air, the Animals die a great deal sooner then if it were left in the Vessel; though by that Exsuction the ambient space is left much more free to receive the steams that are either breathed out of the Lungs of the Animal, or discharg'd by insensible Transpiration through the Pores of his Skin. (Boyle, R. *New experiments physico-mechanicall, touching the spring of the air, and its effects, [made, for the most part, in a new pneumatical engine].* Oxford, H. Hall, 1660. 399 pp. [pp. 350-352].)

EXPERIMENT XI

OCTOBER 1, 1678

About 10 of the Clock in the morning, I included a Shrew-Mouse with common Air, in a Receiver, fortified against the external Air; about 11 the Mouse was brought to such straits, that he could hardly breathe: I threw in another strong and lusty Mouse into the same Receiver, and presently put on the stopple again: But because the first Mouse had consumed some of the Air, it came to pass that the external Air was forcibly impelled into the Receiver, and so was able to dispel a great part of the Air stagnant there; and indeed, when this was done, the first Mouse seemed to be much better, neither did it die much sooner than the other, but both of them died about noon. About 4 in the afternoon, I thrust a fresh strong Mouse into the same Receiver, and lest the external Air might again expel the included Air, I put him in very slowly and liesurely; The issue was, that this third Mouse lived not 3 minutes entire.

Whence we may conjecture, That that portion of Air which hath once served the respiration of Animals as much as it could, is no longer useful for the respiration of another Animal, at least of the same kind. (Boyle, R. *A continuation of new experiments physico-*

mechanical, touching the spring and weight of the air, and their effects. The second part. . . . London, Miles Flesher, 1682. 198 pp. [p. 94].)

Richard Lower

1631-1691

Richard Lower, Oxford anatomist, physiologist, and physician, has already been mentioned in Chapter II. In February 1665 he carried out the first direct transfusion of blood from one animal to another and suggested that the manoeuvre might have a clinical application. An account of his experiments was published in the *Philosophical Transactions* in 1666 (vol. 3, pp. 226-232). Denis of Paris, adopting Lower's suggestion, carried out a transfusion upon a human being on 15 June 1667. Those interested in blood transfusion should consult a remarkable two-volume work by Scheel which deals exclusively with the history of the subject.[5]

Lower's chief contribution to physiology was his book, *Tractatus de corde* (Pl. 20), published in London in 1669. He proved that the dark venous blood, when passed through the lungs, became bright in color and he suggested, as the following passage shows, that the blood absorbed from the air a definite chemical substance necessary for life, and that this was, in fact, the chief function of the pulmonary circulation.

THE MOVEMENT AND COLOUR OF THE BLOOD

[p. 166] . . . I have shown that the bright red colour of arterial blood is not acquired through any heating in the heart or anywhere else at any time. In like manner also the dark colour of venous blood is independent of any extinction of its heat within the veins. For, if this were so, why should the arterial blood not take on a like colour after it has left its vessels, since it has now beyond all doubt lost its heat?

This being so, we must next see to what the blood is indebted for this deep red coloration. This must be attributed entirely to the lungs, as I have found that the blood, which enters the lungs completely venous and dark in colour, returns from them quite arterial and bright. For, if the anterior part of the chest is cut away and the lungs are [p. 167] continuously insufflated by a pair of

[5] Scheel, P. *Die Transfusion des Blutes und Einsprützung der Arzeneyen in die Adern. Historisch und in Rücksicht auf die practische Heilkunde bearbeitet.* Copenhagen, F. Brummer, 1802-1803. 2 vols.

bellows inserted into the trachea, and they are also pricked with a needle in various places to allow free passage of air through them, then, on the pulmonary vein being cut near the left auricle, the blood will flow out into a suitably placed receptacle completely bright-red in colour. And, as long as the lungs are supplied with fresh air in this way, the blood will rush out scarlet, until the whole perfusate reaches several ounces, nay pounds, just as if it were being received from a cut artery. What I had written earlier about the blood withdrawn from the pulmonary vein being like venous blood was said as a result of experimental work, but at a time when I did not yet know from experiment that one could keep life in an animal by continuous insufflation of pricked lungs; so that all the air had been forced out of the lung before I was able to seize and to lance the pulmonary vein. I acknowledge my indebtedness to the very famous Master *Robert Hooke* for this experiment—by which the lungs are kept continuously dilated for a long time without meanwhile endangering [p. 168] the animal's life—and the opportunity thereby given me to perform this piece of work. . . .

Further, that this red colour is entirely due to the penetration of particles of air into the blood, is quite clear from the fact that, while the blood becomes red throughout its mass in the lungs (because the air diffuses in them through all the particles of blood, and hence becomes more thoroughly mixed with the blood), when venous blood is received into [p. 169] a vessel, the surface and uppermost part of it takes on this scarlet colour through exposure to the air. If this is removed with a knife, the part lying next below will soon change to the same colour through similar contact with the air.

Indeed, if the cake of blood is turned over after remaining stationary for a long while, its outer and uppermost layer takes on the red colour in a short space of time (provided the blood is still fresh). It is a matter of common knowledge that venous blood becomes completely red when received into a dish and shaken up for a long time to cause a thorough penetration of air into it. And let no one be surprised at a loss or admixture of air causing such marked colour-changes in the blood, since we see other fluids also acquiring various colorations, according as their pores take up or refract in greater or lesser amount the rays of light.

If you ask me for the paths in the lungs, through which the nitrous spirit of the air reaches the blood, and colours it more deeply, do you in turn show me the little pores by which that other nitrous spirit, which exists in snow, passes into the drinks of gourmets and cools their summer wines. For, [p. 170] if glass or metal cannot prevent the passage of this spirit, how much more easily will it penetrate the looser vessels of the lungs? Finally, if we do not deny the outward passage of fumes and of serous fluid, why may we not concede an inward passage of this nitrous foodstuff into the blood through the same or similar little pores?

On this account it is extremely probable that the blood takes in air in its course through the lungs, and owes its bright colour entirely to the admixture of air. Moreover, after the air has in large measure left the blood again within the body and the parenchyma of the viscera, and has transpired through the pores of the body, it is equally consistent with reason that the venous blood, which has lost its air, should forthwith appear darker and blacker. (Lower, R. *Tractatus de corde item de motu & colore sanguinis et chyli in eum transitu.* London, James Allestry, 1669. xvi, 220, 20 pp. Facsimile edition with introduction and translation by K. J. Franklin in R. T. Gunther's *Early science in Oxford,* Oxford, 1932. [Vol. IX].

Robert Hooke

1635-1703

Robert Hooke started his career as a chorister at Christ Church, Oxford, later becoming Robert Boyle's technical assistant. As such, he designed and probably built with his own hands the air pump, thus making possible the great experiments on the "Spring and Weight of the Air" which Boyle published in 1660 and 1662. Hooke's genius had early become evident, and Boyle was quick to recognize it and to give him full credit.

Hooke was one of the early Fellows of the Royal Society (1663), becoming their Curator in 1664 and frequently carrying out experiments at their meetings. On 9 November 1664 he acquainted the Society in writing with the fact that "by means of a pair of bellows and a pipe thrust into the wind-pipe of a dog"[6] he had been successful in keeping alive for over an hour an animal whose chest had been cut open to reveal the heart and lungs. On this occasion he had simply followed a technique described earlier by Vesalius in the *Fabrica* (Hooke may not have been aware of it since he does not mention it) in which a bellows

---

[6] Birch, Thomas. *The history of the Royal Society.* London, A. Millar, 1756-1757. 4 vols. [vol. I, pp. 485-486].

is used alternately to inflate and collapse the lungs. He found that continued ventilation of the lungs in this way was necessary to sustain the heart beat, but found no direct correlation between the movement of lungs and heart.

Malpighi had thought that the expansion and contraction of the lungs in breathing, which necessarily kneads and squeezes the blood vessels, would have the function of assisting the blood to flow through the capillary network. According to this view, the movement of the lungs in breathing would be indispensable for the passage of the blood from the right side of the heart to the left and, therefore, for the maintenance of the heart beat. Hooke's experiment cast some doubt on this necessity but did not disprove it.

The question seems to have continued to bother Hooke because three years later, on 10 October 1667, he and Richard Lower repeated the experiment before the Society, this time with the significant addition of a second bellows to supply a steady current of air to the lungs which he had perforated with his pen knife. The lungs were therefore held motionless in an expanded state while air passed through them. Hooke considered as a result of this experiment "that the true use of respiration was to discharge the fumes of the blood,"[7] but a week later, on 17 October, he was more hesitant and considered the experiment showed only that a continued supply of fresh air rather than the motion of the lungs was necessary to sustain life, and that the movement of the lungs did not assist the circulation of blood through them. At this meeting the Fellows discussed "whether it was the emission and discharge of fumes, or the intromission of fresh air, that preserved the animal alive."[8] In the account of the experiment submitted on 24 October Hooke leaned toward the idea that it was the entrance of fresh air, and therefore something derived from the air, which was essential.

This experiment of Hooke is important not only because it established the indispensable role of fresh air in respiration but also because it provided the experimental technique which allowed his collaborator, Richard Lower, to demonstrate that the change in color of the blood occurs as a result of its passage through the lungs.

AN ACCOUNT
OF AN EXPERIMENT MADE BY M. HOOK, OF PRESERVING ANIMALS ALIVE BY BLOWING THROUGH THEIR LUNGS WITH BELLOWS

This Noble Experiment came not to the Publisher's hands, till all the preceding Particulars were already sent to Press, and almost all Printed off, (for which cause also it could not be mentioned among the Contents:) And it might have been reserved for the next opportunity, had not the considerableness thereof been a motive to hasten its Publication. It shall be here annexed in the Ingenious

[7] Birch, vol. II, p. 198.
[8] *Ibid.*, p. 200.

Author his own words, as he presented it to the Royal Society, Octob. 24, 1667. The Experiment it self having been both repeated (after a former successful trial of it, made by the same hand a good while agoe) and improved the week before, at their publick Assembly. The Relation it self follows:

I Did heretofore give this *Illustrious Society* an account of an Experiment I formerly tryed of keeping a Dog alive after his *Thorax* was all display'd by the cutting away of the Ribbs and *Diaphragme;* and after the *Pericardium* of the Heart was also taken off. But divers persons seeming to doubt of the certainty of the Experiment (by reason that some Tryals made of this matter by some other hands, failed of success) I caus'd at the last Meeting the same Experiment to be shewn in the presence of this *Noble Company,* and that with the same success, as it had been made by me at first; the Dog being kept alive by the Reciprocal blowing up of his Lungs with Bellowes, and they suffered to subside, for the space of an Hour or more, after his *Thorax* had been so display'd, and his *Aspera arteria* cut off just below the *Epiglottis,* and bound upon the nose of the Bellows.

And because some Eminent Physitians had affirm'd, that the *Motion of the Lungs* was necessary to Life upon the account of promoting the Circulation of the Blood, and that it was conceiv'd the Animal would immediately be suffocated as soon as the Lungs should cease to be moved, I did (the better to fortifie my own *Hypothesis* of this Matter, and to be the better able to judge of several others) make the following additional Experiment; *viz.*

The Dog having been kept alive, (as I have now mentioned) for above an houre, in which time the Tryal had been often repeated, in suffering the Dog to fall into *Convulsive* motions by ceasing to blow the Bellows, and permitting the Lungs to subside and lye still, and of suddenly reviving him again by renewing the blast, and consequently the motion of the Lungs: This, I say, having been done, and the Judicious Spectators fully satisfied of the reallity of the former Experiment; I caused another pair of Bellowes to be immediately join'd to the first, by a contrivance, I had prepar'd, and pricking all the outer coat of the Lungs with the slender point of a very sharp pen-knife, this second pair of Bellows was mov'd very quick, whereby the first pair was alwayes kept full and alwayes blowing into the Lungs; by which the Lungs were also alwayes kept very full, and without any motion; there being a continued Blast of Air forc'd into the Lungs by the first pair of Bellows, supplying it as fast, as it could find its way quite through the Coat of the Lungs, by the small holes pricked in it, as was said before. This being continued for a pretty while, the Dog, as I expected, lay still, as before, his Eyes being all the time very quick, and his Heart beating very regularly: But, upon ceasing this blast, and suffering the Lungs to fall and lye still, the Dogg would immediately fall into Dying convulsive fits; but be as soon reviv'd again by the renewing the fulness of his Lungs, with the constant blast of fresh Air.

Towards the latter end of this Experiment a piece of the Lungs was cut quite off; where 'twas observable, that the Blood did freely circulate, and pass thorow the Lungs, not only when the Lungs were kept thus constantly extended, but also when they were suffer'd to subside and lye still. Which seem to be Arguments, that as the *bare* Motion of the Lungs *without fresh Air* contributes nothing to the life of the Animal, he being found to survive as well when they were not mov'd as when they were; so it was not the subsiding or movelesness of the Lungs, that was the immediate cause of Death, or the stopping the Circulation of the Blood through the Lungs, but the *want* of a sufficient *supply of fresh Air.*

I shall shortly further try, whether the suffering the Blood to circulate through a vessel, so as it may be openly exposed to the fresh Air, will not suffice for the life of an Animal; and make some other Experiments, which, I hope, will thoroughly discover the *Genuine use of Respiration;* and afterwards consider of what benefit this may be to Mankinde. (Hooke, R. "An account of an experiment made by M. Hook, of preserving animals alive by blowing through their lungs with bellows." *Phil. Trans.,* 1667, 2, 539-540.)

John Mayow

1641-1679

John Mayow, another of that constellation of Oxford physiologists which included Lower, Willis, Boyle, and Hooke among its number, is perhaps best known for his discussion of the substance we now know to have been oxygen, termed by him "spiritus nitro-aereus." Mayow (Pl. 21) was born in Cornwall in 1641 and matriculated at Oxford in 1658. He was elected in 1660 Fellow of All Soul's College, where he studied law, receiving a B.C.L. in 1665 and D.C.L. in 1670. Little is known for certain about his later life. No record has been found of medical studies yet he is said to have practised medicine at Bath "especially in the summer time." Details concerning his marriage and where and when he did his experimental work are sparse. Hooke proposed him for fellowship in the Royal Society and he was elected in November 1678. A year later he died in London.

Mayow's first publication, the so-called *Tractatus duo,* appeared in November 1668 (when he was 27) (Pl. 22a) and included an account of his memorable experiments on respiration and his tract on rickets (Pl. 22b). Five years before his death he published at Oxford (from the Sheldonian Theatre, 1674) these two tracts together with three others under the title, *Tractatus quinque medico-physici. Quorum primus agit de sal-nitro, et spiritu nitro aereo.* In this, his last work, is found the important tract on muscular movement.

The full significance of Mayow's studies was not recognized until after Lavoisier had announced the discovery of oxygen. Thomas Beddoes, an erratic genius who fancied that with oxygen he could cure many of the ailments to which flesh is heir, published an anonymous account of Mayow's work under the title *Chemical experiments and opinions extracted from a work published in the last century* (Oxford, 1790).

This perhaps extravagant appreciation of Mayow's role as a precursor of Lavoisier led to a misunderstanding of the nature of Mayow's real contribution and true historical position. In an effort to correct some of the inflated and inappropriate claims made for Mayow, Professor T. S. Patterson of the University of Glasgow was led in 1931 to make an extreme and intemperate attack upon Mayow's work and reputation—an attack which perhaps created misunderstandings as serious as those it attempted to remove.[9] More recently, articles by Henry Guerlac,[10] Douglas McKie[11] and J. R. Partington[12] have done much to reveal the historical background of Mayow's thought and to establish the facts of his life and work and later influence. Mayow was undoubtedly an acute thinker and a particularly ingenious and accurate experimenter.

ON RESPIRATION

[p. 183] The lungs are placed in a recess so sacred and hidden that nature would seem to have specially withdrawn this part both from the eyes and from the intellect; for, beyond the wish, it has not as yet been granted to any one to fit a window to the breast and re-

[9] Patterson, T. S. "John Mayow—in contemporary setting." *Isis,* 1931, *15,* 47-96.

[10] Guerlac, Henry. "John Mayow and the aerial nitre." *Int. Congr. Hist. Sci., Actes VII,* Paris, 1953, pp. 332-349; also "The poets' nitre." *Isis,* 1954, *45,* 243-255.

[11] McKie, Douglas. "The birth and descent of John Mayow: a tercentenary note." *Philos. Mag. J. Sci.,* 1942, *33,* 51-60; see also "Fire and the *flamma vitalis:* Boyle, Hooke and Mayow" in: *Science, medicine and history, essays in honour of Charles Singer,* edited by E. A. Underwood. Oxford, 1953. 2 vols., vol. I, pp. 469-488.

[12] Partington, J. R. "The life and work of John Mayow (1641-1679)." *Isis,* 1956, *47,* 217-230, 405-417; also "Some early appraisals of the work of John Mayow." *Isis,* 1959. *50,* 211-226.

deem from darkness the profounder secrets of nature. For of all the parts of the body, the lungs alone, as if shrinking from observation, cease from their movement and collapse at once on the first entrance of light and self-revelation. Hence such an ignorance of Respiration and a sort of holy wonder. Still, let me draw near to the inmost vitals, and, concerning so obscure a matter, make at least a guess.

In discussing on Respiration I shall follow the method pointed out by nature and begin therefore with inspiration. . . .

[pp. 184-185] With respect, then, to the entrance of the air into the lungs, I think it is to be maintained that it is caused in the following manner by the pressure of the atmosphere. For as the air, on account of the weight of the superincumbent atmosphere, not only rushes into all empty places, but also presses forcibly upon whatever is next it (as Boyle's experiments have put beyond doubt), it follows that the air, passed through the nostrils and the trachea, up to the bronchia or gates of the lungs, presses against the lungs from within and seeks an entrance into them. Hence it is that when the inner sides of the thorax (which by compressing the lungs from without were resisting the pressure of this air) are drawn outwards by muscles whose function it is to dilate the chest, and the space in the thorax is enlarged, the air which is nearest the bronchial inlets, now that every obstacle is removed, rushes under the full pressure of the atmosphere into the cavities of the lungs, and by inflating them occupies and fills the space of the expanded chest.

The structure of the lungs is adapted for their inflation as thus described, for their substance is composed, as the eminent Dr. Malpighi has noted, of very fine membranes, which form an almost infinite number of spherical vesicles whose mutual connection is such that there is easy access from the trachea to those nearest to it, and from these again to others. Consequently when these vesicles are inflated by an inrush of air, the whole substance of the lungs must necessarily expand. . . . .

[p. 191] Whenever, I say, a muscle attached to two bones contracts, the bone which is less fixed moves towards the other which is more fixed. Wherefore, since every lower rib is less fixed than the one above it, each of the lower ribs must be elevated when the intercostal muscles, even the internal ones, contract. For a quite similar reason holds with the internal as with the external muscles; nor is it an objection to this that the former are attached to the ribs in a different position, as is obvious from Plate II [Pl. 22c], where the interior muscle, *a, a,* will raise the lower and more mobile rib, in contracting, as well as the exterior muscle, *b, b.* And here it is to be noted that the ribs are so articulated with the spine that when they are pulled by the said muscles they easily ascend and are raised with rotation.

Nay, the very position of the muscles makes this plain, for if the interior muscle which is placed between the two lowest ribs were to pull the upper of the two downwards, all the ribs, since they are firmly attached to each other, would necessarily be drawn downwards at the same time, a thing which that weak and membrane-like muscle cannot do. How much more probable is it that the lower ribs are all drawn upwards together by the internal muscles between the upper ribs, for these are sufficiently strong and broad, while the weaker muscles between the lower ribs contribute merely to elevate the lower ribs. These things will be more clearly seen from Plate II [Pl. 22c], which shows the ribs and the internal muscles.

And this view is also supported by the oblique and contrary position of the intercostal muscles. For Nature seems to have inserted these muscles obliquely in the ribs (although a direct insertion would have suited better for moving them up or down) because the intervals between the ribs are so small that if these muscles had been inserted at right angles, they would have been shorter than the nature of muscles admits. Wherefore, that these muscles should have a suitable length, they had to be inserted obliquely (as they are) to the ribs. Yet as this oblique position is less suitable for elevating the ribs, Nature, that most wise engineer, has arranged the muscles with divers aspects so that while they pull the ribs obliquely with equal force in this direction and in that, the ribs meanwhile rise straight upwards, as is shown in Plate I [Pl. 22c], where, when the external muscle *a, a,* and the internal *c, c,* contract together, the lower and more mobile rib will rise not obliquely but straight upwards, just as though it were pulled by a muscle attached to it at right angles. So that clearly the external and internal muscles contract simultaneously, and by their united effort elevate the ribs and expand the chest. Moreover, that the internal muscles do not cause expiration, may be gathered from the fact that the thorax in a dead animal is always contracted, for to die and to expire mean the same thing; but in the dead, the action of the muscles altogether ceases; and so this contraction of the chest cannot be caused by the internal muscles, since they no longer contract. Should any one remark here that that contraction of the thorax is caused by the internal muscles immediately before the death of the animal, I ask, in reply, how then is it that the external muscles (since the two cases are similar) never contract in the dying, so that the chest should remain for some time dilated? . . .

[p. 197] Similarly in *Orthopnœa,* in which the patient can only breathe in an erect position, it is probable that the abdominal viscera press too much on the diaphragm and keep it up in the chest, so that space enough for breathing cannot be provided in the thorax. If, however, the patient be placed in an upright position, the diaphragm, feeble though it be, aided by the weight of the same viscera, can force them downwards. And so, as the abdomen sinks, the chest dilates and the patient is able to breathe. (Mayow, John. *Tractatus duo quorum prior agit de respiratione: alter de rachitide.* Oxford, Henry Hall, 1668. 108 pp. Translation from treatise "On respiration," pp. 183-210 in: Mayow, John. *Medico-physical works.* Alembic Club Reprint No. 17. Edinburgh, The Alembic Club, 1907. xxiii, 331 pp. [pp. 183, 184-185, 191, 197].)

Joseph Priestley
1733-1804

Joseph Priestley was born at Fieldhead, a farmhouse in Birstall parish, Yorkshire, and was educated at Daventry Academy. He served as a parson at Needham Market in Suffolk, and later as Unitarian minister to a meeting-house in Cheshire. While there, he came in contact with that vigorous community in Warrington where the presence of John Aikin, Ferriar, Henry, and Percival made it one of the most active centers of intellectual life in eighteenth century England. The Warrington Academy, to which Priestley was appointed in 1761, fed the better known Manchester Philosophical Society with rich and varied intellects. Priestley's output during these years was prodigious. One finds his essays on education, a catechism for children, a long monograph on electricity, treatises on government, and later numerous theological tracts. During the French Revolution his letter to Burke so enraged his fellow townsmen that they burned his house and his manuscripts. He fled to America, where he lived until his death in 1804.

Priestley's isolation of oxygen has been the subject of much dispute. That he prepared the pure gas is commonly accepted, but he could not divest himself of the doctrine of phlogiston, with the result that full credit for the discovery was left for Lavoisier. In addition to his study of the composition of the air and its role in respiration, Priestley studied the relationship between the air and the blood in a remarkable series of experiments which foreshadow Magnus' later demonstration of the presence of oxygen and carbon dioxide in the blood. All of these experimental results were made possible by Priestley's remarkable ingenuity and technical proficiency (Pl. 23).

THE DISCOVERY OF OXYGEN

[II, pp. 33-34] . . . But having afterwards procured a lens of twelve inches diameter, and twenty inches focal distance, I proceeded with great alacrity to examine, by the help of it, what kind of air a great variety of substances, natural and factitious, would yield, putting them into the vessels represented fig. *a,* which I filled with quick-silver, and kept inverted in a bason of the same. Mr. Warltire, a good chymist, and lecturer in natural philosophy, happening to be at that time in Calne, I explained my views to him, and was furnished by him with many substances, which I could not otherwise have procured.

With this apparatus, after a variety of other experiments, an account of which will be found in its proper place, on the 1st of August, 1774, I endeavoured to extract air from *mercurius calcinatus per se;* and I presently found that, by means of this lens, air was expelled from it very readily. Having got about three or four times as much as the bulk of my materials, I admitted water to it, and found that it was not imbibed by it. But what surprized me more than I can well express, was, that a candle burned in this air with a remarkable vigorous flame, very much like that enlarged flame with which a candle burns in nitrous air, exposed to iron or liver of sulphur; but as I had got nothing like this remarkable appearance from any kind of air besides this particular modification of nitrous air, and I knew no nitrous acid was used in the preparation of *mercurius calcinatus,* I was utterly at a loss how to account for it. . . .

[p. 37] At the same time, I had no suspicion that the air which I had got from the mercurius calcinatus was even wholesome, so far was I from knowing what it was that I had really found; taking it for granted, that it was nothing more than such kind of air as I had brought nitrous air to be by the processes above mentioned; and in this air I have observed that a candle would burn sometimes quite naturally, and sometimes with a beautiful enlarged flame, and yet remain perfectly noxious.

At the same time that I had got the air above mentioned from mercurius calcinatus and the red precipitate, I had got the same kind from *red lead* or *minium.* In this process, that part of the minium on which the focus of the lens had fallen, turned yellow. One third of the air, in this experiment, was readily absorbed by water, but, in the remainder, a candle burned very strongly, and with a crackling noise. . . .

[p. 38] This experiment with *red lead* confirmed me more in my suspicion, that the mercurius calcinatus must get the property of yielding this kind of air from the atmosphere, the process by which that preparation, and this of red lead is made, being similar. As I never make the least secret of any thing that I observe, I mentioned this experiment also, as well as those with the mercurius calcinatus, and the red precipitate, to all my philosophical acquaintance at Paris, and elsewhere; having no idea, at that time, to what these remarkable facts would lead.

Presently after my return from abroad, I went to work upon the *mercurius calcinatus,* which I had procured from Mr. Cadet; and, with a very moderate degree of heat, I got from about one fourth of an ounce of it, an ounce-measure of air, which I observed to be not readily imbibed, either by the substance itself from which it had been expelled (for I suffered them to continue a long time together before I transferred the air to any other place) or by water, in which I suffered this air to stand a considerable time before I made any experiment upon it. . . .

[pp. 40-41] Till this 1st of March, 1775, I had so little suspicion of the air from mercurius calcinatus, &c. being wholesome, that I had not even thought of applying to it the test of nitrous air; but thinking (as my reader must imagine I frequently must have done) on the candle burning in it after long agitation in water, it occurred to me at last to make the experiment; and putting one measure of nitrous air to two measures of this air, I found, not only that it was diminished, but that it was diminished quite as much as common air, and that the redness of the mixture was likewise equal to that of a similar mixture of nitrous and common air.

After this I had no doubt but that the air from mercurius calcinatus was fit for respiration, and that it had all the other properties of genuine common air. But I did not take notice of what I might have observed, if I had not been so fully possessed by the notion of there being no air better than common air, that the redness was really deeper, and the diminution something greater than common air would have admitted. . . .

[pp. 43-44, 45] On the 8th of this month I procured a mouse, and put it into a glass vessel, containing two ounce-measures of the air from mercurius calcinatus. Had it been common air, a full-grown mouse, as this was, would have lived in it about a quarter of an hour. In this air, however, my mouse lived a full half hour; and though it was taken out seemingly dead, it appeared to have been only exceedingly chilled; for, upon being held to the fire, it presently revived, and appeared not to have received any harm from the experiment. . . .

This experiment with the mouse, when I had reflected upon it some time, gave me so much suspicion that the air into which I had put it was better than common air, that I was induced, the day after, to apply the test of nitrous air to a small part of that very quantity of air which the mouse had breathed so long; so that, had it been common air, I was satisfied it must have been very nearly, if not altogether, as noxious as possible, so as not to be affected by nitrous air; when, to my surprize again, I found that though it had been breathed so long, it was still better than common air. . . .

[pp. 54-55] Though there was a difference in the result of these experiments, which I shall consider hereafter, I was now convinced that it was the nitrous acid which the red lead had acquired from the air, and which had enabled it to yield the dephlogisticated air, agreeable to my original conjecture. Finding also, as will be seen in the following section, that the same kind of air is produced by moistening with the spirit of nitre any kind of earth that is free from phlogiston, and treating it as I had done the red lead in the last-mentioned experiment, there remained no doubt in my mind, but that *atmospherical air,* or the thing that we breathe, *consists of the nitrous acid and earth,* with so much phlogistion as is necessary to its elasticity; and likewise so much more as is required to bring it from its state of perfect purity to the mean condition in which we find it. . . .

[pp. 101-102] From the greater strength and vivacity of the flame of a candle, in this pure air, it may be conjectured, that it might be peculiarly salutary to the lungs in certain morbid cases, when the common air would not be sufficient to carry off the phlogistic putrid effluvium fast enough. But, perhaps, we may also infer from these experiments, that though pure dephlogisticated air might be very useful as a *medicine,* it might not be so proper for us in the usual healthy state of the body: for, as a candle burns out much faster in dephlogisticated than in common air, so we might, as may be said, *live out too fast,* and the animal powers be too soon exhausted in this pure kind of air. A moralist, at least, may say, that the air which nature has provided for us is as good as we deserve.

My reader will not wonder, that, after having ascertained the superior goodness of dephlogisticated air by mice living in it, and the other tests above mentioned, I should have the curiosity to taste it myself. I have gratified that curiosity, by breathing it, drawing it through a glass-syphon, and, by this means, I reduced a large jar full of it to the standard of common air. The feeling of it to my lungs was not sensibly different from that of common air; but I fancied that my breath felt peculiarly light and easy for some time afterwards. Who can tell but that, in time, this pure air may become a fashionable article in luxury. Hitherto only two mice and myself have had the privilege of breathing it.

The Presence of Air in the Blood

[III, p. 76] That blood has a power of taking phlogiston from air, as well as imparting phlogiston to air, I satisfied myself by exposing blood of a very beautiful florid colour to nitrous air, inflammable air, and phlogisticated air. The two first-mentioned kinds of air were considerably diminished by the process, which was continued two days, during which time the blood had been changed five or six times. . . .

[p. 78] It may be objected to this hypothesis, concerning the use of the blood, that it never comes into actual contact with the air in the lungs, but is separated from it, though as Dr. Hales states it, at the distance of no more than a thousandth part of an inch. The red globules also swim in a large quantity of serum, which is a fluid of a quite different nature.

In order to ascertain the effect of these circumstances, I took a large quantity of black blood, and put it into a bladder moistened with a little serum, and tying it very close, hung it in a free exposure to air, though in a quiescent state; and the next day I found, upon examination, that all the lower surface of the blood, which had been separated from the common air by the intervention of the bladder (which is an animal membrane, similar to that which constitutes the vesicles of the lungs, and is at least as thick) and likewise a little serum, had acquired a coating of a florid red colour, and as thick, I believe, as it would have acquired, if it had been immediately exposed to the open air; so that this membrane had been no impediment to the action of the air upon the blood. . . .

[p. 79] I observed also, that when I cut out a piece of the crassamentum, and left the remainder in the vessel with the serum, not only that part of the surface which was exposed to the air, but that which was surrounded with serum, and even covered with it to the depth of several inches, acquired the florid colour; so that this deep covering of serum, which must have effectually prevented all evaporation, was no more an impediment to the mutual action of the blood and the air, than the bladder had been. The serum of the blood, therefore, appears to be as wonderfully adapted to answer its purpose, of a vehicle for the red globules, as the red globules themselves: for the slightest covering of water, or *saliva*, effectually prevents the blood from acquiring its florid colour; and M. Cigna found that this was the case when it was covered with oil. (Priestley, Joseph. *Experiments and observations on different kinds of air.* London, J. Johnson, 1774-1777. 3 vols. [Vol. 2, 1775, pp. 33-34, 37, 38, 40-41, 43-44, 45, 54-55, 101-102; Vol. 3, 1777, pp. 76, 78, 79].)

Antoine-Laurent Lavoisier

1743-1794

Antoine-Laurent Lavoisier, whose discoveries and writings destroyed the phlogiston theory and altered the whole theoretical structure of chemistry, was a martyr of the French Revolution. "It took but a moment to cut off that head," said Lagrange, "though a hundred years perhaps will be required to produce another like it."

Born at Paris, the son of a lawyer, Lavoisier was educated at the Collège Mazarin and at the Sorbonne where he was graduated Bachelor of Law in 1763. At the same time he pursued science and in addition to studies in botany and geology he attended the lectures on chemistry of Guillaume François Ronelle (1703-1770) at the Jardin des Plantes. In 1768 Lavoisier was elected to the Académie des Sciences and thereafter frequently devoted himself to the writing of scientific reports on a variety of subjects (Pl. 24). In the same year he joined the Tax Farm—a connection which involved him in public administration and was to lead to his untimely death.

Lavoisier's serious chemical researches began in 1772 when he showed that sulphur and phosphorus on burning combined with a large quantity of air. He later identified this air with the *dephlogisticated air* isolated by Priestley in 1774 and christened it *oxygen,* or the acid-forming substance. By his use of quantitative methods Lavoisier was able to show that combustion and the calcination of metals always involved combination with oxygen. With a few incisive phrases he outlined the great facts of respiration: absorption of oxygen through the lungs with the liberation of "fixed air" which he showed to be the oxide of carbon. He also gave conviction to the then unproved suspicion that the respiration of living bodies was analogous to combustion and that it provided the source of the "animal heat." Of Lavoisier's paper of 1775 only the paragraph containing his conclusions is given. The portion of his joint memoir with Laplace on animal heat which demonstrates the relation between respiration and combustion is also included.

ON THE NATURE OF THE SUBSTANCE WHICH COMBINES WITH METALS DURING CALCINA-TION AND INCREASES THEIR WEIGHT

It seems proved that the substance which combines with metals during calcination, thereby increasing their weight, is none other than the purest part of the air surrounding us which we breathe, and which passes during this process from a state of elasticity to that of fixation. If therefore this result can be obtained of fixed air [carbon dioxide] whenever charcoal is used in the reduction of metals, the consequent increase of weight is due to the combination of charcoal with the pure part of the air and it is very probable that the calces, not only of mercury but of all metals would yield only highly respirable air, if they could be reduced like mercury, which becomes precipitated *per se.*

Since charcoal disappears completely during the revivifying of mercury calx and there remain after the process only mercury and fixed air it follows that the substance which has hitherto been called fixed air [carbon dioxide] results from a combination of the highly respirable air and charcoal. I propose to develop this conclusion more thoroughly in a series of further notes. (Lavoisier, A.-L. "Mémoire sur la nature du principe qui se combine avec les métaux pendant leur calcination, & qui en augmente le poids." *Mém. Hist. Acad. roy. Sci.* (1775), Paris, 1778, pp. 520-526 [p. 526].)

EXPERIMENTS ON THE RESPIRATION OF ANIMALS

AND ON THE CHANGES EFFECTED ON THE AIR IN PASSING THROUGH THEIR LUNGS

Of all the phenomena of the animal Economy, none is more striking, none more worthy the attention of philosophers and physiologists than those which accompany respiration. Little as our acquaintance is with the object of this singular function, we are satisfied that it is essential to life, and that it cannot be suspended for any time, without exposing the animal to the danger of immediate death. . . .

The experiments of some philosophers, and especially those of Messrs. Hales and Cigna, had begun to afford some light on this important object; and, Dr. Priestley has lately published a treatise, in which he has greatly extended the bounds of our knowledge; and has endeavoured to prove, by a number of very ingenious, delicate, and novel experiments, that the respiration of animals has the property of phlogisticating air, in a similar manner to what is effected by the calcination of metals and many other chemical processes; and that the air ceases not to be respirable, till the instant when it becomes surcharged, or at least saturated, with phlogiston.

However probable the theory of this celebrated philosopher may, at first sight, appear; however numerous and well conducted may be the experiments by which he endeavours to support it, I must confess I have found it so contradictory to a great number of phenomena, that I could not but entertain some doubts of it. I have accordingly proceeded on a different plan, and have found myself led irresistibly, by the consequences of my experiments, to very different conclusions.

Now air which has served for the calcination of metals, is, as we have already seen, nothing but the mephitic residuum of atmospheric air, the highly respirable part of which has combined with the mercury, during the calcination: and the air which has served the purposes of respiration, when deprived of the fixed air, is exactly the same; and, in fact, having combined, with the latter residuum, about $\frac{1}{4}$ of its bulk of dephlogisticated air, extracted from the calx of mercury, I re-established it in its former state, and rendered it equally fit for respiration, combustion, &c. as common air, by the same method as that I pursued with air vitiated by the calcination of mercury.

The result of these experiments is, that to restore air that has been vitiated by respiration, to the state of common respirable air, two effects must be produced: 1st. to deprive it of the fixed air [carbon dioxide] it contains, by means of quicklime or caustic alkali: 2dly. to restore to it a quantity of highly respirable or dephlogisticated air, equal to that which it has lost. Respiration, therefore, acts inversely to these two effects, and I find myself in this respect led to two consequences equally probable, and between which my present experience does not enable me to pronounce. . . .

The first of these opinions is supported by an experiment which I have already communicated to the academy. For I have shewn in a memoir, read at our public Easter meeting, 1775, that dephlogisticated air [oxygen] may be wholly converted into fixed air by an addition of powdered charcoal; and, in other memoirs, I have proved that this conversion may be effected by several methods: it is possible, therefore, that respiration may possess the same property, and that dephlogisticated air, when taken into the lungs, is thrown out again as fixed air. . . . Does it not then follow, from all these facts, that this pure species of air has the property of combining with the blood, and that this combination constitutes its red colour. But whichever of these two opinions we embrace, whether that the respirable portion of the air combines with the blood, or that it is changed into fixed air in passing through the lungs; or lastly, as I am inclined to believe, that both these effects take place in the act of respiration, we may, from facts alone, consider as proved:

1st. That respiration acts only on the portion of pure or dephlogisticated air contained in the atmosphere; that the residuum or mephitic part is a merely passive medium which enters into the lungs, and departs from them nearly in the same state, without change or alteration.

2dly. That the calcination of metals, in a given quantity of atmospheric air, is effected, as I have already often declared, only in proportion as the dephlogisticated air, which it contains, has been drained, and combined with the metal.

3dly. That, in like manner, if an animal be confined in a given quantity of air, it will perish as soon as it has absorbed, or converted into fixed air, the major part of the respirable portion of air, and the remainder is reduced to a mephitic state.

4thly. That the species of mephitic air, which remains after the calcination of metals, is in no wise different, according to all the experiments I have made, from that remaining after the respiration of animals; provided always, that the latter residuum has been freed from its fixed air: that these two residuums may be substituted for each other in every experiment, and that they may each be restored to the state of atmospheric air, by a quantity of dephlogisticated air, equal to that of which they had been deprived. A new proof of this last fact is, that if the portion of this highly respirable air, contained in a given quantity of the atmospheric, be increased or diminished, in such proportion will be the quantity of metal which we shall be capable of calcining in it, and, to a certain point, the time which animals will be capable of living in it. (Lavoisier, A.-L. "Expériences sur la respiration des animaux, et sur les changemens qui arrivent à l'air en passant par leur poumon." *Mém. Hist. Acad. roy. Sci.* [1777], Paris, 1780, pp. 185-194. Selections from Lavoisier, A.-L. *Essays, on the effects produced by various processes on atmospheric air; with a particular view to an investigation of the constitution of the acids.* T. Henry, Translator. Warrington, W. Eyres, 1783 [pp. 1, 2-3, 10-12, 13-16].)

MEMOIR ON HEAT

In the experiment on the animal heat of a guinea pig, the animal emerged from our machine with almost the same heat with which it entered it, for we know that the internal heat of animals is always nearly constant, yet without the continual renewal of its heat all that it had at first would be gradually dissipated and we would have withdrawn it from the interior of the machine cold, like all the inanimate bodies which we have placed there in our experiments. But its vital functions restore to it unceasingly that heat which it communicates to everything around it and which in our experiments is distributed to the internal ice of which it melted 13 ounces in 10 hours. This quantity of melted ice thus represents approximately the heat renewed during the same period of time by the vital functions of the guinea pig. Perhaps it is necessary to reduce this by one or two ounces or even more by taking into account that the extremities of the animal's body are chilled in the machine while the interior of the body has retained nearly the same temperature. In addition the liquids which its internal heat has evaporated have, in cooling, melted a small quantity of ice and have become re-united with the water which flows away from the machine.

By reducing that quantity of ice about two ounces and a half, one will have the quantity melted by the effect of the respiration of the animal upon the air. Now if one takes into account the errors inevitable in these experiments and in the factors which we have abstracted in order to make our calculations, one will see that it is not possible to hope for a more perfect agreement between these results. Therefore one may consider the heat released in the conversion of pure air to fixed air by respiration as the principal cause of the maintenance of animal heat, and if other causes help to produce it, their effect is negligible.

Respiration is thus a [process of] combustion, in truth very slow, but otherwise exactly like that of charcoal. It proceeds in the interior of the lungs without giving off any perceptible light because the matter of fire as soon as it is released is immediately absorbed by the moisture of these organs. The heat developed in this combustion is transferred to the blood which circulates through the lungs and thence is distributed through the whole animal system. Thus the air that we breathe serves two ends equally essential to our survival. It removes from the blood the basis of fixed air, an excess of which would be very harmful, and the heat that this combination deposits in the lungs compensates for the continual loss of heat to the atmosphere and surrounding bodies. . . . (Lavoisier, A.-L. and Simon, Pierre, Marquis de La Place: "Mémoire sur la chaleur." *Mém. Acad. roy. Sci.*, 1780 (1784), 355-408 [pp. 405-406. Translated by L.G.W.].)

Adair Crawford
1748-1795

Adair Crawford, eminent chemist and physician, was a versatile Scotsman who served simultaneously as professor of chemistry at Woolwich Military Academy and physician to St. Thomas's Hospital. As a chemist he supported Joseph Priestley's phlogiston hypothesis, but he is best known for his work on animal calorimetry, albeit the description of his experiments in this field is couched in language less precise than one might have anticipated from a man whose thought was ahead of his time. Michael Foster says that he believed: "Inspired air contains elementary fire, and meets in the lungs with the inflammable principle present in the blood. The elementary fire leaves the air of the lungs to join the blood, the capacity for heat of which is increased. In the course of the circulation the blood again becomes impregnated with the inflammable principle by which the capacity of the blood for heat is diminished. It accordingly gives up heat to the tissues. Thus in the lungs the blood discharges inflammable principle and absorbs heat, in the system it imbibes this principle and emits heat.

"It must be remembered that Black and Crawford, and indeed Lavoisier, regarded heat or caloric not, as we now do, as a form of energy, but as a thing or substance which combined with the thing heated, a something which was the physical analogue of the chemical phlogiston."[13]

The following passage is taken, not from the first edition of his *Animal Heat* (1779), but from the second "with very large additions" (1788) based on experiments begun at Glasgow in 1777.

OF THE INFLAMMATION OF COMBUSTIBLE BODIES

From the above experiments we learn, that atmospherical air contains much elementary fire or absolute heat; that when it is converted into fixed air and aqueous vapour, the greater part of this heat is detached; that the capacities of bodies for containing heat are increased by the changes which they undergo in the process of combustion. Hence we infer, that the heat which is produced by combustion, is derived from the air, and not from the inflammable body.

For inflammable bodies contain little absolute heat; atmospherical air, on the contrary, abounds with this principle. In the process of inflammation, the air is converted into fixed air and aqueous vapour, and at the same time gives off a very great proportion of its absolute heat, which, when extricated suddenly, bursts forth into flame, and produces an intense degree of sensible heat. We have found by calculation, that the heat which is produced by the conversion of atmospherical into fixed air, is such, if it were not dissipated, as would be sufficient to raise the air, so changed, to four times the excess of the heat of red hot iron above the common temperature of the atmosphere. It appears, therefore, that, in the process of inflammation, a very great quantity of heat is derived from the air.

It is manifest, on the contrary, that no part of the heat can be derived from the combustible body; for the combustible body, during the inflammation, undergoes a change similar to that which is produced in the blood by the process of respiration, in consequence of which its capacity for containing heat is increased; it therefore will not give off any part of its absolute heat, but like the blood in

[13] Foster, Michael. *Lectures on the history of physiology.* 2d ed. Cambridge. At the University Press, 1924. 306 pp. [pp. 246-247].

its passage through the lungs, it will absorb heat. (Crawford, Adair. *Experiments and observations on animal heat, and the inflammation of combustible bodies; being an attempt to resolve these phenomena into a general law of nature.* 2d ed. London, J. Johnson, 1788. 491 pp., 4 pl. [pp. 368-370].)

Heinrich Gustav Magnus
1802-1870

Born at Berlin where in 1827 he took his Phil. Dr. degree at the University, *Gustav Magnus* was appointed in 1831 *Privat Dozent* of technology and physics and in 1834 professor at Berlin. In 1840 he was made a member of the Berlin Academy of Science.

It was Magnus' great distinction to show that oxygen and carbon dioxide are both transported in considerable quantities in the circulating blood, and that therefore the seat of respiration is not in the capillaries of the lungs, where Lavoisier believed it to be, but rather in the tissues served by the capillaries which form the periphery of the general systemic circulation. In his study of the blood gases Magnus' thorough training in physics and chemistry and his technical proficiency as an experimenter were both indispensable to his success. These qualities are evident in the following passage.

ON THE ABSORPTION CAPACITY OF THE BLOOD FOR OXYGEN

... We turn now to the determination of the absorption capacity of the blood for oxygen. ...

Blood was shaken continuously with atmospheric air and this was continually renewed so that one could assume that oxygen and nitrogen would be absorbed at the same pressure under which each exists in the atmosphere. Thereupon the blood was brought into a vessel which was closed at one end by an iron stop-cock and at the other by a greased stopper and above was completely filled with mercury. Then the stopper was opened under mercury, carbonic acid was admitted and the mercury displaced. Next the opening, which was always under the mercury, was again closed with the stopper and the vessel lifted out and shaken continuously. In order to determine the amount of oxygen and nitrogen developed, a second vessel, which was likewise fitted with an iron stop-cock, was entirely filled with mercury and screwed to the stop-cock of the first vessel and both stop-cocks were opened. In this way the mercury fell downward from the upper vessel and the air rose into the latter. When the whole quantity had accumulated there, the stop-cock was closed and the vessel unscrewed. Then the carbonic acid was absorbed by caustic potash, the remaining air measured and the oxygen gas determined by explosion with hydrogen. The remainder was assumed to be nitrogen.

In this manner I carried out a considerable number of experiments with different kinds of blood. They have, to be sure, yielded no perfectly corresponding numbers, but they agree as far as they can be expected to in a fluid which is as variable as blood. However, with the absorption coefficient thus determined, one may calculate the amount of oxygen which could be absorbed by the blood at the pressure under which it was presented to it in the lungs, yet this would not be sufficient to admit the hypothesis that all the inspired oxygen gas absorbed may be contained in the blood. The absorption coefficient thus determined is only correct when the absorption of the gas by the blood follows Dalton's law. I had, however, grounds for supposing that this may not be the case and therefore undertook a new series of experiments which were carried out in the following way.

The blood was shaken continuously with ever renewed portions of atmospheric air and then conveyed into a vessel above, entirely filled with mercury, which was closed by an iron stop-cock. This was screwed to a second vessel, likewise closed by a stop-cock, which contained carbonic acid. By opening the stop-cock the mercury fell downward and the carbonic acid rose to the blood. At that point the vessel was closed and the blood continuously shaken with carbonic acid. Then another vessel, entirely filled with mercury, was screwed on to the vessel with the blood, and the gas accumulated in it. Then carbonic acid was again brought in the same way to the blood, was shaken again, and the gas again likewise conveyed into this vessel, and this process was repeated many times. Finally this gas thus accumulated was studied in the manner aforementioned. Thus I can hope to obtain at least a not insignificant portion of the absorbed gas, since it was not possible to attain to the whole amount.

Simple though these experiments are, yet it was originally impossible to carry them out because the time which elapsed until the foam had settled after each shaking was so great that the blood began to decompose before the conclusion of the whole experiment. Not until later did it happen that this difficulty was overcome by the application of a drop of oil which, placed on the surface of the blood, very soon made the foam disappear.

Before I describe the results which have been obtained by this method, I must mention that each time immediately before the application of the carbonic acid, a quantity of it was brought into a special vessel and shaken with caustic potash in order to see whether it would be completely absorbed and thus be free from oxygen and nitrogen. . . .

The proportion in which oxygen and nitrogen occur in the air obtained from the blood, yields in addition a direct proof that during the experiment air has not penetrated from outside into the vessels since in this case the measured amounts of both gases must stand in that proportion to one another in which they occur in the atmosphere while here the oxygen amounted ordinarily to three, and often four and five times as much as the nitrogen. . . . (Magnus, Gustav. "Ueber das Absorptionsvermogen des Bluts für Sauerstoff." *Ann. Physik. Chem.*, 1845, *66*, 177-206 [pp. 193, 194-198. Translated by L.G.W.].)

Paul Bert

1833-1886

Paul Bert, physiologist, was born at Auxerre in Burgundy and following attendance at the communal school and the Collège Amyot went to Paris to study law without any strong inclination for the profession. While in law school he also attended lectures in comparative anatomy and after receiving his law degree in 1857 he went on to take the licentiate in natural science in 1860. One of his examiners for the licentiate was Claude Bernard who was so impressed with Bert's abilities that he invited him to become his laboratory assistant. Bert, who had decided to study medicine first, completed his course for the M.D. in 1863 and was then Bernard's assistant for two years. In 1865, he won the prize in experimental physiology of the Paris Academy of Sciences and a year later received the doctorate of natural science. In 1868, after little more than a year as professor of zoology at Bordeaux, Bert returned to Paris to Claude Bernard's chair at the Sorbonne, Bernard having resigned to leave it vacant for him. It was at Paris that he carried out the fundamental studies on the effects of different partial pressures of oxygen upon the respiration of animals which laid the foundations for aviation medicine.

In March 1874, J. E. Crocé-Spinelli and H. T. Sivel, who had served as subjects in Bert's experiments, accompanied by a physician, ascended to 23,000 feet in a balloon and came down safely. On April 15th Crocé-Spinelli and Sivel, accompanied this time by Gaston Tissandier, decided to make a second ascent to a greater height. Since Bert was away from Paris, Croce-Spinelli wrote to tell him of their plans. Bert realized immediately that the quantity of oxygen which they planned to take was not enough for the height to which they intended to rise and wrote to warn them, but his letter arrived too late. On April 15th the men ascended to 26,300 feet. All lost consciousness, and Tissandier alone survived (Pl. 25).

EFFECTS OF ALTERING OXYGEN PARTIAL PRESSURE

1. *Aeronauts.*

Let us begin with the simplest case, and let us consider first the aeronaut, who, *without making any effort*, is lifted in the upward course of his balloon.

As he rises and the pressure diminishes, his blood loses its oxygen, as my experiments have shown: a very slight weakening at first, whose existence, nevertheless, my analyses have permitted me to prove as soon as the pressure is not more than 56 centimeters. Even then, the oxygen loss cannot have a very definite immediate effect; the difference is like those one observes between individuals who are in equally good health, like those which changes in respiratory rhythm or the different states of activity or of rest, of digestion or of abstinence bring in the same individual. The aeronaut cannot feel it.

If he rises higher, the loss of oxygen increases: at 2000 meters it was on the average 13%; at 3000, it becomes 21%; at 6500, 43%; at 8600 meters (26 centimeters pressure), the height at which Croce-Spinelli and Sivel died, they must have lost half of the oxygen of their arterial blood [Fig. 5]. My animals at 17 centimeters pressure had lost 65%; their arterial blood then contained only 7 volumes instead of 20 per 100 volumes of blood, less than ordinary venous blood coming from a contracted muscle. This is the blood which, in the arteries, was given the task of nourishing and animating the muscles, the spinal cord, the sense organs, the brain! In considering these facts, we recall the celebrated experiment of Bichat, on dark blood injected into the vessels of the nervous centers.

We know that, in a general way, the effects of the rarefaction of the air began to be felt quite plainly about the height of 4000 meters, corresponding to a pressure of 46 cm. It is also at about this pressure that in our bells our animals ceased to move about and showed signs of discomfort. Now the graph of Figure 31 shows

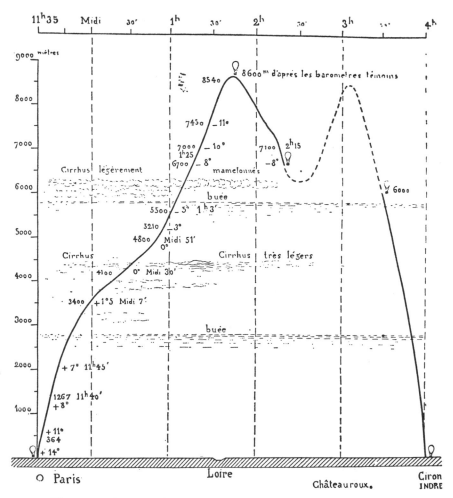

Figure 5. Diagram of the great balloon ascent on 15 April 1875.

that at about this moment the proportion of oxygen in the blood diminishes more rapidly; there is a remarkable agreement here.

This decrease in the quantity of oxygen contained in the blood is the prime factor. From it are derived all the symptoms of decompression. Its cause, we have seen, is double: first, the proportion of oxygen which the blood can absorb grows proportionately less as the pressure lowers . . .; in the second place, if we suppose that the respiratory rhythm has not changed, the quantity of oxygen which circulates in the lungs during a given time diminishes in the same proportion as the pressure. Now under normal pressure, the arterial blood, we have seen, is never completely saturated with oxygen, the agitation of the blood and the air not taking place with sufficient energy in the lungs. . . .

The data given in the second part of this work, and the theories which are deduced from them, and which are summarized in the third part, can be condensed in the following conclusions . . . :

A. The diminution of barometric pressure acts upon living beings only by lowering the oxygen tension in the air they breathe and in the blood which supplies their tissues (anoxemia of M. Jourdanet), and by exposing them thus to the dangers of asphyxia.

B. The increase in barometric pressure acts only by increasing the oxygen tension in the air and in the blood.

Up to about three atmospheres, this increase in tension results in somewhat more active intra-organic oxidations.

Beyond five atmospheres, the oxidations diminish in intensity, probably change in character, and, when the pressure rises sufficiently, stop completely. . . .

In the vertebrates, the sudden symptoms due to too great oxygen tension begin to appear only at the moment when the oxygen goes into solution on coming in contact with the tissues, since the hemoglobin is saturated with it. We can say then that the anatomical elements are *anaerobes*. . . .

D. The harmful effects of lowered pressure can be effectively prevented by breathing an air sufficiently rich in oxygen to maintain the tension of this gas at its normal value (20.9).

Those of increased pressure will be prevented by using air sufficiently low in oxygen to secure the same result.

E. In a general way, the benign or harmful gases (oxygen, carbonic acid, etc.) act on living beings only according to their tension in the surrounding atmosphere, a tension which is measured by multiplying their percentage by the barometric pressure; the increase of one of these factors can be compensated for by the decrease of the other. . . .

G. Sudden decompression beginning with several atmospheres has an effect (except for a few cases included in F) only by allowing to return to the free state the nitrogen which had become dissolved in the blood and the tissues under the influence of this pressure. . . .

I. The barometric pressure and the percentage of oxygen have not always been the same on our globe. The tension of this gas has probably been diminishing and no doubt will continue to diminish. That is a factor which has not yet been taken into account in biogenic speculation. . . .

K. It is inexact to teach, as is ordinarily done, that plants must have appeared on earth before animals, in order to purify the air of the large quantity of CO_2 which it contained. In fact, germination, even that of molds, does not take place in air that contains enough CO_2 to be fatal to warm-blooded animals.

It is just as inexact, as I remarked long ago, to explain the earlier appearance of reptiles with reference to warm-blooded animals by the impurity of air containing too much CO_2; reptiles, in fact, fear this gas even more than birds, and especially more than mammals. (Bert, Paul. *La pression barométrique*. . . . 1878. 1,178 pp. Translated by Mary Alice and Fred A. Hitchcock. *Barometric pressure. Researches in experimental physiology*. Foreword by John F. Fulton. Columbus, Ohio, College Book Company, 1943. xxxii, 1,055 pp. [pp. 981-982; 1036-1038].)

John Scott Haldane
1860-1936
and
John Gillies Priestley
1880-1941

John Scott Haldane, Oxford physiologist of respiration without portfolio, was a pioneer in the study of respiratory problems through the use of improved quantitative methods of gas analysis; he was also known for his writings upon the philosophical implications of physiological thought. His apparatus for the analysis of the respiratory gases was first described in 1892;[14] this was followed in 1899 by a book on methods of gas analysis.[15] His monograph, *Respiration,* based on his Silliman Lectures at Yale University, was published in 1922.[16]

Haldane and *John Gillies Priestley* were the first to bring forward convincing evidence that the carbon dioxide tension of the blood served as the normal stimulus for the respiratory center. They proved that ventilation of the lungs

[14] Haldane, J. S. "A new form of apparatus for measuring the respiratory exchange of animals." *J. Physiol. (Lond.),* 1892, *18,* 419-430.

[15] Haldane, J. S. *Methods of air analysis.* London, C. Griffin and Company, Ltd., 1899. (3d ed., 1920, x, 137 pp.)

[16] Haldane, J. S. *Respiration.* New Haven, Yale University Press, 1922. xviii, 427 pp.

normally depended upon the carbon dioxide concentration of the alveolar air and although they at first believed that this was the only factor, it was later pointed out that in certain circumstances oxygen-want may itself be an adequate cause of increased ventilation. The explanation of apnoea following forced breathing was a direct corollary to their observations upon the influence of carbon dioxide tension.

EFFECTS OF EXCESS OF CO_2 ON THE RESPIRATORY VENTILATION

For the purpose of studying the effects of CO_2 on the respiratory ventilation we placed the small box already described over the head of the subject in the plethysmograph. He thus breathed air in which the CO_2 produced by himself gradually accumulated. Samples of this air were taken at intervals with the precautions already described; and the depth and frequency of the respirations at the corresponding times were calculated from the corresponding parts of the tracing. Usually about four samples of air were taken during each experiment.

The following table summarises the results obtained [Fig. 6]. As the normal respirations while the subject was breathing pure air were also recorded at the beginning of each experiment, it was possible to calculate for each observation the increase in the depth and frequency of the respirations; and the results of these calculations are shown in separate columns. In calculating the alveolar ventilation, which is shown in one of the columns, we assumed a dead space of 190 c.c. for J.S.H. and 140 c.c. for J.G.P. (see above). The last column shows the calculated percentage of CO_2 in the alveolar air, assuming that the percentage at the beginning of the experiment was 5.6 for J.S.H., 6.3 for J.G.P., and that the respiratory exchange remained the same during the experiment.

It is quite evident from this table that the smallest increase in the CO_2 percentage of the air breathed is accompanied by a compensatory increase in the alveolar ventilation, the latter increase being just about sufficient to keep the alveolar CO_2 percentage constant. The results thus confirm those obtained by direct determinations of the CO_2 percentage in alveolar air while the subject was breathing air rich in CO_2 (see above). It will also be seen that the increased alveolar ventilation was at first almost entirely obtained by increased depth of the respirations, there being little or no alteration in their frequency until the alveolar ventilation had been increased to about five times the normal. Owing to the existence of the dead space this

Figure 6. The table from Haldane and Priestley's paper on the influence of CO_2 on the respiratory centres.

Subject and number of experiment	% of CO_2 in inspired air	Average depth of respirations in c.c.	Average frequency of respiration per minute	Depth of respirations, normal=100	Frequency of respirations, normal=100	Volume breathed per minute, normal=100	Ventilation of alveoli with inspired air, normal=100	Calculated CO_2% in alveolar air
J.S.H. 2	0·79	739	14	112	100	111	116	5·5
,, 2	1·47	978	13	147	93	137	149	5·0
,, 2	1·52	793·5	15	120	107	128	137	5·55
,, 1	1·97	849	13·5	150	84	128	147	5·7
,, 2	2·02	864	15	130	107	139	153	5·6
,, 4	2·28	911	15	142	100	141	161	5·8
,, 3	2·31	919	14·5	155	91	140	164	5·7
,, 4	2·84	1154	16	178	107	191	227	5·3
,, 4	3·07	1216	15	189	100	186	226	5·5
,, 4	3·11	1232	15	192	100	191	230	5·5
,, 3	3·73	1330	14	224	88	196	273	5·9
,, 3	4·84	1662	14	284	88	245	322	6·5
,, 1	5·14	1771	19	313	120	373	498	6·2
,, 3	5·48	1845	16	311	100	311	411	6·8
,, 1	6·02	2104	27	372	169	631	857	6·6
J.G.P. 5	0·60	516	15	103	100	103	104	6·6
,, 2	1·64	605	19	116	112	130	136	6·2
,, 1	1·65	540	15·5	121	94	114	123	6·7
,, 5	2·53	664	16	133	107	141	155	6·5
,, 6	2·62	747	15	150	94	140	158	6·6
,, 2	2·63	750	18	144	106	152	170	6·3
,, 1	2·71	570	17	128	103	132	144	7·0
,, 6	3·22	922	15	185	94	168	203	6·3
,, 2	3·23	750	17	144	100	144	160	7·1
,, 5	3·42	791	16	159	107	168	192	6·6
,, 3	3·47	465	17·5	144	107	154	189	6·8
,, 1	3·51	724	20	162	121	197	231	6·2
,, 4	3·89	698	18	168	106	178	215	6·8
,, 2	4·16	935	18	179	106	190	218	7·0
,, 1	4·16	895	21	201	127	255	314	6·1
,, 4	4·56	969	19·5	233	114	267	343	6·3
,, 3	4·58	575	20·5	177	126	223	297	6·6
,, 3	4·88	760	20	234	123	288	413	6·35
,, 3	5·22	910	21	281	129	362	540	6·3
,, 4	5·23	1094	19·5	263	114	301	395	6·8
,, 4	5·67	1331	20·5	320	121	385	520	6·8

17—2

means of increasing the alveolar ventilation is evidently much more economical than a simple increase in the frequency would be, since, as the table shows, with increasing depth of respirations the alveolar ventilation increases more rapidly in proportion than the total respiratory ventilation. Mere observations of the frequency of respiration evidently afford no measure of the alveolar ventilation, and may be very misleading. It will be seen, for instance, that even when the alveolar ventilation was increased to three times the normal, there might be an actual diminution in the frequency of the respirations.

DISCUSSION OF RESULTS AND FURTHER EXPERIMENTS ON APNŒA

The experiments which have been detailed above indicate clearly that under normal conditions the regulation of the lung-ventilation depends on the pressure of CO_2 in the alveolar air. Even a very slight rise or fall in the alveolar CO_2 pressure causes a great increase or diminution in the lung ventilation. Thus we found that a rise of 0.2% of an atmosphere in the alveolar CO_2 pressure was sufficient to double the ventilation of the lung alveoli. For each individual the normal alveolar CO_2 pressure appears to be an extraordinarily sharply defined physiological constant.

By what paths do variations of the alveolar CO_2 pressure affect the respiratory centre? All the available evidence appears to us to point clearly to the conclusion that the arterial blood, and this alone, furnishes the connection. Against the existence of a nervous connection through the vagus or sympathetic, suggested originally by Marshall Hall, are the facts that, as shown by Geppert and Zuntz, hyperpnœa occurs as usual, and in the same degree, whether or not the vagus and sympathetic have first been cut, and whether or not the nervous connections between the active muscles and the respiratory centre have been severed. . . .

There is clear positive evidence that the blood is itself a carrier to the respiratory centre of stimuli which produce hyperpnœa. The most striking proof has been furnished by Fredericq, who showed that apnœa is produced in an animal whose respiratory centre is supplied with arterial blood from a second animal to which artificial respiration is applied.

The previous experiments of Geppert and Zuntz on this point are equally convincing. Hence, assuming that CO_2 is the normal stimulus to the respiratory centre, there is no room for doubt that it is through a rise in the CO_2 pressure of the blood supplying the centre that the stimulus is furnished.

Normal hyperpnœa, such as that due to muscular work, may be explained as follows. The venous blood, returning to the lungs in larger quantity, and probably also more highly charged with CO_2, causes a rapid rise in the alveolar CO_2 pressure, and consequent rise in the arterial CO_2 pressure. The respiratory centre is thus stimulated to increased activity, with consequent lowering of the alveolar CO_2 pressure, until a point is struck at which an equilibrium is maintained between the effect of the increased supply of venous blood in raising the arterial CO_2 pressure and that of the increased respiratory activity in lowering it. . . .

For "chemical" apnœa (as distinguished from "vagus" or "distention" apnœa, if such a thing exists) the following explanation seems to agree with the facts recorded by previous observers and by ourselves. The forced or artificial respiration causing the apnœa lowers the CO_2 pressure in the alveolar air and consequently in the arterial blood. The consequence is that CO_2 is washed out of the centre, and the CO_2 pressure in its cells is lowered below the threshold value at which activity of the centre begins. Not only so, but CO_2 is washed out of the tissues of the body generally, so that even the venous blood may have a lower CO_2 tension than corresponds to the threshold value for the respiratory centre; and blood which is quite dark in colour may thus fail to excite the centre. As a consequence it will be a considerable time after the forced or artificial respiration has ceased before the CO_2 pressure in the cells of the respiratory centre again arises to the threshold value; and it may happen that the centre is first again actually excited, not by CO_2 but by deficiency of oxygen. (Haldane, J. S. and Priestley, J. G. "The regulation of the lung-ventilation." *J. Physiol. [Lond.]*, 1905, *32*, 225-266 [pp. 248, 249, 250, 252, 253, 254, 255].)

Yandell Henderson

1873-1944

Yandell Henderson, the professor of applied physiology at Yale University from 1921 to 1938, carried out important investigations upon the physiology of respiration, especially in relation to clinical medicine, and upon the volume output of the heart. His early experiments upon acapnia focussed the attention of physiologists upon this important problem and as a result of his observations, Henderson was led to recommend the administration of carbon dioxide in conditions of shock, e.g., from anesthesia, drowning, and carbon monoxide poisoning. The report of his first experiments, read in May 1907, is given in full below.

This was followed between 1907 and 1911 by a series of significant papers on acapnia which appeared in the *American Journal of Physiology*. In the fourth paper of the series Henderson showed that fatal apnœa might follow excessive forced breathing,[17] and in the sixth paper the relation of acapnia to anesthesia was first pointed out, and the inhalation of carbon dioxide recommended as a means of combating collapse due to anesthesia.[18]

PRODUCTION OF SHOCK BY LOSS OF CARBON DIOXIDE, AND RELIEF BY PARTIAL ASPHYXIATION

The writer is led by a large number of experiments to advance the following hypothesis to explain the causation of shock by extreme pain: Pain induces violent and prolonged hyperpnœa. The carbon dioxide content, not only of the arterial blood but of the tissues of the body as well, is thus greatly reduced. This condition of acapnia lowers the tonus of the peripheral blood vessels, and induces tachycardia, shallow respiration, failure of reflexes, and the mental condition characteristic of surgical shock.

The liability to shock which attaches to the exposure of the abdominal viscera is to be explained by the exhalation of carbon dioxide from the organs exposed, and the consequent loss of tonus in their blood vessels. Thus it was found that when a loop of intestine of a cat was exposed to a current of air warmed to 35° to 38° C. and saturated with moisture, an extreme congestion rapidly developed. When the loop was placed in saline saturated with carbon dioxide, the congestion rapidly disappeared. When the abdominal viscera of a dog under moderate anæsthesia were thus exposed for one hour, and moderate hyperpnœa was thereafter induced for ten minutes by stimulation of the sciatic nerve, shock developed. Arterial pressure fell to 60 mm. Respiration was very shallow. The animal was comatose, and wholly insensitive to stimulation of afferent nerves.

Rapid recovery was effected by assisting in the restoration of the normal carbon dioxide content of the body. The dead space of the respiratory tract was increased by attaching to the trachea a piece of hose a metre in length and 2 cm. in diameter. A moderate volume of saline saturated with carbon dioxide was perfused into the fem-

[17] Henderson, Y. "Acapnia and shock. IV. Fatal apnœa after excessive respiration." *Amer. J. Physiol.*, 1910, *25*, 310-333.

[18] Henderson, Y. and Scarbrough, M. M. "Acapnia and shock. VI. Acapnia as a factor in the dangers of anæsthesia." *Amer. J. Physiol.*, 1910, *26*, 260-286.

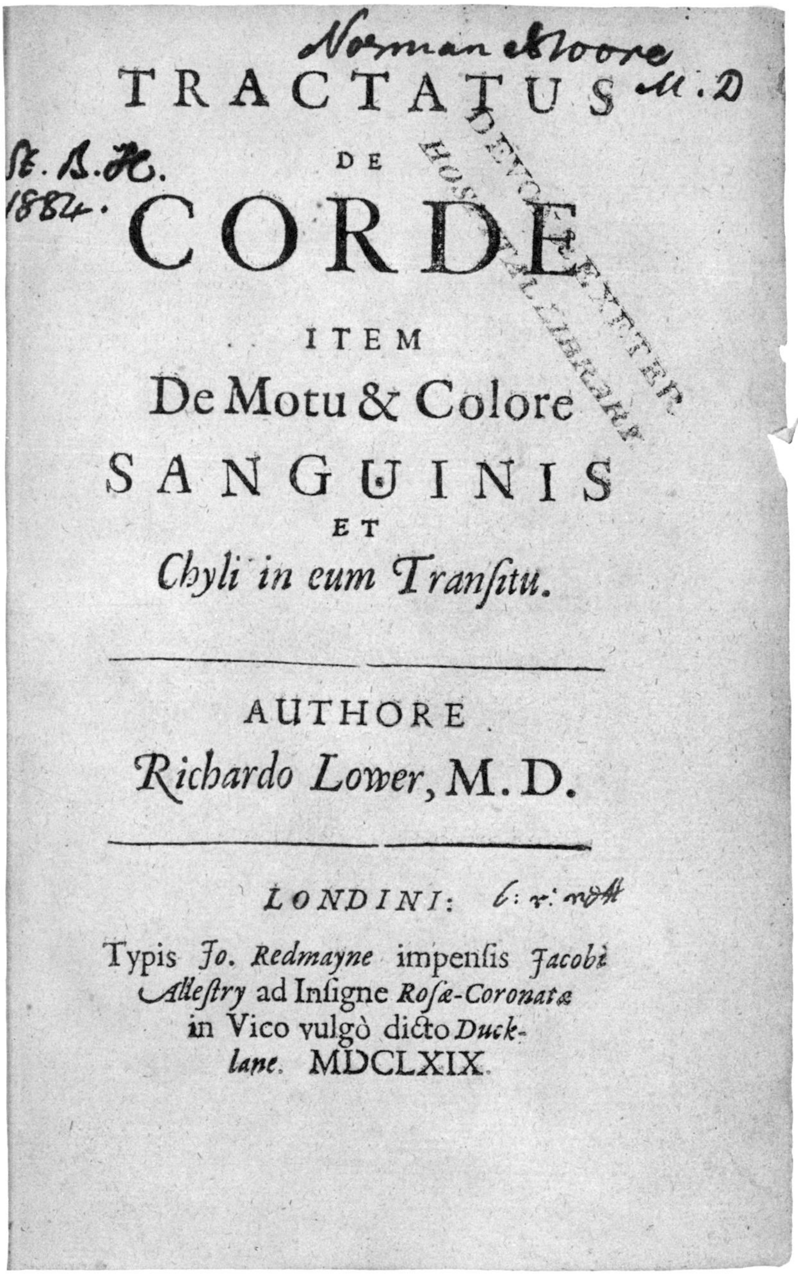

TRACTATUS

DE

CORDE

ITEM

De Motu & Colore

SANGUINIS

ET

Chyli in eum Transitu.

AUTHORE

Richardo Lower, M.D.

LONDINI: *b: r: off*

Typis *Jo. Redmayne* impensis *Jacobi*
Allestry ad Insigne *Rosæ-Coronatæ*
in Vico vulgò dicto *Duck-*
lane. MDCLXIX.

PLATE 20. The title-page of Lower's book on the heart, 1669.

PLATE 21. A portrait of John Mayow which appears as the frontispiece in his *Tractatus quinque*, Oxford, 1674.

TRACTATVS DVO
Quorum prior agit
DE
Respiratione:
Alter De
Rachitide.
A
JOH: MAYOW, Coll: Omn:
An: Socio.
OXON:
Excudebat HEN: HALL, Impensis
RIC: DAVIS. 1669.

PLATE 22A. The cancelled title-page of Mayow's *Tractatus duo* with the date 1669. It had originally appeared in November 1668, but the printer had substituted a new title with the new year.

TRACTATUS
SECUNDUS.
DE
Rachitide.
A
JOH: MAYOW, Oxon. Coll:
Omn: An: Socio.
OXON:
Excudebat HEN: HALL, Impensis
RIC: DAVIS. 1668.

PLATE 22B. The separate title of the tract on rickets in which the printer had not bothered to change the date.

Tab:1mo
fig:1
fig:2
fig:3
fig:4

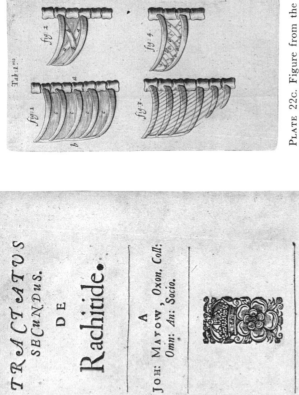

PLATE 22C. Figure from the tract on respiration showing the action of the intercostal muscles.

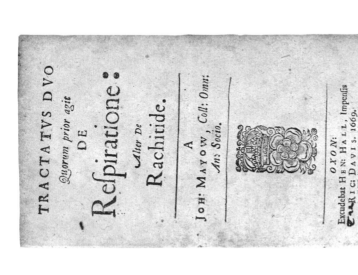

PLATE 23. Frontispiece of the first edition of Priestley's *Experiments and observations upon different kinds of air*, 1774, showing some of the receivers in which he collected air. Mice are to be seen in the receiver number 3.

PLATE 24. Lavoisier in his laboratory, showing experiments on respiration in men at work and at rest. (From Edouard Grimaux's *Lavoisier 1743-1794*, Paris, 1888.)

Fig. 86. — La nacelle du *Zénith* dans les hautes régions de l'atmosphère.

SIVEL	G. TISSANDIER	CROCÉ-SPINELLI
coupe les cordelettes qui retiennent à la nacelle les sacs de lest remplis de sable.	observe les baromètres.	après avoir fait les observations spectroscopiques, va respirer l'oxygène.

PLATE 25. A picture showing the three members who made the catastrophic ascent on 15 April 1875. Tissandier was the sole survivor. (From Paul Bert's *La Pression barometrique. Recherches de physiologie expérimentale*, Paris, 1878, opposite p. 1664.)

PLATE 26. Sir Joseph Barcroft (1872-1947).

PLATE 27. Sir Frederick Gowland Hopkins (1861-1947). Reproduced with the permission of the *British Medical Bulletin* and Ramsay and Muspratt, Cambridge.

oral vein. Within fifteen minutes arterial pressure had risen above 160 mm. Respiration was full and deep. The animal came out of the coma, and the reactions to sensory stimuli were restored to normal character and intensity.

All of the above quoted experiments have been performed repeatedly. (Henderson, Y. "Production of shock by loss of carbon dioxide, and relief by partial asphyxiation." *Amer. J. Physiol.,* 1907, 19, xiv-xv [*Proc.*].)

Joseph Barcroft
1872-1947

Sir Joseph Barcroft, professor of physiology at Cambridge from 1925 until 1937 (Pl. 26), was educated at King's College, Cambridge. He was eminent for his studies of hemoglobin and physiology of life at high altitudes; later he concerned himself with the functions of the spleen and the physiology of the developing foetus. He was elected a Fellow of the Royal Society in 1910 and knighted in 1935.

Barcroft maintained the belief that the exchange of substances through the epithelium of the lungs and the tissues occurs by virtue of the simple process of diffusion, and he obtained strong experimental evidence in favor of this theory. Not the least significant step in his argument came from his studies upon the effect of altitude. His powers of logical analysis, set forth in singularly attractive language, are nowhere better illustrated than in the following passage from the second edition of his well-known monograph. The first two paragraphs of his original preface are also included.

PREFACE

At one time, which seems too long ago, most of my leisure was spent in boats. In them I learned what little I know of research, not of technique or of physiology, but of the qualities essential to those who would venture beyond the visible horizon.

The story of my physiological "ventures" will be found in the following pages. Sometimes I have sailed single handed, sometimes I have been one of a crew, sometimes I have sent the ship's boat on some expedition without me. Any merit which attaches to my narrative lies in the fact that it is in some sense at first hand. I have refrained from discussing subjects which I have not actually touched, but which might fittingly have been included in a modern account of the blood as a vehicle for oxygen. Such are the relation of narcosis to oxygen-want and the properties of intracellular oxidative enzymes. The omission of these and other important subjects has made the choice of a title somewhat difficult. I should like to have called the book, what it frankly is—a log; did not such a title involve an air of flippancy quite out of place in the description of the serious work of a man's life. I have therefore chosen a less exact, though more comprehensive title.

THE HYDROGEN-ION CONCENTRATION OF THE BLOOD

After this somewhat lengthy digression let me return to the subject of mountain sickness. I had mentioned that the symptoms were attributed by Paul Bert to an actual want of sufficient molecules of oxygen in each cubic foot of air inspired into the lungs. This view of the matter was not allowed to go unchallenged for long. Mosso, who, as I have said, was the great moving force in the study of high altitudes, put forward a rival theory, based on the fact that the expired air contained less carbonic acid at high altitudes than at the sea-level. . . .

The position then at the end of Mosso's life may be briefly stated in the following table:

SCHEME 1

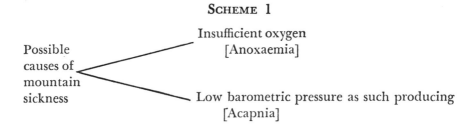

Possible causes of mountain sickness
 — Insufficient oxygen [Anoxaemia]
 — Low barometric pressure as such producing [Acapnia]

Granting the possibility of the existence of acapnia, the further question would arise: How does the acapnia produce its supposed results? There are two possible ways in which it might be held to act. The first is that the absence of CO_2 *per se* should affect the functions of the body, the second is that other things being equal the evaporation of CO_2 from the blood would render that fluid more alkaline. This alkalinity would be reflected by the tissues generally and might affect their function.

The table which I have given above as expressing the causes of mountain sickness then might be expanded as follows and the alternatives then would be:

SCHEME 2

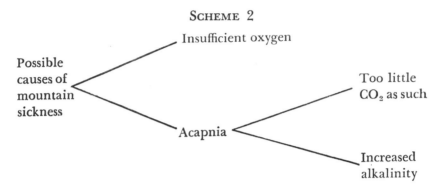

Such then was the position when the subject became one of first hand interest to me. In 1909 the late Professor Zuntz of Berlin sent me a very pleasant invitation. It contained the news that he was about to organize an expedition to Teneriffe the following year. This expedition was to be international in character and he asked me to accompany him and to bring another English worker with me. I was fortunate in having Dr. Douglas as my colleague. The results which we brought back from Teneriffe shed some light on each of the possible mechanisms of acapnia. Let us first consider whether or not the mere reduction of CO_2, as such, in the blood is responsible for mountain sickness.

Pressure of CO_2 in alveolar air mm.

	Sea Level Europe	Cañadas	Alta Vista
Douglas.	41	36	32
Barcroft.	40	41	38
Zuntz.	35	29	27

The above table shows that as between the sea-level and the Alta Vista Hut, there was a drop of more than 20 per cent. in the alveolar CO_2 tensions of Zuntz and Douglas. There was no such drop in my case. The drop of 7 or 9 mm. in the alveolar CO_2 is caused of course

by increased total ventilation on their parts, as a corollary to which
there was a corresponding rise in alveolar oxygen. Zuntz and Douglas have alveolar oxygen pressures of some ten millimetres above
my own. Now if reduced CO_2 pressure were the cause of mountain
sickness Zuntz and Douglas should have been the sufferers, if reduced oxygen pressure in the alveolar air were the cause I would
be the victim, as, in fact, I was to some extent. This experiment
was controlled on Monte Rosa where my carbonic acid pressure
dropped in the ordinary way and where I did not suffer at all. I am
prepared therefore to delete "reduction of CO_2 as such" from the
scheme of possible causes of mountain sickness which now stands as
follows:

Scheme 3

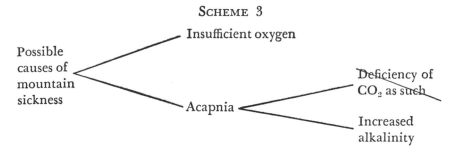

Let us now turn to another possibility which the acapnia theory
presents, namely that of decreased alkalinity of the blood. On our
return from Teneriffe I was quite of the opinion that it might be
deleted as well. The argument was as follows. The affinity of haemoglobin for oxygen depends upon the circumstances under which the
haemoglobin is placed, it decreases with a rise of temperature, with
a rise in hydrogen-ion concentration, and it is also influenced by
salts. Small additions of salt to blood do not however produce any
appreciable effect on the affinity of the haemoglobin for oxygen.
On the other hand, small changes in hydrogen-ion concentration do
produce a very marked effect. At constant temperature then my idea
was that if the alkalinity of the blood increased the haemoglobin
would gain in its affinity for oxygen to an extent which might be
discernible. This matter was tested on the bloods of each member
of the party. As the result of these tests it appeared that when the
blood, drawn at any given altitude was exposed to any standard
pressure of oxygen, in the presence of the concentration of carbonic

acid which the actual blood contained in the body at that altitude. Scheme 3 then turned into Scheme 4.

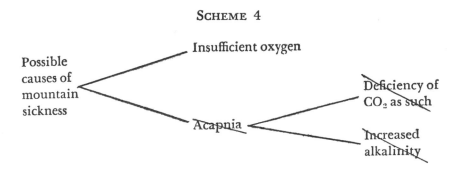

SCHEME 4

(Barcroft, J. *The respiratory function of the blood.* Cambridge, University Press, 1914. x, 320 pp. [p. vii]; 2d ed., 1925-1928, 2 pts. [pt. 1, pp. 88, 89, 90-91].)

Frederick Gowland Hopkins
1861-1947

Sir Frederick Gowland Hopkins, professor of biochemistry at Cambridge until his retirement in 1943 (Pl. 27), was associated with three great developments in modern physiology (see Chs. VI and XII also. Hopkins was educated at University College (B.Sc. 1890) and studied medicine at Guy's Hospital, qualifying in 1894. Four years later he went to Cambridge where he spent the rest of his professional life. He became a Fellow of the Royal Society in 1905, winning the Copley Medal in 1926 and serving as president 1930-1935. Other honors included knighthood (1925) and the Order of Merit (1935). He shared a Nobel Prize with Christiaan Eijkman in 1929 "for his discovery of the growth-stimulating vitamins."

He had begun his experiments on accessory factors in the normal diet in 1906. At about the same time, in collaboration with Sir Walter Morley Fletcher, he undertook the chemical analysis of muscular activity, establishing for the first time the importance of lactic acid; finally, he discovered glutathione, a respiratory enzyme of the tissues, which shed highly significant light upon the metabolic processes occurring peripherally.

GLUTATHIONE

The research described in this paper, though its actual point of departure had an intention quite different,* ultimately resolved itself into an endeavor to throw light upon the chemical nature and physiological significance of a constituent of living tissues, which, though hitherto of unknown nature, has long carried a name. There can scarcely be a doubt that the substance to be described is the "Philothion" of de Rey-Pailhade.

In 1888 this author showed that yeast cells and aqueous extracts of yeast have the property of reducing sulphur to hydrogen sulphide [de Rey-Pailhade, 1888]. Later he showed that many animal tissues possess the same property. Throughout a long series of communications upon the subject he has courageously maintained the view that the labile hydrogen thus shown to exist in living cells has important respiratory functions. His views as to the probable nature of the hypothetical substance (named as above) which he supposed to carry this labile hydrogen, have been modified from time to time. In his latest writings he speaks of it as the hydride of a protein ("hydrure d'albumine"). After the publication of Heffter, to which reference will immediately be made, he accepted the view that the labile hydrogen exists in sulphydryl groups, HS—. . . .

Section III

ISOLATION OF A DIPEPTIDE

Yeast has been chiefly used as a source of the substance to be described, but the same product has been obtained from mammalian muscle, and mammalian liver.

There was every reason in advance to expect that it would be found to have a very low concentration in the tissues. As already stated, the nitroprusside reaction is extremely delicate, and tissue

---

* My attention was directed to the subject in two separate ways. Some years ago I was endeavouring to discover if vitamins were to be found among sulphur-containing compounds, and was led part of the way towards the separation of the substance now described. A little later, acting on the suggestion that acid formation in muscle is a necessary factor in contraction I wished to discover if by chance in the absence of carbohydrate, aceto-acetic acid from fat might function instead of lactic acid. This led me to apply the nitro-prusside test to tissues. At this time Arnold's papers had not yet appeared and I was ignorant of Heffter's publication. The above mentioned enquiries were nugatory but they led to the present one.

extracts when completely freed from proteins contain only very small amounts of organic sulphur. The actual yield of H_2S when yeast cells or animal tissues are treated with sulphur (supposing this to measure sulphydryl groups with any accuracy) is minute.

The discovery of a method of isolation cost much labour; but could the nature and properties of the substance have been known in advance, greater difficulties might well have been expected. . . .

The following shows the acceleration of reduction due to the addition of oxidised dipeptide to the system in neutral or slightly alkaline conditions. The solution in each case was a phosphate buffer solution, the P_h being adjusted after the addition of the dipeptide. Chloroform was added to all the tubes and there was a layer of toluene on the surface. The tubes were filled with nitrogen.

Tissue preparation	Buffer solution	Methylene blue	Oxidised dipetide added	P_h	Reduction time
0.2 g.	5 cc.	0.5 cc.	0 mg.	7.4	5 hrs. 45 mins.
0.2 g.	5 cc.	0.5 cc.	4 mg.	7.4	2 hrs. 40 mins.
0.2 g.	5 cc.	0.5 cc.	0 mg.	7.8	3 hrs. 45 mins.
0.2 g.	5 cc.	0.5 cc.	4 mg.	7.8	1 hr. 40 mins.
0.5 g.	5 cc.	0.5 cc.	0 mg.	7.8	2 hrs. 30 mins.
0.5 g.	5 cc.	0.5 cc.	4 mg.	7.8	0 hr. 55 mins.

The conditions can be adjusted to give more rapid reduction and sharper contrasts than the above.

Tissue	Buffer solution	Methylene blue	Oxidised dipeptide	P_h	Reduction time
Liver .15 g.	5 cc.	0.3 cc.	4 mg.	7.4	0 hr. 25 mins.
Liver .15 g.	5 cc.	0.3 cc.	0 mg.	7.4	6 hrs. +
Muscle (washed) 0.2 g. .	5 cc.	0.3 cc.	8 mg.	7.4	0 hr. 10 mins.
Muscle (washed) 0.2 g. .	5 cc.	0.3 cc.	0 mg.	7.4	3 hrs. +

It seems clear that in the reactions described the -S-S-group of the oxidised dipeptide acts first as a hydrogen acceptor and under conditions of even slight acidity the resulting HS-groups are too stable to transfer the hydrogen to another acceptor. In neutral or slightly alkaline solution on the other hand the hydrogen is transferred to the methylene blue. If this view be the right one we have to recognise the important fact that the two reactions involved in the transference of hydrogen to the disulphide group under the influence of a tissue enzyme, and its subsequent transference from sulphydryl groups to the methylene blue acceptor, together run faster than the single reaction in which the dye is directly reduced by the tissue enzyme. The dipeptide then possesses what are essentially catalytic properties and would be fairly spoken of as a co-enzyme. Indeed, if tissues are very thoroughly washed, as in the observations of Thunberg referred to earlier, so that their power to reduce methylene blue is practically removed, the restoration of this power when the oxidised dipeptide is added at once gives the impression that it has the function of a co-ferment exerted on the lines suggested. . . .

SUMMARY

A substance responsible for the nitroprusside reaction which is given by nearly all animal tissues, and was applied by Heffter and by Arnold in proof of the presence of sulphydryl groups in the cell, has been isolated from yeast, from muscle, and from mammalian liver. It has the properties of the philothion of de Rey-Pailhade.

Evidence is given to show that the substance is a dipeptide containing glutamic acid and cysteïn. The relation of the two amino-acids in the molecule has not yet been determined. Though present in low concentration (0.01 to 0.02% of the fresh tissue) the dipeptide contains practically the whole of the non-protein organically bound sulphur of the cell.

The substance is autoxidisable, and, owing to the changes in the sulphur group of its cysteïn moiety from the sulphydryl to the disulphide condition and *vice versa*, it acts readily under varying conditions either as a hydrogen acceptor or an oxygen acceptor (hydrogen "donator"). It can be both reduced and oxidised under the influence of factors shown to be present in the tissues themselves.

Evidence is discussed which suggests that the substance has actual functions in the chemical dynamics of the cell. (Hopkins, F. G. "On the autoxidisable constituent of the cell." *Biochem. J.*, 1921, *15*, 286-305 [pp. 286, 288, 303, 304].)

V

Digestion

Knowledge of gastric function had inevitably to await the rise of modern chemistry, inorganic as well as organic, but more particularly the chemistry of proteins and enzymes. Inorganic chemistry had its beginnings in the seventeenth century with the French chemist-physician Jean Rey, and two Oxford men, Robert Boyle and John Mayow, who were followed in the eighteenth century by a host of vigorous experimenters, the most notable being Antoine-Laurent Lavoisier. However, organic chemistry, especially study of protein[1] structure, did not come into its own until well into the nineteenth century. Recognition of the amino acids as the building-stones of the proteins (into which the digestive process breaks them down) came with the work of two men of genius, Edmund Drechsel (1843-1897), who in 1891 published his discovery that the protein molecule contains both mono- and di-amino acids, and Emil Fischer (1852-1919), who began to study the proteins in 1898 and in 1906 published his classic monograph, *Untersuchungen über Aminosäuren, Polypeptide und Proteine*. In this he showed animal and vegetable proteins to be composed of individual amino acids united by elimination of water from their separate molecules.

Prior to the nineteenth century, one encounters terminology and views that bespoke the mystic alchemical vagaries of a previous age. The term "fermentation" was used to describe the changes which occur in the stomach; however, the word was of uncertain connotation, and the failure on the part of writers of the sixteenth and seventeenth centuries to define their terms tended to confuse their own contemporaries as well as those of later generations who have sought to understand them. The first man to sound a modern note in the study of digestion was Santorio Santorio who performed

---

[1] The name "protein" was introduced by a Dutchman, Gerard Johann Mulder (1802-1880), in 1838 in a paper bearing the significant title, "Action de l'acide hydrochlorique sur la protéine." (*Bull. Sci. Phys. nat. (Leyde)*, 1838, p. 153). Mulder was a collaborator and contemporary of the great German organic chemist Justus von Liebig (1803-1873).

the simple experiment of weighing a human being (usually himself) before and after a meal, finding that his weight increased by the weight of the food ingested. Franciscus de le Boë [Sylvius] (1614-1672) and J. B. van Helmont (1577-1644) speculated concerning digestion, but it remained for de le Boë's youthful pupil, Regner de Graaf, to perform one of the first significant experiments in the history of gastric physiology. He isolated the pancreatic duct of a dog and, by making a permanent fistula, was able in 1664 to collect pure pancreatic juice. After de Graaf the next observations of importance are those of René Antoine F. de Réaumur on the properties of gastric juice in birds.

Then came a group of four brilliant young men, all of whom (except possibly Stevens) died tragically—"doubly dead in that they died so young"—William Hewson who succumbed at thirty-four to a dissection wound, William Stark (1740-1770) who died at twenty-nine of an over-zealous diet experiment, Edward Stevens (*fl.* 1770) of whose life nothing is known, and Charles Darwin who, like Hewson, died of a dissection infection at nineteen. Through study of the properties of gastric juice *in vivo* and *in vitro*, Hewson and his young contemporaries laid the foundations for the work of Lazaro Spallanzani, John R. Young (who published his celebrated thesis in 1803 when twenty-one), Prout, and Beaumont. Spallanzani established for human gastric juice properties similar to those which Réaumur had found for birds and which the young men just mentioned had disclosed in other animals. Like many enquirers in the history of physiology, Spallanzani performed human experiments using himself as subject.

The correlation of gastric physiology with chemistry did not really begin, however, until William Prout (1785-1850) found that the human stomach contained free hydrochloric acid (1824). Meanwhile William Beaumont (1785-1853) had started his remarkable observations upon Alexis St. Martin, and once more the human experiment led to a far-reaching advance in knowledge of physiological processes (1833). It is probably true that Beaumont carried out his observations without knowledge of what had been done before him, and that his discoveries were therefore arrived at independently of his predecessors. However, he gives an excellent historical discussion in his book though one suspects that this was prepared at the time the book was being written, while the observations had been made long before. Developments of the early twen-tieth century for which Pavlov, Rubner, Benedict, Cannon, Bayliss, and Starling were largely responsible and those in later years of this era (*c.* 1925-1955), for which *their* followers must be given chief credit (men such as Carlson, Ivy, Koska, Lim, Ågren, Wolf, and Wolff), are too numerous for special comment.

Santorio Santorio
1561-1636

Santorio Santorio, physician of Capodistria, capital of the Venetian province of Istria on the upper reaches of the Adriatic opposite Venice, is probably the greatest figure in the history of physiology and experimental medicine prior to the time of William Harvey. Santorio introduced the use of instruments of precision for making his measurements and is regarded as the founder of the modern study of metabolic processes. He devised a special watch for counting the pulse, clinical thermometers, and a weighing bed and weighing chair (shown in the frontispiece of this volume). His fame grew rapidly among his contemporaries.

Santorio's universal curiosity caused him to be an indefatigable traveller, and it is probable that he visited every country in Europe. In 1602 while travelling in Poland he wrote his first book on how to combat errors in medicine (*Methodus vitandorum errorum omnium qui in arte medica contingunt*). He mentions his pulse watch which made it possible for him to compare the pulse in any patient from one day to the next. This and other publications led to wide recognition, and in 1610 he was called to Padua to occupy the chair of medicine. He took up his duties the following year, when, at the age of fifty, he was at the height of his powers. At Venice in 1614 he published the little book of 84 text pages *Ars de statica medicina* which brought him enduring fame. Arturo Castiglioni (1874-1953) lists 28 Latin editions and two separate Italian translations;[2] there were also editions in English, French, and German.

It is usually stated that Santorio's chief contribution to physiology lay in his study of insensible perspiration. Thus, in his weighing chair, he was able to make accurate determinations of the body weight at various times before and after eating, sleeping, and the execution of other physiological functions. Although he does not describe his experiments in the first edition of his book, they are described, and in great detail, in a later book entitled *Commentaria in primam fen primi libri canonis Avicennae.*

[2] Castiglioni, A. *Life and work of Sanctorius.* Emilie Recht, Translator. Sanctorius number of *Medical Life,* 1931, *n.s. 38,* 729-786.

INSENSIBLE PERSPIRATION

Aphorism I. If there daily be an Addition of what is wanting, and a Subtraction of what abounds, in due Quantity and Quality, lost Health may be restor'd, and the present preserv'd. . . .

Aph. II. If a *Physician* who has the Care of another's Health, is acquainted only with the sensible Supplies [actual food intake] and Evacuations, and knows nothing of the Waste [Weight-loss] that is daily made by Insensible Perspiration, he will only deceive his Patient, and never cure him.

Aph. III. He only who knows how much, and when the Body does more or less insensibly perspire, will be able to discern, when, and what is to be added or taken away, either for the Recovery or Preservation of Health.

Aph. IV. Insensible Perspiration alone, discharges much more than all the sensible [known] Evacuations together. . . .

Aph. V. Insensible Perspiration, is either made by the Pores of the Body, which is all over Perspirable and covered with a Skin like a Nett; or it is performed by Respiration through the Mouth, which usually in the space of one Day amounts to about the quantity of half a Pound. . . .

Aph. VI. If eight Pounds of Meat and Drink are taken in one Day, the Quantity that usually goes off by Insensible Perspiration in that Time, is five pounds. . . .

Aph. VII. The Quantities insensibly perspir'd, vary according to the Differences of Constitutions, Ages, Countries, Seasons, Distempers, Diet, and the rest of the Non-naturals [i.e., environmental factors]. . . .

Aph. VIII. If the Body be weighed in the Morning before and after sensible Evacuation, then it will be easier to determine the Quantity that is wasted that Night by Perspiration.

Aph. IX. If the Body encreases beyond its usual Weight without Eating or Drinking more than customary, there must either be a Retension of some of the sensible Excrements, or an Obstruction of the Perspirable Matter. . . .

Aph. XX. There are two Kinds of Insensible Perspiration the one is during Sleep, of Humours that are well digested, and after which there is an increase of Strength: The other is when awake, and arises from indigested Humours, and is weakning more or less, according to the greater or lesser Actions of the Muscles during that Time. . . .

Aph. XXI. That Perspiration which is beneficial, and most clears the Body of superfluous Matter, is not what goes off with Sweat, but that insensible Steam or Vapour, which in Winter time exhales to about the Quantity of Fifty Ounces in the space of one natural Day. . . .

Sect. III

Aph. XI. A full or an empty Stomach, lessens Perspiration, for a full one diverts it by a Corruption of the Aliment; and an empty one draws it back that it may be filled. . . .

Aph. XII. When a full Meal is not perfectly digested, it is to be known by an increase of Weight; for the Body will not then perspire well: But an empty Stomach is filled with Vapours. (Santorio, S. *Medicina statica: being the aphorisms of Sanctorius translated into* [quaint, and at times incomprehensible] *English with large explanations* [and now (1958) modified for clarity (by J. F. F.)]. John Quincy, Translator. London, William Newton, 1712. lvi, 312 pp. [pp. 1-2, 3, 4, 5, 9, 10, 117].)

Gasparo Aselli
1581-1626

Gasparo Aselli, a Milanese surgeon and anatomist (Pl. 28), discovered, apparently by accident, the structures now known as the lacteals. Their recognition represents an important milestone in the development of knowledge concerning nutrition. Aselli erroneously believed that the "lacteal veins" led to the liver, and it was not until Jean Pecquet (1622-1674) discovered the thoracic duct and proved that its lower end, the receptaculum chyli, was continuous with the lacteals that their relation to the process of absorption became more clearly established. Foster's translation of Aselli's original description[3] (Pl. 29) of his disclosure follows.

[3] Aselli, G. *De lactibus sive lacteis venis, quarto vasorum mesaraicorum genere novo invento. . . . Dissertatio qua sententiae anatomicae multae, vel perperam receptae . . . illustrantur. . . .* Milan, G. B. Bidelli, 1627. 10 *ll.,* 79 pp. 4 pl. in color, portrait. The plates accompanying this tract are the first colored anatomical illustrations of importance in the history of bookmaking. The work was published posthumously through the generosity of that liberal patron of science, Nicholas Fabry de Peiresc. Peiresc's own uncut copy, stamped with his mark of ownership, was subsequently owned by Jean Paul Marat and was acquired by J.F.F. in 1931. The engraving of Aselli (reproduced in Pl. 28) which is present in some copies of his book, was made in the 42d year of his age, thus coinciding closely with his discovery of the lacteals (23 July 1622).

THE LACTEALS

On the 23rd of July of that year (1622) I had taken a dog in good condition and well fed, for a vivisection at the request of some of my friends, who very much wished to see the recurrent nerves. When I had finished this demonstration of the nerves, it seemed good to watch the movements of the diaphragm in the same dog, at the same operation. While I was attempting this, and for that purpose had opened the abdomen and was pulling down with my hand the intestines and stomach gathered together into a mass, I suddenly beheld a great number of cords as it were, exceedingly thin and beautifully white, scattered over the whole of the mesentery and the intestine, and starting from almost innumerable beginnings. At first I did not delay, thinking them to be nerves. But presently I saw that I was mistaken in this since I noticed that the nerves belonging to the intestine were distinct from these cords, and wholly unlike them, and, besides, were distributed quite separately from them [Pl. 30]. Wherefore struck by the novelty of the thing, I stood for some time silent while there came into my mind the various disputes, rich in personal quarrels no less than in words, taking place among anatomists concerning the mesaraic veins and their function. And by chance it happened that a few days before I had looked into a little book by Johannes Costaeus written about this very matter. When I gathered my wits together for the sake of the experiment, having laid hold of a very sharp scalpel, I pricked one of those cords and indeed one of the largest of them. I had hardly touched it, when I saw a white liquid like milk or cream forthwith gush out. Seeing this, I could hardly restrain my delight, and turning to those who were standing by, to Alexander Tadinus, and more particularly to Senator Septalius, who was both a member of the great College of the Order of Physicians and, while I am writing this, the Medical Officer of Health, "Eureka" I exclaimed with Archimedes, and at the same time invited them to the interesting spectacle of such an unusual phenomenon. And they indeed were much struck with the novelty of the thing. (Foster, Michael. *Lectures on the history of physiology* . . . 2d ed. Cambridge, At the University Press, 1924. 306 pp. [pp. 48-49].)

Olof Rudbeck

1630-1702

Olof Rudbeck, anatomist, physician, botanist, and world-recognized "littérateur," precocious son of one of the oldest noble families of Sweden, was born in 1630 in the village of Arosen (*Lat.* "Arosiâe") in the province of Westerôs, near Upsala. In 1650, he discovered that the lacteals of Aselli (1622; published 1627) drain into the receptaculum chyli, thence into the thoracic duct (sheep) and thence into the great veins of the neck, and that on opening the duct, milky chyle flows out in profusion if, before the experiment, the animal has been well fed.[4] This disclosure gave new meaning to Aselli's account of the mesenteric lacteals, indicating the chief channel by which digested food enters the blood stream to nourish the tissues. Young Rudbeck had demonstrated this to Queen Christina who forthwith befriended the talented young experimenter and later provided a travel grant ("pension") which made it possible for him to study in Leyden, Paris, and other great academic centers of Western Europe. In the course of his travels he visited Padua and there saw the dissection amphitheatre of Fabricius ab Aquapendente; on returning to Upsala he planned an anatomical theatre in design similar to that in Padua, and his Queen made possible its erection. This building is the oldest surviving structure amongst the present University buildings at Upsala, having weathered two disastrous fires that virtually destroyed other parts of the University.

In 1650, Rudbeck distinguished between the lacteal system, with its thoracic-duct "chyle," and the true lymphatic system, with its *vasa serosa* which contain not milky "chyle," but a clear, watery fluid.[5] He had found these vessels passing from the liver and the intestines, and had noted that some at least, like the lacteals, also flow into the thoracic duct.

Rudbeck became a great leader in Swedish science and in his writings touched many fields; he was probably best known as botanist and horticulturist as evidenced by his *Catalogus plantarum* (Upsala, 1658) and *Hortus botanicus* (Upsala, 1685). The well-known genus of plants, Rudbeckia, was named for this indefatigable Upsala professor of botany.[6]

[4] Rudbeck, O. *Disputatio anatomica, de circulatione sanguinis. . . .* Vesterås, E. Lauringer, 1652. 16 pp., 1 pl. Dr. Erik Waller, the great Swedish collector (whose library is now at the University of Upsala), possessed four copies, of which two have an extra plate drawn and colored by Olof Rudbeck.

[5] Rudbeck, O. *Nova exercitatio anatomica, exhibens ductus hepaticos aquosos, & vasa glandularum serosa. . . .* Vesterås, E. Lauringer, 1653. 48 pp., 2 pl. Facsimile, Upsala, 1930.

[6] Smith, J. E. *Reliquiae Rudbeckianae, sive, Camporum elysiorum libri primi, quae supersunt, adjectis nominibus Linnaeanis.* London, 1789. viii, 35 pp.

THE DISCOVERY OF THE LYMPHATICS

During the years 1650 and 1651, while engaged in studying the origin and course of the lacteal veins, when I placed a ligature around the portal vein and the bile duct, sometimes ducts became visible, distinctly gorged between the liver and the ligature, but collapsed below the latter. That these ducts could have been chylous vessels was inconceivable to me, because when the ligature was released, they collapsed, the watery fluid they contained rushed toward the pancreas and they disappeared; but again became filled with fluid when the ligature was tightened. Having repeated this experiment several times and convinced myself of its correctness, it occurred to me that the fluid in question was, so to speak, useless for the sustenance of the body and was excreted in the pancreas and driven out through Wirsung's duct. I was so sure of my point, that during the public demonstration of the thoracic lacteals which I once arranged in the presence of Europe's great lady, our illustrious and gracious Queen Christina, and of the nobility, the honorable senate of the university and a number of students, I also demonstrated these ducts.

When, however, somewhat later I tied the lacteal veins of the mesentery between the pancreas glandulosum and the chyle vesicle so as to make apparent in the course of a few days the lacteal fluid contained in them, by good luck both the origin and the orifice of these ducts, about which I thus far had been uncertain, became perfectly clear. Concerning this I shall now give a fuller account in accordance with the plan of my work. (Nielson, A. E. "A translation of Olof Rudbeck's *Nova exercitatio anatomica*." *Bull. Hist. Med.*, 1942, *11*, 304-339 [p. 315].)

Regner de Graaf

1641-1673

Regner de Graaf, a brilliant young pupil of Sylvius de le Boë, carried out at the early age of twenty-two an important series of experiments on the physiology of the pancreas (Pl. 31). He records that they were commenced in 1663, and they were published in the following year as a dissertation for his doctor's degree. He succeeded in introducing a temporary cannula, made of the quill of a wild duck, into the pancreatic duct of a living dog, and he studied the properties of the liquid so obtained, observing its clear colour, its reaction, which he believed to be acid, and its bitter taste (Pls. 32a & b). De Graaf's account of his unsuccessful attempts to collect pancreatic juice, followed by his eventual success, is one of the most interesting passages in the history of the experimental method and is given below. De Graaf also studied the reproductive organs, both of male and female, and was the first to describe the ovarian follicles which still bear his name.

CHAPTER III

IN WHAT MANNER THE PANCREATICK JUICE WAS FOUND OUT

THE First Experiment by which we undertook to collect the Pancreatick juice in a living Dog, was a Ligature with which we tied the upper-part of the Pancreas, together with the thin Gut; for, by this manner, we hoped that after some Hours we should have found the Pancreatick Duct swell'd with Juice, but in vain: which seemed to our Judgment to happen by reason that the motion of the Blood being hindered to the Pancreas, and separation of the Juice from it was prevented also.

The Second Experiment was also by Ligature made about the Insertion of the Ductus into the Intestinum Duodenum, but also in vain. The Reason perhaps was the Glandules of the pancreas being hurt, by whose Ductus all the Pancreatick Juice might the more easilier [sic] have flown out, by reason that neither in the great Ductus nor in the lateral branches is there any valves found.

The Third Experiment was by two boards or planks, higher in the middle, than at the ends, applyed and straightly bound to the Duodenum, at the ingress of the Pancreatick Ductus; from whence, after some hours, the Abdomen being opened again, which before had been lightly stitched up, we found the Pancreatick Ductus swelled with a clear and limpid Juice; nevertheless, we could not conveniently either take it out, or taste it. By which success we being animated the more, resolved a fourth Tryal, by opening the Intestinum Duodenum, according to the Longitude thereof; and presently applying a little vessel to the orifice of the Ductus Pancreaticus, as the first Figure of the following Table *A*. [Pl. 32a] demonstrates: afterwards by straightly tying the said Intestine about the neck of the vessel: so that its orifice was diametrically opposite to the end of the Ductus Pancreaticus, not doubting but by this means we should gather a rare quantity of the Pancreatick Juice; but this also in vain; without doubt, because the air included within the vessel, denyed entrance to the Pancreatick Juice, lightly touching it. Therefore we resolved to try a Fifth Experiment, with a little vessel smally perforated, as the first Figure of the Second Table shews under the letter B. By which advantage, in the space of five hours, we collected so great a quantity of Liquor, that the vessel was almost half full; whose contained Liquor was of a bitter relish, and of a yellowish colour; which we judged to happen because the bile, (by reason the Intestine was not first cleansed) was intermixed with the Succus Pancreaticus. . . . (de Graaf, R. *Disputationum medicarum de natura et usu succi pancreatici.* Leyden, Hackian, 1664. 90 pp., 1 pl. A French translation appeared in Paris in 1666, a second Latin edition with many additions to the text in 1671. Quotation is from the English, translated from the second Latin, edition by Christopher Pack, *De succo pancreatico: or A physical and anatomical treatise of the nature and office of the pancreatick juice. . . .* London, N. Brook, 1676, 11 *ll,* 152 pp., 8 *ll* [pp. 26-27].)

René Antoine Ferchault de Réaumur
1683-1757

René Antoine Ferchault de Réaumur was born at La Rochelle, the son of a prominent judge. Not wishing to enter the law himself, he went to Paris where he applied himself so diligently to the study of mathematics, physics, and natural history that at the age of twenty-five he was elected to the Académie des Sciences. For his discovery of the art of converting wrought iron into steel (published in 1722) the king gave him a pension of 12,000 francs which he accepted only on condition that it revert to the Académie after his death.

Réaumur lived in an age when versatility in science was still a possibility and he wrote on many subjects. Most of his work consists of papers scattered among the *Mémoires* of the Académie. Like Boyle he invented a thermometer, and the temperature scale which he introduced still bears his name. He also published six volumes of a great work on the natural history of insects.

By far the most picturesque of his studies relate to his observations on digestion. He had in his possession a pet kite, a bird of prey which is accustomed to eject from its stomach unpalatable articles of food. Réaumur took advantage of this unique opportunity and trained his pet to swallow sponges. When they were brought up, soaked with gastric juice, he found that the fluid squeezed from the sponge caused liquefaction of meat. Unfortunately the buzzard died in the course of his observations and he was forced to continue his studies upon less obliging animals such as ducks and chickens.

GASTRIC JUICE OF THE BUZZARD

It will be easily seen that sponge is the most convenient substance to use in these experiments, for birds of prey do not normally eat it and therefore, judging by previous observations, we may conclude that they cannot digest it. I had no doubt as to the success of the experiment which I was about to undertake, and I accordingly put several small pieces of sponge into a tube, without filling it too full; numerous small holes were then made in the tube and it was swallowed by the bird and brought up as usual. Before the pieces of sponge were placed in the tube they weighed only 13 grains, but when I took them out their weight was 63 grains; they therefore absorbed 50 grains of fluid, most of which I was easily able to squeeze out into a vessel prepared for the purpose.

This experiment alone proves that a fairly large quantity of juice can be obtained quite easily. Two or three of these tubes containing sponge, administered in the course of the day would yield double or treble the above amount, *i.e.* 100 or 150 grains of fluid, while for a small outlay two or three birds could be kept for a week or two and thus 200, 300, or even 450 grains of juice obtained daily. . . . My buzzard died before the series of experiments which I had intended to perform upon it were completed, and I blame my negligence in not replacing it by another buzzard or similar bird of prey. However, I shall make amends for this and try some further experiments which seem to me desirable: I shall now indicate which of these I consider to be the most important, in order to encourage other physicians to attempt them if they have the opportunity.

Before my buzzard died I had only twice obtained, by means of sponges, this juice which can dissolve bones and meat. When I squeezed the fluid out of the sponges into a dish it was quite unlike the clear liquid which is got by different distillations, for it was thick and cloudy and a muddy yellowish white in colour. I am not sure whether its natural colour and transparency had been altered, but further observations will elucidate this point. In the first experiments which I made I did not take the precaution of thoroughly washing the sponges, so that if there were any sediment or other matter in them it would change the consistency of the fluid and make it cloudy.

Apart from anything which the fluid might absorb from the sponges, there may be another reason for its impurity. If, before entering the tube, it came in contact with fragments of meat in the stomach it would not fail to act upon them to a certain extent, and some part of this meat would, when digested and reduced to pulp, almost certainly be mixed with the juice. Therefore, although the juice contained in the sponges could dissolve meat it must not be supposed that it is pure. To obtain fluid which is absolutely pure,— or at least much purer than that which we have just mentioned,— it is only necessary to make sure that the bird swallows the tube containing the sponge on an empty stomach, and that it does not have any food while it retains it. This will not be such a hardship as one might imagine, for nature enables these birds to endure very long fasts; they are not always successful in their search for prey and often go for days without catching, and consequently without eating, anything. . . .

When I put some of the juice from the buzzard's stomach on my tongue, it tasted salt rather than bitter, although, on the contrary, the bones which had been reduced to a jelly by a similar fluid, and their remains, on which the fluid had acted, had not a salt but a bitter taste.

When blue [litmus?] paper was moistened with the fluid it became red.

One of the first experiments that ought to be tried with this fluid,—both because it would be most interesting and because it would prove that it is this juice which reduces meat and bones to pulp, —would be to make it dissolve meat in a vessel just as it dissolves it in the stomach. Actual digestion of aliments taking place under such abnormal conditions would be a most singular and interesting phenomenon. (Réaumur, R.A.F. de. "Sur la digestion des oiseaux. Première mémoire. Expériences sur la manière dont se fait la digestion dans les oiseaux qui vivent principalement de grains et d'herbes, et dont l'estomac est un gésier." *Mém. Acad. roy. sci., Paris,* 1752, pp. 266-307; "Seconde mémoire. De la manière dont elle se fait dans l'estomac des oiseaux de proie." *Ibid.,* 1752, pp. 461-495 [pp. 481-484].)

William Hewson

1739-1774

William Hewson, anatomist, surgeon, and pupil of William and later of John Hunter (1728-1793), wrote, while still a Reader in Anatomy at Great Windmill Street (the dissecting laboratory of the Hunters in London), an important paper on the lymphatic system of birds (Pl. 33). William Hunter (1718-1783) sent it to the Royal Society where it was read on 8 December 1768. Five days earlier a postscript had been added saying that the author had observed similar lymphatic systems in fish and in "a turtle." The paper on fish lymphatics which followed in 1769 was also published in the *Philosophical Transactions,* and for it Hewson was awarded the Copley Gold Medal of the Royal Society and a year later was elected a Fellow.

Hewson (Pl. 34a), however, is better known for his book, *An Experimental Inquiry into the Properties of the Blood* (1771). In Part III, "A description of the red particles of the blood," he not only gave one of the best early descriptions of the erythrocytes and lymphocytes, but he also established for the first time that "coagulable lymph" (now known as fibrinogen) is essential for blood clotting. In a later addition to his *Experimental Inquiry* (1774) he gave the first adequate account of human lymphatics, thus completing his well-planned comparative study of these important structures. It was during this last study that he accidently pricked his finger, and shortly thereafter came his tragic death at the age of thirty-four. Hewson's collected works were published in 1846 by the Sydenham Society. The following passage is taken from his first paper on the lymphatics of birds.

ACCOUNT OF LYMPHATIC SYSTEM IN BIRDS

Having been so fortunate, in a series of experiments made with that view, as to trace out the lymphatic system in birds. I have ventured to offer the following account of it to you, in order to be presented, if you think proper, to the Royal Society; and, I flatter myself, this discovery will be looked upon as some acquisition to physiology.

The lymphatic system has been supposed to be wanting in birds; and absorption in that kind of animals to be carried on by branches of the common veins. Physiologists were led into this opinion by observing, that though the lacteals and mesenteric glands were easily seen even in the smallest quadruped, yet the most acute anatomists had not been able to find in any bird the least appearance either of those vessels or glands. The difficulty of discovering the lacteals in birds was, no doubt, principally owing to the transparency, or want of colour, in the fluid which they contain. In quadrupeds the lacteals are easily found, as they are filled with chyle, which is mostly opaque and white; whereas, in birds, the chyle is as pellucid and colourless as the vessels themselves. The want of mesenteric glands was another cause of our remaining so long ignorant of those vessels.

This system may be divided in birds, as it is in quadrupeds, into the branches, viz. the lacteals and lymphatics, and their trunk, or thoracic duct. The lacteals indeed, in the strictest sense, are, in birds, the lymphatics of the intestines, and like the other lymphatics carry a transparent lymph. And instead of one thoracic duct there are two, of which one goes to each jugular vein (Fig. 36). In these circumstances it would seem, that birds differ from quadrupeds, so far at least as I may judge from the dissection of a goose, which was the bird I chose as most proper for this enquiry. . . .

For the greater satisfaction of those who may think this paper worthy their attention, I have prepared two birds, whose lymphatic systems are filled with quick-silver, in order to be compared with the figure: these have already been shewn to several members of the learned Society, who honoured me with their presence whilst the subjects were fresh; and who, I flatter myself, were then satisfied with the exactness of the drawing.

> *Postscript* Dr. William Hunter adds: "Mr. Hewson begs leave to add, that since the above paper on the lymphatic system in birds was put into the hands of the Secretary of the Royal Society, he has discovered the same system in fish; and has likewise been so fortunate as to procure a Turtle, whose lymphatic system he has traced out, and has got delineated. An account of those dissections, with the figures, he intends soon to have the honour of laying before the Society."
> *Windmill Street, Dec. 3, 1768.*

(Hewson, William. "An account of the lymphatic system in birds." [A letter to William Hunter, M.D., F.R.S. and by him communicated to the Society. Received October 3, 1768.] *Phil. Trans.*, 1769, *58*, 217-226 [pp. 217-218, 224].)

Edward Stevens

fl. 1770

Edward Stevens was an obscure Edinburgh student whose dates have never been ascertained beyond that of his thesis which was defended and published in 1777. It is notable for its description of the isolation of human gastric juice, although, despite statements to the contrary, he was not the first to study its properties. An earlier student at Edinburgh, Benjamin Rush, had performed experiments on himself which were reported in his thesis in 1768 and William Hewson's work has already been described (pp. 171-2). Stevens was the first to study digestion *in vitro*, thus establishing that in the gastric juice there is an active principle necessary for assimilation of food. An English translation of a portion of Stevens' thesis was given in 1784 in the first volume of Spallanzani's *Dissertations relative to the natural history of animals*.

HUMAN STONE-SWALLOWING REGURGITATOR OF EDINBURGH

The following experiments were made at Edinburgh upon an Hussar, a man of weak understanding, who gained a miserable livelihood, by swallowing stones for the amusement of the common people, at the imminent hazard of his life. He began this practice at the age of seven, and has now followed it twenty years. His stomach is so much distended, that he can swallow several stones at a time; and these may not only be plainly felt, but may be heard, whenever the hypogastric region is struck.

EXPERIMENT I

At eight o'clock in the evening, I gave the subject of my experiments a hollow silver sphere, divided into two cavities by a partition, and perforated on the surface with a great number of holes, capable of admitting a needle: into one of these cavities was put four scruples and a half of raw beef, and into the other five scruples of raw bleak [small river fish]. The sphere was voided in twenty-one hours, when the beef was found to have lost one scruple and a half, and the fish two scruples. The rest was much softened, but had no disagreeable smell.

II. A few days afterwards he took the same sphere, containing in one cavity a scruple and four grains of raw beef, and in the other four scruples and eight grains of the same boiled. In forty-three hours the sphere was returned, and the raw flesh had lost one scruple and two grains, and the boiled one scruple and sixteen grains.

III. Suspecting that if these substances were divided, so that the solvent could have freer access to them, more of them would be dissolved, I procured another sphere with holes, so large as to receive a crow's quill, and enclosed some beef a little masticated in it. It was voided quite empty, thirty-eight hours after it was swallowed.

IV. Seeing how readily the chewed meat was dissolved, I thought of trying whether it would be as soon dissolved in a sphere with large holes, but without being chewed. I therefore put a scruple and eight grains of pork into one cavity, and into the other the same quantity of cheese. The sphere was retained forty-three hours, at the end of which not the smallest remains of either pork or cheese could be found.

V. He afterwards swallowed the same sphere, containing in one partition some roasted turkey, and in the other some boiled salt herring. In forty-six hours it was voided, and nothing of the turkey or herring now appeared, both having been completely dissolved. (Stevens, Edward. "Experiments concerning digestion," translated from the inaugural dissertation of Dr. Stevens, published at Edinburgh in 1777, in: *Dissertations relative to the natural history of animals and vegetables, translated from the Italian of the Abbé Spallanzani.* [No translator given.] London, J. Murray, 1784, 2 vols., vol. 1, 303-316 [pp. 303-305].)

Charles Darwin I
1758-1778

Charles Darwin, medical student at Edinburgh, was the precocious eldest son of the poet-naturalist and physician Erasmus Darwin (1731-1802) F.R.S., and brother of Robert Waring Darwin (1766-1848) M.D., F.R.S., who was the father of Charles Robert Darwin (1809-1882) F.R.S., naturalist and author of the book, *On the Origin of Species by Means of Natural Selection* (London, J. Murray, 1859). Charles Darwin received his early education from his father aided by a private tutor; he also attended local schools in Lichfield, Staffordshire. In 1775, when sixteen, Darwin entered Christ Church, Oxford, where one finds a cryptic entry in the college records (Foster's *Alumni oxoniensis*):

Charles D.

S. Erasmus of Lichfield W. Staff.

Ch. Ch. Matriculated 30 March 1775 age 16.

This was just after the time of Edward Gibbon (1737-1794), who had found the dons of Magdalen "plunged in port and prejudice," and young Darwin keenly disliked the similar atmosphere at Christ Church where he felt his mind was going to seed in the pursuit of "classical elegance." As a burgeoning young scientist, he "sigh'd to be removed to the robuster exercises of the medical schools of Edinburgh," so to Edinburgh he went, either in December 1775 or, more probably, in January of 1776 and there pursued and completed his medical studies, writing and successfully defending a Latin M.D. thesis on the lymphatics. In the thesis he set down his conviction that "dropsical" fluid is removed via lymphatic channels, "the absorbent vessels of animal bodies," as a result of the stimulating effects on the heart of the powerful agent contained in the decoction of foxglove. His father Erasmus, who had learned about digitalis from his one-time neighbor William Withering (1741-1799) F.R.S., undoubtedly told Charles about the drug, and Charles in turn had been encouraged to "try it out" by his chief Andrew Duncan (1744-1828). Darwin's observations on the action of digitalis, published by his father two years after Charles's death (appended to his thesis which Erasmus had translated into English), coincided closely with those of Withering whose book (published five years later), *An Account of the Foxglove and Some of its Medical Uses: With Practical Remarks on Dropsy, and Other Diseases* (London, 1785), is a classic in medical literature.

Charles Darwin's book bore the title, *Experiments Establishing a Criterion between Mucaginous and Purulent Matter. And an Account of the Retrograde Motions of the Absorbent Vessels of Animal Bodies in Some Diseases* (Lichfield, 1780, edited by Erasmus Darwin with a life of the author). In Withering's book he mentions Erasmus only once and this in connection with seeing a Miss Hill on 25 July 1776 in consultation with Dr. Darwin (Case IV); similarly, Charles is referred to only once (on page 8, "Dr. [Andrew] Duncan also tells me that the late very ingenious and accomplished Mr. Charles Darwin, informed him of its [digitalis leaf] being used by his father and myself . . .").

Nevertheless, Charles Darwin, the "ingenious and accomplished" Edinburgh medical student, deserves credit for a pioneer study of the action of decoction of foxglove and for having made the highly original suggestion that the "absorbent vessels" which carry foodstuffs to the blood stream also carry fluids when these are accumulated in excessive amounts in tissues (as in progressive heart-failure) and return them to the circulating blood.

SECRETION OF LYMPH

7. As the capillary vessels receive blood from the arteries, and separating the mucus, or perspirable matter from it, convey the remainder back by the veins; these *capillary vessels are a set of*

glands, in every respect similar to the secretory vessels of the liver, or other large congeries of glands. The beginnings of these capillary vessels have frequent anastomoses into each other, in which circumstance they are resembled by the lacteals; and like the mouths or beginnings of other glands, they are a set of absorbent vessels, which drink up the blood which is brought to them by the arteries, as the chyle is drank up by the lacteals: for the circulation of the blood through the capillaries is proved to be independent of arterial impulse; since in the blush of shame, and in partial inflammations, their action is increased, without any increase of the motion of the heart. (Darwin, Charles. *Experiments establishing a criterion between mucaginous and purulent matter.* . . . Lichfield, Printed for J. Jackson; T. Cadell, London; and W. Creech, Edinburgh, 1780. 134 pp. [p. 38].)

Lazaro Spallanzani

1729-1799

The most important contributions to the physiology of digestion after the observations of Réaumur and contemporaneous with those of the young British investigators, Hewson, Stevens, and Stark, were the studies of the gifted Roman Catholic abbé of Modena and Pavia, *Lazaro Spallanzani.*

Lazaro Spallanzani was born the son of a lawyer at Scandiano, a suburb of Modena, and educated at Reggio and at Bologna where he studied law. Under the influence of Vallisnieri he entered the church in order to pursue the study of natural science. In 1754 he was appointed professor of logic, metaphysics, and Greek literature in the University of Reggio, but in 1760 moved to Modena where he carried on investigations on the regeneration of the polyp Hydra and the physiology of the circulation. His work on the circulation so increased his reputation that he was offered the chair of natural history at Pavia. There he translated Charles Bonnet's *Contemplation de la nature* into Italian, and his interest in Bonnet's theory of generation led him to make the studies on infusoria published in his *Opuscules de physique* (1776).

In order to be able to explain to his students at Pavia the mechanism of digestion, Spallanzani studied the action of saliva on foodstuffs and verified Réaumur's conclusions on the digestive powers of gastric juice in animals, proving in addition that it prevented putrefaction. He also carried out a large number of daring experiments upon himself which are well illustrated by the following selection. Although Stevens is usually given credit for being the first to isolate human gastric juice for study, Spallanzani succeeded in doing it independently at about the same time.

OBSERVATIONS ON HUMAN DIGESTION

CCIII. To complete my researches on animals with membranous stomachs, it remained to examine that of Man. One may indeed draw very plausible inferences concerning human digestion, from observations on this numerous class; especially from birds of prey, the cat and dog, which resemble us so much in the structure of the stomach. But analogical arguments are probable indeed, but not conclusive. And it is an object of much higher importance to attain certainty in Man than in animals. In the writings of antient and modern physicians no topic is more frequently discussed, yet there is little else besides supposition: direct experiments made upon Man are entirely wanting, and their researches are illuminated only by the twilight of conjecture, and supported by precarious hypotheses. If therefore it was necessary on other occasions to have recourse to experiment, on the present it was absolutely indispensible. Upon reflection it appeared, that the principal experiments were reducible to two heads, viz. to procure human gastric fluid, in order to examine it in the manner that of animals has been examined; and to swallow tubes full of various vegetable and animal substances, in order to see what changes they undergo in the stomach. I will candidly own, that the latter kind gave me some apprehension. The histories of indigestible substances occasioning troublesome symptoms, and being vomited after a considerable time, occurred to my mind. I also recollected instances where such bodies had stopped in the alimentary canal. Other facts however where the result was contrary, and of more frequent occurrence, gave me confidence. Thus we every day see the stones of cherries, medlars, plums, &c. swallowed and voided with impunity. This consideration at last determined me to make a trial with as great caution as possible.

CCIV. I swallowed in the morning fasting a linen bag, containing fifty-two grains of masticated bread. All the following experiments were made under the like circumstances. I retained the purse twenty-three hours without experiencing the smallest inconvenience, and then voided it quite empty. The string used for sewing and tying it was entire, nor was there any rent in the bag itself. Hence it is plain, that it had not received any damage either in my stomach or intestines. The fortunate result of this experiment gave me great encouragement to undertake others. I immediately repeated it with two of the same bags, with this variation, that one was double, and the other had three folds. My motive obviously was to see, whether these additional folds would impede digestion. The bags were voided in twenty-seven hours, and the double one was empty; but the other still contained a small quantity that had yet the characters of bread. . . .

CCVI. Finding that I could digest dressed meat that had been masticated, I wished to know whether I was capable of digesting it without mastication. I swallowed eighty grains of the breast of a capon, enclosed in a bag. The bag was retained thirty-seven hours. So long a space had produced considerable effects, for it had lost fifty-six grains. The surface of the remainder was dry, but the internal fibres appeared to be more succulent. The piece seemed to have been digested equally, for it retained its original shape. . . . (Spallanzani, L. *Dissertazioni di fisica animale e vegetabile*, Vol. 1, "Della digestione degli animali." Modena, 1780. 275 pp. English translation [anonymous], *Dissertations relative to the natural history of animals and vegetables, translated from the Italian of the Abbé Spallanzani*. London, J. Murray, 1784, 2 vols. [Vol. 1, Introduction, pp. v-vi; 217-218, 219-220, paragraphs CCIII, CCIV, CCVI].)

William Cumberland Cruikshank

1745-1800

William Cumberland Cruikshank, the personal physician of Dr. Johnson, was born at Edinburgh and educated at the universities of Edinburgh and of Glasgow where he was graduated M.A. in 1767. He began the study of medicine at Glasgow under Moore but in 1771 went to London as William Hunter's assistant and pupil. He later became a partner with Hunter in the Windmill Street School and carried it on after the latter's death.

In conjunction with both John and William Hunter and their lamented collaborator, William Hewson, Cruikshank laid the foundation of modern knowledge concerning the function of the lymphatics. He was an exceptionally handsome man (Pl. 34b) who had a large practice as a physician, but he found time to cultivate scholarly tastes and to develop a literary style which received the commendation of Johnson. He had in addition an historical sense, unusual among English medical writers of the eighteenth century.

THE HUMAN LACTEALS

Though Asellius had not seen the lacteals in men, he inferred their existence from analogy, and firmly asserted it. But this doctrine was far from being generally received; and the doctrine of Hippocrates and Galen, which taught that the chyle was absorbed from the intestines by the red veins, more generally prevailed; and Asellius's vessels were considered by the greater number of anatomists as fictitious. Nor was this to be wondered at: they were not only influenced from respect to the ancients, but Harvey, the great discoverer of the circulation of the blood, then in his career of glory, opposed the doctrine, and never believed in the existence of Asellius's lacteals. . . .

Though, in compliance with anatomists in general, I have considered the Absorbent System as consisting of two parts, and have given the history of the discovery of each part; yet, in fact, lacteals and lymphatics are branches of one common trunk; and therefore Veslingius, Rudbeck, Bartholin, and Jolyffe, may be rather said to have seen the vessels first seen by Asellius, in other parts of the body than the intestines, mesentery, and liver. They did not properly discover a new set of vessels, but some more branches of the same system. On the other hand, Asellius had an idea that his vessels were formed only for the purpose of carrying the chyle into the blood; he had no conception of their existing any where else; so that, without the discovery of the lymphatics, we must have remained ignorant of the greatest part of the absorbent system; and therefore they are equally entitled to the honor bestowed on discoverers of so important a part of our machine.

Chapter VIII

FURTHER CONFIRMATION OF THE ABSORPTION OF FLUIDS BY THE LYMPHATIC VESSELS

That the lacteals absorb from the intestines, has been so fully proved, that there is not now an anatomist living, who has the smallest doubt concerning the fact. They have not only been seen absorbing the chyle, but they take up, very readily, coloured fluids thrown into the intestines. Every experiment Mr. Hunter made on the intestines of living animals, at the same time that it refuted absorption by red veins, in the strongest manner confirmed absorption by the lacteals. They quickly absorbed the milk, the solution of starch in water, coloured with indigo, the muskwater; in short, every fluid which was thrown into the cavity of the intestines. I have already mentioned the arguments which induced Dr. Hunter to advance the doctrine, that lacteals and lymphatics were the same spe-

cies of vessels, and that both absorbed. I come now to offer some
additional proofs of this. An accustomed eye finds very little difficulty in distinguishing lymphatics from every other species of
vessel, in men or quadrupeds; their valves, their general appearance,
their intercourse with conglobate glands, sufficiently mark them.
Now the lymphatics are not only branches of the same trunk, as
Dr. Hunter observed, but there is such a connection between them,
such an anastomosis, that the fluids absorbed by the lacteals are in
part transmitted to the lymphatics, and through them, at last, conveyed into the blood. A very remarkable instance of this kind I
demonstrated at lecture in Windmill Street, about two years ago.
The lymphatics of the diaphragm were seen turgid with chyle,
which they had received from the lacteals, some of which were passing that way, towards the subclavian veins. A stronger proof that
lymphatics are absorbents, is, that whenever fluids are extravasated
on surfaces, or into cavities, or whenever such fluids preternaturally
distend their reservoirs, the lymphatics belonging to these surfaces
and cavities are found full of the same fluid. This is better demonstrated, when the fluids mentioned happen to be of a strong colour.
Thus I have repeatedly seen, in animals dying of hæmoptoe, and
in the human subject itself, the lymphatics of the lungs, which at
other times contain a transparent fluid, turgid with blood, which
they had absorbed from the air-cells. Where gall-stones, in the ductus communis coledochus, or in the cystic duct, have prevented the
bile from flowing into the intestines, and the gall-bladder, in consequence of this, became preternaturally distended with that fluid,
I have also seen the lymphatics of that reservoir full of the bile they
had absorbed from its cavity. Baron Haller asserts, that he had repeatedly seen the lymphatics, as well as the lacteals, full of the
coloured fluid he had thrown into the living body. "In animale, cui
plena fuerunt aut chylo, aut lympha, aut cæruleo liquore, quem
animalia, absorbere coegi, sub ipsis intentis meis oculis, toties vidi
haec, sive lymphatica vascula, sive lactea evanesere." Malpighi suspected that the lymphatics persisted in absorbing, even for some
time after death; and I found this to be true in quadrupeds: on
making ligatures on the trunks of the principal blood vessels, no
lymphatics were then visible; but in an hour after I found them
turgid with lymph. Mascagni, Professor of Anatomy at Sienna, in
his Prodrome to his History of the Lymphatics, asserts, that fluids
thrown into cavities, get into the absorbents many hours, or even

days, after the body is dead. After what I have said of transudation in dead bodies, it may be doubted whether this penetration of fluid was absorption, or transudation only. (Cruikshank, W. C. *The anatomy of the absorbing vessels of the human body*. London, G. Nicol, 1786. viii, 192 pp., 3 pl. [pp. 33, 36, 41-42].)

John Richardson Young
1782-1804

John R. Young, pioneer physiologist and biochemist, was the son of an Irish physician, Samuel Young, who had graduated from Trinity College, Dublin, received his medical degree from Edinburgh, and after the Revolution had come to the Colonies where he settled in Hagerstown, Maryland. John Young was graduated from the College of New Jersey (Princeton) at the age of seventeen, was an apprentice to his father for three years, and then entered the University of Pennsylvania in 1802. There he came under the influence of Benjamin Smith Barton and Benjamin Rush and seven months later had completed all necessary courses and had prepared his thesis on digestion. Published in 1803 (when Young was twenty-one years old), it marked the most significant advance in gastric physiology prior to the work of Prout (1824) and William Beaumont (1825, 1833).

It is clear that this gifted student, who died a year later (possibly from tuberculosis contracted from his mother), was an objective and resourceful experimenter and thus a worthy predecessor of William Beaumont whose great monograph on gastric juice was to appear exactly thirty years later. John R. Young was also a clear and precise writer, as the following passage from his thesis indicates.

EXPERIMENTS ON DIGESTION

4thly. The basis of this doctrine [acetous fermentation] is the presence of an acid in the stomach: that this is the case we are fully convinced. But from what has already been said, it appeared to us, an acetous fermentation did not take place in the human stomach. We were therefore, lead at first to suppose, the acid was only present when this viscus was in a morbid state; but experiments proved to us the contrary: In all the different animals we examined, an acid was almost constantly found present. Hunter observes, "that in all the animals, whether carnivorous or not, which he examined, he always found an acid present in their stomachs, though not a strong one." It was before observed, that when small frogs, were digested in the stomachs of larger ones, the dissolved mass was always acid;

here "nature was interrupted in her regular operations," nothing morbid could therefore be said to be present.

The following experiments satisfied us to what this acid was to be referred. A piece of fresh veal was introduced into the empty stomach of one of the large frogs—In two hours it was examined— the surface was a little tender; upon being touched with litmus paper, it was turned red. Here digestion was progressing quite regular, yet an acid was present. It appeared impossible at the same time to conceive, the meat could become sour, in so very short a time, and in so very low a temperature; it was therefore conjectured, the acid was to be referred not to the meat, but to the gastric juice; which the following experiments confirmed us in. A frog was kept starving for two days: a piece of litmus paper was then forced into its empty stomach, by means of a pair of forceps; upon being drawn out, it was covered with gastric juice, and the litmus turned red. The naked gastric juice was afterwards, often examined, by bringing it out of their stomachs with a tea spoon, and constantly found to be slightly acid. Being thus fully persuaded the acid, in the digested food of frogs, did not arise from a fermentation, but was to be referred to their gastric juice, we were lead by analogy to suppose, the acid of our own stomachs was to be attributed to the same origin. But this analogical reasoning might be called mere probability: the following experiment was therefore performed. Early in the morning my stomach being empty, I irritated my fauces, with a view of throwing up some gastric juice: though many efforts were made, none could be vomited. The following day, I took some meat on an empty stomach: in half an hour afterwards, by irritating my fauces, the meat was thrown up, and with it some gastric fluid: Upon being tested, an acid was very evidently present. Here no one can suppose the acid was to be referred to the meat. We have little hesitation, therefore, in saying, that the acid so constantly found in the stomach of man, and almost (probably) all animals, is to be referred to their gastric fluid.

Having thus, we hope, traced the acid of the stomach to its proper origin, we next attempted to ascertain its nature by chemical tests. Mr. Mitchell being in good health, and having the power to ruminate, frequently threw up the contents of his stomach for me; which being filtered a transparent and acid fluid was obtained: on this fluid the following experiments were performed.

I. To a portion of this fluid, acetate of lead was added, a white

precipitation immediately took place: this being washed, muriatic
acid was added, which decomposed it, a very white powder remaining at the bottom, and a fluid above.

Comparative precipitations of urine and this fluid, by the above
agents, were in every respect the same. The explanation of urine
treated in this manner is, that the phosphoric acid of this fluid,
decomposes the acetate of lead, forming an insoluble phosphate of
lead; this being washed, by the addition of muriatic acid it is decomposed, Plumbum cornuum or a muriate of lead formed, while
the phosphoric acid remains in a liquid state above, which by dis-
oxygenation affords phosphorus.

Though great accuracy, and many varied experiments are required to ascertain certainly, the presence of an unknown acid, yet
we are disposed to believe any person who had witnessed the great
similarity in the comparative precipitations just mentioned, would
have pronounced the same explanation was to be applied to both,
or that the acid in the filtered fluid was the phosphoric. . . .

There is as yet one point remaining, which it is necessary for us
to notice.—The powerful action of the gastric fluid has been frequently mentioned in the preceding pages, as dissolving animal and
vegetable matter: If animal substances are so readily dissolved by it,
why does not this fluid also dissolve the stomach?

Hunter in the course of his dissections, frequently observed the
large curvature of the stomach to be dissolved, particularly in such
subjects as were carried off by sudden death: This dissolution he
ascribes to the agency of the gastric fluid, but in the living body he
supposed, the vital principle of the stomach effectually resisted its
action. This ingenious explanation has been objected to, the solution mentioned is said to arise from a putrefaction, that the same
takes place in the intestines, where no such solvent fluid is to be
found: Spallanzani though he appears to accede in great measure to
Hunter's idea, yet he observes; "Too much is attributed to this principle." He supposes whatever possesses life is capable of resisting the
action of the gastric fluid; his arguments by no means prove this.
The following considerations will render the general proposition
doubtful. Fish dissolve and digest living crabs, lobsters, &c. The
leech is concocted by the human stomach, though it has no pores,
and can sustain a temperature equal to that of man.

As the large frogs swollow animals alive, it was supposed they
would answer very well to investigate this principle. As it was ob-

served of the fish above, these large frogs without doubt swollowed living animals, and very soon digested them. But does the gastric fluid act upon them before death? The following experiment proved to us clearly it did not. . . .

Two threads were tied around the fore legs of a live, and common sized spring frog; its whole body, except the head and fore legs was introduced into the stomach of one of the large frogs: the fore legs of the lesser were made to clasp around the lower jaw of the larger frog, and firmly tied in this situation, each of the threads were then tied to the fore legs of the larger frog also: thus situated it was impossible the small frog could be entirely swallowed down, or thrown out of the stomach of the larger one. They were then put in a bason containing a little water, where they remained undisturbed for one day and a half. The small frog upon being drawn out was perfectly alive, and its whole body covered with gastric juice, and not the least dissolved in any part. The same frog was then killed, and again introduced into the stomach of the large one in the very same situation as just described. In five hours it was drawn out, when its whole surface was completely dissolved. Having this clear proof of the living principle, resisting the action of the gastric fluid, it was next proposed to try whether the action of this fluid would be resisted by a part in which the living principle was weakened—The great sciatic nerve of a living frog was therefore divided, and introduced into the stomach of a large one as above—it was drawn out in twelve hours, when it was still alive, and the paralized extremity was quite sound. (Young, J. R. *An experimental inquiry into the principles of nutrition, and the digestive process.* Philadelphia, Eaken & Mecum, 1803. 48 pp. [pp. 39-42, 46-48]. Reprinted with introduction by W. C. Rose by University of Illinois Press, Urbana, 1959. xxvi, 48 pp.)

William Prout

1785-1850

William Prout, the first English physiological chemist, was born at Horton, Gloucestershire, and educated at the University of Edinburgh where he was graduated M.D. in 1811. He then began to practise medicine at London and at the same time to carry on chemical investigations. In 1815 he showed that the urine of the boa constrictor contains 90 per cent uric acid and in 1818 isolated pure urea for the first time. Prout is well known to historians of pure chemistry for his extraordinary speculation that the atomic weights of all the elements are exact multiples of that of hydrogen or half that of hydrogen. Though he had not the facilities at that time to obtain the necessary evidence for his theory, it has perhaps stimulated more investigation during the nearly 150 years since it was put forward than any other generalization in the field of chemistry. As a physiologist Prout is scarcely less distinguished, and his discovery, made in 1823, that the stomach contains free hydrochloric acid will always remain one of the classics of physiological literature. It has the virtue of being brief, clear, and final.

ON THE NATURE OF THE ACID AND SALINE MATTERS USUALLY EXISTING IN THE STOMACHS OF ANIMALS

That a free, or at least an unsaturated acid usually exists in the stomachs of animals, and is in some manner connected with the important process of digestion, seems to have been the general opinion of physiologists till the time of SPALLANZANI. This illustrious philosopher concluded, from his numerous experiments, that the gastric fluids, when in a perfectly natural state, are neither acid nor alkaline. Even SPALLANZANI, however, admitted that the contents of the stomach are very generally acid; and this accords not only with my own observations, but with that, I believe, of almost every individual who has made any experiments on the subject. . . .

The contents of the stomach of a rabbit, fed on its natural food, were removed immediately after death, and repeatedly digested in cold distilled water till they ceased to impart anything to that fluid. The whole of these different portions of fluid, which always exhibited strong and decided marks of acidity, were then intimately mixed together, and after being allowed to settle, were divided into four equal portions. 1. The first of these portions was evaporated to dryness in its natural state, and the residuum burnt in a platinum vessel; the saline matter left was then dissolved in distilled water, and the quantity of muriatic acid present determined by nitrate of silver in the usual manner; the proportion of muriatic acid, in union with the *fixed* alkali, was thus determined. 2. Another portion of the original fluid was super-saturated with potash, then evaporated to dryness, and burnt, and the muriatic acid contained in the saline residuum determined as before. In this manner the total quantity of muriatic acid present in the fluid was ascertained. 3. A third portion was exactly neutralised with a solution of potash of known strength, and the quantity required for that purpose accurately noticed. This gave the proportion of *free* acid present; and by adding this to the quantity in union with a fixed alkali, as determined above, and subtracting the sum from the total quantity of muriatic acid present, the proportion of acid in union with ammonia, was estimated. But as a check to this result, the third neutralised portion above mentioned was evaporated to dryness, and the muriate of ammonia expelled by heat, and collected. The quantity of muriatic acid this contained was then determined as before, and was always found to represent nearly the quantity of muriate of ammonia as before estimated; thus proving the general accuracy of the whole experiments beyond a doubt. 4. The remaining fourth portion of the original fluid was reserved for miscellaneous experiments, and particularly for the purpose of ascertaining whether it contained any other acid besides the muriatic. The experiments abovementioned seemed to preclude the possibility of the presence of any destructible acid; and the only known fixed acids likely to be present were the sulphuric and phosphoric; the muriate of barytes, however, neither alone, nor with the addition of ammonia, produced any immediate precipitate,* showing the absence of these two acids in any sensible quantity, and still farther confirming the results as before obtained. (Prout, William. "On the nature of the acid and saline matters usually existing in the stomachs of animals." *Phil. Trans.*, 1824, *114*, 45-49 [pp. 45-48].)

William Beaumont

1785-1853

While stationed at Mackinac Island in northern Michigan, *William Beaumont,* a United States Army physician (Pl. 35), grasped the unique opportunity to study the processes of digestion offered by the permanent gastric fistula created by a gunshot wound in a young French Canadian voyageur, Alexis St. Martin. That he should have seized and used this opportunity so well is some measure of this remarkable man.

Beaumont was born at Lebanon, Connecticut. At twenty-one he left home to go to Champlain, New York, where he taught school and studied medicine for three years. In 1810 he became an apprentice to Dr. Benjamin Chandler of

---

* It may be proper to remark, that ammonia, after some time, caused a flocculent precipitate, consisting of the earthy phosphates in union with vegetable and animal matter, and that after combustion, traces of sulphuric acid, the result of that process, were very perceptible. But it is evident, from the experiment related in the text, that neither of these acids previously existed in the original fluid in a free state.

St. Albans, Vermont, and two years later was licensed to practise by the Third Medical Society of Vermont. After serving as an Army physician during the War of 1812, he entered private practice at Plattsburgh, New York, but rejoined the Army in 1820 and was sent to Fort Mackinac. On 6 June 1822 he was called upon to dress the apparently mortal wound of Alexis St. Martin.

Contrary to Beaumont's expectations, St. Martin recovered, but his wound when healed left a permanent opening into the stomach which Beaumont attempted to close by repeated dressings over the next two years. Failing to do so, he decided to make physiological studies and began his first series of experiments in May 1825. A preliminary account of his observations was published in the Philadelphia *Medical Recorder* (1825, *8*, 4), but was mistakenly attributed to Surgeon-General Joseph Lovell who had submitted the manuscript on behalf of Beaumont. A full account of his work was published in a separate volume in 1833.

By a series of ingenious arguments he concluded that, in addition to free hydrochloric acid, which Prout had previously observed, there was also present in the gastric juice another active chemical substance, to which Schwann in 1835 gave the name of pepsin. Beaumont's observations illustrate the enormous contribution which may come from painstaking clinical observation, and those who read his little book must inevitably feel the inspiration of his great example.

PREFACE

The present age is prolific of works on physiology; therefore in offering to the public another book relative to an important branch of this science, it will perhaps be necessary to assign my motives.

They are, first, a wish to comply with the repeated and urgent solicitations of many medical men who have become partially acquainted with the facts and observations it is my intention to detail; men, in whose judgment I place confidence, and who have expressed their conviction of the deep importance of the experiments, the result of which I mean herewith to submit to the public: secondly, (and it is that which mainly influences me,) my own firm conviction that medical science will be forwarded by the publication. . . .

The experiments which follow were commenced in 1825, and have been continued, with various interruptions, to the present time (1833). The opportunity for making them was afforded to me in the following way.

Whilst stationed at Michillimackinac, Michigan Territory, in 1822, in the military service of the United States, the following case of surgery came under my care and treatment.

Alexis St. Martin, who is the subject of these experiments, was a Canadian, of French descent, at the above mentioned time about eighteen years of age, of good constitution, robust and healthy. He had been engaged in the service of the American Fur Company, as a voyageur, and was accidentally wounded by the discharge of a musket, on the 6th of June, 1822. . . . The whole mass of materials forced from the musket, together with fragments of clothing and pieces of fractured ribs, were driven into the muscles and cavity of the chest.

I saw him in twenty-five or thirty minutes after the accident occurred, and, on examination, found a portion of the lung, as large as a Turkey's egg, protruding through the external wound, lacerated and burnt; and immediately below this, another protrusion, which, on further examination, proved to be a portion of the stomach, lacerated through all its coats, and pouring out the food he had taken for his breakfast, through an orifice large enough to admit the fore finger.

[He then tells the details of his stormy convalescence and gradual recovery with the formation of a gastric fistula through which all his food passed when his side was not tightly bandaged.]

EXPERIMENT I

August 1, 1825. At 12 o'clock M., I introduced through the perforation, into the stomach, the following articles of diet, suspended by a silk string, and fastened at proper distances, so as to pass in without pain—viz.:—a piece of high seasoned *a la mode beef;* a piece of *raw, salted, fat pork;* a piece of *raw, salted, lean beef;* a piece of *boiled, salted beef;* a piece of *stale bread;* and a bunch of *raw, sliced cabbage;* each piece weighing about two drachms; the lad continuing his usual employment about the house.

At 1 o'clock P.M., withdrew and examined them—found the *cabbage* and bread about half digested: the pieces of *meat* unchanged. Returned them into the stomach.

At 2 o'clock P.M., withdrew them—found the *cabbage, bread, pork,* and *boiled beef,* all cleanly digested and gone from the string; the other pieces of meat but very little affected. Returned them into the stomach again.

At 2 o'clock P.M., examined again—found the *a la mode beef* partly digested: the *raw beef* was slightly macerated on the surface, but its general texture was firm and entire. The smell and taste of the fluids of the stomach were slightly rancid; and the boy complained of some pain and uneasiness at the breast. Returned them again.

The lad complaining of considerable distress and uneasiness at the stomach, general debility and lassitude, with some pain in his head,

I withdrew the string, and found the remaining portions of aliment nearly in the same condition as when last examined; the fluid more rancid and sharp. The boy still complaining, I did not return them any more.

August 2. The distress at the stomach and pain in the head continuing, accompanied with costiveness, a depressed pulse, dry skin, coated tongue, and numerous white spots, or pustules, resembling coagulated lymph, spread over the inner surface of the stomach, I thought it advisable to give medicine; and, accordingly, dropped into the stomach, through the aperture, half a dozen *calomel pills,* four or five grains each; which, in about three hours, had a thorough cathartic effect, and removed all the foregoing symptoms, and the diseased appearance of the inner coat of the stomach. The effect of the medicine was the same as when administered in the usual way, by the mouth and oesophagus, except the nausea commonly occasioned by swallowing pills.

This experiment cannot be considered a fair test of the powers of the gastric juice. The cabbage, one of the articles which was, in this instance, most speedily dissolved, was cut into small, fibrous pieces, very thin, and necessarily exposed, on all its surfaces, to the action of the gastric juice. The stale bread was porous, and, of course, admitted the juice into all its interstices; and probably fell from the string as soon as softened, and before it was completely dissolved. These circumstances will account for the more rapid disappearance of these substances, than of the pieces of meat, which were in entire solid pieces when put in. To account for the disappearance of the fat pork, it is only necessary to remark, that the fat of meat is always resolved into oil, by the warmth of the stomach, before it is digested. I have generally observed that when he has fed on fat meat or butter, the whole superior portion of the contents of the stomach, if examined a short time after eating, will be found covered with an oily pellicle. This fact may account for the disappearance of the pork from the string. I think, upon the whole, and subsequent experiments have confirmed the opinion, that fat meats are less easily digested than lean, when both have received the same advantages of comminution. Generally speaking, the looser the texture, and the more tender the fibre, of animal food, the easier it is of digestion.

This experiment is important, in a pathological point of view. It confirms the opinion, that undigested portions of food in the stomach produce all the phenomena of fever; and is calculated to warn us of the danger of all excesses, where that organ is concerned. It also admonishes us of the necessity of a perfect comminution of the articles of diet. (Beaumont, William, *Experiments and observations on the gastric juice and the physiology of digestion.* Plattsburgh, N.Y., F. G. Allen, 1833. 280 pp. [pp. 5, 9-10, 125-127].)[7]

Theodor Schwann
1810-1882

The name of *Theodor Schwann,* zoologist, looms large in the history of biological thought—indeed it is virtually enshrined with that of his co-worker, Matthias Jakob Schleiden (1804-1881), botanist, for their promulgation of the "cell theory" which led to the close study of the finer structure of cells of animals and plants, their protoplasm, nucleus, nucleolus, and the structural changes which occur during their division (karyokinesis), and the identification of individual "genes" as the ultimate unit transmitting hereditary characters. The studies and deductions of Schleiden and Schwann also led to the great neurophysiological concept of the "neurone theory."

Although the part played by Schwann in developing the cell theory is well known, his many other important contributions are seldom mentioned. These include the medullated nerve fibers, "sheath of Schwann," the "yeast cell theory" of putrefaction (1837), and his several important papers on the digestive process, one written in 1836 with his mentor Johannes Müller (1801-1858) on digestion of egg white, and his still more important independent discovery of the enzyme "pepsin" in the gastric juice. In connection with this, Schwann reëstablished the fact first stated by Prout and later by Beaumont that the free acid in the stomach is hydrochloric, not lactic as some had maintained (1836), and in 1844 he likewise established that bile from the liver and gall bladder is indispensible to digestion.

THE DISCOVERY OF PEPSIN

The questions on the nature of the digestive process resolve themselves into two: What are the materials acting in digestion? and, How do they work?

In answering the first question the free acid must next be taken into account. In all experiments performed hitherto free acid was present in artificial as well as natural digestion. It follows there-

[7] A facsimile reproduction with Sir William Osler's essay on Beaumont was published in 1929 by the Harvard University Press. A paperbound edition (1959) of the original is now available from Dover Books, New York City.

from, although not directly, that its action is essential and necessary in digestion. The acid could serve for the formation of another essential digestive substance which, once formed, carries on digestion independently. In order to test this idea I neutralized gastric juice with potassium carbonate and then digested it with protein. The protein, however, was not digested at all nor altered in any way. If I again merely added muriatic acid in suitable quantity, then the protein was completely digested. Free acid is therefore essential in digestive action.

The acid is, however, not the only active element. Müller, Eberle, Beaumont as well as myself have carried out experiments to try to digest substances simply with dilute acid without any result. . . .

From these experiments the protein-digesting principle accordingly may be characterized in the following way. It is soluble in water and in dilute muriatic acid and acetic acid. It is destroyed by alcohol but it is not known whether it is insoluble in the latter or not. It is likewise altered by boiling heat, but it is uncertain whether it was thereby precipitated or not. Acetate of lead precipitated it even from acid and even more from neutral solution. It was precipitated from neutral solution also by corrosive sublimate [mercuric chloride]. Gall apple infusion probably destroyed its digestive power, while tannin formed an insoluble precipitate with it. . . .

The fibrous material and muscle were thus digested in the same way as the coagulated egg albumen, namely, by free acid in combination with another substance active in very small amounts. Since the latter really carries on the digestion of the most important animal nutrient materials, one might with justice apply to it the name *pepsin*. This substance also acts initially on uncoagulated curd, milk and so forth, so that it coagulates it in the course of digestion. Its action therefore extends over animal materials related to egg white. The dissolving and transformation of the above nutrient materials, gelatine, starch, gluten does not appear to result from the albumen-digesting principle. For when these substances were digested with dilute acid and dilute gastric juice, no change was noted. Even in concentrated muriatic and acetic acid, digestive fluids, as in the artificial gastric juice prepared according to Eberle's method, no significant alteration was noticeable. (Schwann, Theodor. "Ueber das Wesen des Verdauungsprocesses." *Arch. Anat. Physiol. wiss. Med.*, 1836, 90-138 [pp. 93-94, 121, 136. Translated by L.G.W.].)

Ivan Petrovitch Pavlov
1849-1936

Ivan Petrovitch Pavlov, the great Russian physiologist and the creator of two new and particularly fruitful fields of physiological thought, was born at Ryazan, Russia, and educated at the University of St. Petersburg where he was graduated in 1875 (Pl. 36). On completing his work for a scientific degree he entered the Military-Medical Academy and received his medical qualifications in 1879 and his M.D. in 1883. From 1884 to 1886 he studied in Germany under Ludwig and Heidenhain. In 1895 he was appointed professor of physiology at the Military-Medical Academy where he continued to work until the end of his life.

Pavlov first became interested in the physiology of digestion when he visited Heidenhain's laboratory at Breslau in the summer of 1877. Heidenhain had made artificial fistulae in the dog, but in performing the operation, the nerve supply of the stomach had been largely impaired. After many trials, Pavlov in 1889, by virtue of his ambidexterity and extraordinary operative skill, succeeded in making a miniature stomach as a special pouch attached to the main stomach, both retaining their nerve supply. The miniature stomach opened to the outside of the body and when food was received into the main stomach, the small pouch secreted gastric juice of the same quality as that secreted to deal with the food. By this means he succeeded for the first time in obtaining samples of gastric juice uncontaminated with food.

In the animal with gastric fistula Pavlov observed that after it saw or smelled food, an abundant flow of gastric juice occurred. This flow he termed "psychic secretion" and showed that it depended upon reactions integrated at the level of the cerebral cortex since removal of the cortex abolished the response. For this work Pavlov received the Nobel Prize in 1904. It also marked the beginning of his interest in higher nervous function which ultimately led to the enunciation of the concept of the conditioned reflex.

THE NERVOUS CONTROL OF GASTRIC SECRETION

The question as to whether the gastric glands have likewise a special secretory innervation is now a very old one and has had an interesting career. In this matter physiology stood for a long time in sharp conflict with practical medicine. Physicians bringing forward their observations in proof, had long answered the question in the affirmative, and looked upon the existence of secretory nerves to the stomach as undoubted. They had even come to recognise different morbid conditions of the innervation apparatus. Physiologists, on the other hand, had fruitlessly endeavoured for decades to arrive at definite results upon this question. . . .

As a matter of fact, I am now able to demonstrate experiments to you which yield absolutely constant and unequivocal results. We have here before us a dog operated upon in the manner I have described in the first lecture. It possesses an ordinary gastric fistula with metallic cannula, and has had its oesophagus divided as well, so that the mouth is cut off from all communication with the cavity of the stomach. Its stomach has been washed out before the beginning of the lecture, and, as you see now, not a single drop of fluid escapes from the fistula. I give the dog food. The animal eats greedily, but the whole of the food swallowed, comes out again at the oesophageal opening in the neck. After feeding in this way (which for shortness we will henceforth name "sham feeding") for five minutes, perfectly pure gastric juice makes its appearance at the fistula, the stream steadily becomes greater and greater, and now, five minutes after the commencement of secretion, we have already 20 c.c. of juice. We may continue to feed the dog as long as we wish, the secretion will flow at the same rate for one, two, or more hours. We have even had dogs so greedy that they did not tire of eating in this fashion for five or six hours, secreting during the time a total quantity of up to 700 c.c. of the purest gastric juice. The meaning of this experiment is clear. It is obvious that the effect of the feeding is transmitted by nervous channels to the gastric glands. (Pavlov, J.P. *The work of the digestive glands.* W.H. Thompson, Translator. London, Charles Griffin and Co., 1902. xii, 196 pp. [pp. 46, 50].)

Walter Bradford Cannon
1871-1945

Walter Bradford Cannon, the successor of Henry Pickering Bowditch as professor of physiology at the Harvard Medical School, was born at Prairie du Chien, Wisconsin, and was educated at Harvard University where he received an A.B. in 1896 and an M.D. in 1900. He then became instructor in physiology under Bowditch and in 1906 succeeded him as professor, a post which he held throughout his life (Pl. 37). He thus remained active in both teaching and research over an unusually long span of years and in both activities his influence has extended far.

While he was yet a medical student, Cannon realized from watching the shadow of a metal ball passing down the oesophagus of a goose revealed on a fluorescent screen by x-rays that x-rays might be used for the study of gastrointestinal movements. He found that bismuth salts, which are opaque to x-rays, served admirably to bring out the contour of the stomach and intestines during activity and in so doing he introduced a clinical method of diagnosis which since 1898 has been widely used in every hospital in the world (and also a method for study of normal intestinal movements in the intact animal). The diagnosis of gastric ulcer and malignancy of any part of the gastro-intestinal tract by means of the bismuth or barium meal and fluoroscope is now an every-day occurrence and it is often forgotten that the original contribution came from the physiological laboratory. The following passage is taken from Cannon's description of his first experiments.

THE MOVEMENTS OF THE STOMACH STUDIED BY MEANS OF THE RÖNTGEN RAYS

Since the stomach gives no obvious external sign of its workings, investigators of gastric movements have hitherto been obliged to confine their studies to pathological subjects or to animals subjected to serious operative interference. Observations made under these necessarily abnormal conditions have yielded a literature* which is full of conflicting statements and uncertain results. The only sure conclusion to be drawn from this material is that when the stomach receives food, obscure peristaltic contractions are set going, which in some way churn the food to a liquid chyme and force it into the intestines. How imperfectly this describes the real workings of the stomach will appear from the following account of the actions of the organ studied by a new method. The mixing of a small quantity of subnitrate of bismuth with the food allows not only the contractions of the gastric wall, but also the movements of the gastric contents to be seen with the Röntgen rays in the uninjured animal during normal digestion. An unsuspected nicety of mechanical action and a surprising sensitiveness to nervous conditions have thereby been disclosed. . . .

Within five minutes after a cat has finished a meal of bread, there is visible near the duodenal end of the antrum a slight annular con-traction which moves peristaltically to the pylorus: this is followed by several waves recurring at regular intervals. Two or three minutes after the first movement is seen, very slight constrictions appear near the middle of the stomach, and, pressing deeper into the greater curvature, course slowly towards the pyloric end. As new regions enter into constriction, the fibres just previously contracted become

* Poensgen (Die motorische Verrichtungen des menschlichen Magens und ihre Störungen, Strassburg, 1882), gives a comprehensive review of the literature to that date.

relaxed, so that there is a true moving wave, with a trough between two crests. When a wave swings round the bend in the pyloric part the indentation made by it deepens; and as digestion goes on, the antrum elongates and the constrictions running over it grow stronger, but, until the stomach is nearly empty, they do not entirely divide the cavity. After the antrum has lengthened, a wave takes about thirty-six seconds to move from the middle of the stomach to the pylorus. At all periods of digestion the waves recur at intervals of almost exactly ten seconds. So regular is this rhythm that many times I have been able to determine within two or three seconds when a minute had elapsed simply by counting six similar phases of the undulations as they passed a given point. It results from this rhythm that when one wave is just beginning, several others are already running in order before it. Between the rings of constriction the stomach is bulged out, as shown in the various outlines in Figures 3, 4, and 5 [Fig. 7]. The number of waves during a single period of digestion is larger than might possibly at first be supposed. In a cat that finished eating fifteen grams of bread at 10.52 A.M., the waves were running regularly at 11:00 o'clock. The stomach was not free from food until 6.12 P.M. During that time the cat was fastened to the holder at intervals of half an hour and the waves were always observed, following one another in slow and monotonous succession. At the rate of three hundred and sixty an hour, approximately two thousand six hundred waves passed over the antrum during that single digestive period. . . .

The part played by the fundus apparently has not hitherto been properly appreciated. It has been regarded as the place for peptic digestion or as a passive reservoir for food; but it is in fact a most interestingly active reservoir.

The action of the cardiac portion will be best understood by comparing the appearances the stomach presents at various stages in a digestive period. In order to show these stages I carefully made a set of three tracings of the outlines of the stomach as soon as possible after a cat had finished eating, and another set of three every half hour thereafter, until the contents had disappeared (Figs. 3, 4, and 5 [Fig. 7]). These tracings were made by placing white tissue paper over the fluorescent screen, and drawing with a thick lead pencil, easily seen, as much of the boundary of the stomach as I could at the end of each expiration. Between the times for making the drawings the cat was allowed to rest quietly on a mat, but care was taken to lay her in the

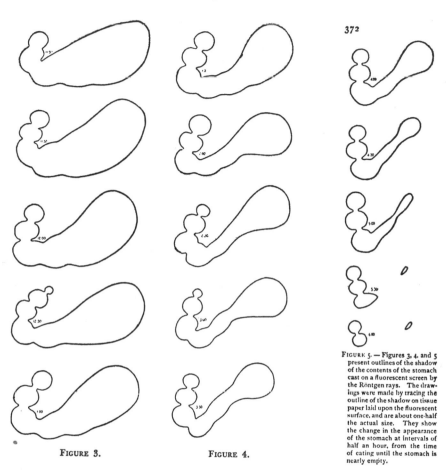

372

FIGURE 5. — Figures 3, 4. and 5 present outlines of the shadow of the contents of the stomach cast on a fluorescent screen by the Röntgen rays. The drawings were made by tracing the outline of the shadow on tissue paper laid upon the fluorescent surface, and are about one-half the actual size. They show the change in the appearance of the stomach at intervals of half an hour, from the time of eating until the stomach is nearly empty.

FIGURE 3.   FIGURE 4.

Figure 7. Cannon's original tracings of the outlines of a cat's stomach at successive intervals following a bismuth meal.

same position on the holder for each drawing. The drawings of each set were afterwards fastened over one another, so that the lines coincided as closely as possible. Another piece of tissue paper was then put over these, and all four sheets were laid on an illuminated pane of glass. It was thus easy to get a composite tracing, which, considering the movement imparted to the stomach by respiration, and the dimness of the shadows in the later stages of digestion, probably represents more exactly than any single drawing the outline of the stomach for each successive period.

A comparison of these drawings shows that as digestion proceeds the antrum appears gradually to elongate and acquire a greater capacity, and that the constrictions make deeper indentations in it. But when the fundus has lost most of its contents, the longitudinal and circular fibres of the antrum contract to make it again shorter and smaller. Its change of form, however, compared with the rest of the stomach, is slight.

The first region to decrease markedly in size is the preantral part of the pyloric portion. The peristaltic undulations, caused by the circular fibres, start at the beginning of this portion, and gradually, by their rhythmic recurrence, press some of the contents into the antrum. As the process continues, the smooth muscle fibres with their remarkable tonicity contract closely about the food that remains, so that the middle region comes to have the shape of a tube (Fig. 4—1.30 P.M. to 2.30 P.M. [Fig. 7]), with the rounded fundus at one end and the active antrum at the other. Along the tube very shallow constrictions may be seen following one another to the pylorus.

At this juncture the longitudinal fibres which cover the fundus like radiating fingers, and the circular and oblique fibres reaching in all directions about this spherical region, begin to contract. Thus the contents of the fundus are squeezed into the tubular portion. This process, accompanied by a slight shortening of the tube, goes on until the shadow cast by the fundus is almost wholly obliterated (Fig. 5—5.30 P.M. [Fig. 7]).

The waves of constriction moving along the tubular portion press the food onward as fast as they receive it from the contracting fundus; and when the fundus is at last emptied they sweep the contents of the tube into the antrum (Fig. 5—5.00 P.M. to 6.00 P.M. [Fig. 7]). Here the operation is continued by the deeper constrictions till finally (in this instance, at 6.12 P.M.) with the exception of a slight trace of food in the fundus, nothing is to be seen in the stomach at all. (Cannon, W. B. "The movements of the stomach studied by means of the Roentgen rays." *Amer. J. Physiol.*, 1898, *1*, 359-382 [pp. 359-360, 367, 370-372].)

William Maddock Bayliss
1860-1924
and
Ernest Henry Starling
1866-1927

Sir William Maddock Bayliss and *Ernest Starling,* both professors at University College, London, greatly enriched modern physiology through their prolonged and fruitful collaboration.

William Bayliss was born at Wolverhampton, England, the son of an iron manufacturer, and educated at University College (B.Sc. 1882) and at Wadham College, Oxford (D.Sc. 1888), where he went to study physiology with John Scott Burdon-Sanderson. He then returned to Schäfer's laboratory at University College where early in 1890 E. H. Starling (whose biography is given in Chapter XI) joined forces with them. Together they investigated the electrical phenomena accompanying the heart beat, the arrangement of the vasomotor fibers in the sympathetic nervous system, and the innervation of the intestine among other problems.

In 1912 Bayliss was appointed professor of general physiology at University College (Pl. 38) and in 1914 published his *Principles of General Physiology,* a great pioneering work, prophetic of a new direction and new lines of investigation in physiology. He was awarded the Copley Medal of the Royal Society in 1919, the first physiologist to receive it since the Reverend Stephen Hales in 1739; he was knighted in 1922.

The discovery by Bayliss and Starling in 1902 of secretin was peculiarly dramatic, and the simplicity and directness of their original description has an appeal felt even by the uninitiated.

IV. THE CRUCIAL EXPERIMENT

On January 16th, 1902, a bitch of about 6 kilos weight, which had been fed about 18 hours previously, was given a hypodermic injection of morphia some 3 hours before the experiment, and during the experiment itself received A.C.E. in addition. The nervous masses around the superior mesenteric artery and coeliac axis were completely removed and both vagi cut. A loop of jejunum was tied at both ends and the mesenteric nerves supplying it were carefully dissected out and divided, so that the piece of intestine was connected to the body of the animal merely by its arteries and veins. A cannula was inserted in the large pancreatic duct and the drops of

PLATE 28. The Bassanus engraving of Aselli at the age of 42 which is to be found in a few copies of *De lactibus,* 1627.

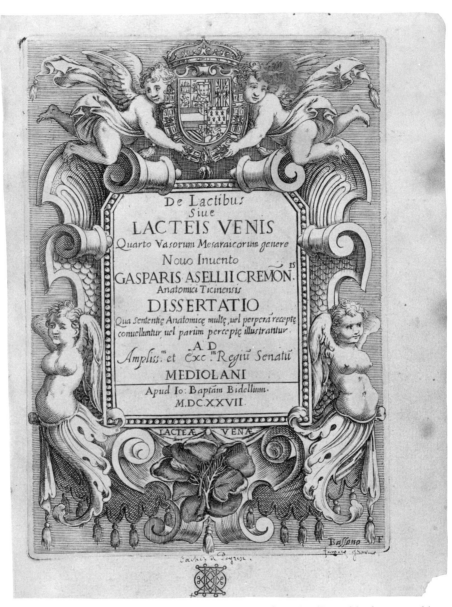

De Lactibus
Siue
LACTEIS VENIS
Quarto Vasorum Mesaraicorum genere
Nouo Inuento
GASPARIS ASELLII CREMON.
Anatomici Ticinensis
DISSERTATIO
Qua Sententię Anatomice multę, uel perperā receptę
conuelluntur, uel parum perceptę illustrantur.
A D
Ampliss.me et Exc.mo Regiū Senatū
MEDIOLANI
Apud Io: Baptam Bidellium.
M.DC.XXVII.

PLATE 29. The handsomely engraved title-page of *De lactibus* with the ownership
mark of Nicholas Fabry de Peiresc, famous contemporary patron of science.

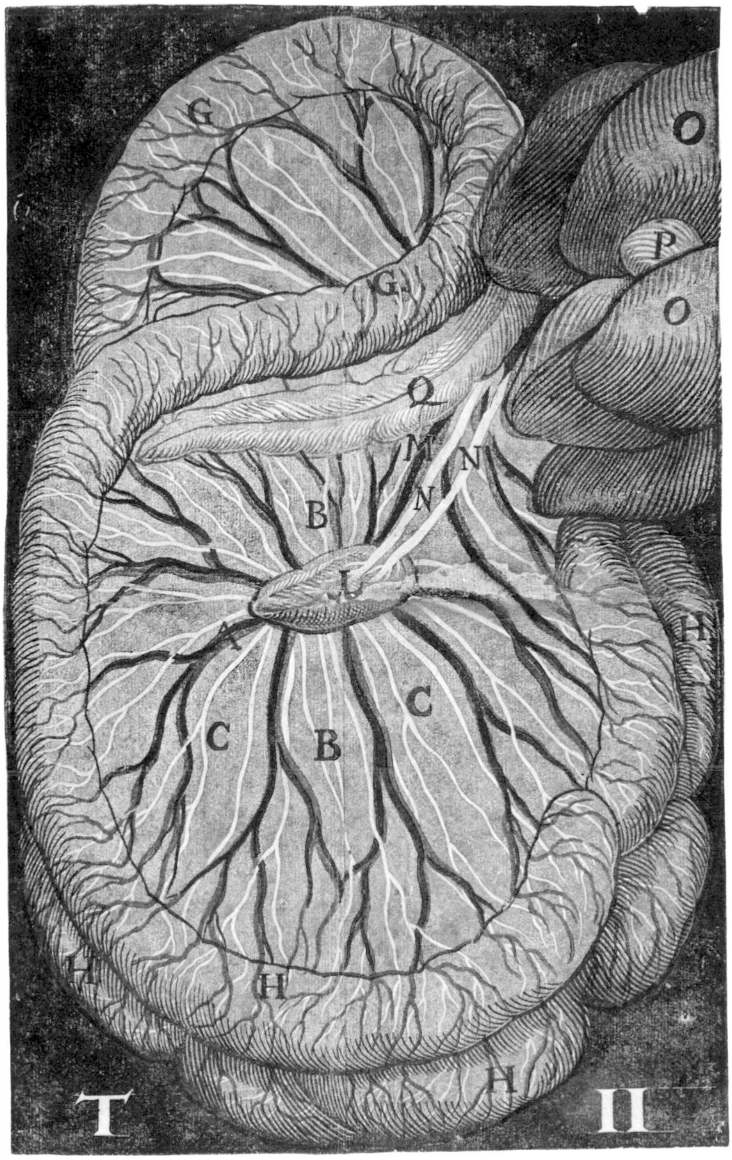

PLATE 30. The second of four large folding plates printed in four
colors showing the distribution of the lacteals in the mesentery.

REGNERUS de GRAAF
Medicinæ Doctor
A°. Ætatis suæ 25.
1666.

H. watch pin.   *a Paris*   *G. Edelinck fecit.*

PLATE 31. De Graaf at 25. (From the first edition of his *De virorum organis generationi*, 1668.)

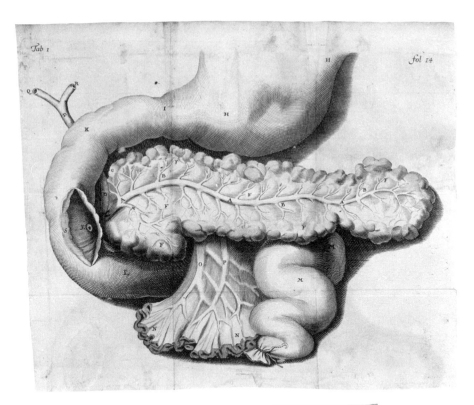

PLATE 32. Two engravings from de Graaf's *De succo pancreatico*, 1671: a. The pancreas and the opening of the pancreatic duct; b. De Graaf's illustration of the ingenious operative techniques which he used to collect pancreatic juice and parotid saliva by inserting catheters directly into the ducts of these glands. Since the dog had to be kept muzzled he also had to perform a tracheotomy upon it.

J. V. Riemsdyk del.

PLATE 33. The plate, drawn by Riemsdyk, which accompanied Hewson's "Account of the lymphatic system in birds" communicated to the Royal Society by William Hunter on 8 December 1768.

PLATE 34A. William Hewson (1739-1774). (From *The works*, London, 1846.)

PLATE 34B. Dickinson's engraving of William Cruikshank.

PLATE 35. William Beaumont at the age of 66. (From an old daguerreotype.)

PLATE 36. Pavlov at the age of 27 when working in Ludwig's laboratory. (Found by Dr. Daniel P. O'Brien at Leipzig in 1936.)

PLATE 37. Walter B. Cannon at Franklin, N. H., in 1923 with two of the Yerkes chimpanzees, Chim and Panzee.

PLATE 38. Sir William Maddock Bayliss (1860-1924). (Reproduced through the kindness of L. E. Bayliss.)

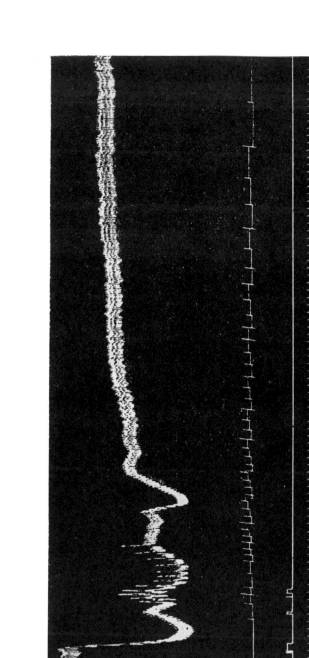

Fig. 2. *Effect of injecting acid extract of jejunal mucous membrane into vein.* Explanation as Fig. 1. The steps on the drop-tracing are due to a gradual accumulation of secretion on the lever of the drop-recorder, which fluid falls off at intervals. Blood-pressure zero=level of drop recorder.

PLATE 39. Bayliss and Starling's original figure showing the effect on pancreatic secretion and blood-pressure of the intravenous injection of an acid extract of jejunal mucous membrane (*J. Physiol.*, 1902, 28, 331.)

secretion recorded. The blood-pressure in the carotid was also recorded in the usual way. The animal was in the warm saline bath and under artificial respiration.

The introduction of 20 c.c. of 0.4% HCl into the duodenum produced a well-marked secretion of 1 drop every 20 secs. lasting for some 6 minutes; this result merely confirms previous work.

But, and this is the important point of the experiment, and the turning-point of the whole research, the introduction of 10 c.c. of the same acid into the enervated loop of jejunum produced a similar and equally well-marked effect.

Now, since this part of the intestine was completely cut off from nervous connection with the pancreas, the conclusion was inevitable that the effect was produced by some chemical substance finding its way into the veins of the loop of jejunum in question and being carried in the blood-stream to the pancreatic cells. Wertheimer and Lepage have shown,* however, that acid introduced into the circulation has no effect on the pancreatic secretion, so that the body of which we were in search could not be the acid itself. But there is, between the lumen of the gut and the absorbent vessels, a layer of epithelium, whose cells are as we know endowed with numerous important functions. It seemed therefore possible that the action of acid on these cells would produce a body capable of exciting the pancreas to activity. The next step in our experiment was plain, viz. to cut out the loop of jejunum, scrape off the mucous membrane, rub it up with sand and 0.4% HCl in a mortar, filter through cotton-wool to get rid of lumps and sand, and inject the extract into a vein. The result is shown in Fig. 2 [see Pl. 39.]. The first effect is a considerable fall of blood-pressure, due, as we shall show later, to a body distinct from that acting on the pancreas, and, after a latent period of about 70 secs. a flow of pancreatic juice at more than twice the rate produced at the beginning of the experiment by introduction of acid into the duodenum. We have already suggested the name "secretin" for this body, and as it has been accepted and made use of by subsequent workers it is as well to adhere to it.

In the same experiment we were able to make two further steps in the elucidation of the subject. In the first place the acid extract was boiled and found undiminished in activity, secretin is therefore not of the nature of an enzyme. In the second place, since Wertheimer and Lepage have shown that the effect of acid in the small intestine

* *Journal de Physiologie*, III, p. 695, 1901.

diminishes in proportion as the place where it is introduced approaches the lower end, so that from the last 6 inches or so of the ileum no secretion of the pancreas is excited, it was of interest to see whether the distribution of the substance from which secretin is split by acids is similar in extent. Fig. 3 shows the result of injecting an extract from the lower 6 inches of the ileum made in the same way as the jejunum extract. The fall of blood-pressure is present, but there is no effect on the pancreas. Another preparation from the ileum just above this one also had no effect on the pancreas. A preparation from the jejunum below the previous one had a marked effect, but less than that of the loop above. The distribution of "prosecretin," as we have proposed to call the mother-substance, corresponds therefore precisely with the region from which acid introduced into the lumen excites secretion from the pancreas. (Bayliss, W. M. and Starling, E. H. "The mechanism of pancreatic secretion." *J. Physiol.* [*Lond.*], 1902, *28,* 325-353 [pp. 330-332].)

VI

Muscle
and Peripheral Nerves

The contractile activity of muscles was a phenomenon which greatly interested the ancient Greeks and was studied by them in detail. Aristotle does not appear to have distinguished individual muscles as functional units. Instead he considered muscular tissue in the aggregate simply as flesh and seems to have thought that it served the purpose merely of giving form to the body. The relation between muscle and nerve could not of course be understood before the individual muscles were distinguished as anatomical units nor before the nerves were recognized as the peripheral branches of a *system* arising from the spinal cord and brain. The first recognition that the nerves form a connected system extending throughout the body came with the work of Herophilus and Erasistratus at Alexandria around the beginning of the third century B.C. It was therefore natural that the first person to develop a theory of muscle contraction should be Erasistratus. Galen says Erasistratus held that in muscular contraction, breath or *pneuma* entered the muscle through the nerve and filled its cavities thereby causing it to swell. When the muscle was thus filled with *pneuma,* its breadth increased while its length diminished, and as a result it was contracted. This simple explanation of muscular contraction in terms of swelling and inflation was to endure in physiology until the seventeenth century. Galen was also much interested in the contractility of muscle and in the fact that it depends on the nerve. He showed that section of the nerve going to a muscle paralyzes that muscle, and section of the spinal cord paralyzes all the muscles of the body supplied by nerves arising below the point of section. Mere injury or compression of the nerve may also cause the muscle to lose all movement and sensitivity.

Galen believed that muscle was made up of fibres and flesh. The fibres of a muscle are continuous with those of its tendons at either end. In the body of the muscle the fibres are spread apart by the flesh contained in the interspaces between them. Each of the continuous fibres extending through both tendon and muscle Galen considered to be made up of finer fibres—on the one hand, of inert and insensitive fibres of the same kind as occur in tendons, and on the other, of sensitive fibres which are simply fine extensions of the branches of nerves. In contrast to Erasistratus, Galen does not devote particular attention to the actual mechanism of contraction. He considers the contractility of muscle simply as a manifestation of the motor faculty which comes to the muscle from the brain.

In the early seventeenth century, writers were using Erasistratus' concept of muscle contraction in an essentially unmodified form. Since the Latin equivalent of the Greek word *pneuma* for breath is *spiritus* and since the breath or *spiritus* which flows into muscles, causing them to contract, comes from the brain, this is the breath of the mind or *spiritus animi*. This, then, is the animal spirit to which, for instance, Frans de le Boë refers as the cause of muscular contraction in his lectures on medicine at Leyden in 1640 and 1641: "And the contraction of a muscle is nothing else than the distension of its fibres swollen with Animal Spirit and hence its shortening."[1] Descartes in his *Traité de l'Homme* (1664) attempted to suggest the mechanisms within nerve and muscle which would be necessary to allow this traditional scheme to work. He imagined that the nerves might be like hollow tubes with their central ends open to the cavities of the brain and their peripheral ends opening in the muscles. Descartes postulated that the animal spirits flowed through the hollow nerves from the brain into the muscle thereby causing it to inflate. This flow was controlled by valves similar to the valves in the veins. Once in the muscles the spirits, which Descartes conceived as composed of very fine particles, oozed out through the surface of the muscle and through the skin. Thus a muscle subsided quickly from its contracted state.

Therefore, when William Croone published his *De ratione motus musculorum* in 1664, he inaugurated a new epoch in muscle physiology, for, while he retained the hypothesis of contraction by the inflation of the muscle, he attributed this inflation to a chemical interaction between the juice of the nerves and the blood in the muscle. However, it was soon shown by Swammerdam and Glisson that

[1] Boë, Frans de le (Franciscus Sylvius). "Dictata ad Casparis Bartholini institutiones anatomicas (1640-1641)." Chapter V in his *Opera medica*. Cologne, 1680, p. 676.

muscles did not swell in contraction. In fact, there was, if anything, a very slight reduction in their volume. For this reason Croone later published a modified version of his theory designed to show that the contraction of a muscle might take place by the change of shape of a multitude of small internal spaces. This concept of the internal structure of muscle as a latticework enclosing a multitude of fine spaces was also developed independently by Borelli in an attempt to solve the same problem—namely, how to account for the contraction of a muscle by an internal fermentation which swelled and changed the shape of its internal spaces without altering its external volume. Borelli was indebted to Croone for the original idea that muscular contraction might be produced by a process of fermentation within the muscle, but he was not aware of the identity of his source because Croone had published anonymously.

The idea of animal spirits, which is still present in the theories of Croone and Borelli, although in the more substantial form of a *succus nerveus* or juice of the nerves, persisted in nerve and muscle physiology to a much later period. The first Croonian lecturer, Alexander Stuart, thought that by introducing a blunt probe into the spinal canal he was forcing fluid into the nerves and that this was responsible for the muscular convulsions resulting from this procedure. The discovery of animal electricity by Galvani tended to reinforce rather than to remove the concept of animal spirits, but with Helmholtz's measurement of the rate of transmission of the nerve impulse, the improved understanding of the behavior of electric charges, and the concept of polarized membranes, the animal spirits gradually faded away. Possibly a faint echo of them survives in the concept of the secretion of acetylcholine at nerve endings.

In recent years the all-or-none principle has served to define the physico-chemical activity present in muscular contraction, and the new knowledge concerning the dynamics of the biochemical processes in muscle and the structure of muscle proteins has begun to reveal the complex physical chemistry involved in muscular contraction. In several respects the emerging pattern is surprisingly like that suggested by Croone and Borelli in the seventeenth century. At the same time the study of the electrical phenomena of isolated nerves and receptors has shown that the intensity of a sensation depends on the number of nerve impulses as measured by the frequency of impulses travelling along a single nerve fibre. Since 1936 the nature of the nerve impulse itself has been greatly illuminated by studies of the electrical changes which occur inside the giant nerve fibres of the squid. Undoubtedly study of the internal activity of the neurone may be even more important in the future.

Galen

131-201 A.D.

Galen, who is mentioned elsewhere (Ch. II), made many interesting observa tions upon the physiology of muscle and nerve. His experiments on the spinal cord suggest at times that he appreciated the significance of reflex action. However, he put forward the theory that the nervous system controlled muscle through the passage of fluid ("animal spirits") down the nerve trunks, and the concept dominated thought in this field until 1792. Much more significant were Galen's simple observations concerning the action of individual muscles and muscle groups. He objected to the theory, apparently prevalent at this time, that there existed more than one type of contractile activity. The following passage from his little book, *De motu musculorum,*[2] (Pl. 40) illustrates his beliefs concerning contraction and contains, incidentally, some of his observations upon reciprocal innervation. It illustrates also his obscure and redundant style.

Each muscle has only one active movement (that of contraction, since muscles are only extended in passive obedience to the active movement of the opposing muscle) not six, as was commonly believed. Proof of this statement by reason and experiment.

The primary object of our investigation is to discover whether there are as many muscle movements as appear after vivisection before dissection, or if there are many fewer kinds of movement than it would appear. It seems absurd, apart from any other reason, that there should be more than one kind of muscle movement (see infra chap. v and vi), just as it would seem absurd to say that every artery has a different motion, for indeed, nature always appears to act in the same way in organs which are alike. The theory, which has

---

[2] Galen. *De motu musculorum.* Bk. 1, Chapter 4. The first printed edition of this work, edited and translated from the Greek by Thomas Linacre, appeared in London in 1522 from the press of Pynson. The first French translation was published by Étienne Dolet in 1541. See also Charles Daremberg's *Oeuvres anatomiques, physiologiques et médicales de Galien.* Paris, J. B. Baillière, 1870. 2 vols., vol. 2, pp. 321-375. Further details concerning the book can be found in J. F. Fulton's *Muscular contraction and the reflex control of movement.* Baltimore, The Williams and Wilkins Co., 1926, pp. 8-10.

already been advanced, that each muscle has six movements, is obviously fallacious. In reality no muscle in the arms or legs has a third movement apart from extension and contraction. The same is obviously true of the temporal muscles, each of which has two movements. If the whole limb is moved by its muscles in six places, there is yet no reason to doubt that each muscle has a double movement. Actually if one muscle had to move the whole limb it would need to be capable of as many movements as the limb has movements; but since there are many more than six muscles in every limb, it is not surprising that the various movements should be performed for the limb by different muscles. I think that those who express such opinions have been deceived by the tongue, which they believed to consist of a single muscle. If this were really the case it would clearly prove that one muscle is capable of many different movements. Since the tongue is not really a single muscle, but is moved by a number of muscles, I think one may conclude, on the contrary, that each individual muscle is incapable of diverse movements; if it were otherwise the existence of a great number of muscles would be unnecessary, because one alone could perform all movements. But, it is said each of the eyes perform four distinct movements; that is true, my friends, for they have, in fact, four different muscles each, but there would only be one for each eye if it were capable of performing all these four movements. As one would conclude that this muscle had four movements if it were the only one, so, since there are as many muscles as there are movements one is led to believe that each muscle performs only a single movement; just as one movement only is performed by each of the two rotator muscles of the eye.

But, some of us say, it is admitted that each muscle performs two movements, if not more. How, then, can reason mean that there is only one muscle movement? [In reply I say] there is nothing absurd in that. Each muscle has only one active movement, it is only capable of the opposing movement by accident. A muscle is active when it pulls the limb which is in motion towards it, and not when it is brought back again by an opposing muscle. This is the reason why every part which can move has more than one muscle. For every muscle situated up above there is also one situated down below; and if there is a muscle on the right there is one on the left too; for, since each limb, set in motion by muscles—as though by reins—has to divide its activity between two sides, has one muscle tense and one relaxed alternately. The contracted muscle pulls towards itself, while the relaxed muscle is pulled along with its part; therefore both muscles move during the performance of each of the two movements, [but they are not both active] for activity consists in tension of the part which moves, and not in the action of obeying; and a muscle obeys when it is pulled in a passive state, just like any other part of the limb.

Dare we then now assert that only one innate movement exists in each muscle or must we first find out whether the various peculiarities of muscle fit in with this view. The latter course seems to me more preferable. Let us then at once state the peculiarities which can be observed in muscle, omitting nothing. There is one peculiarity, the first which we mentioned in the beginning (Chap. I) and that is that if whole muscles are cut through, their lower portion is completely deprived of movement, while if they are partially cut, movement is only injured. The gravity of the injury is in proportion to the incision; the larger the incision the greater the injury and vice versa. Supposing that these same observations are applied to tendons also; indeed if you cut a tendon through you deprive it of movement; if you make an incision the injury is in proportion to it. If then when a single muscle is cut through, all movement is destroyed one may conclude, I think, that this one muscle was the source of all movement [in that limb]. If, on the other hand, when a single muscle is cut only one movement was done away with, one might then conclude that the cut muscle was the source of one movement only.

As it happens that not one movement alone, nor yet all movement, but invariably two movements are done away with, it would seem to follow that two movements are performed by one single muscle. At the same time, since incision of a muscle or a tendon situated on opposite sides destroys the same two movements, we may conclude, by an absolutely identical method of reasoning that this muscle or tendon is possibly the source of the same two movements, which it governs or performs equally; so that the loss of any muscle entails the destruction of [active] movement in the opposing muscle, and they cannot both be equally capable of actively producing two opposing movements; each one of them can only perform one of the two movements. One of these propositions is necessarily true; we shall try and discover which, after explaining more clearly, in the first place, that in these successive movements, when one is destroyed the other must necessarily perish also. Suppose that the movement which extends a limb is destroyed, it will be possible to flex the limb again once, but, after that, it will remain in that position and can never extend again because it has been deprived of its extensor movement; being therefore incapable of extension it cannot, in consequence, flex either. In the same way if a limb is deprived of its flexor movement, it is possible to extend it once more, but after that the limb will be immovable since it can never return to the flexed position which must precede extension. It seems, therefore, indisputable that successive opposing movements are simultaneously destroyed, and it is in consequence reasonable to try and discover whether the two movements are produced by both muscles, or whether one movement being produced by each one of them, the second is abolished immediately after the first. (Translated from Daremberg's French text [see note 2], pp. 329-332.)

William Croone
1633-1684

William Croone is one of the picturesque figures among the physiologists of the seventeenth century (Pl. 41), and there is no better way of describing the state of knowledge concerning muscle physiology at that time than by citation from his writings. It will be recalled that he was one of the original founders of the Royal Society of London, which had been officially incorporated in 1662, and on 4 May 1664 he presented the Society[3] with a copy of his "little treatise," *De ratione motus musculorum* (Pl. 42), which had appeared anonymously in London in that year.[4]

FERMENTATION IN MUSCLE CONTRACTION

For since it has now been proven sufficiently that a certain force is carried from the brain through the nerves into the muscle, nor, if faith may be placed in the eyes, does there appear in the nerves anything which is more suitable to this purpose than that very rich and spirituous juice which is drawn all through the nerves in a constant circuit, what, I ask, is more likely than that the force is carried with this liquor or rather, that this liquor itself, or animal spirit of the

[3] Birch, T. *History of the Royal Society,* 1756, vol. 1, p. 422.

[4] Croone, W. *De ratione motus musculorum.* London, J. Hayes, 1664. 34 pp., 1 pl. (anon). In the same year and again in 1666 the work was appended to an edition of Willis' *Cerebri anatome,* published in Holland and erroneously attributed to this author. A fourth edition signed, also in Latin, appeared in Amsterdam in 1667 from the press of Caspar Commelinus.

fibres, is struck out from the branchlets of the nerves by some impulse? If this be so, it will also be highly probable that from the mixture of this liquor or spirit with the spirits of the blood there occurs continuously a great agitation of all the spirituous particles which are present in the vital juice of the whole muscle, as when spirit of wine is mixed with the spirit of human blood. For I have stated above that all parts of living things are swollen with a certain vivifying and spirituous liquor; . . . and no one is such a novice in Chemistry as not to know how great a commotion and agitation of the particles is accustomed to occur from different liquors mixed with each other, as may be discerned in the example just mentioned and also in common water with oil of vitriol or Butter of Antimony dissolved with spirit of Nitre and in an almost infinite number of other cases of this kind. . . .

Moreover, since it has been shown already that all motions of the spirits in the parts of a muscle are contained within certain spaces and, in addition, that these spaces are broader and more definite where the belly of the muscle is, we would consider that single space A.P.C. [see Croone's diagram, Pl. 43], I say that the agitation of the spirits which is made by the different liquors within the heaving membranes of the muscle necessarily impels them with a great effort through straight lines towards A and C. And since, in the intervals or spaces, they always strike against the smaller ends, they are turned back on themselves and are accumulated in greater quantity around the middle or belly of the muscle B (it may be anywhere) and hence the Muscle begins to swell. . . .

. . . But I may say that all these things are accomplished even in an instant by these causes. For at the same time as the fibrils of the taut nerve HEG are struck in the brain, immediately these droplets of liquor exude from all its branchlets just as, when the piston of a syringe is pushed in very lightly, liquid at once spurts out—for it must be understood that the whole body is filled with spirituous and vital juices. Like water mixed with oil of vitriol, so this liquor creates an effervescence in the blood in an instant. And in the same instant blood flows through the artery IKO like water from an opened pipe. No sooner does the muscle begin to swell at its boundary than are the fibres also contracted, and so everything occurs at one and the same time in the twinkling of an eye. However, that effervescence, which I have mentioned, ceases almost immediately and the very active spirits are dissipated through the membranes of the muscle nearly in an instant and, unless a new impulse arrives at once, the muscle is immediately pulled back and made flaccid by the inequality of the circulation of the blood through the fibres of the antagonist, and the blood flows out in greater quantity through the vein LMN. Hence violent exercises also remove the spirits and make them break out through sweats. This is also the reason why the limbs are very painful and stiff after more violent movements of the body (especially in those who are not accustomed to them). However, the blood flows in and again flows out rapidly, as may be illustrated from that sudden erection of the penis from venereal thoughts and its flaccidity after the emission of the semen, the instantaneous suffusion of the whole face from Shame; and in Fear, the immediate recession of the blood from every part of the body to the interior. In this connexion, the smaller the proportion of the sustained weight to the moving force, the more rapidly are the distances Ed and qD traversed. Hence great weights are elevated rapidly enough by the inflation of a bladder attached to them or by the forcing of water into the same bladder. ([Croone, William]. *De ratione motus musculorum.* London, J. Hayes, 1664. 34 pp. [p. 21, Sect. 27; p. 22, Sect. 28; p. 33, Sect. 35. Translated by L.G.W.].)

AN HYPOTHESIS OF THE STRUCTURE OF A MUSCLE, AND THE REASON OF ITS CONTRACTION; READ IN THE SURGEONS THEATRE ANNO 1674, 1675. BY DR. C.

Having shewn and proved at large, That the motion of a *Muscle,* is performed only by the Carnous *Fibres,* and that each distinct Carnous *Fibre* had a power of Contracting it self; I offered an *Hypothesis* of the Structure of one Carnous *Fibre,* since the force of the whole *Muscle* is but an Aggregate of the Contractions of each particular *Fibre:* And this I did in farther Explication of an Hypothesis, printed in the year 1664, grounded on an Experiment made for that purpose before the *R.S.* a little before that time. In that printed Paper 'twas said, a *Muscle* in Contraction swell'd like a Bladder blown up, which would raise a great weight according to the Experiment shown to the Society: An Objection rose, That we did not see any such conspicuous swelling in the Belly of a *Muscle;* to answer which, and explicate the *Hypothesis* more clearly, I made this farther addition.

1. I supposed each distinct Carnous *Fibres* as A E F to consist of an infinite number of very small *Globules,* or little Bladders, which

for explication sake I here express as so many little Triangles, *e.g.* four in this *Fibre,* A L B, B M C, C L D, D O E, all opening into one another at the Points A, B, C, D, E.

2. I did not only suppose, but endeavoured to prove, That from the *Artery* of each particular *Muscle,* the nourishing Juice of the *Muscle* was thrown out and extravasated to run at large among the Carnous *Fibres,* and insinuating it self by the constant Pulse of the Heart was driven on, and after mixing with another Liquor it meets with between the *Fibres* in the *Muscles,* came to be strain'd through the Coat of each Globule or little Bladder into the Cavity of it: And likewise, that from each ramification of the *Nerve* within the *Muscle,* that second sort of Matter much more fluid and active than the former is extravasated, and these mixt together as I said, enter into each little Bladder, and by these constant agitations, ebullition, or effervescence, which with the natural heat that is partly the cause, and partly the constant assister of this motion, and makes that which we call the very life of every part, as long as the Animal lives, keeps these Globules or small Vesicles always distended. How it enters in, and sends out its effete Particles again into the mass of Blood to be discharged by Transpiration, and every moment takes in fresh, I endeavoured in those Lectures to shew at large. . . . These and several other Particulars I did endeavour to make out at large in those Lectures; yet only in the way of an *Hypothesis,* not as if I did presume to believe I had found out the true secret of *Animal Motion,* when I am almost persuaded, no Man ever did or will be able to explicate either this or any other *Phenomenon* in Nature's true way and method: But because I reckon such Speculations among the best Entertainments of our Mind, I may chance to collect and publish sometime or other what I then said, and have lately try'd about it. And I am the more willing. First, because Mr. *Lewenhook* has since told us, That he finds by his Microscope the Texture of a carnous Fibre to be of innumerable small Vesicles or Globules, which gives an appearance of reality to the said Hypothesis, and them, [*sic*] because a sheet or two, and two or three schemes, of that long expected Work of *Borelli, de Motu Animalium,* having been sent to the *Royal Society,* I find there some Schemes for explicating Muscular Motion, the very same with those I make use of; and the same Experiment of the Bladder applied in another Scheme to this occasion likewise: How he has explain'd or manag'd them, as yet I know not, but his using them, has made me have a better opinion of this Thought than

else I should ever have had. . . . (Croone, William. "An hypothesis of the structure of a muscle, and the reason of its contraction; read in the Surgeons Theatre Anno 1674, 1675." In Hooke's *Philosophical Collections*, 1681, No. 2, sec. 8, pp. 22-25 [pp. 22-23, 25].)[5]

Jan Swammerdam
1637-1680

There can be few careers of greater pathos than that of Swammerdam—nor few instances of a sharper contrast between the magnificent achievement of his work and the acute misery of his personal life. He was born at Amsterdam and in 1661 entered the University of Leyden where he studied under Frans de le Boë and met Steno as a fellow student. After a brief sojourn at Paris in 1665 he returned to Leyden where he was graduated in 1667 with a thesis on respiration. He then settled at Amsterdam where his life was made unhappy by quarrels with his father who quite naturally wanted Jan to earn his own living. Despite frequent promises to do so, Jan Swammerdam devoted almost all his time for the remainder of his short life to his researches. Most of his work dealt with the anatomy and life history of insects, but he also made a thorough study of the anatomy and development of frogs. His experiments on the contraction of frog muscles, described here, were carried out while he was a student at Leyden in the period 1661-1665 but were not published until the general publication of his papers as the *Biblia naturae* in 1737-1738 (Pl. 44). In 1758, there appeared an English translation of this great work by Thomas Flloyd from which the following passage is taken.

EXPERIMENT TO DEMONSTRATE CONTRACTION OF FROG MUSCLE

[p. 123]. Another very delicate and useful experiment may be made, if one of the largest muscles be separated from the thigh of a Frog, and, together with its adherent nerve, prepared in such a manner as to remain unhurt. For if, after this, you take hold, Tab. XLIX. Fig. v. *a a,* of each tendon with you[r] hand, and then irritate *b* the propending nerve with scissors, or any other instrument, the muscle will recover its former motion, which it had lost. You will see that it is immediately contracted, and draws together, as it were, both the hands, which hold the tendons. . . .

[5] Hooke's "Collections" was a private publication which filled the gap during the years that the *Philosophical Transactions* of the Royal Society had been abandoned owing to lack of funds. Croone's lecture was also published (in Latin) in the *Acta Eruditorum* (1682, pp. 194-197).

[p. 125]. . . . We very clearly find also by experiments, that the motion produced in the muscle by irritating the nerve, is always propagated out of the larger into the smaller branches, and goes afterwards continually descending. The nerves designed for the senses are circumstanced in a quite different manner; for in these, the sensitive motions, doubtless, tend upwards. In order to contract any muscle, it is necessary that its nerve be irritated in the region above the muscle, or at its insertion into it; since that motion never tends upwards, but always downwards. . . .

[p. 127]. If, instead of the heart, we should chuse to make use of some other muscle, we may proceed in the manner represented in the eighth figure, where the glass siphon, Tab. XLIX. Fig. VIII. *a,* contains within its hollow the muscle, *b,* and the nerve hanging from the muscle is fastened, without being cut or bruised to a slender twisted silver wire, *cc,* that runs at the other end, an eye made in a piece of brass wire, soldered to the embolus or piston of the siphon, *d.* Things being thus made ready, a drop of water, *e,* must be let into the slender tube of the siphon by a very fine funnel. Now, if after this, the silver wire be cautiously drawn with a leisurely hand *f* through the ring or eye of the brass wire, till the nerve is irritated by the compression, it must by this means undergo, the muscle will contract itself in the same manner with the inflated heart, whose alterations, upon a similar occasion, I have already described, even the drop of water will in some measure sink, though afterwards it never rises again. But this experiment is very difficultly sensible, and requires so many conditions to be exactly performed, that it must be tedious to make it; for which reason, I have bethought myself of another that may be more easily understood and performed.

You must have ready a little glass siphon, Tab. XLIX. Fig. IX. *a,* cut through with a diamond near the extremity of its slender tube, *b;* then pass through the hole thus made, the nerve of the muscle *c:* but as the air can easily make its way through this hole, while the nerve is irritated, till it contracts itself, so as to keep the water from sinking; it is absolutely necessary to stop that passage on the outside, which may be easily done with a little ising-glass and starch. But I must own, that in this experiment, the sinking of the drop is so inconsiderable, that it can scarce be perceived: . . . (Swammerdam, Jan. *The book of nature; or the history of insects.* . . . Translated by Thomas Flloyd, revised and improved by John Hill. London, C. G.

Seyffert, 1758. Two parts: I: xx, 4 *ll.*, 236 pp.; II: 153, lxiii pp., 6 *ll.*, 53 plates [II, pp. 123, 125, 127].)

Nicolaus Steno
1638-1686

Nils Stensen, or as he is better known under the Latin form of his name, Nicolaus Steno, was born at Copenhagen where he began his medical studies under Thomas Bartholin. He later studied briefly at Amsterdam and for a longer period at Leyden where he carried out a brilliant series of anatomical researches. He also met there Jan Swammerdam, a fellow student with whom he travelled to Paris in the summer of 1665. As the following passages indicate, they discussed the question of muscular contraction, and Swammerdam appears to have demonstrated for Steno his experiments to show that muscles do not swell during contraction. In the autumn of 1665 Steno travelled on southward alone from Paris to Montpellier. In that city there were a number of visiting Englishmen, among them William Croone. Steno and Croone discussed the question of muscular contraction, the subject upon which Croone had published his short tract only the year before. It was probably from Steno that Croone first learned that muscles do not change in volume during contraction. From Montpellier Steno went to Florence, where he arrived in the spring of 1666 and where a year later he published his *Elementorum myologiae specimen* from which these passages are taken.

THE MOTOR FIBRE IN THE CONTRACTION OF THE HEART AND SKELETAL MUSCLE

The motor fibre is contracted in the same way when the arteries, veins and nerves are cut as when these same structures are entire. There is no one who has not noticed the convulsive movements of the fleshy parts in recently slaughtered animals in which both heart and head have been removed. I have observed that when the cartilaginous part of the ribs has been cut through the junctures with the sternum no one believed that the action of the intercostal muscles waited upon an impulse communicated from the heart. My friend Swammerdam has often demonstrated to us that a Frog may swim a long time with its heart excised. In a tortoise, movement has been noted in the feet and tail 24 hours after the head has been cut off. When the heart has been excised it continues its movement for the same time. At Leyden, while intent on examining the experiment of Bils when, after the scapula had been raised in a dead dog,

I was dissecting the plexus of nerves passing out to the left front limb, I saw the muscles be convulsed not only when I was dissecting the intact nerves of the former but also when I pressed strongly, or was dissecting the intact nerves adhering to the resected muscles in the same way that my friend Swammerdam had observed previously in Frogs.

What therefore is surprising is that the heart, extracted from the body, is moved with repeated beats, although neither new blood flows into its vessels nor does new spirit enter it through the nerves from the brain. Therefore, since the structure of the motor fibres is not only as I have observed three years ago [1664], but their movement may be observed as clearly in the heart as in the muscles, as has been said so often, I hope that it has been demonstrated with sufficient clearness that, as the ancients said, the heart is a muscle.

What I have here proposed concerning the movement of muscles, refers to the changes which occur in the muscles themselves, when they are contracted, without suggesting any cause from which that movement proceeds. Hence, concerning the power of the will, I add nothing, since I believe that it is evident that all voluntary movement is accomplished by the muscles, but that not every movement which is executed by a muscle is voluntary, so that a particular individual muscle, but not all nor at all times, happens to be an organ of voluntary motion. . . .

Concerning the fluids of muscle our knowledge is so uncertain as to be non-existent.

It is certain that there is fluid in the fibrils of which the motor fibre is composed, between these fibrils, between the motor fibres themselves, in the membranous fibres of the muscle and finally between these same membranous fibres, but indeed these fluids may not all be of the same kind. Whether they are as different in their material properties as in their separate locations is not at all certain.

Nor is it known to which of those fluids, which we consider known to us, any one of these fluids may be similar. Many people talk of the animal spirits, the more subtle part of the blood, the juice of the nerves—but these are mere words signifying nothing.

Those who would continue further would introduce salty and sulphureous parts, or those analogous to spirit of wine; which may be true perhaps, but are neither certain, nor sufficiently distinct. Experience teaches us that exhausted strength may be restored by drinking spirit of wine, but whether to ascribe this to the fluid which we call spirit itself or to another material which the fluid spirit provides, or to another cause closely linked to it—who will determine?

Just as the substance of this fluid is unknown to us, similarly its movements are uncertain; seeing that it has not yet been established definitely, either by arguments or experiments, whence it comes, by what means it proceeds or whither, on departing, it is received.

Whether the surrounding fluid has the arteries, nerves, or opposed muscles for its source cannot be known. The apertures of the veins, the pores of the body and perhaps those in the bones and the nerves can be discovered. In the muscle itself there can be induced a simple movement from the middle towards the ends, from the ends towards the middle, from one end towards the other; and it can also be stimulated to a less simple motion.

There remains another difficulty no less momentous and not yet decided: namely, in what respect the movement of fluid in a muscle is different, when it is contracted, from the movement of fluid in the same muscle when it is at rest, uncontracted: is its quantity changed or does it remain the same? If fluid enters, is the incoming fluid of the same nature, or different from what was previously there? Is the fluid which contracts the solid itself moved—if indeed the contraction of the solid proceeds by the movement of a fluid? (Steno, Nicolaus. *Elementorum myologiae specimen, seu musculi descriptio geometrica.* . . . Florence, Stellae, 1667. 123 pp. [pp. 58-60; 63-64. Translated by L.G.W.].)

Thomas Willis

1621-1675

Born at Great Bedwyn, Wiltshire, the son of a farmer, *Thomas Willis* was educated at Christ Church, Oxford (B.A. 1639; M.B. 1646). He began to practise medicine at Oxford and took part in the meetings which were later to give rise to the Royal Society. In 1666 he moved to London where he carried on a large practice.

Willis (Pl. 45) has been much underrated as a contributor to physiology. His methods of experiment and his process of reasoning were at times erratic and did not conform with the standards set by some of his contemporaries such as Boyle and Lower. Yet Willis had wide clinical experience, he recorded what he saw, and he frequently gave evidence of penetrating vision. His description of the anatomy of the brain though inaccurate in places is at times masterly, and those who now read his tracts on scurvy and on nervous diseases will detect his shrewd powers of observation. His tract on muscular motion, which first appeared in Latin as an appendix to his treatise on melancholia,[6] was translated into English and was published at London in 1684 in *Dr. Willis's Practice of Physick.* . . . The following passage indicates that Willis made experiments for himself; it also illustrates his tendency to speculation.

THE CAUSE OF MUSCULAR CONTRACTION

As often as the motion of a living Muscle was beheld by me, I considered and weighed in my mind by what means all the fleshy fibres were contracted and released by turns, I could conceive or collect no other thing than that in every contraction, the Spirits or certain elastick Particles did rush into the fleshy fibres from either Tendon, and did intumifie and force them nearer towards themselves or together; then the same Particles presently coming back from the flesh into the Tendons, the relaxation of the muscles happened. In a bare or naked Muscle, when I had separated every fleshy fibre or a company of them apart from the rest in the whole passage by help of a Microscope, I most plainly perceive the Tumor, begun at either end of the flesh, to be carried towards the middle, as it were by the Spirits, entred here and there at once. Further (which I mentioned before) each fibre being tyed about the middle, being as it were as yet free and compacted with the others, was contracted or drawn together; but a Ligature being put to both ends, is remained flaggy constantly above or beyond the bound place. But that I might no longer doubt concerning this, I applied two Ligatures, at equal distances from the middle and the ends, about the same bundle of fleshy fibres, which being done, a contraction and swelling up arising presently from either fleshy extreme to the places bound, went no farther; the middle part between in the mean time being unmoved, remained flaccid; whence it may be well concluded, that in every musculary contraction the animal Spirits or elastick Particles do leap out from the tendinous fibres into the fleshy, and vicissively in the relaxation, recede or run back from these into those.

However this being proved and granted, there yet remain very many difficulties concerning Musculary Motion; for first, it may be asked how the animal Spirits, which enter silently, or without any incitation, or Tumor, the tendinous fibres do so blow up the fleshy

[6] Willis, T. *Affectionum quae dicuntur hystericae et hypochondriacae pathologia spasmodica vindicata contra responsionem . . . N. Highmori. Cui accesserunt exercitationes medico-physicae duae: 1. De sanguinis accensione. 2. De motu musculari.* Leyden, F. Lopez and C. Driehuysen, 1671.

fibres, that they are able to force them altogether into shorter spaces. . . .

But that the fleshy belly of the Muscle, whilst it is contracted, doth swell up, is not at all to be doubted, because this is evidently beheld by the sight and touch in the dissection of living Creatures: to wit, all the fleshy fibres being wrinkled together, are made more tumid and sharper, and so shorten the Muscle, and make it also thicker and broader: For the more certain belief of this, when I had bound some of the fleshy fibres, separated from the knitting of the rest, and had left others near them loose, there appeared a notable difference between those flaccid or not swelled, and these intumified or swelled up in every contraction of the Muscle.

But if it be demanded, of what nature, to wit, whether spirituous saline, as may be believed, or of any other disposition, the animal Spirits, derived from the Brain into the Muscles, may be; and then whether the other Latex, immediately carried to them from the blood, is sulphureous or nitrous. Concerning these, because it appears not to the sense, we shall pronounce nothing rashly or positively. But even as in other natural things, the active Particles of a various kind, which being unlike among themselves, are found apt mutually to grow hot, or to be struck off from one another, otherwise to be rarified or expanded; and as the intestine motions of Bodies, and especially the elastick, such as are the contractions of the Muscles, can only proceed from the congressions of such like, certainly it may be lawful to presume, that these do wholly depend upon such a cause.

Therefore as to the Muscular Motion in general, we shall conclude after this manner, with a sufficiently probable conjecture, *viz.* that the animal Spirits being brought from the Head by the passage of the Nerves to every Muscle (and as it is very likely), received from the membranaceous fibrils, are carried by their passage into the tendinous fibres, and there they are plentifully laid up as in fit Storehouses; which Spirits, as they are naturally nimble and elastick, where ever they may, and are permitted, expanding themselves, leap into the fleshy fibres; then the force being finished, presently sinking down, they slide back into the Tendons, and so vicissively. . . . (*Dr. Willis's practice of physick,* . . . London, T. Dring, C. Harper, & J. Leigh, 1684. Treatise V, "Of muscular motion." [2d pagination, pp. 33-34].)

Francis Glisson
1597-1677

Francis Glisson, Regius Professor of Physic at Cambridge from 1636 until his death, is remembered for his description of the fibrous sheath of the liver, still known as Glisson's capsule, and for having written the first authoritative monograph to be published in England on a single disease (Rickets, 1651). In physiology Glisson (Pl. 46) is remembered more especially for the theory of irritability and for being the first to oppose the then prevalent theory of animal spirits as a cause of muscular contraction. The following passage is his description of an experiment indicating that the volume occupied by muscle during contraction did not increase but, in point of fact, seemed actually to diminish.

MUSCLE VOLUME CONSTANT DURING CONTRACTION

I come to the second important reason proving animal spirits not to be the immediate cause of sense and movement. The flux and reflux of matter in the same channels is rarely to be met with in nature's arrangements. In breathing, expiration and inspiration go on in the same organs, but the cartilaginous windpipe was made for that purpose, and the thorax is in turn both contracted and dilated. The fact of the flux and reflux of the intestinal juices is admitted but the peristaltic movement is provided for the same purpose, *i.e.* for repeatedly shifting the chyle. But in the nerves there is hardly sufficient cause to show why the spirits should sometimes be carried inwards and sometimes outwards, unless in the nerves too we assume a peristaltic movement or think that the animal spirits, just as if they were small tubes, run both up and down, and flow out and back at will. But they go forth to nourish the parts and determine the organs of sense according to their suitable functions. The sensation of the same objects sometimes lasts several hours. . . . Do the animal spirits in the nerves both go forth and return during the whole of that time so that the object of sensation continues a long time in both the outer and inner organs? I cannot solve these riddles. Moreover, these spirits flow to swell the mobile fibres so that in proportion as their bellies swell in breadth they are shortened in length and draw away the bones attached to the tendons. However, as a result of the following experiment, the idea of the explosion of spirits and of the inflation of muscles has for some time now been silenced.

Take an oblong glass tube of suitable size and shape, and in its side at the top near its mouth, fix another upright tube shaped like a funnel. Get a strong brawny man to thrust the whole of his bared arm into the opening of the larger tube, and then let the opening of the tube be luted up all round the man's shoulder so that no water can escape: then pour through the funnel as much water as the glass can hold and allow some water to overflow into the funnel. When this has been done, order the man now alternately to contract strongly, and now to relax, all his arm muscles. During contraction the water in the tube sinks, but during relaxation rises. Hence it is clear that the muscles when taut or contracted, are not at that time inflated or swollen, but are on the contrary unswollen and actually diminished. For if they were swollen, the water would ascend higher in the glass and would not descend. Therefore one must conclude that the fibres are shortened by their own vital motion, and have no need of plentiful afflux of animal or vital spirits by which they might be inflated in order to be shortened and in order that their movements might obey the commands of the brain.

I fear, in this digression concerning animal spirits, I have been rather irksome to my readers, but obviously I could not avoid it nor put more succinctly what had to be said. Although I have touched lightly on the heads of the discussion only, yet the work has grown in size beyond my expectations. Now I return to the main theme and I shall try to elucidate another doubt previously mentioned, namely how the wishes of the brain communicate themselves to the nerves whose function it is to execute them.

Para. 10. The second uncertainty is whether the nerves recognise, by natural perception or sense, the particular movement of the brain above described by which they are excited, or the fibres the movement of the nerves. That I may lead no other mind but my own into error, I warn readers that every complete action that has its origin in sense and sensory desire is animal in its particular feeling, and similarly what proceeds immediately from the understanding and will is free. I have said in my book "De vita naturae," Chapter 15, n. 3, that there are three successions of vital faculties, and that the perceptive faculty among them is the leader of the others. Here I must say again that the natural faculties are frequently interwoven with the sensitive faculties, and these again with the intellectual into one compound operation. But in this occurrence the whole action is generally named from the higher faculties. But if the same process originates with a higher faculty, however much the lower faculties also are subject to its sway, it is still named from the former only. However, we must not overlook in the evolution of the whole action the contribution made by the lower faculties in fulfilling that same action. The present investigation can be taken as an example in which, although we have agreed that the whole action is animal because it has its origin in sense and sensory desire, yet we are not thereby prevented from asking whether in its production, some natural actions are connected with it. Indeed, we are not examining the whole matter sufficiently thoroughly unless we accurately investigate what kind these actions are. Therefore, granted these premises, I say that the brain notices its own movements, the nerves the brain's movements and the fibres the nerves' movements, not by sense but by natural perception alone. I think that the truth of all this can be shown by one argument. We judge that whatever we recognise by sense, we feel because the sense has drawn our attention to it. Indeed whatever we seek by sensual desire we obviously apprehend with our inner senses also, so that no animal operation is altogether concealed from our senses; but the brain, when stimulated by its own desire and when moving outwards to accomplish that desire, is not aware by sense that it moves thus, nor does it distinguish by sense in what way it communicates its movements to the nerves to which it goes. Similarly the nerves are not aware of the movement which they communicate to the fibres they stimulate. Finally the fibres do not distinguish by sense their excitability at the movement stimulated by the nerves. They are aware of all this by natural perception alone and by its medium are the respective parts stimulated to the performance of their various functions. For the muscle, with regard to the stimulus it feels, is obviously unaware by what means or by what mechanisms it is set in motion by the brain. (Glisson, F. *De ventriculo et intestinis. Cui praemittitur alius, de partibus continentibus in genere; & in specie, de iis abdominis.* London, Henry Brome, 1677. 509 pp. [Ch. 8, para. 9-10, pp. 166-168].)

Giovanni Alfonso Borelli
1608-1679

Giovanni Alfonso Borelli, the author of *De motu animalium* is included in this series of readings not for any important discovery, but rather because of the influence which he exerted upon this field of work. His book, an extensive work in two volumes (Pl. 47), contains an analysis of the mechanics of contraction: how muscles act at joints, what tension they must develop in order to overcome a given mechanical disadvantage, etc. It also contains interesting observations upon reciprocal innervation and tonus. His theory of contraction, though little in advance of Galen, is of some interest as showing the influence which the new chemistry of his day had already exerted. This is well illustrated in the following selection.

THEORY OF MUSCULAR CONTRACTION

Since all muscles, with some few exceptions, do not manifest vital movement otherwise than in obedience to the will, since the commands of the will are not transmitted from the brain which is the instrument of the sensitive, and the seat of the motive soul, by any other channels than the nerves as all confess and as the most decided experiments shew, and since the action of any incorporeal agency or of spirituous gases must be rejected, it is clear that some corporeal substance must be transmitted along the nerves to the muscles or else some commotion must be communicated along some substance in the nerves, in such a way that a very powerful inflation can be brought about in the twinkling of an eye.

And since the inflation, hardening, and contraction do not take place in the channels which serve for bringing them about and in which the motor influence resides, namely, in the nerves themselves, but takes place outside the nerves, namely, in the muscles, it is evident that the substance or the influence which the nerves transmit is not taken by itself alone sufficient to bring about that inflation. It is necessary, therefore, that something else must be added, something which is to be found in the muscles themselves; or that in the muscles there is some adequate disposition of material so that on the arrival of the influence transmitted by the nerves there takes place something like a fermentation or ebullition, by which the sudden inflation of the muscle is brought about. That such an action is possible is rendered clear by innumerable experiments which are continually being made in chemical elaborations as when spirits of vitriol are poured on oil of tartar; indeed all acid spirits when mixed with fixed salts at once boil up with a sudden fermentation. In like manner, therefore, we may suppose that there takes place in a muscle a somewhat similar mixing from which a sudden fermentation and ebullition results, with the mass of which the porosities of the muscle are filled up and enlarged, thus bringing about the turgescence and the inflation. . . .

In the same way, if one of the extremities of the nerve fibre be compressed or pushed, or struck or pinched, forthwith the commotion and concussion or undulation ought to be communicated right to the other end, because by reason of their contiguity, the parts lying first in an ordered series by pressing on those following, communicate the blow and the impulse right to the end.

Hence it follows that the fibres or spongy ducts of certain nerves turgid with the spirituous juice can be shaken or pinched by that gentle motion of the spirits by which the acts of the command of the will are in the brain carried out, and then, by concussing the whole length of the nerve through the convulsive irritation, can squeeze out and discharge from their extreme orifices some spirituous droplets into the appropriate muscle, whence the ebullition and explosion follow by which the muscle is contracted and rendered tense.

And on the other hand when the extremities of the sensory nerves which end in the skin, nose, ears or eyes, are compressed or struck or titillated, it necessarily follows that forthwith the concussion, undulation, or titillation of the spirituous juice contained within the tubules is conveyed along the whole length of the nerve and reaches the particular part of the brain to which the nerve fibres are joined. And here the faculty of the sensitive soul according to the region of the brain thus percussed, according to the vehemence of the blow and the fashion and mode of the motion, is able to form a judgment concerning the object causing the movement.

[He insists that the] juices, however spirituous and active, are always corporeal and cannot act at a distance, and cannot, without physical contact, increase, intensify, or depress the animal spirits; it is by means of their corporeal presence that they either increase the animal spirits which are also corporeal, mixing themselves with them, or expel them, or transform them. Wherefore it cannot be conceived that nervous action can take place without some local movement of the nervous juice passing along the whole length of the nerve right to the brain. . . . (Borelli, G. A. *De motu animalium.* Rome, Angelo Bernabo, 1680-1681. Selections translated by Sir Michael Foster, *Lectures on the history of physiology.* Cambridge, At the University Press, 1924. 306 pp. [pp. 72-73, 280-281].)

Alexander Stuart
1673-1742

Alexander Stuart, the first Croonian Lecturer, was born in Scotland and received his M.D. from Leyden in 1711, presenting for the degree a dissertation bearing the title *De structura et motu musculari.* Stuart was Physician-in-Ordinary to the Queen and was attached to Westminster and St. George's Hospitals. The following passage has been included to show that the theory of reflex action had not at this time found its way into physiological thought, even though Descartes had already referred to it in vague and halting terms. This passage serves also to illustrate that Galenical doctrine still held sway in the field of the nervous system. The figure reproduced from Stuart's *Lectures on Muscular Motion* (Pl. 48) is the first to depict the familiar manœuvre of pithing a frog.

THE MANNER, EXPLANATION AND USE OF THE Vth EXPERIMENT

1st, This Experiment is performed by suspending a live Frog by the fore legs in a frame, or in any other commodious manner, as in Tab. 3. fig. 1. [Pl. 49] when having cut off the head from the first vertebre of the neck with a pair of scissars, a small probe, the button at its extremity being first filed flat, is to be pushed very gently down upon the upper extremity of the *medulla spinalis,* in the first vertebre of the neck; upon which the inferior limbs, which hung down loose, will be immediately contracted, as they appear in fig. 2, tab. 3 [Pl. 49]. The same probe pushed gently through the hole of the occiput of the scull on the *medulla oblongata,* will make the eyes move, and sometimes the mouth to open.

2dly, The same being repeated at some small interval of a few seconds, succeeds for several times in the same manner; until the extremity of the spinal marrow be either pushed down too far out of the reach of the probe, or contused by it, which last effect appears soonest on the *medulla oblongata:* but after this the Experiment will not farther succeed, the compression then ceasing to be equal or uniform.

OBSERVATION ON THIS EXPERIMENT

Obs. 1. It must be observed, that this Experiment succeeds better in the summer months some time after the Frogs have spawned, than it does early in the spring, or in winter when those creatures are almost dead by cold, and want of food.

Obs. 2. The interval of a few seconds in repeating this Experiment on the same Frog, seems to be necessary for recovering the equality of the circulation, which was disturbed by the immediate preceding convulsion, as it throws the blood violently out of the muscles in the time of their contraction or systole, which cannot be restored immediately in such a languid state of circulation, as this Experiment must bring on; and as the assistance of the blood will appear by the following scheme to be necessary to muscular motion, where it is deficient, the motion must also be defective or imperfect, as it appears in repeating the pushes too quick.

Obs. 3. As the inferior process of the brain called the *medulla oblongata,* and its continuation called the spinal marrow, are only a continued or prolonged collection of the nerves arising from the brain and *cerebellum;* by this Experiment it appears, that the nerves contribute remarkably to muscular motion; and their assistance in it is owing to the fluid they contain, I have endeavoured to prove, by shewing the non-elasticity of the nerves in the first Experiment.

Obs. 4. The motion here excited is in the muscles of voluntary or spontaneous motion, which are under the command of the will.

Obs. 5. The effect of the impulse by the probe is the same, which is or may be produced in these muscles by the mind or will; or is the very same in its manner as voluntary or spontaneous motion, and performed by mediation of the same instruments, to wit, the animal spirits, or fluid of the nerves, and the muscles of voluntary motion.

Obs. 6. The extremity of the probe applied in this Experiment being flat, cannot produce this effect by irritation, but by compression; and the compression of the pliable extremities of tubes full of any fluid, must depress or propel the contained fluid towards the lower or opposite extremities, with an increased degree of velocity. Therefore at least the beginning of this motion may be justly ascribed to a propulsion of a small quantity of the contained fluid, through these slender canals into the muscles, in which they terminate, with some greater degree of velocity, and in some greater quantity than usual. Whence we may conclude, that voluntary muscular motion in a living animal is begun in the same manner, by an impulse of the mind or will on the animal spirits through the nerves, into the muscles. (Stuart, A. *Three lectures on muscular motion, read before the Royal Society in the year MDCCXXXVIII*. London, T. Woodward, 1739. x, 54 pp. [pp. 37-39]. A Latin edition of the same lecture entitled *Dissertatio de structura et motu musculari* was published the year before.)

Luigi Galvani
1737-1798

Luigi Galvani, the virtual discoverer of animal electricity, was born and spent his life, as did Malpighi, in the city of Bologna. The history of his discoveries concerning "animal electricity" is confusing and difficult. Galvani's original description shows naïve enthusiasm without penetrating analysis, and it is in consequence difficult to select a passage from his own writings which gives his crucial observation. From the maze of controversy which followed the publication of the *De viribus electricitatis in motu musculari commentarius*[7] (1791, Pl. 50), there emerged two important facts, both of which can probably be attributed with some justification to Galvani himself: 1) *The contraction with metals*. In the passage quoted below, though Galvani mentions that the blade of his scalpel was held in place by rivets of a dissimilar metal, the contraction of the frog's leg in his first experiment was clearly due to a potential conducted from the static machine. After a prolonged series of experiments it became obvious that dissimilar metals when brought into contact with each other generated an electric current, and it was this in the hands of Volta that led to the great discovery of the battery and the voltaic pile. 2) *Contraction without metals*. Galvani had maintained that contraction resulting from metallic contact was due to electricity generated within the tissue, and in his efforts to prove that electricity could in fact be generated by animal tissues he found that if a nerve were made to touch another tissue at two points, one injured and one uninjured, the muscle supplied by the nerve would be thrown into contraction. This demonstrated unequivocally the existence of animal electricity. The experiment appeared in an anonymous pamphlet in 1794 which was undoubtedly by Galvani himself, since a manuscript of it in his own handwriting is known to have existed. His nephew Aldini, however, claimed authorship after Galvani's death. The details of the difficult historical controversy between Galvani, Volta, and Aldini are fully set forth in the first volume of Émil du Bois-Reymond's *Untersuchungen über thierische Elektricität*, Berlin, 1848.

[7] The original Latin edition appeared in Bologna in 1791, was issued twice that year, and the next year at Modena, was translated into German twice (1793, 1894), into French (1939), and English (twice in 1953). A bibliography of the editions and translations will be found in *Luigi Galvani. Commentary on the effects of electricity on muscular motion*. Translated into English by Margaret Glover Foley, with notes and a critical introduction by I. Bernard Cohen. Norwalk, Conn., Burndy Library, 1953. This book also includes a facsimile reproduction of the first edition.

THE EFFECTS OF ANIMAL ELECTRICITY
ON MUSCULAR MOTION

Since I had upon occasion remarked that prepared frogs, which were fastened by brass hooks in their spinal cord to an iron railing which surrounded a certain hanging garden of my home, fell into the usual contractions not only when lightning flashed but even at times when the sky was quiet and serene, I surmised that these contractions had their origin in changes which occur during the day in the electricity of the atmosphere. . . . I finally became tired of waiting in vain and began to press and squeeze the brass hooks which penetrated the spinal cord against the iron railing. I hoped to see whether muscular contractions were excited by this technique and whether they revealed any change or alteration related to the electrical state of the atmosphere. As a matter of fact, I did observe frequent contractions but they had no relation to the changes in the electrical state of the atmosphere. . . .

But when I brought the animal into a closed room, placed it on an iron plate, and began to press the hook which was fastened in the spinal cord against the plate, behold!, the same contractions and movements occurred as before [Pl. 51]. I immediately repeated the experiment in different places with different metals and at different hours of the day. The results were the same except that the contractions varied with the metals used; that is, they were more violent with some and weaker with others. . . . (Galvani, Luigi. *Commentary on the effects of electricity on muscular motion.* Margaret Glover Foley, Trans. Norwalk, Connecticut, Burndy Library, 1953. 176 pp. [p. 59].)

William Bowman

1816-1892

Sir *William Bowman,* ophthalmic surgeon of Kings College Hospital, London, distinguished himself in physiological research before he settled on surgery of the eye as his profession. This eminent physiologist, histologist, and morbid anatomist, like his near contemporary Thomas Young, reached the zenith of his scientific attainments before the age of twenty-six after which his career as a creative scientist terminated almost completely because of his preoccupation with medical practice.

Bowman was born at a time when a group of young men in Britain and in Germany were, through the use of the newly introduced compound microscope, to transform scientific medicine—men such as Robert B. Todd, James and Stephen Paget, Herbert Mill, Richard Partridge, Robert Graves, Wharton Jones, William Sharpey, Joseph Hodgson, Peyton Blakiston, Johannes Müller, F. G. J. Henle, J. E. Purkinje, M. J. Schleiden, and Theodor Schwann. It can be said of Bowman that, when in 1838 Schleiden and Schwann first propounded the "cell theory," he, perhaps more than any of his distinguished contemporaries, was thoroughly prepared for it, for he had been studying the finer structure of skeletal muscle and recognized it as being made up of individual cellular units. At the age of sixteen he had been apprenticed to a master surgeon Joseph H. Hodgson, F.R.S., and he had also come to know that remarkable physician Peyton Blakiston who, in recognition of Bowman's assistance in his studies on heart muscle, presented him with a compound microscope. He was therefore only in his late teens when his studies on muscle had begun. When he first entered Kings College, London, to study for his membership examination for the Royal College of Surgeons, he was already well launched on a research career.

When he was twenty-four, i.e., on 18 June 1840, his celebrated paper, "On the minute structure and movements of voluntary muscle," was communicated to the Royal Society for him by Robert B. Todd, Professor of Anatomy and Physiology at Kings College. On the basis of this paper, Bowman was made a Fellow of the Royal Society the following year. His preoccupation with the activity of the individual cell is well illustrated in the first paragraph below; his far-reaching conclusions follow.

ON THE MINUTE STRUCTURE AND FUNCTIONS OF VOLUNTARY MUSCLE

A contracted fasciculus has often a somewhat uneven or undulated margin, which is sometimes occasioned by very slight irregularities or puckerings of the fibrillae, but more frequently by a transverse wrinkling of the sarcolemma, which, when this is extensively separated by fluid from the fibrillae, is almost a necessary consequence of the shortening of the fasciculus. I have not seen this in contracted fasciculi that have not been wetted, and, therefore, conclude the sheath to be endowed with the requisite elasticity for accommodating it to the varying form of its contents. But where bullae are developed, the folds thus occasioned are strongly marked, and have very probably been not unfrequently mistaken for transverse rugae upon the fasciculus. The fibrillae, however, are entirely independent of them, as may be seen in specimens taken from the Newt and Mouse. In those Birds that have been examined, the irritability has so speedily ceased, that no contraction has been observed. . . .

1. The *primitive fasciculi* of voluntary muscle consist of elongated polygonal masses of *primitive component particles,* or *sarcous elements,* arranged and united together endways and sideways, so

as to constitute in these directions respectively, *fibrillae* and *discs*, either of which may, in certain cases, be detached as such, and both of which, in the unmutilated organ, always exist together. It is the assemblage of these particles, which may most properly be styled "Sarcous tissue."

2. The dark longitudinal striae are shadows between fibrillae, the dark transverse striae, shadows between discs [Pl. 52].

Every primitive fasciculus is invested by a highly delicate, transparent, and probably elastic membrane, the *sarcolemma,* which is adherent to its surface, and isolates the sarcous tissue from every other part.

Every primitive fasciculus contains upon or among its primitive particles, numbers of *corpuscles,* which either actually are, or are analogous to, the nuclei of the original cells of development; and it is certain, that during growth, these corpuscles increase in number.

The *extremities* of the primitive fasciculi, in certain cases at least, are directly continuous with tendinous structure, and are not tapered, but obliquely or transversely truncated. This is at variance with the common opinion that the tendon embraces each fasciculus, and is continued along it from end to end, constituting its cellular sheath.

In *contraction* of the fasciculi, observed *after death,* the primitive particles are approximated and flattened in the direction of the length of the fasciculi, and expanded in their transverse direction.

Such *contraction may* engage a few such particles only, or the whole fasciculus, may oscillate from end to end, without occurring at any special situations or intervals, and may be independent of immediate nervous co-operation.

Rugae and *zigzag inflexions are* a mere consequence of the approximation of the extremities of a fasciculus, otherwise than by its own contraction, and are necessarily obliterated by either its own contraction, or its elongation by other forces.

It is highly probable, that in all *contractions* of voluntary muscle in the *living body,* the same mechanism is employed as in the dying; and that in the living body, these contractions engage only parts of fasciculi at a time, and oscillate along them, as well as occur alternately in different sets of fasciculi.

These results are true as regards the *vertebrate* and *articulate* classes of the animal kingdom. (Bowman, Sir William. "On the minute structure and functions of voluntary muscle." *Phil. Trans.,* 1840, *130,* 457-501; 1841, *131,* 69-72 [pp. 490-491, 493-494].)

Henry Pickering Bowditch
1840-1911

As the first full-time professor of physiology in America *Henry Pickering Bowditch* established in 1871 in two small attic rooms of the old Harvard medical building on North Grove Street the first physiological laboratory for the teaching of medical students in this country, and equipped it with apparatus bought abroad at his own expense. Born at Boston, Bowditch (Pl. 53) was a grandson of Nathaniel Bowditch, the distinguished mathematician and author of the *Practical Navigator,* and through his mother, Lucy O. Nichols, was related to Edward and William Pickering, the astronomers.

He was educated at Harvard (A.B. 1861) and then entered the Lawrence Scientific School to study chemistry and natural history, but his studies were interrupted by his service with the United States Army during the Civil War. After the war he entered the Harvard Medical School (M.D. 1868) and then went to Europe. After some months at Paris studying with Claude Bernard, Ranvier, and Charcot, Bowditch went to the laboratory of Carl Ludwig of Leipzig. While there he published the memorable paper in which the "all-or-none" principle of contraction of cardiac muscle was for the first time enunciated; in the same communication the phenomenon of the staircase ("Treppe") was described. Thus when he returned to teach physiology at Harvard at the invitation of President Eliot, he had had the training of a mature scientist and thenceforward applied his knowledge to the training of a whole generation of American physiologists of whom perhaps the most outstanding was his own successor, Walter B. Cannon.

The following passage contains Bowditch's description of the "all-or-none" principle.

STIMULATION OF HEART MUSCLE

The weakest induction shock which will just cause a contraction of the heart, does not evoke a minimal contraction, and the size of the contractions does not increase to an absolute maximum as the intensity of the stimulus is raised. An induction shock produces a contraction or fails to do so according to its strength; if it does so at all, it produces the greatest contraction that can be produced by any strength of stimulus in the condition of the muscle at the time. From this it follows directly that the cause of the varying degrees of contraction of the heart is to be sought in changing [initial] conditions of the muscle fibres themselves. It is scarcely necessary to point out the great practical significance of this generalization. (Bowditch, H. P. "Über die Eigenthümlichkeiten der Reizbarkeit, welche die Muskelfasern des Herzens zeigen." *Arb. physiol. Anst. Leipzig,* 1871, *6,* 139-176 [p. 174].)

Walter Morley Fletcher
1873-1933
and
Frederick Gowland Hopkins
1861-1947

Sir Walter Morley Fletcher, physiologist and medical administrator, was one of the most colorful figures of British medicine during the opening years of the twentieth century (Pl. 54).[8] Educated at Cambridge, he became a fellow of Trinity College and in so doing joined "the unseen company of those who down the centuries have poured their riches into this great society." It was "a real and constant delight to him," for it was the society of William Bentley, Isaac Newton, J. J. Thomson, to name but a few. In the physiology laboratories where he worked, he took further inspiration from men such as Michael Foster, J. N. Langley, and Sir William Hardy, and came through with flying colors in his Physiology Tripos after which he proceeded to St. Bartholomew's Hospital where he obtained his medical qualification in 1899.

As Senior Demonstrator in the Cambridge Physiology Laboratory he had as pupils Keith Lucas, A. V. Hill, and Edgar Douglas Adrian, and in his early research endeavors he collaborated with Frederick Gowland Hopkins and Edward Mellanby (1884-1955). It was natural that in this company Fletcher, himself an athlete of distinction, should have become interested in the metabolism of muscle, and one of his earliest papers (1898) dealt with this subject.[9] It was followed in 1907 by the classic paper with Hopkins on the relation of lactic acid to muscle metabolism. The general conclusions reached at this time are given in the following passage. This paper was followed by a number on the same theme, all written in collaboration with Hopkins.

SURVIVAL RESPIRATION OF MUSCLE

We have given proof that the survival processes in excised unstimulated muscle lead from the moment of excision onwards to a steady accumulation of lactic acid, which, under most conditions,

---

[8] Fletcher, Maisie. *The bright countenance, a personal biography of Walter Morley Fletcher.* London, Hodder and Stoughton, 1957. 351 pp.

[9] Fletcher, W. M. "The survival respiration of muscle." *J. Physiol. (Lond.),* 1898, *23,* 10-99; "The influence of oxygen upon the survival respiration of muscle." *Ibid.,* 1902, *28,* 354-359; 474-498.

ceases entirely with loss of irritability. The increase of acid in the intact muscle is most rapid under anærobic conditions, is slower in air, and is not to be observed (at any rate for long periods after excision) in an atmosphere of pure oxygen. In the unstimulated muscle the production is, for the greater part of the survival period, very nearly proportional to the lapse of time; but stimulation produces an acceleration which may convert the curve of production velocity from a linear type into one showing exponential characters. Partial disintegration of the muscle represents a strong stimulus, inducing this acceleration to a marked degree, and a want of recognition of the rapidity of the change so induced has led many observers to ascribe much too high values to the lactic acid content of "resting" muscle. This is an error which has necessarily prevented the ascription of right values to the changes occurring during survival processes or fatigue. Exposure of the intact fibres to poisons, such as chloroform or coal gas, also accelerates the velocity of production, and, as has been shown in Part II of this paper, the action of alcohol in this respect is so marked that its uninformed use as a solvent has introduced large errors into many published estimations of lactic acid.

Our experiments make it clear that the excised but undamaged muscle when exposed to a sufficient tension of oxygen has in itself the power of dealing in some way with the lactic acid which has accumulated during fatigue. While the fibers are recovering from fatigue and regaining irritability in an atmosphere of pure oxygen, their content of lactic acid is greatly reduced. As already stated, exposure to pure oxygen also inhibits the production of the acid in fresh resting muscle. In air a slowing of the rate of production is seen, but exposure to an atmospheric tension of oxygen does not inhibit the process of formation.

There is no reason to suppose at present that an increase of oxygen tension has any influence more special than that of accelerating the penetration of the gas into the muscle mass. If, as can hardly be doubted, there occur, in the surviving tissue, processes (encouraged by anærobic conditions) which lead to acid production, opposed to others (demanding oxygen) which make, possibly, for actual inhibition of production, and, certainly, for removal after production, then it is clear that whether we shall observe an accumulation of the product or a balance, or, as a third alternative, removal of the product when formed, will depend upon the rate at which oxygen is supplied. There is every reason to believe that a sufficient tension of oxygen (not reached in air) partially restores to an excised muscle one normal asset otherwise lost on excision, a supply, namely, of the gas sufficiently rapid to turn the balance, from an accumulation to a removal, of the particular breakdown product under consideration. (Fletcher, W. M. and Hopkins, F. G. "Lactic acid in amphibian muscle." *J. Physiol. (Lond.)*, 1907, *35*, 247-309 [pp. 297-298].)

Louis Lapicque
1866-1952

Louis Lapicque, who occupied the chair of Claude Bernard at the Sorbonne from 1919 to 1936, for many years investigated, in collaboration with his wife, the excitatory process of irritable tissues (Pl. 55). They discovered a striking correlation between such properties as the rate of conduction, the speed of contraction, the latent period, etc., and the least interval of time required to produce excitation; this has shed important light upon the intimate nature of the excitatory processes. Prior to the work of the Lapicques, excitation had been described in vague and inexact terms; but with the introduction of "chronaxie" —a precise and easily determined characteristic—the subject was at once clarified and quantitative methods were made possible.

The theory of isochronism formulated in their first paper on the curare effect was based on the belief that the ability of one tissue to excite another rests on the existence of similar excitatory time factors between the two. A nerve fibre transmitting an impulse to a skeletal muscle fibre must, according to the theory, have the same time relations—the same chronaxie—as the muscle fibre which it innervates. To account for the neuromuscular block produced by curare the Lapicques believed, on the basis of their experiments, that curare had specifically augmented the chronaxie of the muscle fibre without affecting that of nerve, thus making the nerve incapable of stimulating the muscle elements in question. Any agent which would restore the muscle's chronaxie would abolish the neuromuscular block. Similarly, they postulated that the agents which altered the chronaxie of nerve would cause a like block and they found it true experimentally that strychnine shortened the chronaxie of nerve, leaving that of muscle unaffected. They therefore regarded curare and strychnine as antagonists at the neuromuscular junction and assembled much evidence to show that this was true.

The following passage is taken from Lapicque's paper in which the term "chronaxie" was originally defined. Though this paper was published in 1909, the work had been begun in 1903 and hence antedates the excellent studies of Lucas published in 1907.

EXPERIMENTAL DEFINITION OF EXCITABILITY

The excitability of a tissue cannot be considered as defined when but *one* threshold of stimulation has been determined. Indeed, such an isolated determination cannot be used even in the simplest and most direct comparison, *e.g.* to discover whether excitability increases or diminishes under a given influence. Even when it has been ascertained if the stimulus originally used should be increased or diminished, the conclusion reached is only applicable to that particular stimulation and not to the general excitability of the tissue; in fact another stimulus differing from the first merely by its duration might give an entirely different, or even a contrary result.

For example, under the influence of curare, as Brücke clearly stated more than 40 years ago, the excitability of the gastrocnemius of the frog is hardly changed at all for constant currents, while it is considerably diminished for induction shocks.

To take another example: if the temperature is lowered the excitability of nerve and muscle in general is diminished for induction shocks and increased for a constant current*—or to put it more exactly—is diminished for brief shocks and increased for prolonged currents. If one compares the excitability of two different tissues, it is even more essential to take the time element into consideration in addition to the threshold.

A smooth muscle which remains motionless to a violent induction shock contracts under the influence of a fairly weak constant current of several seconds duration; this constant current loses none of its force though it is of slow onset and takes a second or more to establish itself. On the other hand, the gastrocnemius of a frog which would react strongly to an induction shock or to a constant current of abrupt onset would not be affected by a much stronger constant current taking several tenths of a second to establish itself.

Is it then permissible to say that either of these muscles is *more* or *less* excitable than the other, if at the same time the method of stimulation is not indicated? The significance of the terms 'more' and 'less' changes according to the type of stimulation and they are therefore inadequate even when defining relative excitability. . . .

The best method, it seems to me, is to establish the two essential

* Gotch and Macdonald. *Journal of Physiology*, 1896. L. and M. Lapicque. *Comptes rendus de la Soc. de Biol.*, Jan. 12, 1907. Keith Lucas. *Journal of Physiology*, Dec. 31, 1907.

elements of excitability by two direct experimental measurements. This can be be done as follows:

One must determine:

1. The intensity of a constant current of abrupt onset and prolonged duration which gives the threshold of excitability. I propose to call this intensity the *rheobase* (lowest point of current). In practice it is unnecessary to measure this intensity; if the circuit of stimulation does not need to be altered in any way it is sufficient if the voltage corresponding to that of the *rheobase* is known.

2. The duration of a constant current of abrupt onset which attains the threshold of stimulation with an intensity equal to double that of the rheobase, *i.e.* with a voltage of double that of the rheobase. I propose to call this duration the *chronaxie* (αξια, value, χρονου, of time).

This time interval is in reality characteristic of the true excitability of the tissue under consideration, and it agrees more or less with the ratio a/b of the hyperbolic formula; all that I have written on this subject since 1903, on my own or with Madame Lapicque, applies to it. I have proved that it (the *chronaxie*) varies, according to the tissue under consideration—not to mention the influence of temperature—from three ten-thousandths of a second (gastrocnemius of a green frog) to one second (stomach of the same animal), *i.e.*, scale of variation of 1-3000; and it is certain that excitability exists above and below these limits.

Determination of the time interval requisite for establishing the rheobase is necessarily inexact, since it is reached asymptomically. It equals about ten times the *chronaxie*.

Excitability is thus defined without theory or calculation by means of two experimental values. (Lapicque, L. "Définition expérimentale de l'excitabilité." *C. R. Soc. Biol.* [*Paris*], 1909, *67*, 280-283 [pp. 280-281, 282-283].)

Shiro Tashiro

1882-1963

Shiro Tashiro was born at Togo, Japan, and educated at the University of Chicago where he received an S.B. in 1909 and a Ph.D. in 1912. In 1918 he became professor of biochemistry at the University of Cincinnati where he remained until his retirement in 1952. Tashiro's discovery in 1913 that the production of the nerve impulse depends upon the metabolic activity of the nerve fibre was fundamental to the understanding of neural function.

CO_2 IN RESTING AND STIMULATED NERVE TRUNKS

In spite of all the negative evidence against the presence of metabolism in the nerve fibre, we have established three important facts: namely, (1) A resting nerve gives off a definite quantity of carbon dioxide; (2) stimulation increases CO_2 production; and (3) CO_2 production from the resting nerve proportionally decreases as irritability diminishes. These facts prove directly that the nerve continuously undergoes chemical changes, and that nervous excitability is directly connected with a chemical phenomenon. There is still another question left, namely, Is there any direct relation between excitability and tissue respiration? To put this question more directly, we may ask: Does excitability depend on the respiratory process in the protoplasm? To answer these questions we must refer to two facts; namely, the direct relation between the rate of respiratory activity and the decrease of excitability; secondly, the influence of reagents on CO_2 production and their effects on the state of excitability. (Tashiro, Shiro. "Carbon dioxide production from nerve fibres when resting and when stimulated; a contribution to the chemical basis of irritability."* *Amer. J. Physiol.*, 1913, *32*, 107-136 [pp. 132-133].)

Alexander Forbes
1882-1965
and
Alan Gregg
1890-1957

Alexander Forbes was a member of the department of physiology, Harvard Medical School, from 1912 and professor of physiology from 1936 to 1948 when he became Emeritus professor. *Alan Gregg* collaborated with Forbes in the investigations described here while he was a medical student at Harvard where

* The preliminary report of these investigations was given in part in Biochemical section of Eighth International Congress for Applied Chemistry, September 1912. See original communications, Eighth International Congress for Applied Chemistry, xxvi, p. 163. See also this Journal, 1913, *31*, p. xxii.

he took his M.D. degree in 1916. Gregg later went to the Rockefeller Foundation where from 1931 till 1951 he was director of the division of medical sciences.

In 1915 Forbes and Gregg made the earliest systematic analysis of nerve impulses set up in the central nervous system and compared them with those evoked by artificial stimulation of a peripheral nerve. It had been supposed by some physiologists that impulses arising within the brain and spinal cord differed in kind from those elicited faradically in isolated preparations, and Forbes and Gregg were the first to provide satisfactory evidence that, however elicited, nerve impulses were always of the same nature. This gave added significance to the observations of Gotch, Lucas, Adrian, and others who had studied the responses of nerve trunks after removal from the body, and it proved that the all-or-none principle must be taken into account in any consideration of reflex action. In a well-reasoned argument Forbes and his co-worker gave the accepted explanation of the differences between action currents of a reflex and those set up by stimulation of a motor nerve. Forbes in continuing these investigations acquired further evidence for his and Gregg's original interpretations, but the fundamental observations are contained in their first joint communication from which the following selection is made.

ACTION CURRENTS OF THE FLEXION REFLEX

In general, it may be said that as compared with the direct response, the reflex action current appears after a latency of about 9σ, then rises to a maximum which is reached from four to ten times as long after its onset as is the case in the impulses directly evoked from the nerve by a single shock; and the maximum when reached is much smaller even in a maximal reflex than is evoked by maximal stimulation of the nerve. . . .

The more gradual rise of the electrical disturbance in the case of the reflex may be quite as easily explained in a way which harmonizes perfectly with the view that the impulse is essentially the same however evoked. It has already been suggested that we have no grounds for the conclusion that in the flexion reflex the impulses in the many neurones making up the motor nerve are discharged "in a volley" rather than in "platoon fire," to use Brücke's phrase. They might conceivably start down the nerve trunk simultaneously in all the fibres. Yet it is quite as likely, if not even probable, that the reflex times in the hundreds of separate arcs will not be exactly the same, and that the arrival of the various outgoing impulses at a given point in the nerve will be spread out over a considerable period of time. Just such a scattering in time would perfectly explain the more gradual development of the observed electrical disturbance at the point where it is recorded. It would also contribute another factor to account for the greatly reduced intensity of disturbance as compared with the direct response; for if at any given instant only a small percentage of all the fibres taking part in the reflex are at the height of their activity, at no time will there be so great a disturbance as if all were active at once. This consideration taken in connection with those already mentioned, namely, the fact that nearly half the fibres involved in the direct response are afferent and the fact that by no means all of the motor fibres are called into action by stimulation of a single afferent nerve, may well account for the smallness of the action current obtainable from the maximal reflex. (Forbes, A. and Gregg, A. "Electrical studies in mammalian reflexes. I. The flexion reflex." *Amer. J. Physiol.*, 1915, *37*, 118-176 [pp. 147, 148-149].)

Frederick Haven Pratt

1873-1958

Frederick Haven Pratt took his A.B. at Harvard University and after a period of study at Göttingen returned to the Harvard Medical School where he took his M.D. in 1906. From 1912 to 1919 he was professor of physiology at the University of Buffalo but in 1921 moved to the chair of physiology at Boston University which he occupied until 1942 when he became Emeritus professor. Pratt established the all-or-none principle of contraction of skeletal muscle fibres by means of direct observation. His ingenious method involved recording the movement of mercury droplets on the surface of a muscle, one fibre of which was stimulated by a pore electrode several μ in diameter. The following selection will serve to indicate the significance of his studies.

THE ALL-OR-NONE PRINCIPLE

The amount of energy transformed in muscle is characteristically far greater than that manifest in the process necessary to arouse the transformation. Passage from stimulus to response involves a distinct breach of continuity. A change, discrete and transitory, precedes a change revealing sources of energy relatively vast, governed in duration and intensity by no conceivable presiding extension of the original excitatory force; and yet, in skeletal muscle particularly, response is docile to behest of stimulus from its readiness to fulfil the requirements of instrumental calibration up to the marvel of emotional expression.

The determination of the general type of mechanism involved in the factor of control is plainly fundamental to the whole conception of the energetics of muscle. That a minimal stimulus should be capable of awakening the massive charge of an unstable system, and at once restoring equilibrium in relative accordance with its own subtle measure of intensity, is a conception fraught with an assumption of organic complexity unique in its nature, and one which places the problem of muscle contraction in a hazardous field. If, on the contrary, the mechanism of control be regarded as discontinuous with the responding system, conceding to the latter an inherent, determinate capacity for energy release, it is possible to reinstate the control factor as a mechanism for simply utilizing multiples of energy yielding elements. The excitatory process, in accordance with its access to one or more systems of definite dynamic capacity, will then discharge one or more in strict relation to that access; that is, in strict relation to its own demands.

The alternatives present so great a divergence, on the score of both nature and complexity of mechanism, that the acceptance of one or the other must determine widely different interpretations of contractile phenomenon—gross, microscopic and physico-chemical. For in one case we must recognize the events in sequence as follows:

Excitation→initiation of discharge in responding system→limitation of magnitude of discharge (massive) in strict conformity to magnitude of excitation (relatively meagre); and in the other.

Excitation→full discharge in every responding system to which the excitatory influence has effective access.

Thus the first alternative involves, in the same system, initiative plus limitation; the second, initiative without limitation in all systems excited. In the first, control necessitates an inhibition of discharge, quantitatively selective, in a disturbed unstable system; in the second, it requires only that excitation penetrate to each quantum of energy needed in the response. (Pratt, F. H. "The all-or-none principle in graded response of skeletal muscle." *Amer. J. Physiol.*, 1917, *44*, 517-542 [pp. 517-518].)

Genichi Kato

1890-

For many years professor of physiology at Keio University, Tokyo, *Genichi Kato* was by common consent the leader of the great school of physiology in Japan. He was born at Okayama-ken and educated at Kyoto University Medical School where he was graduated in 1916. In 1918 he began to teach at Keio University and soon afterward carried out a series of important experiments upon the effect of narcotics on peripheral nerve. Taking advantage of the species of enormous toad common in Japan, he was able to secure long stretches of nerve which could be subjected to the action of a narcotic. His experiments were beautifully conceived and had a simplicity and directness which made them appealing and convincing to a degree seldom felt of observations in this special field of work. Largely as a result of his investigations it became possible to adopt a satisfactory hypothesis concerning the nature of the nerve impulse.

DECREMENTLESS CONDUCTION

My "theory of decrementless conduction" of nervous impulse in narcotised region of nerve was first brought to publication at the second general meeting of the Japanese Physiological Society which was held in April, 1923, at Kyushu Imperial University in Fukuoka, and secondly, in November of the same year it was delivered as a special lecture at the fourth general meeting of the Keio Medical Society, Tokyo. I have rewritten this lecture to form the present monograph. . . .

In the experiments we have used principally the male species of the large healthy Japanese toads, Bufo vulgaris Japonicus, which often weigh as heavy as about 350 gram, and from them we made nerve-muscle preparations, sciatic-gastrocnemius, the nerve of which was, as a rule, not shorter than 10 centimeters. This extraordinary large toad facilitated us to expose so long a stretch of nerve as eight centimeters to the action of narcotics. . . .

INFLUENCE OF THE LENGTH OF NARCOTISED NERVE ON THE DEPTH OF NARCOSIS REQUIRED TO ABOLISH CONDUCTION

I. PRELIMINARY TEST

As it was stated in the foregoing chapter, the firing of a train of gunpowder closely resembles to the conduction of nervous impulse.

The combustion of gunpowder, however, takes place too instan-
taneously to observe the mode of progression closely. So Dr. Maki
took a Japanese incense, a stick of slowly combusting substance, as
a model of nerve. Attention was at first attracted to the rate of conduction: After he had tested that the combustion propagated along
an "incense" with a slow but constant rate, he immersed the both
ends (AB, CD) of it in a saturated $KCLO_3$ solution and dried. Let
us suppose the part BC, free from $KCLO_3$, as a stretch of nerve that
is narcotised. The combustion propagated with a constant rate along
the "incense" so treated from A to B but more rapidly than before
and from B to C with reduced but constant (not progressively reduced) rate and from C to D as rapidly as in between A and B.
The reduction of the rate of progression in the region BC occurred
at once in the immediate neighbourhood of B and no further reduction was observed along its course. Thus, no decrement in the rate
of conduction! . . .

II. Main Test

The most important experiment upon which "decrement theory"
has been based is, as mentioned before, that the time required to
abolish conduction becomes gradually less as the length of nerve to
be narcotised is made greater. . . .

I suggested, therefore, to Dr. Maki that he should make experiments on this line, and special precautions were taken in following
points:

1. that two sciatic-gastrocnemius preparations were taken from the
same toad and the different lengths of these two nerves were narcotised and the times required to suspend conduction from "outside
electrodes" A and A′ were determined with fully maximal stimulus
and they were compared with each other, and the comparison was
never made between those from different toads or frogs.

2. that the nerves were exposed to narcotic simultaneously in the
same narcotising chamber, so that the different lengths of the two
nerves taken from the same toad could be exposed to the action of
narcotic in the same condition.

3. that special cares were taken in making nerve-muscle preparation as well as in setting it up in narcotising chamber. To avoid inequality of the action of narcotic in any part of the nerve, all the nervous branches were ligated as far as possible from the main trunk.

Before we proceed further to compare the times required to abolish conduction in different lengths of narcotised nerves, we must stop a moment to determine experimentally to what extent the times necessary for extinction of conduction in the same length of two narcotised nerves coincide.

A. *The extent of diversity of the times required to abolish conduction in the same length of two narcotised nerves.*

Under the precaution mentioned above, Dr. Maki has determined the times required to abolish conduction in the same length of nerves taken from the same toad. The differences of the times so determined are given as % of the time for B. In some cases the times were the same for both A and B but it was not a matter of usual occurrence. Some diversity was found in most of the cases, the maximum diversity being as large as twenty percent, though such a difference occurs very rarely.

B. *The times required to suspend conduction in the different lengths of narcotised nerves.*

In the narcotising chamber specified in the precautions different lengths of two nerves taken from the same toad were exposed simultaneously to the action of ether vapour. By regulating the rate of bubbling of ether vapour, the concentration of the narcotic, to which the nerves were exposed, was changed in every experiment, so that the comparison could be made in the wide range of times. In No. 5 the conduction abolished within 7 minutes, while in No. 15 it lasted as long as about 80 minutes. As I have mentioned before, the comparison should be made only between the times given in the same number of experiments (these were determined in two nerves taken from the same toad).

The diversity of the times are given as % of the time determined in the shorter region of narcotised nerve, + indicates a case in which the conduction abolished earlier in longer region of nerve, as previous investigators have informed, while — indicates a case, in which the conduction was suspended earlier in the shorter narcotised region. In No. 3 it will be seen that the times determined were practically the same both in short and long narcotised regions, the conduction being suspended in the shorter region one second earlier. In the other cases the differences oscillated equally on both sides and there could be seen no tendency that the conduction would be abolished earlier in the longer stretch of narcotised nerve. If it be true that the longer is the narcotised region, the shorter is the time for abolition of conduction, then there must be a marked difference of times in No. 19, 20 and 21 in which the lengths of the nerves narcotised were in such a ratio as 11.4 to 1.8. It must, therefore, be concluded that the length of narcotised nerve has no influence at all on the depth of narcosis required to abolish conduction. [The same result was also obtained using as narcotics chloroform, alcohol, urethane, chloral-hydrate and cocaine.]

ETHER AS A NARCOTIC

No.	Time for longer region	cm.	Time for shorter region	cm.	%
1	15' 10"	3.5	15' 0"	2.5	−1.11
2	18' 20"	3.5	18' 25"	2.5	+0.45
3	22' 35"	3.5	22' 34"	2.5	−0.07
15	80' 9"	3.5	82' 18"	1.8	+2.65
19	58' 13"	11.5	45' 36"	1.8	−6.62
20	19' 33"	11.5	18' 32"	1.8	−5.49
21	11' 10"	11.5	12' 0"	1.8	+6.94

(Kato, G. *The theory of decrementless conduction in narcotised region of nerve*. Tokyo, Nankodo, 1924. v, 166 pp. [pp. 1, 11, 13, 14-18]. See also *The further studies on decrementless conduction*. Toyko, Nankodo, 1926. xiii, 163 pp.)

Joseph Erlanger
1874-
and
Herbert Spencer Gasser
1888-1963

Joseph Erlanger was born at San Francisco and took his B.S. degree at the University of California in 1895. From California he went to Johns Hopkins to study medicine (M.D. 1899) and in 1910 was appointed professor of physiology at Washington University Medical School, St. Louis (Emeritus professor 1946-   ).

Herbert Spencer Gasser was born at Platteville, Wisconsin, and studied first at the University of Wisconsin (A.B. 1910; A.M. 1911). He then went to Johns Hopkins University Medical School (M.D. 1915) and in 1916 began teaching (he was professor of pharmacology 1921-1931) at Washington University, St. Louis, where he collaborated with Joseph Erlanger in the researches from which a selection is presented here. Gasser was director of the Rockfeller Institute, New York, from 1935 until his retirement in 1953 and an emeritus member until his death on 11 May 1963.

In 1921 Erlanger and Gasser began the series of joint studies which over a period of time completely revolutionized knowledge concerning conduction in peripheral nerve. Through application of the principle of amplification by means of thermionic valves and the use of an inertialess recording system (the cathode ray oscillograph), they were able to distinguish in a mixed nerve the action currents of fibres subserving different functions. Their correlation of rate of conduction with fibre diameter—itself an important contribution—was overshadowed by their success in allocating distinct functions to the different waves in their action current records.

ACTION CURRENTS OF INDIVIDUAL FIBERS

Discussion and crucial experiment. Turning now to a consideration of the nature of the waves of the compound action current, the evidence we have thus far presented is so clearly in favor of their being discrete action currents originating simultaneously under the stimulating electrode and traveling along the nerve at different rates, that no other plausible way of accounting for them seems possible. In our preliminary statement, published before the evidence had become so convincing, other possibilities were mentioned, but even at that stage of the investigation these were easily disposed of. The waves cannot, for instance, be due to strong stimulation because they are not evident in the phrenic nerve under any circumstances. For the same reason they cannot be attributed to the development of discrete, regular, decremental states resulting from injury to the nerve in preparation. As a matter of fact injuring the phrenic nerve by manipulating it roughly, or by painting it with scalding water, or with 95 per cent alcohol, does not cause waves to appear in its action current.

The phrenic differs from the sciatic nerve in that branches in the former are insignificant, but constitute a striking feature of the latter. The advisability of ascertaining whether the branches have anything to do with the waved nature of the action current in the sciatic nerve became apparent during the course of some experiments that have recently been performed. In these experiments it has been found that when an inert conductor, such for example, as an idle non-polarizable electrode, rests upon the nerve anywhere *between* the leads, the action current is deformed by a notch or by a wave in a manner to be described elsewhere. Not only is this deformation produced by a foreign conductor, but also by the stumps of the nerve's own branches. It has, however, been found that the waves with which the present paper concerns itself are not due to the presence of branches. The waves appear when there are no stumps between leads; indeed they have been obtained when the preparation has consisted only of the part of a very large bull frog's sciatic nerve that is entirely free of branches. . . .

The waves then represent discrete action currents in different nerve fibers. In the present state of our knowledge it is, however, impossible to assign to the waves definite functions; and speculation on this phase of the subject based on the results we have thus far accumulated has failed as yet to suggest even a satisfactory working hypothesis. To be sure it is not at all surprising in view of the varied histological composition of mixed nerves to find that the action current of such a nerve as the sciatic is compound. Indeed the varied histological composition of nerve has led Langley recently to venture the opinion "that the size" for instance "of the fibers has some definite connection with the kind of tissue in which the fiber ends." Now that the action current of a mixed nerve has been found to be compound one would naturally be inclined to infer that each component is concerned with the mediation of some particular type of response. For a clue to the solution of the problem one would naturally turn first to the two great groups of fibers of the peripheral nervous system, namely, motor and sensory. It is, however, currently believed that the conduction rate of the action current is of the same order of magnitude in afferent and efferent fibers. The fact that thus far we have observed only two waves in the action current of the saphenous nerve (dog) whereas the action current of the tibial nerve dissociates into three, sometimes into four, waves, would naturally lead one to attribute this difference to the absence of voluntary motor fibers in the former nerve. But this possibility seems to be precluded by our data in that they show that the leading wave both in the saphenous and in the sciatic action currents has essentially the same rate of conduction. That motor and sensory fibers of a mixed nerve have discrete action currents traveling at different rates is negatived also by the form of the action current in the phrenic nerve.

Despite the fact that this nerve contains, in addition to motor fibers "an abundance of fibers from sensory ganglia" its action current has always been simple in form. . . .

Differences in the nature of nerve impulses on the afferent side have been invoked by Head and collaborators, if we read these authors aright, in order to account for the regrouping of somatic impressions which they describe as occurring within the central nervous system. "Each end organ in the skin," they write, "is capable of reacting to the mass stimulation of the environment in a specific manner . . . When these *peculiar impulses* (italics ours) reach the spinal cord, they are discharged into secondary systems each of which is guarded by specific receptors . . . It is as if the gallery of a concert hall were fitted with a series of resonators, each of which was tuned to a certain note." The indications we have obtained of differences in the properties of groups of fibers composing a nerve supply an experimental basis for the "peculiar impulses" which Head and Thompson find it necessary to predicate in order to account for their clinical observations. Granting the existence of peculiar impulses in particular nerve fibers, the only further condition that would be needed to effect a regrouping of somatic impulses is that the secondary systems, in the sense of Head and Thompson, respond most readily, as do the peripheral receptors, to their adequate stimuli.

These few examples will suffice to indicate the possible applications of our finding that the fibers composing a mixed nerve are not all alike in a physiological sense. To repeat, these differences may mean that the stimuli the fibers deliver are different and perhaps adequate to the structures they innervate. It should be made clear, however, that we have not yet succeeded in obtaining any experimental evidence that can be regarded as proving the existence of differences in the stimulating values of the impulses delivered by the different types of fibers. The results of our investigations do, however, prove that in certain of the mixed nerves the action current is compound. Furthermore they indicate the possibility, which is being investigated further, that each of the potential waves of any action current is a composite of potential changes slightly out of phase in individual nerve fibers. However this may be, we suggest for the sake of convenience that action currents from which discrete waves separate out be called *compound* and that the potential waves which lengthen on propagation be designated *simple* action currents.

(Erlanger, J. and Gasser, H. S. "The compound nature of the action current of nerve as disclosed by the cathode ray oscillograph." *Amer. J. Physiol.*, 1924, *70*, 624-666 [pp. 659-660, 662-663, 665].)

Edgar Douglas Adrian
1889-
and
Yngve Zotterman
1899-

Edgar Douglas Adrian (Lord Adrian, Master of Trinity College, Cambridge) was educated at Trinity College and studied medicine at St. Bartholomew's Hospital, but his election to a fellowship at Trinity in 1913 permitted him to pursue a career of research in neurophysiology. From 1929 to 1937 he was Foulerton Research Professor of the Royal Society; he served as president of the Society 1950-1955. Among his many honors are the Order of Merit and the Nobel Prize in Medicine (1932), shared with Sir Charles Sherrington, for his fundamental discoveries concerning the mechanism of sense organs and motor nerve cells and the structure of nerve messages—discoveries which did so much to illuminate Sherrington's own pioneer work on the nervous system.

Yngve Zotterman took his B.A. degree at Cambridge in 1922, studied medicine in his native Sweden, and in 1926 became a Research Fellow at Cambridge under Adrian. He later returned to Sweden to join the faculty of the Royal Veterinary School at Stockholm, and there continued his researches which resulted in 1935 in the isolation of single units in the taste receptors of the tongue and later, in his analysis (with Liljestrand and von Euler) of the chemoreceptors and stretch receptors in the carotid body.

In 1926 Adrian and Zotterman recorded a series of remarkable observations upon the responses of single sensory end-organs to a natural stimulus (tension) on the basis of which they were led to formulate their important conception of "adaptation" of receptors to stimuli. Their prediction that a similar process of adaptation would be found in other units of the nervous system has been amply justified by recent work, and the theory has already begun to assume an importance comparable with Müller's law of specific nerve energies.

NATURE OF ADAPTATION

The gradual decline in rhythm which occurs with a steady stimulus has already been described, but its cause has not been dealt with. It might be due to a gradual decrease in the excitability of the end-organs or to a gradual increase in their refractory period, or to both

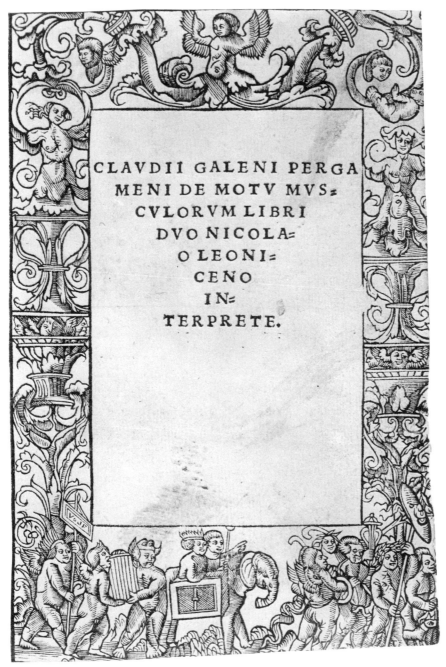

CLAVDII GALENI PERGA
MENI DE MOTV MVS=
CVLORVM LIBRI
DVO NICOLA=
O LEONI=
CENO
IN=
TERPRETE.

PLATE 40. Title-page of the 1522 Pynson edition of Galen's *De motu musculorum* edited by Leoniceno. (Courtesy of the Bodleian Library, Oxford.)

PLATE 41. William Croone (1633-1684). (Obtained through the courtesy of the Royal College of Physicians, London.)

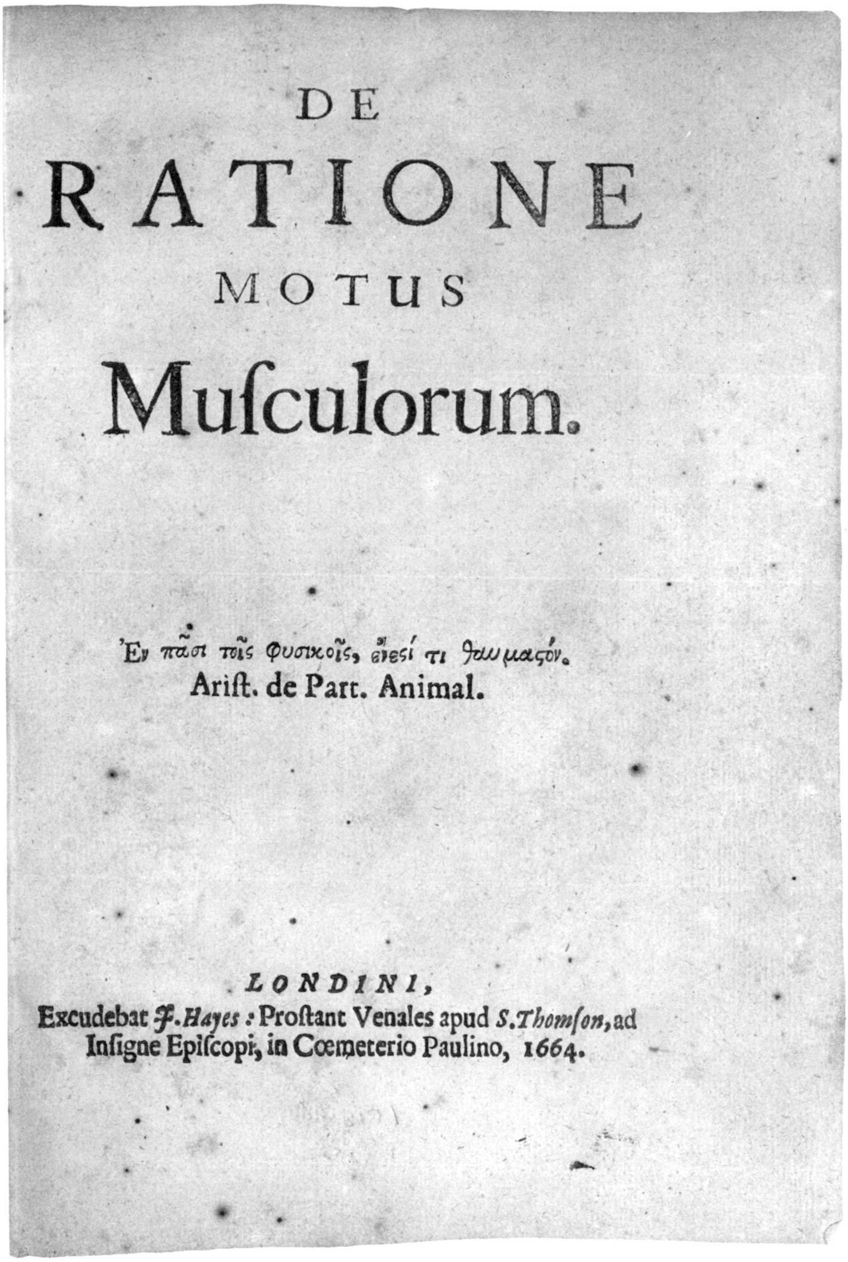

DE
·RATIONE
MOTUS
Muſculorum.

Ἐν πᾶσι τοῖς φυσικοῖς, ἀεί τι θαυμαςόν.
Ariſt. de Part. Animal.

L O N D I N I,
Excudebat *J. Hayes :* Proſtant Venales apud *S. Thomſon,* ad
Inſigne Epiſcopi, in Cœmeterio Paulino, **1664.**

PLATE 42. Title-page of the first edition of Croone's anonymous tract on muscular motion.

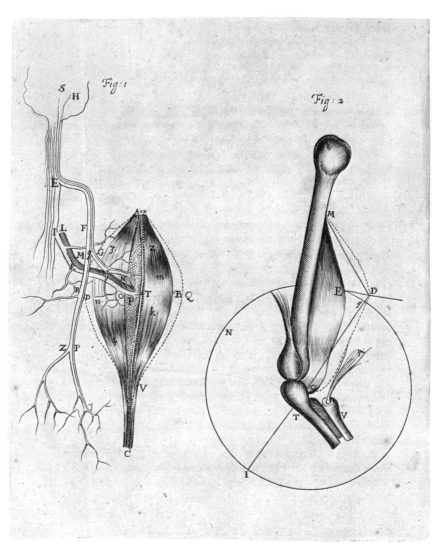

PLATE 43. Croone's diagram illustrating his beliefs concerning the relation of the circulation and nerve supply of muscle to contraction and the direction of forces exerted by certain muscles at the elbow. (From *De ratione motus musculorum*, 1664.)

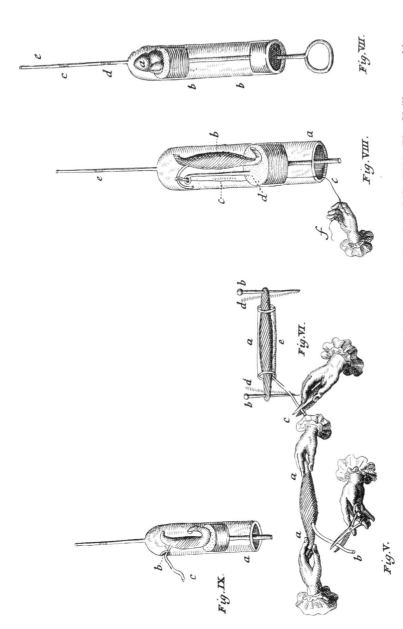

Fig. VII.

Fig. VIII.

Fig. VI.

Fig. V.

Fig. IX.

PLATE 44. Part of Plate XLIX in Jan Swammerdam, _Biblia naturae_ (Leyden 1737-1738). Fig. V illustrates his mode of stimulating the contraction of an excised frog's muscle by squeezing the attached nerve. Fig. VI Swammerdam used to demonstrate the degree to which a muscle is thickened at the same time that it is contracted. Fig. VII shows how a living frog's heart, which has been inflated with air like a balloon and its vessels tied, diminishes in volume when the heart muscle contracts in systole. At that instant the droplet of water in the capillary glass tube drops from C to D. Figs. VIII and IX illustrate two techniques for showing that the volume of a skeletal muscle does not change during contraction. The droplet of water in the capillary glass tube remains at the same level _e_ when the muscle is stimulated to contract. These minutely elegant experiments represent an extraordinary degree of skill and ingenuity.

PLATE 45. Thomas Willis (1621-1675), the discoverer of the circle of Willis.

PLATE 46. Francis Glisson (1597-1677). (Courtesy of the Bodleian Library, Oxford.)

DE
MOTV ANIMALIVM

IO. ALPHONSI BORELLI

NEAPOLITANI

MATHESEOS PROFESSORIS

Opus Poſthumum.

PARS PRIMA.

ROMAE,
Ex Typographia Angeli Bernabò. M. DC. LXXX.

SVPERIORVM PERMISSV.

PLATE 47. Title-page of the first volume of Borelli's book on the movements of animals. This great work attempted to provide explanations of all forms of physiological activity in terms of physical and chemical forces as well as giving mechanical analyses of various forms of co-ordinated muscular activity.

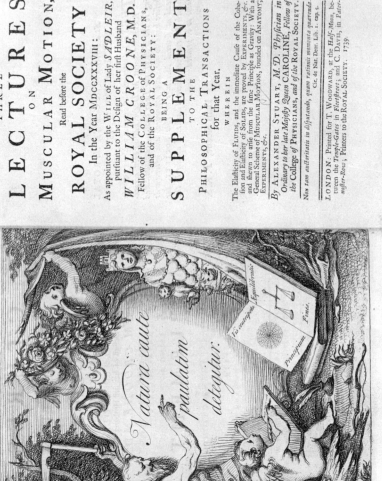

THREE
LECTURES
ON
MUSCULAR MOTION,
Read before the
ROYAL SOCIETY
In the Year MDCCXXXVIII:

As appointed by the WILL of Lady SADLEIR,
purſuant to the Deſign of her firſt Husband
WILLIAM CROONE, M.D.
Fellow of the COLLEGE of PHYSICIANS,
and of the ROYAL SOCIETY:

BEING A
SUPPLEMENT
TO THE
PHILOSOPHICAL TRANSACTIONS
for that Year.

WHEREIN

The Elaſticity of FLUIDS, and the immediate Cauſe of the Cohe-
ſion and Elaſticity of SOLIDS, are proved by EXPERIMENTS, &c.
and ſhewn to ariſe from the ſame Principle as Gravity: With a
General Scheme of MUSCULAR MOTION, founded on ANATOMY,
EXPERIMENTS, &c.

By ALEXANDER STUART, M.D. *Phyſician in
Ordinary to her late Majeſty Queen* CAROLINE, *Fellow of
the* College *of* Physicians, *and of the* Royal Society.

Non tam auchoritatis in diſputando, quam rationis momenta quærenda.
Cic. de Nat. Deor. Lib. 1. cap. 5.

LONDON: Printed for T. WOODWARD, at the *Half-Moon*, between the *Temple-Gates* in *Fleetſtreet*; and C. DAVIS, in *Pater-
noſter-Row*; Printers to the ROYAL SOCIETY. 1739.

PLATE 48. The engraved frontispiece and title-page of the first Croonian Lecture on muscular motion, 1739.

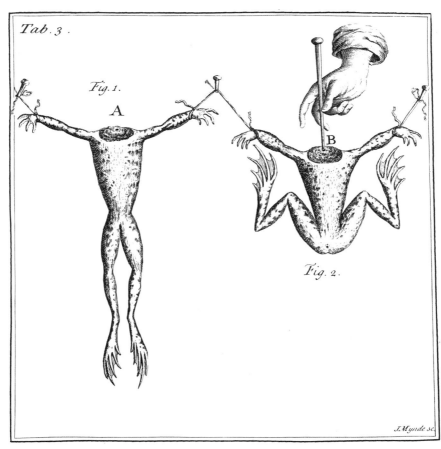

PLATE 49. Stuart's diagram illustrating the motions induced in a decapitated frog on compression of the spinal medulla. He fancied that the movements were due to pressing fluid into the nerves. (From the first Croonian Lecture, 1739.)

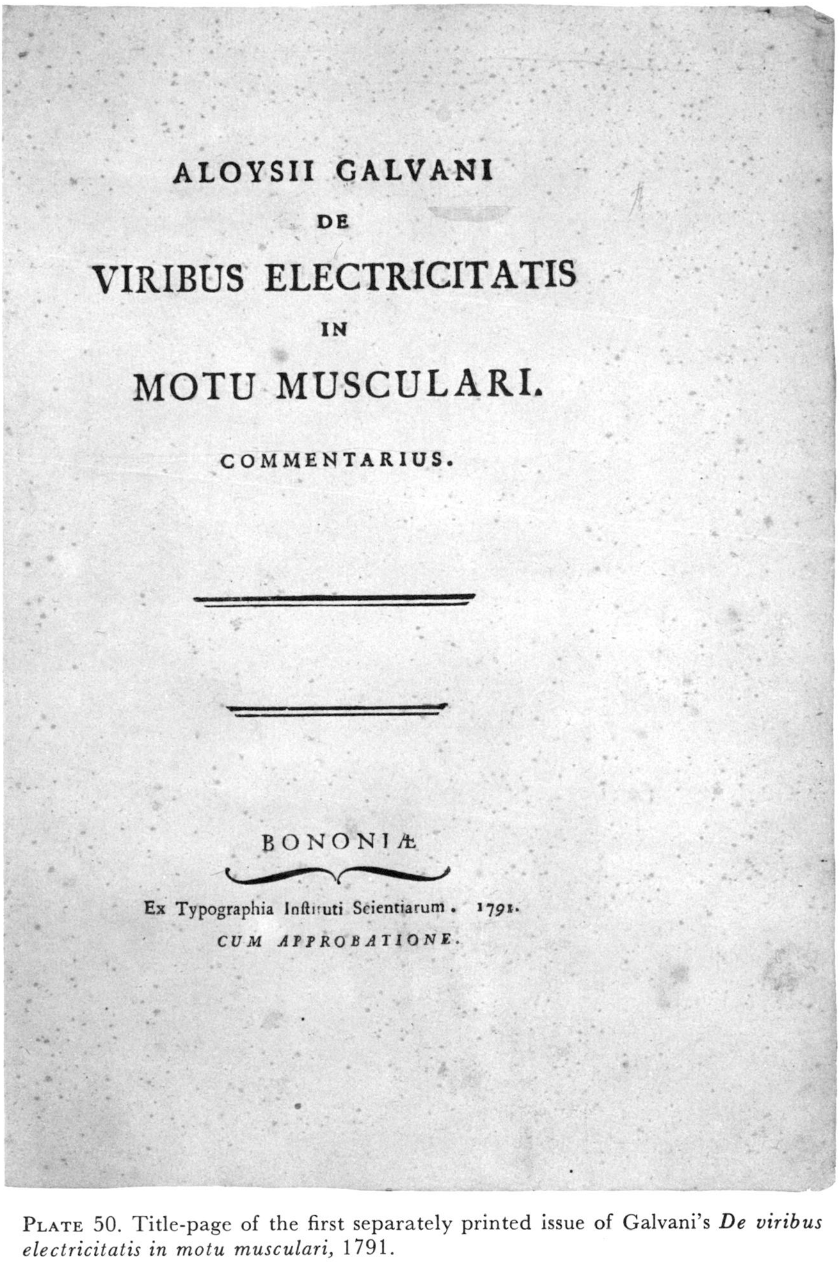

ALOYSII GALVANI

DE

VIRIBUS ELECTRICITATIS

IN

MOTU MUSCULARI.

COMMENTARIUS.

BONONIÆ

Ex Typographia Inftituti Scientiarum. 1791.

CUM APPROBATIONE.

PLATE 50. Title-page of the first separately printed issue of Galvani's *De viribus electricitatis in motu musculari,* 1791.

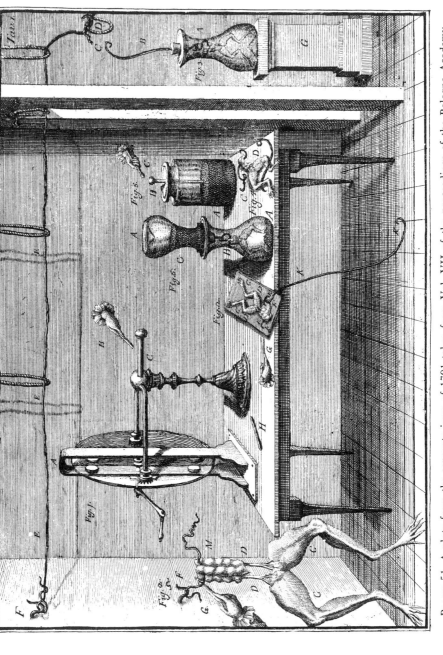

PLATE 51. A plate from the separate issue of 1791 taken from Vol. VII of the proceedings of the Bologna Academy, *De Bononiensi scientiarum et artium instituto atque academia commentarii*, containing Galvani's original announcement of his discovery of animal electricity.

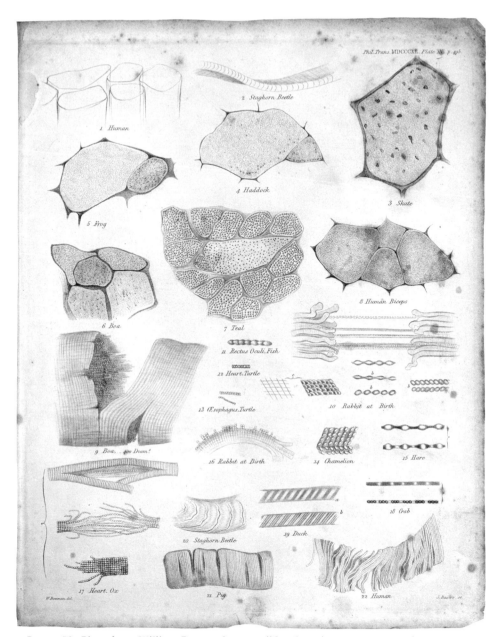

1 Human

2 Staghorn Beetle

4 Haddock

3 Skate

5 Frog

6 Boa

7 Teal

8 Human Biceps

11 Rectus Oculi, Fish

12 Heart, Turtle

13 Œsophagus, Turtle

10 Rabbit at Birth

9 Boa. 400 Diam.t

16 Rabbit at Birth

14 Chamelion

15 Hare

20 Staghorn Beetle

19 Duck

18 Crab

17 Heart, Ox

21 Pig

22 Human

W. Bowman del.

J. Basire sc.

PLATE 52. Plate from William Bowman's paper "On the minute structure and movements of voluntary muscle" published in 1840. Bowman was the first to describe the fibres of striated muscle.

PLATE 53. Henry Pickering Bowditch (1840-1911). (Courtesy of the Library of the School of Medicine, Harvard University.)

Plate 54. Sir Walter Morley Fletcher (1873-1933). (Kindness of Lady Fletcher.)

PLATE 55. Louis Lapicque (*right*) with A. V. Hill and Madame Lapicque at the 1929 International Physiological Congress in Boston. (Photograph by Walter Willard Boyd.)

these causes. If only the former were in action, the effective value of the stimulus would decrease so that longer and longer intervals would have to elapse after each impulse before the end-organ had reached the degree of excitability necessary for the setting up of a fresh impulse. A slowing of the rate of recovery would have the same effect, although the excitability remained unaltered. When a gradually increasing current is applied to a nerve fibre the adaptation which occurs is confined to the mechanism of excitation, for the stimulus may fail to set up an impulse at all if it increases too slowly. Presumably the failure of a constant current to set up more than one impulse is due to the same cause, *i.e.* to the rapid decline in the stimulating value of the current. The rate of recovery may be altered in the region which becomes adapted, and Brücke has shown that the refractory period of the nerve fibre or nerve ending becomes prolonged when a rapid succession of impulses are passing, but this by itself would not account for the complete failure to set up a second impulse. So, if the decline in rhythm from the end-organ is due to a process of adaptation of the same kind as that occurring in the nerve fibre we should expect to find evidence of a change in excitability with or without a change in refractory period in addition.

In order to study the process more thoroughly we have increased the tension on the muscle at varying rates, recording both the tension on the muscle at each moment and the frequency of the afferent impulses. The tension was applied by a short lever fixed in the centre of a twisted elastic band. A similar lever at one end of the band was rotated at varying speeds through a known angle and its movement was communicated to a pointer moving across the slit of the film camera. The lever in the middle of the band is fixed to the thread from the muscle and can only move through a very small arc, but when the end lever is rotated the tension on the thread is increased and its final value depends on the amount of movement of the end lever. The tension developed for different movements of the end lever was determined by hanging weights on the centre lever and finding the amount of movement required to raise them. . . . With very rapid loading the maximum frequency is reached at about the same moment as the maximum tension, but with more gradual loading the maximum frequency is much less and it is reached some time before the stimulus is at its full value. These curves would be the natural result of any process of adaptation and they merely serve to emphasise the fact that the adaptation begins at the moment that the stimulus is applied. A more significant fact is shown in Fig. 10 B, which records also the effects of a rapid unloading after the tension had been at its full value for 17 seconds. In all our experiments the result of this has been a complete cessation of all impulses for a period varying from .75 to 1.5 sec. followed by a gradual return to the normal "resting" frequency of 3-8 per second. . . . It is difficult to explain this pause in the discharges without supposing that a true fall of excitability has occurred. During the period of stimulation the frequency has fallen to about half its initial value. If this fall is due to an increase in the refractory period the latter must have risen to about double its initial value, and we should expect to find a discharge at half the initial resting frequency when the stimulus is removed. Actually the initial frequency is 6 per second but there is a pause of 1.3 sec. at the end of stimulation.

We conclude that the decline in the frequency of response is due in part at least to a fall of excitability in the end-organs when the stimulus is continued and their adaptation is thus brought into line with the much more rapid process which occurs in the nerve fibre.

Remarks

The behaviour of the end-organs which we have examined seems to be explained very simply in terms of the general properties of excitable tissues, in particular by the phenomena of adaptation and of the refractory state. It is probable, therefore, that other types of end-organ will be found to react in much the same way to the particular stimuli which call them into play. This probability is strengthened by the close resemblance of the records of impulses in various types of sensory nerve dealt with in Part I, though an investigation of other single end-organs will be needed to establish it. A point of considerable interest is that the frequency of the discharge from the end-organ is so much slower than the maximum frequency which the nerve fibre can tolerate. If this is true of end-organs in general it means that the frequency of the impulses in the fibres of the auditory and of the optic nerves is lower than is often supposed. This again must wait for experimental confirmation. Finally, it is worth enquiring whether the synapses of the central nervous system may not sometimes react in the same way as the end-organ to the mass of impulses reaching them. (Adrian, E. D. and Zotterman, Y. "The impulses produced by sensory nerve-endings. Part 2. The response of a single end-organ." *J. Physiol.* [*Lond.*], 1926, *61*, 151-171 [pp. 167-170].)

Archibald Vivian Hill
1886-
and
William Hartree
1870-1943

Archibald Vivian Hill, biophysicist, was educated at Trinity College Cambridge (B.A. 1909) where he was elected a fellow in 1910. After a period of teaching at Manchester he was appointed professor of physiology at University College in 1923 (Hon. 1925-1951). From 1926 to 1951 he was Foulerton Research Professor of the Royal Society. His collaborator in the work here presented, *William Hartree,* O.B.E., was born on 8 April 1870 and educated at Trinity College, Cambridge, where he took his degree in 1892 and where he lectured in the Engineering Department until 1913. He was associated with A. V. Hill during the First World War, and in 1919 returned to Cambridge with him to work in physiology, publishing ten papers on the physiology of muscle under his own name, his first in 1920 at the age of fifty, and 24 in collaboration with others, his last at seventy-one. He remained at Cambridge until 1933 when physical disability took him out of the laboratory to collaborate with his son in yet another field, calculation of atomic structures. He died on 27 April 1943.

Hill and William Hartree have contributed extensively to knowledge of the thermodynamics of muscle and have been largely responsible for the modern conception of muscle metabolism. In the course of their fruitful collaboration they have studied from the point of view of the physical chemist not only the reactions of isolated muscle, but also the performance of the intact human organism. The analysis of heat-production of isolated muscle has been made possible through constant improvements in instruments for detecting all thermal changes. The separation of heat-production into four distinct phases, correlated with corresponding phases of mechanical activity, represents perhaps their most important discovery. The first selection has been taken from their original paper describing this result.

Hill has continued to pursue the elusive problem of heat production in muscle and nerve (his contributions were recognized in 1922 by the Nobel Prize shared with Otto Meyerhof) since his first paper on the action of nicotine and curare as determined by temperature coefficients and form of contraction curve of the muscle twitch.[10] At that time his methods for detecting heat led

[10] Hill, A. V. "The mode of action of nicotine and curari, determined by the form of the contraction curve and the method of temperature coefficients." *J. Physiol. (Lond.),* 1909, *39*, 361-373.

him to believe that no heat production was involved in the transmission of the nerve impulse.[11] In the fifty years since the appearance of his first paper, Hill, with a persistence and stubbornness worthy of John Bull himself, has sought ways and means of increasing both the speed and the sensitivity of his heat-detecting thermocouples. The success implied in his recent paper on heat production in the muscle twitch is deserving of praise and unreserved congratulation.

THE FOUR PHASES OF HEAT-PRODUCTION OF MUSCLE

When a muscle is stimulated isometrically it passes gradually into a new elastic condition: as stimulation is continued the elastic condition continues to change up to a certain limit, after which it remains constant; when stimulation ends, the muscle reverts gradually to its original elastic state. Expressed in another way the muscle, on excitation, gradually develops elastic potential energy: as the excitation proceeds this potential energy reaches a constant value; when the excitation ends the potential energy disappears. Finally, in the presence of oxygen there occur certain recovery processes accompanied by an evolution of heat and restoring the muscle to its previous internal condition. These four stages, viz. the development of the mechanical response, its maintenance and its disappearance, followed by the oxidative recovery from activity, will be referred to below as the four phases of muscular contraction. The questions arise "how much of the total heat-production is to be associated with each phase and how is it distributed in time?" The experiments described in this paper represent an attempt to answer this question. The investigation arose originally from the simpler question, "what happens to the potential energy of a muscle excited isometrically, when the muscle relaxes?" There are clearly two possible answers: (i) that the potential energy, if not utilised in doing work, is re-absorbed more or less reversibly by the muscle for use in a subsequent contraction; or (ii) that it is degraded into heat by processes analogous (say) to leakage, diffusion or neutralisation. The experiments have decided in favour of the second alternative. . . .

2. EXPERIMENTAL RESULTS

The present part of this paper deals only with the heat produced during the first few seconds after excitation and is confined to the

[11] Hill, A. V. "The absence of temperature changes during the transmission of a nervous impulse." *J. Physiol. (Lond.)*, 1912, *43*, 433-440.

case of tetanic stimulation, for periods of 0.1 to 6.0 seconds, of the sartorius muscles of the frog (Rana temp.). It is clearly desirable to repeat the investigation on other and more slowly moving muscles and we hope to do this later. The experiments have been carried out at various temperatures, in oxygen and in nitrogen, and under various conditions of fatigue.

The first important point brought out by these experiments is that, provided that advanced fatigue be avoided, no difference can be discerned in the initial stages of the heat-production between muscles kept in oxygen and muscles left for a long time in nitrogen. It is known, and in experiments performed recently we have amply confirmed, that in the later stages there is considerable difference in the heat-production according as the muscles are kept in oxygen or nitrogen; this difference is attributed to slow oxidative recovery processes possible (at least to their full extent) only in the presence of oxygen by which the muscle is restored in some manner to its previous condition.

Oxygen however has no effect whatever on the *initial* heat-production. It is not necessary to give all the evidence in detail as it is negative in kind and we will include below only an account of one experiment devoted specifically to testing this point. The direct comparison of the curves made by the muscle (a) in oxygen and (b) in nitrogen is an extremely sensitive one, as no analysis of the records is required in order to allow us to assert that the two curves are the same; thus any possible error in the analysis is eliminated. Great care was taken in the nitrogen experiments to eliminate the oxygen completely by sweeping it out as far as possible with boiled Ringer's solution in which the muscles were allowed to rest for some time, then leaving the muscles for some time in nitrogen before making an observation, and lastly giving them (in most cases) a few preliminary stimuli in order to assist them to use up any traces of dissolved oxygen. A mild degree of exercise not leading to appreciable fatigue does not appear to alter the type of the thermal response: advanced fatigue however does change it by diminishing the relative amount of heat liberated in the processes of relaxation. Muscles kept in nitrogen are readily fatigued and it is necessary therefore to avoid over-stimulating them. . . .

In a prolonged contraction (*e.g.* 2 secs. tetanus) of the sartorius, the heat production may be resolved into the following four phases: (a) an initial rapid production, diminishing gradually in rate as the stimulus proceeds; (b) a smaller constant heat-production maintained so long as the stimulus is maintained, and ending shortly after the stimulus ceases; (c) a relatively large evolution of heat, occurring rather suddenly during the later stages of relaxation; and (d) a large, but slow, production of heat occurring in the presence of oxygen for some minutes after the contraction is over.

In the twitch evoked by a single shock or by a very short tetanus only three of these phases occur, (a), (c) and (d). It is natural to associate (a) with the development, (b) with the maintenance and (c) with the disappearance of the mechanical response, and to connect (d) with the processes of recovery. It is probable that the heat produced during relaxation is derived from the mechanical potential energy developed on excitation, and lost in relaxation.

The interval between the second and third phases of the initial heat-production depends largely on the temperature. In a short twitch at 0°C. it is of the order of 0.7 sec.: at 25°C. it is too short to be measured directly with the instruments at present employed. All the more reliable experiments have been performed at a low temperature. (Hill, A. V. and Hartree, W. "The four phases of heat-production of muscle." *J. Physiol.* [*Lond.*], 1920, *54*, 84-128 [pp. 84-85, 106-107, 126-127].)

TIME OF HEAT-PRODUCTION IN MUSCLE TWITCH

When a muscle has been soaked in a moderately hypertonic solution its mechanical response to a shock is delayed, but its heat production is almost normal and starts considerably earlier than its shortening. After a more hypertonic solution the mechanical response is abolished, but a substantial part of the heat production remains. These effects are rapidly reversed by soaking in a normal isotonic solution. They strengthen the previous conclusion that chemical reactions triggered by a stimulus precede the mechanical response. . . .

DISCUSSION

The separate identity, and the properties, of the heat of activation were discussed by Hill (1949a)* and the conclusion was drawn that it makes up about one-third to one-half of the whole heat in a twitch

* Hill, A. V. 1949a *Proc. Roy. Soc. B*, 136, 195-211.

undergoing maximal shortening. At 0°C. this is usually about 3×10^{-3} cal/g, so the heat of activation would be 1.0 to 1.5×10^{-3} cal/g. It appeared to reach its full value rather soon after excitation (in about 0.2 or 0.3 s), but accuracy in determining its magnitude and time course was not great. Another estimate of the heat of activation (Hill 1950*b*)* made use of the fact that a muscle very heavily loaded does not shorten at all when excited, so there is neither heat of shortening nor work. Under these conditions the heat that remains is rather less than half the heat production under a small load, say 1.2×10^{-3} cal/g. Both these estimates are rather higher than the heat found after treatment with strong hypertonic solutions. This was not unexpected, for the hypertonic muscles were difficult to excite fully.

The mechanical response considered in this paper, shortening or development of tension, was that recorded by ordinary methods. By special procedures, however, earlier signs of mechanical change can be detected, *e.g.*, (1) the 'latency relaxation,' which is a very slight lengthening (under favourable conditions about 1/1000 of the muscle's length), and (2) increased resistance to rapid stretch (Hill 1951)† which is a much stronger effect. In muscles soaked in hypertonic solutions, and showing no ordinary mechanical response to a shock, Howarth (1958)‡ found a similar increased resistance to stretch. There is no present evidence that the heat production starts earlier than this increase of stiffness; though Professor Sandow (personal communication) informs me that he was unable to detect any latency relaxation in hypertonic muscles showing no ordinary contraction.

It is clear, in any case, that the chemical reactions responsible for the heat production may be well advanced before any detectable shortening occurs. The increased rigidity revealed by a rapid stretch begins much earlier than shortening; it may be an immediate consequence of the first chemical reaction triggered by the stimulus, *e.g.* a removal of the 'plasticizing' effect of ATP when that is broken away from actomysin (see *e.g.* Weber and Portzehl 1954).¶ (Hill, A. V. "The priority of the heat production in a muscle twitch." *Proc. roy. Soc. B.,* 1958, *148*, 397-402 [pp. 397, 401-402].)

* Hill, A. V. 1950*b* *Proc. Roy. Soc. B*, **137**, 330-331.

† Hill, A. V. 1951 *Proc. Roy. Soc. B*, 138, 339-348.

‡ Howarth, J. V. 1958 *J. Physiol.* (in the Press) [144, 167-175].

¶ Weber, H. H. Portzehl, H. 1954 *Progr. Biophys.* 4, 60-111.

Alan Lloyd Hodgkin
1914-
and
Andrew Fielding Huxley
1918-

The discovery of the giant nerve fibres of the squid (*Loligo forbesi*) by J. Z. Young in 1936 opened one of the most exciting chapters in the history of modern neurophysiology because it permitted the study of the electrical phenomena of the nerve impulse in the interior as well as on the surface of a single nerve fibre. The first persons to succeed in the difficult task of inserting electrodes into a living giant nerve fibre and thereby measuring directly the action potential within the fibre were Hodgkin and Huxley. This same feat was accomplished independently and almost simultaneously by Curtis and Cole in the United States in the summer of 1939.[12] Because of the war Hodgkin and Huxley were unable to pursue their work immediately, but in 1945 they succeeded in measuring both the resting and action potentials and showed that the action potential exceeds the resting potential by a large amount.[13] By 1947 they had shown that the generation of the nerve impulse was accompanied by a leakage of potassium ions across the membrane with a resulting marked change in the membrane conductance, and that during recovery the potassium ions were reabsorbed. They then engaged in an intensive series of researches into the electrical and chemical changes which accompanied the nerve impulse and in 1952 were able to publish equations which accurately predicted the form of the conductance changes and the form and amplitude of the action potential during impulse transmission and allowed them to restrict the number of possible kinds of ionic events which might produce these changes.[14] The fundamental significance of this work was recognized in 1963 when Hodgkin and Huxley shared with Sir John Carew Eccles the Nobel Prize in physiology. Eccles' work has thrown a similar degree of light on the mechanism of nerve impulse transmission across the synapse.

Alan Lloyd Hodgkin was born at Danbury, near Oxford, England, and educated at Trinity College, Cambridge. During the war he worked on radar research but since 1945 he has been at the Physiology Laboratory, Cambridge. In 1952 he was appointed Foulerton Research Professor of the Royal Society.

[12] Curtis, H. J. and Cole, K. S. "Membrane action potentials from the squid giant axon." *J. cell. comp. Physiol.*, 1940, *15*, 147-157.

[13] Hodgkin, A. L. and Huxley, A. F. "Resting and action potentials in single nerve fibres." *J. Physiol. (Lond.)*, 1945, *104*, 176-195.

[14] Hodgkin, A. L. and Huxley, A. F. "A quantitative description of membrane current and its application to conduction and excitation in nerve." *J. Physiol. (Lond.)*, 1952, *117*, 500-544.

Also a student and Fellow of Trinity College, Cambridge, *Andrew Fielding Huxley* engaged in research and teaching at Cambridge until 1960 when he became Jodrell Professor of Physiology at University College, London.

ACTION POTENTIALS RECORDED FROM INSIDE A NERVE FIBRE

Nervous messages are invariably associated with an electrical change known as the action potential. This potential is generally believed to arise at a membrane which is situated between the axoplasm and the external medium. If this theory is correct, it should be possible to record the action potential between an electrode inside a nerve fibre and the conducting fluid outside it. Most nerve fibres are too small for this to be tested directly, but we have recently succeeded in inserting micro-electrodes into the giant axons of squids (*Loligo forbesi*).*

The following method was used. A 500μ axon was partially dissected from the first stellar nerve and cut half through with sharp scissors. A fine cannula was pushed through the cut and tied into the axon with a thread of silk. The cannula was mounted with the axon hanging from it in sea water. The upper part of the axon was illuminated from behind and could be observed from the front and side by means of a system of mirrors and a microscope; the lower part was insulated by oil and could be stimulated electrically. Action potentials were recorded by connecting one amplifier lead to the sea water outside the axon and the other to a micro-electrode which was lowered through the cannula into the intact nerve beneath it. The micro-electrode consisted of a glass tube about 100μ in diameter and 10-20 mm. in length; the end of the tube was filled with sea water, and electrical contact with this was made by a 20μ silver wire which was coated with silver chloride at the tip. . . . A small action potential was recorded from the upper end of the axon and this gradually increased as the electrode was lowered, until it reached a constant amplitude of 80-95 mv. at a distance of about 10 mm. from the cannula. In this region the axon appeared to be in a completely normal condition, for it survived and transmitted impulses for several hours. Experiments with external electrodes showed that the action potential was conducted for at least a centimetre past the tip of the micro-electrode.

These results are important for two reasons. In the first place they

* Young, J. Z. *Proc. Roy. Soc.*, B 121, 319 (1936).

prove that the action potential arises at the surface, and in the second, they give the absolute magnitude of the action potential as about 90 mv. at 20°C. Previous measurements have always been made with external electrodes and give values which are reduced by the short-circuiting effect of the fluid outside the nerve fibre.

The potential difference recorded between the interior and exterior of the resting fibre is about 50 mv. The potential difference across the membrane may be greater than this, because there may be a junction potential between the axoplasm and the sea water in the tip of the electrode. This potential cannot be estimated, because the anions inside the nerve fibre have not been identified.

We wish to express our indebtedness to Mr. J. Z. Young, whose discovery of the giant axon in *Loligo* made this work possible. (Hodgkin, A. L. and Huxley, A. F. "Action potentials recorded from inside a nerve fibre." *Nature*, 1939, *144*, 710-711.)

VII

Central Nervous System

Knowledge of the nervous system has developed to a large extent independently of other branches of physiological thought, for, unlike them, it has until recent years drawn but little upon the exact sciences. In the early days the nervous system proved difficult to study, not so much because of the obscurity surrounding the activities of its individual units, but rather because of the complexity of its structure. Even in the eighteenth century physiologists had grasped many of the fundamental facts relating to conduction in nerve trunks, but it is only in modern times, thanks to Waller, Remak, Van Gehuchten, and Ramón y Cajal, that the intricacies of structure have been effectively unravelled. The theory of the integrative action of the nervous system has made possible an intelligent functional analysis in terms of its overwhelming structural complexity.

Enunciation of the concept of reflex action marked the beginning of the modern interpretation. Jean Fernel (1542) and René Descartes (1637) dimly grasped the notion without fully appreciating its significance. Stephen Hales and Alexander Stuart found that decapitated frogs ceased moving when the spinal cord was destroyed, but it remained for Robert Whytt (1751) to define reflex action in terms of experiment in precise language. Prochaska generalized the concept without, however, offering much new experimental data in its support. From the controversy between Bell (1811, 1821) and Magendie (1822) there emerged, largely through the genius of Magendie, the fact that incoming and outgoing pathways of the nervous system are separate morphological entities. Herbert Mayo then proved that a small segment of the nervous system might be sufficient for the maintenance of a reflex, and, soon after, Marshall Hall began to teach that the spinal cord is in reality a series of interrelated segments, each with its own circumscribed reflex arcs. When reflex action had been firmly established, investigators next attempted to analyze the functions of individual regions of the nervous system. Rolando (1809) and Flourens (1824) approached the cerebellum; Fritsch and Hitzig (1870) defined the motor area; and David Ferrier (1873), with the stimulus of the clinic constantly before him, gave the rational explanation of hemiplegia and hemianopsia, and in so doing localized for the first time the more important functions of the cerebral hemispheres. The theory of reflex integration, which is associated with the name of Sherrington (1906), has clarified the bewildering mass of clinical and physiological data concerning the various levels of function in the nervous system which had been accumulating since the time of Hughlings Jackson (1870).

Jean Fernel

1497-1588

Jean Fernel, mathematician, astronomer, physiologist, and personal physician to four French kings, was a remarkable and most versatile man, a great humanist, and certainly one of the foremost figures of French science and medicine during the sixteenth century. At the age of thirty he gave to the world the first accurate measurement of a meridian of longitude. Fernel, however, engages our attention in this volume because he was above all else a *physiologist* and, within the limits of his time, a disciple of Galen's experimental method, especially in study of the nervous system. Nevertheless he was not one to uphold the doctrines of Galen uncritically. Sir Charles Sherrington in *The Endeavour of Jean Fernel* summarizes Fernel's thoughts concerning mind and muscle and concludes that he had an appreciation of the concept of reflex action a century before Descartes. The esteem in which Fernel was held by the men of his time is indicated by Guy Patin whose pen, Sherrington remarked, was so often "dipped in gall, but never for Fernel" (p. 59). "He is of my Saints, along with Galen [Patin wrote]. Never prince did more for the world than our Fernel. He rescued our learning from decay and our calling from disaster. He gave the profession a new lease of life; he bequeathed it a fresh fame. I should glory more to trace descent from him than from the King of Scots or the Emperor of Constantinople."

FERNEL ON MIND

Fernel treats mind as coming within physiology [*Physiol.* v, c. I] It forms the theme of a full third of his "Physiology." He includes the mind and its workings within physiology not because he regards the mental as an affair of matter. That was not his conception at all. *Res incorporeae sunt objecta intelligentiae.* He considered the action of the mind a part of physiology because for him all the workings which went on in the body were, at source, non-material and incorporeal. . . . (C.S.S.)[1]

FERNEL ON THE NERVES OF SENSATION AND MOTION

[Some nerves are for touch and others for motion]

The sense of touch is composed of somewhat harder nerves that the sixth pair of cerebral nerves distributes inwardly to the organs and outwardly to the skin. They are the authors of no motion. Now those nerves that are called the movers are very hard, and even if they do not cause voluntary motion, nevertheless they convey the effective force of motion into the muscles, the special instruments of motion. Let us pause briefly and consider the arrangement of these nerves of which, although the structure is similar, some are for motion, others for sensation. And lest perhaps it be pretended that some issue from the brain, others from the cerebellum and spinal marrow, we declare that both have the same origin. What is the reason therefore that of those that arise from the brain, some are adapted to motion, others to sensation? The origin of both is the same, a similar spirit flows into them, and Galen gives them the same composition; what then is the reason for this distinction, this difference? The harder—he says—are those that cause movement, the soft those that provide sensation. However, those touching nerves that are extended from the sixth pair into the organs, the skin and the extremities of the body, are much harder than those that are extended from the second pair into the eyes to give them motion. Nor is this only in the long course of their passage, but immediately from their origin, because they receive a more posterior origin than that other [second] pair.

[The composition of some is for motion, of others for sensation]

Therefore the cause of this so completely distinguished faculty must not be referred to softness or to hardness. Let us therefore consider composition. But what is the explanation of this composition? I shall say little but suggest many things.

[The brain is moved, the meninges have sensation]

The body of the brain is agitated by constant motion, yet equipped with no sense of touch; on the other hand the meninges which go about it are themselves immobile and very thick; but they are in-

[1] Sherrington, *Sir* Charles S. *The endeavour of Jean Fernel. With a list of his writings.* Cambridge, Cambridge University Press, 1946. x, 223 pp. [pp. 59, 77].

dividually exquisitely sensitive to touch, as has been confirmed by Galen and as we also have detected by feeling them in the wounded and in open skulls. The symptoms of diseases fully declare this, because delirium and frenzy—which arise from a phlegmon of the substance of the brain—are not usually accompanied by pain, and even less so are unconsciousness and lethargy, although accompanied by putridity. However, if the very smallest drop either of a humor or of a sharp vapor is carried to the meninges, severe pain results. These things display the different natures of the brain and of the meninges.

[*The moving force is from the brain, the sentient from the meninges*]

The spine and all the nerves derive their marrow from the brain as its source, and their investing coat from the meninges; individually they have that force and nature which they receive from their origin. Therefore it is necessary that the marrow in the spine and the nerves —even if, unlike the brain, it is not agitated by motion—is the moving force, and the membranes receive its sentient and motor force and transfer it to other parts. For if the body of the brain is lacking in sensation, much more so is that marrow which is in the spine and the nerves. For whence and through what condition did it receive a new force? Or how does the body of the brain confer upon it a sentient force which the brain does not have? And so whatever nerves have the power of both touching and of moving are instruments of each function, yet in a different part. Those which are called sentient are the authors only of touch and not at all of motion, and those which go from the sixth pair to the inward organs and the outer skin are of this kind. Although they do not issue from the meninges alone —as some once believed—yet they receive from them most of their substance and very little from the brain; for immediately after they arise from the thin meninx, as they approach the thicker, they receive a great increase of strength and power. Therefore they effect merely touch and not motion.

[*In what way the brain is the origin of motion and sensation*]

On the other hand, those arisen from the spine are observed to contain a large supply of marrow from their origin. Therefore the anterior part of the brain is the origin and seat of sensation and the posterior of motion, but the meninges are the origin of touch; however, the brain cloaked about by its meninges is the efficient cause of all animal functions. Those nerves which are filled with much marrow are the instruments of motion, but those that issue in greater part from the meninges, of touch. (Fernel, Jean. *Universa medicina.* Paris, Andreas Wechsel, 1567. [De partium corporis humani descriptione. Book V, De animae facultatibus, ch. X, pp. 100-101].)

René Descartes
1596-1650

René Descartes, the philosopher, took the functions of living organisms into the sphere of his speculations and wrote what is sometimes erroneously described as the first European textbook of physiology (Pl. 56).[2] Since he was not an experimentalist, the cold logic of the experimental method had little appeal to his speculative turn of mind. He regarded the human body as a machine directed by the "rational soul" which dwelt in the pineal gland (Pl. 57a), and he dimly grasped the concept of reflex action, as the following paragraph will indicate; but with Descartes the conception was an *ad hoc* assumption unaccompanied by any experimental justification. The same is true of his interesting description of reciprocal innervation of the eye muscles (Pl. 57b), also given below.

L'ÂME RAISONNABLE

For the parts of the blood which penetrate even into the brain do not serve merely to nourish and maintain its substance but instead chiefly to produce a certain very subtle breath or rather a very lively and very pure flame which they call the *Animal Spirits.* . . .

In proportion as the animal spirits enter the cavities of the brain, they pass thence into the pores of its substance, and from these pores into the nerves; where according as they enter, or even only tend to enter, more or less, into this or that nerve, they have the power of changing the shape of the muscles into which the nerves are inserted, and by this means making all the limbs move. Thus, as you may have seen in the grottoes and fountains in our gardens, the force

[2] Descartes, R. *De homine figuris et latinitate donatus a Florentio Schuyl.* Leyden, Francis Moyard & Peter Leff, 1662. [34], 121 [8], 85 pp., 6 pl. The phrase "latinitate donatus" indicates that the manuscript was originally in French. The French text, however, was not published until 1664. The original figures showing the valves of the heart and the diagrams of the pineal gland appear only in the first two Latin editions of 1662 and 1664. In subsequent editions the diagrams were redrawn by Louis de La Forge, the French editor, and many of them are scarcely recognizable when compared with the originals from which they were taken.

with which the water issues from its reservoir is sufficient to put into motion various machines, and even to make them play several instruments, or pronounce words, according to the varied disposition of the tubes which conduct the water. Indeed, the nerves of the machine may very well be compared with the tubes of these waterworks; its muscles and tendons with the other various engines and springs which seem to move these machines; its animal spirits to the water which impels them, of which the heart is the source or fountain; while the cavities of the brain are the central reservoir. Moreover, breathing and other like acts which are as natural and usual to the body or machine, and which depend on the flow of the spirits, are like the movements of a clock, or of a mill, which may be kept going by the ordinary flow of water. External objects which, by their mere presence, act upon the organs of sense; and which, by this means, determine the machine to move in many different ways, according as the parts of the brain of the machine are arranged, may be compared to the strangers who, entering into one of the grottoes of these water works, unconsciously themselves cause the movements which they witness. For they cannot enter without treading upon certain planks which are so disposed that, if they approach a bathing Diana, they cause her to hide among the reeds; and if they attempt to follow her, they see approaching towards them a Neptune, who threatens them with his trident; or if they pass in another direction they cause some sea-monster to dart out who vomits water into their faces; or like contrivances, according to the fancy of the engineers who made them. And lastly, when the rational soul—*l'âme raisonnable*—is lodged in this machine, it will have its principal seat in the brain, and will take the place of the engineer or 'fountaineer', who ought to be in that part of the works or reservoir with which all the various tubes are connected, when he wishes to quicken or to slacken, or in any way to alter their movements. . . .

(The final summary is as follows) : I desire you to consider all the functions which I have attributed to this machine (the body) , as the digestion of food, the pulsation of the heart and of the arteries (Pl. 58); the nutrition and the growth of the limbs; respiration, wakefulness, and sleep; the reception of light, sounds, odours, flavours, heat, and such-like qualities, in the organs of the external senses; the impression of the ideas of these in the organ of common sense and in the imagination; the retention, or the impression, of these ideas on the memory; the internal movements of the appetites and the passions; and lastly, the external movements of all the limbs, which follow so aptly, as well as the action of the objects which are presented to the senses, as the impressions which meet in the memory, that they imitate as nearly as possible those of a real man; I desire, I say, that you should consider that these functions in this machine naturally proceed from the mere arrangement of its organs, neither more, nor less than do the movements of a clock, or other automaton, from that of its weights and wheels; so that so far as these are concerned, it is unnecessary to conceive in it any soul—whether vegetative or sensitive—or any other principle of motion, or of life, than its blood and its spirits agitated by the heat of the fire which burns continually in its heart, and which is in no wise essentially different in nature from all the fires which are met with in inanimate bodies.

RECIPROCAL INNERVATION OF THE EYE MUSCLES

Let us imagine a tube or small nerve, bf, flowing into the muscle D—which I am supposing is one of those which move the eye, and there dividing into several branches, loose in texture, which stretch or shrink according to the quantity of animal spirits which flow in or out of them, and whose ramifications are so arranged that the animal spirits flowing into them cause the whole body of the muscle to swell and shorten, thus pulling the eye to which it is attached towards it; on the other hand when the animal spirits flow out of the muscle it shrinks and lengthens.

Besides bf, there is another tube, ef, through which the animal spirits flow into muscle D, and there is yet another tube, dg, by which they flow out of it. Muscle E, which I assume moves the eye in the opposite direction to muscle D, receives the animal spirits from the brain through the tube cg, while those from muscle D flow through dg to E, which returns them to D by ef. There is no visible exit for the spirits contained in muscles D and E, and apparently they can only flow from one muscle to another, but these spirits are composed of such minute particles, which become even smaller owing to their ceaseless motion, that they are continually escaping through the surface and flesh of the muscles, while more are always flowing in by the two tubes, bf, and cg.

There is a small membrane, Hfi, separating the tubes bf and ef and acting as a kind of door. It has two angles, H and I, so arranged that when the animal spirits which tend to flow down from b towards H are stronger than those which are flowing up from e to i, the former push down this membrane, thus making an opening through which the latter can come through and join them as they flow towards muscle D; but when the spirits flowing up from e to i are stronger, or even as strong, as the others, they raise the membrane Hfi so that it remains closed, thus barring their own exit from muscle E; while if there is not sufficient force on either side to push against Hfi, it normally remains half-open. If, as sometimes happens, the spirits in muscle D tend to flow out through dfe or dfb, the fold H can swell out and block their passage. Between cg and dg there is another small membrane or valvule g, similar to Hfi, which normally remains half-open, and which can be closed by the spirits flowing from dg and opened by those flowing from cg.

From all this it follows naturally that when the animal spirits in the brain do not tend, or hardly tend at all, to flow through the tubes, bf, cg, the two valvules f and g remain half-open and they and the muscles D and E are slack and motionless; the more so because the animal spirits which they contain flow freely from one muscle to the other, from e by f to d and conversely from d by g to e. When the spirits tend to enter the tubes, bf, cg, however, with an equal force from both sides, they immediately close the two passages g and f and fill out the muscles D and E as much as possible, thus causing them to hold the eye firmly in whatever position they find it.

Again, if the animal spirits from the brain tend to flow with more force through bf than cg, they close the valve g and open f—either more or less, in proportion to their strength—through which the spirits in muscle E pass to muscle D by the tube ef, at a speed in proportion to the size of the opening at f, so that muscle D shortens, because the spirits cannot flow out of it, while E lengthens, and thus the eye is turned towards D. On the other hand if the spirits flow with greater force through cg than through bf they close valvule f and open g, so that the spirits from muscle D go back at once by the tube dg to muscle E, which thus becomes shortened and pulls the eye towards that side.

These spirits are like a wind or a very subtle flame and they are bound to flow very rapidly from one muscle to another whenever they can find a passage; and this though no force guides them, but only their inclination to move about according to the laws of nature. And though they are very subtle and lively, yet when they flow into a muscle they cause it to become stiff and swollen, just as air in a balloon makes it hard and stretches the substance in which it is contained. (Descartes, R. *L'Homme et un traitté de la formation du foetus.* Paris, Charles Angot, 1664. 39 *ll.*, 448 pp., 4 *ll.* [pp. 10-11, 12-14, 106-107; 16-21].)

Robert Whytt
1714-1766

Robert Whytt, a neurologist of Edinburgh (Pl. 59), approached the physiology of the central nervous system in the modern spirit, extirpating known regions of the central nervous system and studying how animals reacted thereafter to various stimuli. His book,[3] in which the results are described, is one of the most remarkable in the history of neurology (Pl. 60). In it he establishes that the spinal cord is essential for reflex action and describes the pupillary response to light—which is still known as "Whytt's reflex"—observing that destruction of the anterior *corpora quadrigemina* abolished the reaction. The following passage indicates that he also grasped fully the mechanism and significance of reflex action. To the element within the central nervous system which received sensory impressions he applied the term "sentient principle" and implied that, unlike the "rational soul" of Descartes, it was diffused throughout the brain and spinal cord.

'VITAL' MOTIONS

FURTHER, the motions excited by any pain, or irritation, are so instantaneous, that there can be no time for the exercise of reason, or a comparison of ideas in order to their performance; but they seem to follow as a necessary and immediate consequence of the disagreeable perception. And as the DEITY seems to have implanted in our minds a kind of SENSE respecting *Morals,* whence we approve of some actions, and disapprove of others, almost instantly, and without any previous reasoning about their fitness or unfitness; a FACULTY of singular use, if not absolutely necessary for securing the interests of virtue among such creatures as men! so, methinks, the analogy will appear very easy and natural, if we suppose our minds so formed and connected with our bodies, as that, in consequence of a *stimulus* affecting any organ, or of an uneasy perception in it, they shall im-

---

[3] Whytt, R. *An essay on the vital and other involuntary motions of animals.* Edinburgh, Hamilton, Balfour and Neill, 1751. x, 392 pp. For an excellent account of Whytt, see Leonard Carmichael's "Robert Whytt: a contribution to the history of physiological psychology." *Psych. Rev.,* 1927, *34,* 287-304.

mediately excite such motions in this or that organ, or part of the
body, as may be most proper to remove the irritating cause; and this,
without any previous rational conviction of such motions being necessary or conductive to this end. Hence, men do not eat, drink, or
propagate their kind, from deliberate views of preserving themselves
or their species, but merely in consequence of the uneasy sensations
of hunger, thirst, &c.

THE mind, therefore, in producing the vital and other involuntary motions, does not act as a rational, but as a sentient principle;
which, without reasoning upon this matter, is as necessarily determined by an ungrateful sensation or *stimulus* affecting the organs, to
exert its power, in bringing about these motions, as is a balance,
while, from mechanical laws, it preponderates to that side where the
greatest weight prevails.

THE general and wise intention of all the involuntary motions, is
the removal of every thing that irritates, disturbs, or hurts the body:
hence, those violent motions of the heart, in the beginning of fevers,
small-pox, measles, &c. when frequently the blood, from its being
affected by the mixture of some peculiar *miasma*, acts as a stronger
stimulus than usual upon this organ. Nevertheless, as, in many instances, the very best things may, by excess, become hurtful; so this
endeavour to free the body, or any of its parts, from what is noxious,
is unhappily, sometimes, so strong and vehement as to threaten the
entire destruction of the animal fabric. But, in the main, this FAC-
ULTY must be confessed highly useful and beneficial; since, without it, we should constantly have cherished in our bodies the lurking
principles of diseases, slowly indeed and by imperceptible degrees,
but not less surely, ruining our health and constitutions.

UPON the whole, there seems to be in man one sentient and intelligent PRINCIPLE, which is equally the source of life, sense and
motion, as of reason; and which, from the law of its union with the
body, exerts more or less of its power and influence, as the different
circumstances of the several organs actuated by it may require. That
this principle operates upon the body, by the intervention of something in the brain or nerves, is, I think, likewise probable; though,
as to its particular nature, I presume not to allow myself in any uncertain conjectures; but, perhaps, by means of this connecting *medium*, the various impressions, made on the several parts of the body
either by external or internal causes, are transmitted to, and per-

ceived by the mind; in consequence of which it may determine the nervous influence variously into different organs, and so become the cause of all the vital and involuntary motions, as well as of the animal and voluntary. It seems to act necessarily, and as a sentient principle only, when its power is exerted in causing the former; but, in producing the latter, it acts freely, and both as a sentient and rational agent. (Whytt, R. *Op. cit.* [note 3], pp. 288-291.)

Georgius Prochaska
1749-1820

Georgius Prochaska, a brilliant anatomist of Vienna, known throughout the continent of Europe on account of his attractive lectures and writings, attempted more precise allocation of the elements of a reflex to known structures in the nervous system. He occupies an important position in the history of psychology for his introduction of the concept of a "sensorium commune"—that region of the central nervous system which "reflects" to the motor nerves the sensory impressions received by the brain.[4] There is no suggestion in the writings of Prochaska of sensory and motor roots, but sensory and motor fibres are tacitly assumed. The following excellent translation appeared in 1839 in an anonymous work, by Alexander Walker, entitled *Documents and Dates of Modern Discoveries in the Nervous System.*

INVOLUNTARY MOTIONS REFLECTED FROM THE SENSORIUM COMMUNE

What are the sensorium commune, its functions, and its seat?

External impressions, which are made upon the sensorial nerves, are propagated rapidly through their whole length to their origin; where, when they have arrived, they are reflected according to a certain law, and pass into certain and corresponding motor nerves, through which, again rapidly propagated even to the muscles, they excite certain and determinate motions. This place, in which, as in a centre, the nerves appropriated to sense as well as motion, meet and

---

[4] Prochaska's theory of a "sensorium commune" appeared in his *Adnotationum academicarum fasciculi tres,* which bears the title "De functionibus systematis nervosi et observationes anatomico-pathologicae." The "Adnotationes" were published at Prague, the first fasciculus in 1780 and the last in 1784. The passage translated was reprinted in Latin at Vienna in 1800 in Prochaska's *Opera minorum anatomici-physiologici et pathologici argumenti,* and occurs in the second volume on page 150 ct seq.

communicate, and in which the impressions of the sensorial nerves
are reflected upon the motor nerves, is called the sensorium commune—a term already received by most physiologists.

The whole cerebrum and cerebellum certainly do not seem to belong to the composition of the sensorium commune: these parts of
the nervous system appear to be rather the instruments which the
mind uses immediately in the performance of the actions termed animal; but it seems not improbable that the sensorium commune, properly so called, extends to the medulla oblongata, the crura cerebri
and cerebelli, even to part of the thalami optici, and to the whole
spinal marrow, in a word, as widely as the origin of the nerves. That
the sensorium commune extends to the spinal marrow, we learn
from the motions remaining in decapitated animals, which could not
take place without the consent and cooperation of the nerves arising
from the spinal marrow; for if a decapitated frog be pricked, not
only does it retract the punctured part, but it crawls and leaps,
which could not be without the consent of the sensorial and motor
nerves, of which consent the seat must be in the spinal marrow, the
part of the sensorium commune remaining.

The reflection of sensorial into motory impressions, which takes
place in the sensorium commune, does not obey mere physical laws,
where the angle of reflection is equal to the angle of incidence, and
where action and reaction are equal, but it follows peculiar laws
written, as it were, by nature, in the medullary pulp of the sensorium, which we can know only by their effects, and not discover by
our imagination. Nevertheless, a general law, according to which the
sensorium commune reflects sensorial into motor impressions, is our
preservation: so that certain motory impressions follow external
impressions hurtful to the body, producing motions tending to ward
off and remove the source of injury; and, on the contrary, internal
or motor impressions follow external or sensorial impressions
beneficial to us, producing motions calculated to perpetuate that
benefit. Many examples certainly prove this general law of the
reflections of the sensorium commune, of which it will be sufficient
to adduce a few. Irritation of the internal membrane of the nostrils
excites sneezing, because that impression, made by irritation of the
olfactory nerves, is by them carried to the sensorium commune, is
there reflected, according to a certain law, upon motor nerves going
to the muscles appropriated to respiration, and, through these, pro-

duces a forcible expiration through the nose, in which, by the air forcibly passing, the irritation is removed. So it happens when any irritation is caused to the wind-pipe by a crumb of bread or a drop of liquid falling into it: this irritation, carried to the sensorium commune, and thence reflected upon the nerves appropriated to respiratory motion, excites a forcible cough, the most apt remedy for expelling the irritant, which does not cease until that irritant is removed. If a friend approaches our eye with his finger, although we are persuaded that no harm will be done to us, yet that impression carried by the optic nerve to the sensorium commune, is in the sensorium so reflected upon the nerves appropriated to the motion of the eyelids, that the palpebrae are involuntarily closed so as to avoid the contact of the finger. These and innumerable other examples that might be adduced, show manifestly how much the reflection of sensorial into motor impressions by the sensorium commune regards the preservation of our body. On this account, Tissot properly enumerates the action of the sensorium commune amongst those powers of which the end and union constitute the nature of our living body.

As, therefore, the principal function of the sensorium commune consists in the reflection of sensorial into motor impressions, it is to be observed, that this reflection takes place whether the mind be conscious or unconscious of it. The motion of the heart, of the stomach, and of the intestines, certainly in no respect depend on the consciousness of the mind; but as no muscular motion can be excited, unless a stimulus applied to the sensorial nerves passes by a certain reflection to the motor nerves, and excites muscular contraction, so it is certain that the reflection of impressions proper for inducing these motions, if they take place in the sensorium commune, takes place without the consciousness of the mind. But it is asked whether these impressions ascend to the sensorium commune, to be reflected, or whether, without making this circuit, they are more quickly reflected by the ganglia, whence these parts have many nerves. More on this point hereafter. But that the reflections of sensorial into motor impressions take place quite unconsciously in the sensorium commune, we learn from certain actions remaining in apoplectic patients, in whom all consciousness is destroyed; for they have a strong pulse, breathe strongly, and often even raise the hand unconsciously to the part affected. The sensorium commune acts also without consciousness in producing the convulsive motions of epileptic patients, and even those retractions of the limbs when slightly pricked or pinched, which are sometimes observed in profound sleep, besides motion of the heart and respiration. To these we must add all those motions which for some time remain in the body of a decapitated man, or other animal, and are excited by pinching the body, but especially the spinal marrow, which certainly occur without consciousness, and are governed by the residual part of the sensorium commune, which is in the spinal marrow. All these actions arise from the organisation and physical laws proper to the sensorium commune, and are, therefore, spontaneous and automatic. Those actions, which take place in the animal body with consciousness, are either such, that the mind has no power over its will, or such as the mind can coerce or impede at will: the former, as they are ruled by the sensorium commune alone, in as far as it does not depend upon the mind, are also automatic actions, not less than those which are performed unconsciously; such are sneezing from a stimulus applied to the nostrils, cough from a stimulus applied to the trachea, vomiting from irritation of the fauces, or from an emetic, tremor and convulsions in chorea S. Viti, and in the paroxysms of intermittent fever, &c. But the actions which the mind directs and moderates by its power, although the sensorium commune has its part in producing them, we call, nevertheless, animal, not automatic. ([Walker, Alexander]. *Documents and dates of modern discoveries in the nervous system*. London, John Churchill, 1839. xii, 172 pp. [Prochaska's "Involuntary motions reflected from the sensorium commune," pp. 123-130].)

Alexander Walker

1779-1852

Alexander Walker, an eccentric of the Edinburgh School of Anatomy, deserves credit for having insisted, prior to Bell and Magendie, upon the separate functions of the posterior and anterior roots of spinal nerves. Unfortunately he appears to have based his inferences purely upon anatomy and he assigned to the anterior roots the function of sensibility and to the posterior roots motor power. He was deeply perturbed that no one of his time gave him credit for his speculations, and he died still believing that the posterior roots were motor and the anterior, sensory. The following passage[5] from his paper published in 1809 is

---

[5] Walker, A. "New anatomy and physiology of the brain in particular, and of the nervous system in general." *Archives of Universal Science*, 1809, *3*, 172 et seq.

included here as one of the curiosities of physiological literature. Walker was a scholarly man whose translations from French, German and Latin are above reproach (see his anonymous *Documents and Dates of Modern Discoveries in the Nervous System*, London, 1839). Struthers[6] notes that he was forced to leave London for having pointed out to a group of fellow students that the great Abernethy, during an operation which they witnessed, had tied off a nerve-trunk when intending to ligate the subclavian artery.

NEW ANATOMY AND PHYSIOLOGY OF THE BRAIN

Thus, then, it is proved to us, that medullary action commences in the organs of sense; passes, in a general manner, to the spinal marrow, by the anterior fasciculi of the spinal nerves, which are, therefore, nerves of sensation, and the connexions of which with the spinal marrow or brain must be termed their spinal or cerebral terminations; ascends through the anterior columns of the spinal marrow which are, therefore, its ascending columns; passes forward through the inferior fasciculi of the medulla oblongata, and then through the crura cerebri; extends forward, outward and upward through the corpora striata; and reaches the hemispheres of the cerebrum itself. This precisely is the course of its ascent to the sensorium commune.

From the posterior part of the medulla of the hemispheres, it returns by the thalami, passing backward, inward and downward; flows backward in the fasciculi under the nates and testes; backward and upward through the processus cerebelli and testes or anterior peduncles of the cerebellum; and thus reaches the medulla of the cerebellum itself.

From the cerebellum, it descends through the posterior columns of the spinal marrow, which are, therefore, its descending columns; and expands through the posterior fasciculi of all the nerves, which are, therefore, the nerves of volition, and the connexions of which with the spinal marrow or brain must be termed their spinal or cerebellic origins. This precisely is the course of its descent from the sensorium commune toward the muscular system.

Now, from this course, it is evident, that impressions acting on the organs of sense, and there producing sensations, will reach, by this route, the sensorium commune, and there constitute perception, or, in other words, will have their influence diffused from this central point, and rendered universally cognizable to the system; for all the

[6] Struthers, J. *Historical sketch of the Edinburgh anatomical school.* Edinburgh, Maclachlan and Stewart, 1867. 94 pp. [p. 77].

actions which take place in this system must be cognizable to it, and even the action of other systems can only be cognizable by means of this one.

Volition would similarly appear to consist in the transmission of the impulse from the cerebellum, the new modification which, from its structure, that impulse must undergo, and its rapid descent through the posterior columns to the muscular organs. ([Walker, Alexander). *Documents and dates of modern discoveries in the nervous system.* London, John Churchill, 1839. xii, 172 pp. [pp. 35-36].)

Charles Bell

1774-1842

Sir Charles Bell, an anatomist born in Edinburgh, was a prolific writer whose beautifully illustrated anatomical works still remain among the chief desiderata of anatomical collectors. His claims to priority in the discovery of the functions of the anterior and posterior roots of the spinal cord have been the subject of prolonged controversy. Those who wish authoritative information should consult Gordon-Taylor and Walls's *Sir Charles Bell, His Life and Times,* Norman Moore's life of Bell in the *Dictionary of National Biography,* A. D. Waller and Keith's correspondence in the *Lancet,* 1911-1912, and Carmichael's excellent account of Bell.[7] Bell put forward his beliefs in 1811 in a privately printed pamphlet entitled *Idea of a New Anatomy of the Brain Submitted for the Observation of the Author's Friends.* Only five copies of the tract are known to exist. It will be evident to anyone who studies the tract that Bell's real claim rests on having demonstrated convincingly the motor functions of the anterior roots. In this tract he certainly did not prove the sensory functions of the posterior roots. In an article published in the *Philosophical Transactions* in 1821 the concept was published, but in reserved and halting terms.[8] This paper was reprinted several times after Magendie's discovery had been announced, and Bell was clearly guilty of making changes in the original text, giving more definite shape to the theory, yet retaining the date 1821. Though one hesitates to pass judgment upon claims to priority, one cannot doubt that Bell was dishonest and that the chief credit for elucidating the function of the posterior as well as

[7] Gordon-Taylor, Gordon and Walls, E. W. *Sir Charles Bell, his life and times.* Edinburgh and London, E. S. Livingstone, 1958; Carmichael, L. "Sir Charles Bell: a contribution to the history of physiological psychology." *Psych. Rev.,* 1926, *33,* 188-217.

[8] Bell, C. "On the nerves; giving an account of some experiments on their structure and functions, which lead to a new arrangement of the system." *Phil. Trans.,* 1821, *111,* 398-424.

the anterior roots belongs to Magendie. It will be observed that Bell had clearly in mind the principle of specific nerve energies.

IDEA OF A NEW ANATOMY OF THE BRAIN; SUBMITTED FOR THE OBSERVATION OF HIS FRIENDS

NOTE

The want of any consistent history of the Brain and Nerves, and the dull unmeaning manner which is in use of demonstrating the brain, may authorize any novelty in the manner of treating the subject.

I have found some of my friends so mistaken in their conception of the object of the demonstrations which I have delivered in my lectures, that I wish to vindicate myself at all hazards. They would have it that I am in search of the seat of the soul; but I wish only to investigate the structure of the brain, as we examine the structure of the eye and ear.

It is not more presumptuous to follow the tracts of nervous matter in the brain, and to attempt to discover the course of sensation, than it is to trace the rays of light through the humours of the eye, and to say, that the retina is the seat of vision. Why are we to close the investigation with the discovery of the external organ?

It would have been easy to have given this Essay an imposing splendour, by illustrations and engravings of the parts, but I submit it as a sketch to those who are well able to judge of it in this shape.

The prevailing doctrine of the anatomical schools is, that the whole brain is a common sensorium; that the extremities of the nerves are organized, so that each is fitted to receive a peculiar impression; or that they are distinguished from each other only by delicacy of structure, and by a corresponding delicacy of sensation; that the nerve of the eye, for example, differs from the nerves of touch only in the degree of its sensibility.

It is imagined that impressions, thus differing in kind, are carried along the nerves to the sensorium, and presented to the mind; and that the mind, by the same nerves which receive sensation, sends out the mandate of the will to the moving parts of the body.

It is further imagined, that there is a set of nerves, called vital nerves, which are less strictly connected with the sensorium, or which have upon them knots, cutting off the course of sensation, and thereby excluding the vital motions from the government of the will.

This appears sufficiently simple and consistent, until we begin to examine anatomically the structure of the brain, and the course of the nerves—then all is confusion: the divisions and subdivisions of the brain, the circuitous course of nerves, their intricate connections, their separation and re-union, are puzzling in the last degree, and are indeed considered as things inscrutable. Thus it is, that he who knows the parts the best, is most in a maze, and he who knows least of anatomy, sees least inconsistency in the commonly received opinion.

In opposition to these opinions, I have to offer reasons for believing, That the cerebrum and cerebellum are different in function as in form; That the parts of the cerebrum have different functions; and that the nerves which we trace in the body are not single nerves possessing various powers, but bundles of different nerves, whose filaments are united for the convenience of distribution, but which are distinct in office, as they are in origin from the brain.

That the external organs of the senses have the matter of the nerves adapted to receive certain impressions, while the corresponding organs of the brain are put in activity by the external excitement: That the idea or perception is according to the part of the brain to which the nerve is attached, and that each organ has a certain limited number of changes to be wrought upon it by the external impression.

That the nerves of sense, the nerves of motion, and the vital nerves, are distinct through their whole course, though they seem sometimes united in one bundle; and that they depend for their attributes on the organs of the brain to which they are severally attached.

The view which I have to present, will serve to shew why there are divisions, and many distinct parts in the brain: why some nerves are simple in their origin and distribution, and others intricate beyond description. It will explain the apparently accidental connection between the twigs of nerves. It will do away [with] the difficulty of conceiving how sensation and volition should be the operation of the same nerve at the same moment. It will shew how a nerve may lose one property, and retain another; and it will give an interest to the labours of the anatomist in tracing the nerves. . . .

It is admitted that neither bodies nor the images of bodies enter the brain. It is indeed impossible to believe that colour can be conveyed along a nerve; or the vibration in which we suppose sound to consist can be retained in the brain: but we can conceive, and have reason to believe, that an impression is made upon the organs of the outward senses when we see, or hear, or taste.

In this enquiry it is most essential to observe, *that while each organ of sense is provided with a capacity of receiving certain changes to be played upon it, as it were, yet each is utterly incapable of receiving the impressions destined for another organ of sensation.* [Editor's italics]

It is also very remarkable that an impression made on two different nerves of sense, though with the same instrument, will produce two distinct sensations; and the ideas resulting will only have relation to the organ affected.

As the announcing of these facts forms a natural introduction to the Anatomy of the Brain, which I am about to deliver, I shall state them more fully.

There are four kinds of Papillæ on the tongue, but with two of those only we have to do at present. Of these, the Papillæ of one kind form the seat of the sense of taste; the other Papillæ (more numerous and smaller) resemble the extremities of the nerves in the common skin, and are the organs of touch in the tongue. When I take a sharp steel point, and touch one of *these* Papillæ, I feel the sharpness. The sense of *touch* informs me of the shape of the instrument. When I touch a Papilla of taste, I have no sensation similar to the former. I do not know that a point touches the tongue, but I am sensible of a metallic taste, and the sensation passes backward on the tongue.

In the operation of couching the cataract, the pain of piercing the retina with a needle is not so great as that which proceeds from a grain of sand under the eyelid. And although the derangement of the stomach sometimes marks the injury of an organ so delicate, yet the pain is occasioned by piercing the outward coat, not by the affection of the expanded nerve of vision.

If the sensation of light were conveyed to us by the retina, the organ of vision, in consequence of that organ being as much more sensible than the surface of the body as the impression of light is more delicate than that pressure which gives us the sense of touch; what would be the feelings of a man subjected to an operation in which a needle were pushed through the nerve? Life could not bear so great a pain.

But there is an occurrence during this operation on the eye, which will direct us to the truth: when the needle pierces the eye, the patient has the sensation of a spark of fire before the eye.

This fact is corroborated by experiments made on the eye. When the eye-ball is pressed on the side, we perceive various coloured light. Indeed the mere effect of a blow on the head might inform us, that sensation depends on the exercise of the organ affected, not on the impression conveyed to the external organ; for by the vibration caused by the blow, the ears ring, and the eye flashes light, while there is neither light nor sound present.

It may be said, that there is here no proof of the sensation being in the brain more than in the external organ of sense. But when the nerve of a stump is touched, the pain is as if in the amputated extremity. If it be still said that this is no proper example of a peculiar sense existing without its external organ, I offer the following example: Quando penis glandem exedat ulcus, et nihil nisi granulatio maneat, ad extremam tamen nervi pudicæ partem ubi terminatur sensus supersunt, et exquisitissima sensus gratificatio. . . .

I found that injury done to the anterior portion of the spinal marrow, convulsed the animal more certainly than injury done to the posterior portion; but I found it difficult to make the experiment without injuring both portions.

Next considering that the spinal nerves have a double root, and being of opinion that the properties of the nerves are derived from their connections with the parts of the brain, I thought that I had an opportunity of putting my opinion to the test of experiment, and of proving at the same time that nerves of different endowments were in the same cord, and held together by the same sheath.

On laying bare the roots of the spinal nerves, I found that I could cut across the posterior fasciculus of nerves, which took its origin from the posterior portion of the spinal marrow without convulsing the muscles of the back; but that on touching the anterior fasciculus with the point of the knife, the muscles of the back were immediately convulsed. [Editor's italics]

Such were my reasons for concluding that the cerebrum and the cerebellum were parts distinct in function, and that every nerve possessing a double function obtained that by having a double root. I now saw the meaning of the double connection of the nerves with thc spinal marrow; and also the cause of that seeming intricacy in the connections of nerves throughout their course, which were not double at their origins.

The spinal nerves being double, and having their roots in the spinal marrow, of which a portion comes from the cerebrum and a portion from the cerebellum, they convey the attributes of both grand divisions of the brain to every part; and therefore the distribution of such nerves is simple, one nerve supplying its destined part. But the nerves which come directly from the brain, come from parts of the brain which vary in operation; and in order to bestow different qualities on the parts to which the nerves are distributed, two or more nerves must be united in their course or at their final destination. Hence it is that the 1st nerve must have branches of the 5th united with it: hence the *portio dura* of the 7th pervades every where the bones of the cranium to unite with the extended branches of the 5th: hence the union of the 3d and 5th in the orbit: hence the 9th and 5th are both sent to the tongue: hence it is, in short, that no part is sufficiently supplied by one single nerve, unless that nerve be a nerve of the spinal marrow, and have a double root, a connection (however remotely) with both the cerebrum and cerebellum.

Such nerves as are single in their origin from the spinal marrow will be found either to unite in their course with some other nerve, or to be such as are acknowledged to be peculiar in their operation.

The 8th nerve is from the portion of the *medulla oblongata**
which belongs to the cerebellum: the 9th nerve comes from the portion which belongs to the cerebrum. The first is a nerve of the class called Vital nerves, controlling secretly the operations of the body; the last is the Motor nerve of the tongue, and is an instrument of volition. Now the connections formed by the 8th nerve in its course to the viscera are endless; it seems no where sufficient for the entire purpose of a nerve; for every where it is accompanied by others, and the 9th passes to the tongue, which is already profusely supplied by the 5th. . . .

The cerebrum I consider as the grand organ by which the mind is united to the body. Into it all the nerves from the external organs of the senses enter; and from it all the nerves which are agents of the will pass out.

If this be not at once obvious, it proceeds only from the circumstance that the nerves take their origin from the different parts of

---

* The medulla oblongata is only the commencement of the spinal marrow.

the brain; and while those nerves are considered as simple cords, this circumstance stands opposed to the conclusion which otherways would be drawn. A nerve having several roots implies that it propagates its sensation to the brain generally. But when we find that the several roots are distinct in their endowments, and are, in respect to office, distinct nerves; then the conclusion is unavoidable, that the portions of the brain are distinct organs of different functions.

To arrive at any understanding of the internal parts of the cerebrum, we must keep in view the relation of the nerves, and must class and distinguish the nerves, and follow them into its substance. If all ideas originate in the mind from external impulse, how can we better investigate the structure of the brain than by following the nerves, which are the means of communication betwixt the brain and the outward organs of the senses.

The nerves of sense, the olfactory, the optic, the auditory, and the gustatory nerve, are traced backwards into certain tubercles or convex bodies in the base of the brain. And I may say, that the nerves of sense either form tubercles before entering the brain, or they enter into those convexities in the base of the *cerebrum*. These convexities are the constituent parts of the cerebrum, and are in all animals necessary parts of the organs of sense; for as certainly as we discover an animal to have an external organ of sense, we find also a medullary tubercle; whilst the superiority of animals in intelligence is shewn by the greater magnitude of the hemispheres or upper part of the cerebrum.

The convex bodies which are seated in the lower part of the cerebrum, and into which the nerves of sense enter, have extensive connexion with the hemispheres on their upper part. From the medullary matter of the hemispheres, again, there pass down, converging to the crura, Striæ, which is the medullary matter taking upon it the character of a nerve; for from the Crura Cerebri, or its prolongation in the anterior Fasciculi of the spinal marrow, go off the nerves of motion.

But with these nerves of motion which are passing outward there are nerves going inwards; nerves from the surfaces of the body; nerves of touch; and nerves of peculiar sensibility, having their seat in the body or viscera. It is not improbable that the tracts of cineritious matter which we observe in the course of the medullary matter of the brain, are the seat of such peculiar sensibilities; the organs of certain powers which seem resident in the body. . . .

Again, if those parts of the brain which are directly connected with the nerves, and which resemble them in structure, give pain when injured, and occasion convulsion to the animal as the nerves do when they are injured; and if on the contrary such parts as are more remote from the nerves, and of a different structure, produce no such effect when injured, we may conclude, that the office of the latter parts is more allied to the intellectual operations, less to mere sensation.

I have found at different times all the internal parts of the brain diseased without loss of sense; but I have never seen disease general on the surfaces of the hemispheres without derangement or oppression of the mind during the patient's life. In the case of derangement of mind, falling into lethargy and stupidity, I have constantly found the surface of the hemispheres dry and preternaturally firm, the membrane separating from it with unusual facility.

If I be correct in this view of the subject, then the experiments which have been made upon the brain tend to confirm the conclusions which I should be inclined to draw from strict anatomy; viz. that the cineritious and superficial parts of the brain are the seat of the intellectual functions. For it is found that the surface of the brain is totally insensible, but that the deep and medullary part being wounded the animal is convulsed and pained. . . .

. . . Through the nerves of sense, the *sensorium* receives impressions, but the will is expressed through the medium of the nerves of motion. The secret operations of the bodily frame, and the connections which unite the parts of the body into a system, are through the cerebellum and nerves proceeding from it. (Bell, Charles. *Idea of a new anatomy of the brain; submitted for the observations of his friends.* London, Privately printed [1811]. 36 pp. [pp. 3-6, 8-12, 21-25, 27-30, 32-33, 35-36].)

François Magendie
1783-1855

François Magendie, the pioneer experimental physiologist of France, introduced a new era in physiology (Pl. 61). Impetuous, hard-working, versatile, Magendie left his mark in almost every branch of physiological thought, and though he paved the way for the great developments in experimental physiology of the nineteenth century, his contribution was really more one of isolated facts rather than of broad generalizations. He was fearless, and at times unnecessarily cruel, but he invariably triumphed over the avalanche of criticism which frequently overtook him. In 1821 he began to publish the first journal in French to be devoted exclusively to physiology; it bore the title *Journal de Physiologie expérimentale et pathologique* and passed through ten volumes (1821-1831). His first two papers on the functions of the roots of spinal nerves,[9] translated in full below, appeared in the second volume of this journal.

EXPERIMENTS UPON THE FUNCTIONS OF THE ROOTS OF THE SPINAL NERVES

I had long been desirous of making the experiment of dividing in an animal the posterior roots of the nerves which arise from the spinal marrow. I had several times made the attempt, without being able to succeed, on account of the difficulty of opening the vertebral canal without injuring the spinal marrow, and consequently without destroying or at least seriously wounding the animal. Last month there was brought to my laboratory a litter of eight puppies, six weeks old; these animals appeared to me very suitable for a new attempt at opening the vertebral canal. I was able indeed, with the help of a very sharp scalpel, and I may say at a single cut, to expose the posterior half of the spinal marrow surrounded by its envelopes. There only remained for the complete exposure of this organ to cut the dura-mater which surrounds it: this I did with facility; I then had a complete view of the posterior roots of the lumbar and sacral pairs, and in lifting them up successively with the points of a small pair of scissors, I was able to cut them on one side, the spinal marrow remaining untouched. I was ignorant what might be the result of this attempt; I reunited the wound by a suture, and then observed the animal; I at first thought the member corresponding to the cut nerves, was entirely paralysed; it was insensible to the strongest prickings and pressures, it seemed to me also incapable of moving; but soon, to my great surprise, I saw it move in a manner very apparent, although sensibility was entirely extinct. A second and third experiment gave me exactly the same result; I began to think it probable that the posterior roots of the spinal nerves might have different functions from the anterior roots, and that they were more particularly destined for sensation.

It naturally occurred to the mind to cut the anterior roots, leaving

[9] Magendie, F. "Expériences sur les fonctions des racines des nerfs rachidiens." *J. Physiol. exp. Path.*, 1822, 2, 276-279; "Expériences sur les fonctions des racines des nerfs qui naissent de la moelle épinière." *Ibid.*, 366-371.

the posterior untouched; but such an enterprise was more easily conceived than executed; how expose the anterior part of the spinal marrow, without interfering with the posterior roots? I confess that the thing at first appeared to me to be impossible; nevertheless for two days I continued to think of it, and at last I decided to endeavour to pass before the posterior roots, a sort of cataract knife, the blade of which, being very narrow, would permit of my cutting the roots, by pressing them with the sharp side of the instrument, against the posterior surface of the body of the vertebræ; but I was obliged to renounce this method on account of the large veins which the canal contains on that side, and which I opened at each progressive movement. In making these attempts, I perceived that by pulling the vertebral dura-mater, the anterior roots might be seen united in bundles, exactly where they pierce that membrane. I wanted nothing more, and in a few moments I had cut all the pairs which I wished to divide. As in the preceding experiments, I made the section on one side only, in order to have a point of comparison. It may be conceived with what curiosity I observed the effects of this section: they were not doubtful, the member was completely immovable and flaccid, at the same time preserving an unequivocal sensibility. Finally, that nothing might be neglected, I cut the anterior and posterior roots at the same time; there ensued absolute loss both of sensibility and of motion.

I have repeated and varied these experiments upon several species of animals: the results just announced were confirmed in the most complete manner, both for the posterior and anterior members. I am pursuing these researches, and I shall give a more detailed recital of them in the following number; it is sufficient for me at present to be able to advance as positive, that the anterior and posterior roots of the nerves which arise from the spinal marrow, have different functions, that the posterior appear more particularly destined to sensibility, whilst the anterior seem more especially allied to motion.

EXPERIMENTS UPON THE FUNCTIONS OF THE ROOTS OF THE NERVES WHICH ARISE FROM THE SPINAL MARROW

The facts which I announced in the preceding number are too important to be passed over without my seeking to throw light upon them by new researches.

I at first wished to ascertain if it might not be possible to cut the anterior and posterior roots of the spinal nerves without opening the great canal of the vertebral dura-mater; because, by exposing the spinal marrow to the air and to a cold temperature, the nervous action is sensibly weakened, and consequently the results sought for are obtained in a manner but little apparent.

The anatomical position of the parts did not render the thing impossible; for each bundle of spinal roots goes for some time in a particular canal before uniting and confounding itself with the other bundle. I found indeed that with the help of scissors blunt at the points, a sufficient quantity of the plates and lateral parts of the vertebræ may be taken away to expose the ganglion of each lumbar pair; and then with a small stylet there is not much difficulty in separating the canal which contains the posterior roots, and the section becomes easy. This mode of making the experiment gave me the same results as those I had previously observed; but as the experiment is much longer and more laborious than the preceding one in which the great canal of the spinal dura-mater is opened, I do not think that this mode of making the experiment should be followed in preference to the first.

I afterwards wished to submit to more particular proof the results of which I have previously spoken. Every one knows that nux vomica determines both in man and animals, general and very violent tetanic convulsions. I was curious to ascertain if these convulsions would still take place in a member in which the nerves of motion had been cut, and if they would appear to be as strong as usual, a section of the nerves of sensation having been made. The result accorded entirely with the preceding; that is to say in an animal in which the posterior roots were cut, the tetanus was complete and as intense as if the spinal nerves had been untouched: on the contrary, in an animal in which I had cut the nerves of motion of one of the posterior members, the members remained supple and immovable at the time when, under the influence of the poison, all the other muscles of the body suffered the most violent tetanic convulsions.

On directly irritating the nerves of sensation, or the posterior spinal roots, would contractions be produced? Would a direct irritation of the nerves of motion excite pain? These were the questions which I asked myself and which experience alone could resolve.

With this view, I began to examine the posterior roots or the nerves of sensation. The following are the results of my observations: in pinching, pulling, pricking these roots, thc animal gives signs of pain; but it is not to be compared in intensity with that which occurs if the spinal marrow be only slightly touched at the part where these roots arise. Nearly every time that these posterior roots are thus excited, contractions are produced in the muscles to which the nerves are distributed; these contractions are however but slightly marked, and infinitely weaker than if the spinal marrow itself be touched. If one of the posterior bundles of roots be cut at once, a general movement is produced in the member to which the bundle goes.

I have repeated the same experiments upon the anterior bundles, and I have obtained analogous results, but in an inverse sense; for the contractions excited by the pinching, pricking, &c. are extremely strong and even convulsive, whilst the signs of sensibility are scarcely visible. These facts then are confirmative of those already announced; only they seem to establish that sensation does not belong exclusively to the posterior roots, any more than motion to the anterior.

Nevertheless a difficulty might arise. When, in the preceding experiments, the roots were cut, they were continuous with the spinal marrow: might not the disturbance communicated to the latter have been the real origin, either of the contractions or of the pain felt by the animals? To remove this doubt, I repeated the experiments, after having separated the roots from the spinal marrow; and I ought to say that, with the exception of two animals in which I saw contractions upon pinching and pulling the anterior and posterior bundles, in all the rest I did not observe any sensible effect from the irritation of the anterior or posterior roots thus separated from the spinal marrow.

I had still to make another kind of experiment on the spinal roots; that of galvanism. By its means, I accordingly excited these parts, first leaving them in their ordinary state, and afterwards cutting them at their spinal extremities to place them upon an isolating body. In these various cases, I obtained contractions from each sort of roots; but those which followed the excitation of the anterior roots were in general much stronger and more complete than those which took place when the electric current operated upon the posterior. The same phenomena took place either by applying the zinc or copper pole to the nerve.

It now remains for me to give an account of my researches to endeavour to follow motion and sensation distinctly beyond the roots of the nerves, that is to say, into the spinal marrow; this is the subject of my present occupation.

Before finishing this article, I ought to give some further explanation as to the novelty of the results which I have announced.

When I wrote the note contained in the preceding number, I believed I was the first who had thought of dividing the roots of the spinal nerves; but I was soon undeceived by a small work by Mr. Shaw, which this young and laborious practitioner had the politeness to send me as soon as he had received the number of my journal. It is said in that work that Mr. Charles Bell made this section thirteen years ago, and that he had discovered that the section of the posterior roots did not prevent the continuance of motion. Mr. Shaw adds that Mr. Charles Bell had stated this result in a small pamphlet printed solely for the use of his friends, but not for publication. I immediately asked Mr. Shaw to have the kindness to send me if possible the pamphlet of Mr. Charles Bell, in order that I might render him all the justice that was his due. A few days afterwards I received it from Mr. Shaw.

This pamphlet is entitled:

Idea of a new anatomy of the brain, submitted for the Observations of his Friends, by Charles Bell, F.R.S.E. It is very curious, inasmuch as there is to be found in it the germ of the recent discoveries of the author in the nervous system. At page 22, the passage indicated by Shaw is to be found: I shall transcribe the whole of it.

"Next considering that the spinal nerves have a double root, and being of opinion that the properties of the nerves are derived from their connections with the parts of the brain, I thought that I had an opportunity of putting my opinion to the test of experiment, and of proving at the same time that nerves of different endowments were in the same cord and held by the same sheath.

"On laying bare the roots of the spinal nerves, I found that I could cut across the fasciculus of nerves, which took its origin from the posterior portion of the spinal marrow, without convulsing the muscles of the back; but that on touching the anterior fasciculus with the point of a knife, the muscles of the back were immediately convulsed."

It is seen by this citation of a work which I could not know, since it had not been published, that Mr. Bell, conducted by his ingenious ideas on the nervous system, was very near discovering the functions of the spinal roots; at the same time, the fact that the anterior are destined to motion, whilst the posterior belong more especially to sensation, appears to have escaped him: it is then to the establishment of this fact in a positive manner that I must limit my pretensions. ([Walker, Alexander]. *Documents and dates of modern discoveries in the nervous system*. London, John Churchill, 1839. xii, 172 pp. [pp. 87-91, 92-101].)

Herbert Mayo
1796-1852

Herbert Mayo, physiologist of the Middlesex Hospital, London, took the next step after Bell and Magendie toward clarifying the problem of reflex action. In his *Anatomical and Physiological Commentaries,* part I of which appeared in 1822, he described the functions of the nerves of the face, ascribing motor power to what is termed the VIIth and common sensibility to the Vth. This unfortunately formed the beginning of a bitter and tiresome controversy with Bell, who fancied that he had made the discovery in a paper that had appeared in 1821. As in the controversy with Magendie, it is clear to anyone who will read the evidence impartially that Bell had, in point of fact, just missed the discovery, and that Mayo really deserves the credit. In part II of his "Commentaries" in 1823,[10] he found that a circumscribed segment of the brain composed of the optic tubercles and the crura sufficed to give the pupillary reflex when the stump of the optic nerve was irritated. The following passage contains Mayo's account of this discovery.

DELINEATION OF THE TOPOGRAPHY OF CERTAIN REFLEX ACTIONS

It is clear that an influence, independent of the will, occasionally throws voluntary muscles into action, as appears in tetanus, and other spasmodic disorders; and is shown remarkably in the physiological experiment of irritating the skin on the lower extremities, after the division of the spinal cord in the back, when the occurrence of action limited to the muscles of the lower extremities evinces that a connexion exists, independently of the will, between sentient surfaces and the action of voluntary muscles. I have varied this experiment by dividing the spinal cord at once in the neck and in the

---

[10] Mayo, H. *Anatomical and physiological commentaries,* London, 1823, no. 2 [pp. 17, 138].

back, upon which three unconnected nervous centres exist; and the division of the skin in either part (and especially at the soles of the feet in the two hinder portions) produces a convulsive action of the muscles in that part. The same influence may then possibly regulate the unconscious actions to which these remarks relate. . . .

An influence may be propagated from the sentient nerves of a part to their correspondent nerves of motion, through the intervention of that part alone of the nervous centre, to which they are mutually attached. Thus in vertebral animals, in which alone the fact is questionable, when the spinal cord has been divided in two places, an injury of the skin of either region is followed by a distinct muscular action in that part. Again: if the brain is quickly removed from the head of a pigeon, leaving only the crura cerebri, together with the tubercles and the second and third nerve, on pinching the second nerve, the iris contracts. ([Walker, Alexander]. *Documents and dates of modern discoveries in the nervous system.* London, John Churchill, 1839. xii, 172 pp. [pp. 131, 132].)

Marie-Jean-Pierre Flourens
1794-1867

Marie-Jean-Pierre Flourens, professor of comparative anatomy at the University of Paris, who carried out a prolonged series of experiments on the central nervous system. analyzed the functions of the cerebellum and gave a singularly lucid description of cerebellar ataxia, which would serve for any modern textbook. After describing in his book[11] the consequences of removal of the cerebellum in a large number of animals, he draws his conclusions concerning the normal functions of this organ. Below is a protocol of an experiment on a dog, followed by his general conclusions (based on observations of twenty-one animals of various species). He also studied the effects of alcohol and various other drugs on locomotion and, as the final selection indicates, he concluded that alcohol acted specifically on the cerebellum.

EXPERIMENT XVI. ON A DOG

I made a lesion in the cerebellum of a young and healthy dog by means of incisions which extended deeper and deeper. The animal gradually lost the power of ordered and regular movement, and

[11] Flourens, P. *Recherches expérimentales sur les propriétés et les fonctions du système nerveux, dans les animaux vertébrés.* Paris, Crevot, 1824. xxvi, 331 pp.

when the mid-region of the cerebellum was reached he could only totter along with a zigzag motion. When he tried to go forward he would go back and when he wished to turn to left he would turn right. He made great efforts to move, but being unable to control them he would bound forward suddenly and fall over himself. If there were any obstacle in his way he was quite unable to avoid it, however hard he tried, and he knocked against objects on all sides although he could see and hear perfectly well; when irritated he tried to bite and indeed did bite whatever was annoying him, if he could get hold of it, which was seldom, since he could not control his movements with precision. The animal was in full possession of his intellectual facilities and his senses and there was no trace of convulsion; he was merely deprived of the power to control and regulate his movements. When I extended the lesion to the inmost layer of the cerebellum the animal lost the power of motion and of equilibrium completely. . . .

I shall not add any further experiments here since the absolute similarity of those which have just been described make it unnecessary to do so. Thus 1. A slight injury to the cerebellum invariably produces a corresponding derangement of the power of motion in animals of all ages which increases in proportion to the injury; while complete removal of the cerebellum always causes total loss of the power of regulating movement.

2. At the same time there is a curious fact to be noted about the absolute regularity and repetition of these phenomena, *i.e.* in different animals the movements which are affected by [injury to] the cerebellum invariably correspond to their dominant type of movement. In birds which fly a great deal this derangement is particularly evident in their flight; it affects the gait of those which usually walk; and impedes swimming in birds accustomed to water.

There is therefore a drunken way of swimming and of flying, just as there is a drunken gait, and though the dominant means of progression may be impaired it still prevails.

3. Although removal of the cerebellum invariably coincides with loss of the power of locomotion, the intellectual faculties and the senses are not affected and so long as the operation is confined to the cerebellum there is no sign of convulsions.

The faculty which controls convulsions or muscular contraction, that which coördinates such contractions, and the faculties of the intellect and of the senses are therefore of three essentially different orders and reside in three separate regions of the nervous system.

4. Although with removal of the cerebellum an animal can no longer control its movements or maintain its balance when walking or standing, it still attempts to do so, and though it has lost the power of locomotion it can still move in self-defence.

This tendency to control balance and these movements in self-defence are therefore not derived from the cerebellum: it would be shown presently from whence they do proceed.

VI

EXPERIMENTS ON THE CEREBELLUM

1. I caused a sparrow to swallow a few drops of alcohol and soon after it began to show signs of intoxication. It could only fly in a queer uncertain manner, wavering and twisting itself about in its flight, and when it walked it swayed about and described a zigzag course. After it had swallowed a few more drops (of alcohol) it could not even stand up or indeed stay in any fixed position. It behaved as though half the cerebellum had been removed after the first few drops and entirely removed after the final dose. . . .

6. From these experiments it follows:

1° That a certain amount of alcohol acts exclusively and positively on the cerebellum.

2° That in acting thus exclusively, or, if you prefer it, specifically, on the cerebellum it affects only those functions which in previous experiments I have shown to proceed solely and specifically from that organ.

3° That if this amount is exceeded the action of the alcohol extends beyond the cerebellum.

4° That the action of alcohol always leaves behind it traces which can be recognised and verified.

5° That especially in small birds, the formation and development of these traces are visible to the naked eye. (Flourens, P. *Op. cit.* [note 11], pp. 145-146, 148-149, 259, 261-262.)

Johannes Müller
1801-1858

Johannes Müller, the founder of the great German school of physiology in the nineteenth century, made, as did Malpighi and Haller, distinguished contributions to many branches of biological thought. His textbook (1834-1840) served to crystallize knowledge of the day and it stimulated work in almost every field. Müller, had he not been a physiologist, might have been the leading neurologist of his day. His penetrating analysis of experimental work on the nervous system, as exemplified in his textbook and in his numerous other writings, can still be read with profit today. He interested himself also in psychology, and it was in his attempt to analyse sensation that he enunciated the principle which since 1826 has rightly borne his name. Müller's law of specific nerve energies gives expression to the fact that each sense organ, however it may be stimulated, gives rise to its own characteristic sensation and to no other: electrical stimulation of the optic nerve, for example, causes a sensation of light and nothing else. Though this generalization was set forth as early as 1826,[12] the principle is stated in somewhat more mature form in his textbook from which the following selection is taken.

SECTION IV

OF THE PECULIAR PROPERTIES OF INDIVIDUAL NERVES

CHAPTER I

Of the nerves of special sense

The nerves have always been regarded as conductors, through the medium of which we are made conscious of external impressions. Thus the nerves of the senses have been looked upon as mere passive conductors, through which the impressions made by the properties of bodies were supposed to be transmitted unchanged to the sensorium. More recently, physiologists have begun to analyse these opinions. If the nerves are mere passive conductors of the impressions of light, sonorous vibrations, and odours, how does it happen that the

[12] Müller, J. *Ueber die phantastischen Gesichtserscheinungen*. Coblenz, Jacob Hölscher, 1826. Also: *Zur vergleichenden Physiologie des Gesichtssinnes des Menschen und der Thiere*. Leipzig, C. Cnobloch, 1826.

nerve which perceives odours is sensible to this kind of impressions only, and to no others, while by another nerve odours are not perceived: that the nerve which is sensible to the matter of light, or the luminous oscillations, is insensible to the vibrations of sonorous bodies; that the auditory nerve is not sensible to light, nor the nerve of taste to odours; while, to the common sensitive nerve, the vibrations of bodies give the sensation, not of sound, but merely of tremours? These considerations have induced physiologists to ascribe to the individual nerves of the senses a special sensibility to certain impressions, by which they are supposed to be rendered conductors of certain qualities of bodies, and not of others.

This last theory, of which ten or twenty years since no one doubted the correctness, on being subjected to a comparison with facts, was found unsatisfactory. For the same stimulus as electricity, may act simultaneously on all the organs of sense,—all are sensible to its action; but the nerve of each sense is affected in a different way, becomes the seat of a different sensation: in one, the sensation of light is produced; in another, that of sound; in another, taste; while, in a fourth, pain and the sensation of a shock are felt. Mechanical irritation excites in one nerve a luminous spectrum; in another, a humming sound; in a third, pain. An increase of the stimulus of the blood causes in one organ spontaneous sensations of light; in another, sound; in a third, itching, pain, &c. A consideration of such facts could not but lead to the inference that the special susceptibility of nerves for certain impressions is not a satisfactory theory, and that the nerves of the senses are not mere passive conductors, but that each peculiar nerve of sense has special powers or qualities which the exciting causes merely render manifest.

Sensation, therefore, consists in the communication to the sensorium, not of the quality or state of the external body, but of the condition of the nerves themselves, excited by the external cause.—We do not feel the knife which gives us pain, but the painful state of our nerves: the probably mechanical oscillation of light is itself not luminous; even if it could itself act on the sensorium, it would be perceived merely as an oscillation; it is only by affecting the optic nerve that it gives rise to the sensation of light: sound has no existence but in the excitement of a quality of the auditory nerve; the nerve of touch perceives the vibration of the apparently sonorous body as a sensation of tremour. We communicate, therefore, with the external world merely by virtue of the states which external influences excite in our nerves.

By the knowledge of the fact just announced, we are led not only to recognize the peculiar qualities of the different nerves of sensation, in addition to their general distinction from the motor nerves; but we are also enabled to banish for ever from the doctrines of physiology a number of erroneous notions regarding the supposed power of the nerves to perform the functions of each other. It has been long known that blind persons cannot recognize colours with their fingers, *as colours;* but we perceive now why it is impossible for them to do so; and the facts which show us the impossibility of it, afford an explanation of many other circumstances. However acute the sense of touch in the finger of the blind may be rendered by practice, it can be but the one sense proper to the nerves of the fingers,—*touch.* (Müller, J. *Elements of physiology.* Baly's translation of Müller's *Handbuch.* London, Taylor and Walton, 2 vols.: vol. 1, 1838, xxii, 848 pp.; vol. 2, 1842, xxiii-xxxviii, 849-1715, 22 pp. [pp. 766-767].)

Marshall Hall

1790-1857

Marshall Hall, neurologist and indefatigable experimenter (Pl. 62), who introduced the concept that the spinal cord is a chain of segments whose functional units are separate reflex arcs, added great impetus to the study of experimental neurology. He was one of the first, after Whytt, to attempt systematic correlation of clinical and experimental observations upon the nervous system. Hall was largely unaware of the work of his predecessors, and it is to his credit that, beginning as it were *de novo,* he was able to travel as far as he did. In his important paper read to the Royal Society in 1833, he demonstrated tonic closure of the sphincters by reflex action, cessation of strychnine convulsions after destruction of the spinal cord and that most reflexes were more readily elicited by stimulating appropriate end-organs than through their bared nerve trunks. Several papers embodying his observations were published shortly before his memoir had been read to the Royal Society. Soon after this paper appeared, Hall was denounced as a propagator of absurd and idle theories and, despite the enthusiastic reception of his work abroad, the *Philosophical Transactions* became from that time on closed to him as a channel of publication.

The first passage is from one of the preliminary descriptions of his experiments.

THESE MOTIONS INDEPENDENT OF SENSATION
AND VOLITION

A PAPER was read, containing 'a brief account of a particular function of the nervous system,' in which Dr. Marshall Hall detailed a series of experiments tending to prove the existence of *a source of muscular action distinct from all those hitherto noticed by physiologists, viz. volition, the irritation of the motor nerves in some part of their origin or course, or that of the muscles themselves.* The peculiarity of this motion he stated to consist in its being excited by irritation of the extreme portion of the sentient nerves, whence the impression is conveyed through the corresponding portion of brain and spinal marrow as a centre, to the extremities of the motor nerves.

The animals experimented on were salamanders, frogs and turtles. In the first of these, the tail, entirely separated from the body, moved as in the living animal, on being excited by the point of a needle passed lightly over its surface. The motion ceased on destroying the spinal marrow within the caudal *vertebræ*. The head of a frog having been removed, and the spine divided between the third and fourth *vertebræ,* an eye of the separated head was touched: it was retracted and the eye-lid closed,—a similar movement being observed in the other eye. On removing the brain, these phenomena ceased. On pinching the skin, or the toe of one of the anterior extremities, the whole of this portion of the animal moved. On destroying the spinal marrow, this phenomenon also ceased. Precisely similar effects were observed on pinching the skin or toe of one of the posterior extremities; and on removing the last portion of the spinal marrow, this phenomenon ceased. The head of the turtle continues to move long after its separation from the body: on pinching the eye-lid, it is forcibly closed, the mouth is opened, and the membrane expanded under the lower jaw descends as in respiration. On pinching any part of the skin of the body, extremities, or tail, the animal moves. The posterior extremities and tail being separated together, the former were immovable; the latter moved on the application of the flame of a lighted taper to the skin. Those extremities had no connection with the spinal marrow. All movement ceased in the tail also, on withdrawing the spinal marrow from its canal.

Three things [Dr. Hall observes] are plain from these observations: 1. That the nerves of sensibility are impressible in portions of an animal separated from the rest; in the head, in the upper part of the trunk, in the lower part of the trunk: 2. that motions similar to voluntary motions follow these impressions made upon the sentient nerves: and 3. that the presence of the spinal marrow is essential as the central and cementing link between the sentient and motor nerves. . . . ([Walker, Alexander]. *Documents and dates of modern discoveries in the nervous system.* London, John Churchill, 1839. xii, 172 pp. [pp. 135-137].)

REFLEX ACTION OF MEDULLA OBLONGATA AND MEDULLA SPINALIS

This animal was decapitated in the manner usual with cooks, by means of a knife, which divided the second and third vertebra.

The head being placed upon the table for observation, it was first remarked that the mouth opened and shut, and that the submaxillary integuments descended and ascended, alternately, from time to time, replacing the acts of respiration. I now touched the eye or eyelid with a probe. It was immediately closed: the other eye closed simultaneously. I then touched the nostril with the probe. The mouth was immediately opened widely, and the submaxillary membranes descended. This effect was especially induced on touching the nasal fringes situated just within the anterior part of the maxilla. I passed the probe up the trachea and touched the larynx. This was immediately followed by a forcible convulsive contraction of the muscles annexed to it. Having made and repeated these observations, I gently withdrew the medulla and brain. All the phenomena ceased from that moment. The eye, the nostril, the larynx were stimulated, but no movement followed.

The next observations were made upon the other parts of the animal. The limbs, the tail, were stimulated by a pointed instrument or a lighted taper. They were immediately moved with rapidity. The sphincter was perfectly circular and closed; it was contracted still more forcibly on the application of a stimulus. The limbs and the tail possessed a certain degree of firmness or tone, recoiled on being drawn from their position, and moved with energy on the application of the stimulus. On withdrawing the spinal marrow gently out of its canal, all these phenomena ceased. The limbs were no longer obedient to stimuli, and became perfectly flaccid, having lost all their resilience. The sphincter lost its circular form and its contracted state, becoming lax, flaccid, and shapeless. The tail was flaccid, and unmoved on the application of stimuli. . . .

It is distinctly proved, by this series of observations, that the reflex function exists in the medulla independently of the brain; in the medulla oblongata independently of the medulla spinalis; and in the spinal marrow of the anterior extremities, of the posterior extremities, and of the tail, independently of that of each other of these parts, respectively.

There is a still more interesting and satisfactory mode of performing the experiment: it is to divide the spinal marrow between the nerves of the superior and inferior extremities. We have then two modes of animal life: the first being the assemblage of the voluntary and respiratory powers with those of the reflex function and irritability; the second, the two latter powers only: the first are those which obtain in the perfect animal, the second those which animate the foetus. The phenomena are precisely what might have been anticipated. If the spinal marrow be now destroyed, the irritability alone remains—all the other phenomena having ceased.

The spinal marrow of a frog was divided between the anterior and posterior extremities. It was immediately observed that the head and the anterior extremities alone were moved spontaneously and with design, the respiration being performed as before. But the posterior extremities were not paralysed: they were drawn upwards, and remained perfectly motionless, indeed, unless stimulated; by the application of any stimulus, they were moved with energy, but once only, and in a manner perfectly peculiar. The stimulus was not felt by the animal, because the head and anterior extremities remained motionless at the time it was applied. Nothing could be more obvious, and indeed striking, than the difference between the phenomena of the functions of sensation and volition observed in the anterior part of the animal, and those of the reflex function in the posterior: in the former there were spontaneous movements with obvious design; in the latter, the mere effect of stimulus. (Hall, M. "The reflex function of the medulla oblongata and the medulla spinalis." *Phil. Trans.*, 1833, *123*, 635-665 [pp. 644, 650-651].)

Ernst Heinrich Weber
1795-1878
and
Eduard Friedrich Weber
1806-1871

Ernst Heinrich Weber and his brother *Eduard Friedrich Weber,* both of Leipzig, shared the discovery of the inhibitory power of the vagus nerves upon the beating of the heart. Wilson Philip (1826) had seen the heart lie "quite still for about half a minute" after crushing the brain [see above, p. 84] and concluded that the brain controls the heart, but he did not discover the channels by which this control was exerted. Similarly, Alfred Wilhelm Volkmann (1800-1877), the physiologist of Halle, had in 1837 actually observed inhibition of the heart on vagal stimulation, but being convinced that excitation of nerve always provoked increased activity of the tissue it innervates, he dismissed this chance observation as due to some error of technique. The Webers induced inhibition at first by connecting one pole of an electro-magnetic apparatus to the nostril of a frog and the other to the mid-region of the spinal cord, and they deserve great credit for finally tracing the pathway of the effect which they observed to the vagus. They extended their observations to include not only frogs, but also fish, birds, cats, dogs, and rabbits. At first they believed that both vagi were necessary, but this view they soon abandoned. The experiment is a very important milestone in the history of physiology not merely because of its significance to the circulation, but because it brought to light a wholly new kind of nervous action and it formed the beginning of a series of highly significant researches upon the inhibitory processes occurring within the central nervous system. The discovery of the Webers, which was first communicated to a scientific congress meeting at Naples in September, 1845, was published in November of the same year in an obscure Italian medical journal edited by Annibale Omodei.[13] The following translation has been made from the original brief account in Omodei's 'Annali,' and as far as I am aware it is the first time that it has been rendered into English.

---

[13] Weber, E. F. and Weber, E. H. "Experimenta, quibus probatur nervos vagos rotatione machinae galvano-magneticae irritatos, mortum cordis retardare et adeo intercipere." *Annali Universali di Medicina* (compilati dal Annibale Omodei), Milan, 1845, *116,* fasc. 347 (ser. 3, vol. 20), pp. 227-228. In January 1846 this paper was reprinted in Mandl's *Archives d'Anatomie générale et de Physiologie* (the title borne by a supplementary volume to *Arch. gén. Med.,* 4. sèr., for 1846). These experiments were described in greater detail on pages 42-48 and on p. 120 of an article entitled "Muskelbewegung" which Eduard Weber contributed to Rudolph Wagner's *Handwörterbuch der Physiologie,* 1846, *3,* 1-122.

THE EXPERIMENTS OF *EDWARD* AND *ERNEST HENRY WEBER* BY WHICH IT IS PROVED THAT WHEN STIMULATED WITH A ROTARY ELECTROMAGNETIC APPARATUS THE VAGUS NERVES SLOW DOWN AND, TO A CONSIDERABLE EXTENT, INTERRUPT THE HEART-BEAT

I. If the medulla oblongata of a frog or the ends of the isolated vagus nerves are excited by the rotation of a fairly strong electromagnetic machine, the heart suddenly stops beating, but at the end of excitation begins after a short interval to beat again: at first slowly and weakly, then gradually more strongly and more frequently until finally the original beat observed before excitation is restored.

II. The rotation of a less powerful instrument slows down and weakens the heart-beat. The heart, whose beat is by this means interrupted, is not contracted as in a tetanic convulsion, but remains relaxed and has a flat appearance.

III. The excitation of the vagus nerve on one side only does not change the heart-beat.

If excitation of the vagus nerves is continued long enough for the force producing their excitation to be exhausted, the heart begins to beat again.

IV. If the adjacent parts of the heart in which the sympathetic nerves run or extend their branches, are excited in the same way, the heart-beats, so far from stopping or slowing down, rather become more frequent and, if they had previously been stopped, are restored.

V. But it is uncertain whether this effect depends more on the excitation of the sympathetic nerve than on the electricity directly spreading to the heart by means of the moist animal tissue.

VI. If the wire connection from the electromagnetic machine is applied directly to the heart in a certain way, it can cause the heart to become contracted tetanically, and to cease to beat for as long as response lasts.

VII. The excitation of vagus nerves as described has an effect in rabbits similar to that in frogs. (Weber, E. F. and Weber, E. H. *Op. cit.* [note 13], pp. 227-228.)

Charles Edouard Brown-Séquard
1817-1894

C. E. Brown-Séquard, the first to point out the clinical significance of experimental hemisection of the spinal cord, had a meteoric career (Pl. 63). Born in Mauritius of a French mother and an American father, he moved from place to place expending his phenomenal abilities in the most diverse ways. Poverty-stricken, and given to free expression of radical political views, he was forced in 1852 to leave France for America, where he supported himself in New York by the practice of obstetrics and charged $5 a case for his services. He returned to France, but in 1855 one finds him once more in America, this time teaching the "institutes of medicine" at Virginia Medical College. Later (1864-1867) he occupied the chair of physiology and pathology of the nervous system at Harvard. Following the death of Claude Bernard in 1878, he became his successor as professor of experimental medicine in the Collège de France. His observations on the physiology of the spinal cord cord were carried out over a long period (beginning with his medical thesis in 1846) and were published at intervals in the *Comptes Rendus,* from 1849.[14] It is true that his views were to some extent modified, but the salient points which he emphasized have stood unchallenged. The first two paragraphs below are taken from his lectures on this subject to the Royal College of Surgeons, delivered in May, 1858.

THE RELATIONS OF THE COLUMNS OF THE MEDULLA OBLONGATA

It seems absolutely certain, from the above facts and reasonings, that there is no decussation of the voluntary motor fibres of the trunk and limbs above the crossing of the pyramids. On the other hand, we have already shown, in a previous lecture, that there seems to be no decussation of these fibres in the spinal cord—*i.e.,* below the crossing of the pyramids; so that we are led to admit that most of, if not all, the conductors of the orders of the will to muscles decussate at the lower part of the medulla oblongata, and that these conductors chiefly form the anterior pyramids, after their decussation. An interesting fact, in addition to those already mentioned, concerning these pyramids, is, that when a lesion exists at the place

[14] His original papers describing the consequences of hemisection of the spinal cord are numerous. The most important is the following: "Explication de l'hemiplégie croisé du sentiment." *C. R. Soc. Biol. (Paris),* 1850, 70-73; see also *ibid.,* pp. 134 and 195 and *Recherches expérimentales sur la transmission croisée des impressions dans la moelle épinière.* Paris, Victor Masson, 1855.

of decussation, it produces a paralysis in the two sides of the body, because it destroys fibres belonging to them both. This is a feature quite peculiar to this part of the cerebro-spinal axis.

From the preceding remarks, and from the facts and reasonings contained in our lectures (the third and seventh) on the decussation of the conductors of sensitive impressions, it results that, as regards anæsthesia and paralysis, three different groups of symptoms may be observed, according to the place of the alteration in a lateral half of the cerebro-spinal axis: 1st, above the decussation of the pyramids, a lesion on either the medulla oblongata, the pons Varolii, the crura cerebri, the optic thalami, the corpora striata, or the brain proper, if it produces anæsthesia and paralysis, produces them both in the opposite side of the body; 2d, below the decussation in the pyramids, a lesion in the spinal cord produces paralysis in the same side, and anæsthesia in the opposite side; 3d, at the level of the decussation of the pyramids, and upon the decussating fibres, and also behind them, a lesion produces paralysis in both sides of the body, and anæsthesia only in the opposite side. So that *wherever the lesion, in a lateral half of the cerebro-spinal axis, may be—below, above, or at the level of the crossing of the pyramids—if it produces anæsthesia, it is in the opposite side; while paralysis, in these three cases, is either in the same or the opposite side, or in both sides.* (Brown-Séquard, C. E. *Course of lectures on the physiology and pathology of the central nervous system.* Philadelphia, Collins, 1860. xii, 276 pp., 3 pl. [pp. 199-200].)

STIMULATION OF THE CERVICAL SYMPATHETIC

I have found that the remarkable phenomena which follow the section of the cervical part of the sympathetic, are mere consequences of the paralysis and therefore of the dilatation of the blood-vessels. The blood finding a larger way than usual, arrives there in greater quantity; therefore the nutrition is more active. Now the sensibility is increased because the vital properties of the nerves are augmented when their nutrition is augmented. . . . I base my opinion in part on the following experiments: If galvanism is applied to the superior portion of the sympathetic after it has been cut in the neck, the vessels of the face and of the ear after a certain time begin to contract; their contraction increases slowly, but at last it is evident that they resume their normal condition, if they are not even smaller. Then the temperature and the sensibility diminish in the face and in the ear, and they become in the palsied side the same as in the sound side. When the galvanic current ceases to act, the vessels begin to dilate again, and all the phenomena discovered by **Dr.** Bernard reappear. (Brown-Séquard, C. E. "Experimental researches applied to physiology and pathology." *Med. Exam.* [Philadelphia], 1852, *8*, 481-504 [p. 486].)

John Hughlings Jackson
1835-1911

Hughlings Jackson was born at Green Hammerton, Yorkshire, and studied medicine at York (Pl. 64). In 1859 he went to London where he studied at the London Hospital. From 1862 to 1906 he was a physician at the National Hospital for Epileptics, Queen Square, London, and he used the experience gained at this hospital in the study of nerve physiology and pathology. He related the loss or impairment of various functions to brain disease and brain injury and showed that certain regions of the brain appeared to control certain limb movements. His description of cerebellar rigidity is an instance of his use of pathological manifestations to reveal normal functional relationships. On the basis of such observations Jackson predicted in 1864 and 1870 that an area existed in the cerebral cortex which governed individual movements—that is, he predicted the existence of a motor area in the cortex.

CEREBELLAR RIGIDITY WITH PERIODIC SEIZURES

July 11. There had been no material change in his condition for some time, except a progressive loss of flesh. He was now much emaciated. His mental condition continued of the same character. He lay still and never spoke unless he was spoken to; and his replies were always monosyllabic. He now could utter another street cry—'Any watercresses?'— in good intonation; and, when saying it, smiled, which he never did when saying anything else. When he was asked who any one near him was, he invariably replied 'Granmother'; and, in answer to the question 'How are you today?' he invariably replied 'Nothink'. The great test of his bodily strength each day had been the degree of vehemence with which he could utter 'Dusta-hoy.' To-day his voice was piteously feeble. He was much weaker, but still took his food well. He had had convulsive seizures every few days, several of which Mr. Mackenzie saw. Sometimes, but not always, the seizure was preceded by a loud cry. There was no marked twitching of the face, nor any special deviation of the eyeballs. His hands were clenched; his forearms were flexed on the upper arms, which were generally kept to the sides. The head was drawn back and the back was curved. His legs were always extended to the fullest possible degree, the feet being arched backwards. Sometimes he passed faeces and urine in an attack. The seizures generally lasted about three or four minutes; and, when passing off, they returned if he were moved about. He was not unconscious. There was no clonic spasm. In one attack the two eyes were turned to the left, and the head to the right—not backwards, as usual. (Jackson, J. Hughlings. "Case of tumour of the middle lobe of the cerebellum." *Brit. med. J.,* 1871, 2, 528-529.)

David Ferrier

1843-1928

Sir David Ferrier, the English neurologist, laid the foundation of knowledge concerning the localization of cerebral function (Pl. 65). Fritsch and Hitzig had, by galvanic stimulation, defined the motor area of the brain. Goltz had described the gross results of extirpation of the posterior half and the anterior half respectively of the cerebral hemispheres of dogs, but he denied that there was localization of function. Ferrier, through the study of experimental and of clinical evidence, allocated certain well-recognized functions to specific areas of the hemispheres; as Sherrington has said: "He established the localization of the 'motor' cortex very much as we now know it. He located it as a region accompanying the Rolandic fissure across the lateral aspect of the hemisphere and extending thence over and upon the hemisphere's median aspect. He pointed out that its extent was greater and its character more detailed in the ape than in any of the types less near to man. He showed that its focal movements were obtainable with such definition and precision that 'the experimenter can predict with certainty the result of stimulation of a given region.' He went on to determine the effects of destruction of limited portions of the cerebral cortex. He allocated regions specially concerned with vision and with hearing respectively. He showed that the hemiplegias and monoplegias, ensuing on injuries within the motor region of the ape, were characteristically greater than those produced by similar cerebral lesions in the dog. The symptoms in the ape he stressed as being strikingly akin to those familiar in the clinic. At the International Congress of Medicine of 1881, held in London, he gave a convincing demonstration of his results before a gathering of the neurologists of Europe. Sir Charles Ballance, who was present, relates that on the appearance of one of Ferrier's hemiplegic monkeys, the clinician Charcot, of Paris, exclaimed 'It is a patient!' —words pregnant as a pronouncement on the case for which Ferrier was arguing."[15] Ferrier had begun his studies on the cortex cerebri in 1873 and the results of his first experiments were published in the *Reports* of the West Riding Asylum where he had worked. In 1874 and 1875 appeared his two Croonian Lectures and in 1876 his celebrated book, *The Functions of the Brain,* from which the following passage is taken.

EXTIRPATION OF THE MOTOR CORTEX

The question, however, with which we are more particularly engaged is the determination of the physiological significance of these regions [prefrontal convolutions]. The mere fact of the excitation of movements is, as we have already seen, no proof that the regions stimulated have a motor significance, for the stimulation of a sensory centre may give rise to reflex or associated movements. Whether the centres now under consideration are directly motor, or only give rise to movements in a reflex or indirect manner when stimulated, is a question which has been answered differently by different investigators on this subject. The definite purposive character clearly perceivable in many of the movements, and their correspondence with the ordinary volitional activities and peculiarities of the animals, apart from other considerations, point rather to the conclusion that they are the result of the artificial excitation of the functional activity of centres immediately concerned in effecting volitional movements, and as such truly motor. As the question, however, is one capable of being answered by direct experiments, we may proceed to the consideration of these. If these regions are centres of voluntary motion, paralysis of voluntary motion ought to follow from their destruction, and any apparent exception to this result must be capable of satisfactory explanation, consistently with this view, if it is the correct one.

The following experiments on monkeys give no uncertain reply to the questions stated.

The first experiment I have to record is instructive, as showing the respective effects of irritation and destruction of the convolutions bounding the fissure of Rolando. The right hemisphere of a monkey had been exposed and subjected to experimentation with electrical irritation. The part exposed included the ascending parietal, ascending frontal, and posterior extremities of the frontal convolutions. The animal was allowed to recover, for the purpose of watching the effects of exposure of the brain. Next day the animal

[15] Sherrington, C. S. "Obituary notice of Sir David Ferrier." *Proc. roy, Soc.,* 1928, *103*B, viii-xvi [p. x].

was found perfectly well. Towards the close of the day following, on which there were signs of inflammatory irritation and suppuration, it began to suffer from choreic spasms of the left angle of the mouth and left arm, which recurred repeatedly, and rapidly assumed an epileptiform character, affecting the whole of the left side of the body. Next day left hemiplegia had become established, the angle of the mouth drawn to the right, the left cheek-pouch flaccid and distended with food, which had accumulated outside the dental arch; there being almost total paralysis of the left arm, and partial paralysis of the left leg. On the day following the paralysis of motion was complete over the whole of the left side, and continued so till death, nine days subsequently. Tactile sensation, as well as sight, hearing, smell and taste, were retained. On *post-mortem* examination it was found that the exposed convolutions were completely softened, but beyond this the rest of the hemisphere and the basal ganglia were free from organic injury.

In this we have a clear case, first, of vital irritation producing precisely the same effects as the electric current, and then destruction by inflammatory softening, resulting in complete paralysis of voluntary motion on the opposite side of the body, without affection of sensation.

In the next experiment the lesion was more limited, and the state of paralysis was limited correspondingly. The left hemisphere of a monkey was exposed, and the cortical substance destroyed by the cautery in the post-parietal lobule (foot-centre), ascending parietal convolution (hand and wrist movements), and superior part of the ascending frontal convolution (movements of arm and leg). The centres of the biceps, facial muscles, and mouth and tongue were not involved. Immediately on this being done the right leg was found to be dragged, the foot and ankle especially hanging flaccid and powerless.

The right hand and wrist hung powerless and flaccid, but the animal could flex the forearm and maintain resistance against extension, a fact easily accounted for by the biceps centre remaining intact. There was no trace of facial paralysis or distortion of the angle of the mouth. Cutaneous sensation and the various special senses were unimpaired, and beyond the paralysis mentioned the animal was in good condition, and enjoyed food. In this animal the angular gyrus was subsequently destroyed, with the effect of causing blindness of the right eye.

On *post-mortem* examination next day the lesion was found to occupy the motor regions specified and the angular gyrus, the rest of the brain and the basal ganglia being intact.

In this case the paralysis was confined to the same movements as a result from electric stimulation of the centres specified. In the following experiment the extent of the lesion was still further circumscribed, and the effect, as regards voluntary motion, correspondingly limited. (Ferrier, D. *The functions of the brain.* London, Smith, Elder and Co., 1876, xvi, 323 pp. [pp. 200-203]; 2d ed., 1886.)

Charles Edward Beevor
1854-1907
and
Victor Horsley
1857-1916

Charles Edward Beevor was born at London and studied medicine at University College Hospital. He was later a physician at the National Hospital for the Paralysed and Epileptic, Queen Square, London where he collaborated with Sir Victor Horsley on investigations of the localization of cerebral function.

Sir Victor Horsley was also born at London, son of John Calcott Horsley, the artist, and received his medical training at University College Hospital. From 1884 to 1890 he was at the Brown Institution of the University of London and there engaged in experimental studies on the localization of motor functions in the brain. In 1885 he became an Assistant-Surgeon at University College Hospital and in 1886 Surgeon to the National Hospital where Hughlings Jackson was teaching. His association with these hospitals continued until he became medical consultant to the British Mediterranean Expeditionary Force in 1915; he died at Amarah in Mesopotamia in 1916. Horsley was one of the pioneers in the then newly expanding field of brain surgery and he developed Horsley's wax which is used in the control of hemorrhage in cranial surgery. He was knighted in 1902.

In 1874 Hitzig published his monograph on the cerebral cortex in which he accurately defined the limits of the motor area both in dog and monkey.[16] On this foundation Beevor and Horsley built their series of investigations on the excitable cortex of monkey and orang from which the following selection has been made.

[16] Hitzig, E. *Unteruchungen über das Gehirn.* Berlin, A. Hirschwald, 1874. vi, 276 pp.

CORTICAL CENTRE FOR MONKEY UPPER LIMB

Method of Experimentation. The animal being thoroughly an-
aesthetised with ether, the left cortex was exposed *lege artis,* and the
dura mater raised. A careful drawing was then made of the arrangement of the sulci, upon which was represented the position of the
various points stimulated. The cortex, after being carefully dried to
prevent diffusion of the current, was excited as follows. The apparatus employed was one DANIELL cell and an ordinary DU BOIS-REY-
MOND coil, but no attempt was made to equalise the make-and-
break shock by means of a HELMHOLTZ wire. The electrodes were
the ordinary platinum pattern, and were 2 mm. apart. The coil consisted of a primary bobbin wound round an iron core, with secondary bobbin sliding on a sledge over it, the distance between them
being registered in centimeters, so that the strongest current would
be at zero when the secondary coil completely covered the primary
one. The primary current was interrupted by means of an ordinary
NEEF's hammer, and the secondary currents with this arrangement
were of a strength sufficient to produce the sensation of slight pricking on the human tongue when the secondary coil was at 8, *i.e.* 8 cm.
from the primary. This very weak secondary current* was always employed so as to obviate the fallacy of diffusion. That this object was
attained was obvious, for, if a certain movement was always obtained
at one place, shifting the position of the electrodes for even one mil-
limetre was sufficient to produce a totally different result.

Since in all the brains we have experimented upon the positions
of the principal sulci were perfectly constant, we regarded them as
definite landmarks by which we could accurately ascertain in different brains the position of each centre. . . .

From our experiments it appears to us that the ascending parietal
convolution has less claim than the ascending frontal to be considered as an area of extensive representation of movement. We have
been so impressed with the importance of deciding this fact that we
have usually explored the former gyrus with the current directly
after the skull has been removed, and subsequently repeated our examination of it at various intervals during the experiment, so as to
eliminate any error in the direction of loss of excitability of the cortex
of this gyrus.

We would call attention to the extraordinary degree of symmetry

---

* This was the weakest current which would produce a contraction in the muscles.

which exists in all the Monkeys on which we have experimented, and also that this is not merely morphological, but also physiological. Although this is a matter of great interest, we cannot enter into it in further detail. . . .

We will now consider what appears to us the much more important co-operation of these two movements of flexion and extension of the digits. On this point we have obtained the exceedingly definite result that both movements are represented in the middle ⅓ of the ascending frontal and parietal convolutions, and that, while in the ascending frontal convolution extension precedes flexion, in the ascending parietal convolution this order is reversed, and so extension follows flexion. In view of those centres which are immediately in front of the middle ⅓ of the ascending frontal convolution, we readily understand how it comes about that in the ascending frontal extension *precedes* flexion, whereas behind the fissure of Rolando it *follows* flexion. . . .

Thumb.—The limitation of the representation of the thumb in the cortex (see fig. 6) is a matter of great interest, considering that it is the most highly differentiated member of the body. The representation is limited to the ascending frontal and parietal convolutions. . . . It is interesting to observe that the thumb obeys the same general rules respecting the relations of the movements of flexion and extension as do the digits; thus extension *precedes* flexion in the ascending frontal and *follows* flexion in the ascending parietal. The movement of opposition, which is, of course, the most highly differentiated one, was only obtained on stimulating the lowest part of the thumb area, viz., the centres 7 and 5′; this is in perfect harmony with the general plan of representation, as we have found it to exist in the outer convex surface of the cortex. . . . (Beevor, Charles E. and Horsley, Victor. "A minute analysis [experimental] of the various movements produced by stimulating in the monkey different regions of the cortical centre for the upper limb, as defined by Professor Ferrier." *Phil. Trans.*, 1887, *178B*, 153-168 [pp. 157-158, 161, 162].)

Charles Scott Sherrington

1857-1952

Sir Charles Scott Sherrington, Waynflete Professor of Physiology at Oxford from 1913 until his retirement (1935), was born at London and educated at

Gonville and Caius College, Cambridge (Pl. 66). After receiving his medical degree (M.B.) in 1885 he studied pathology at Berlin with Virchow and Koch, and during the next ten years visited Strasbourg several times to work under Frederick L. Goltz whose chief interest lay in the function of the central nervous system. In 1891 Sherrington succeeded Horsley as Professor-Superintendent of the Brown Institution for Advanced Physiological and Pathological Research, but in 1895 accepted the chair in physiology at the University of Liverpool where he remained for eighteen years until he went to Oxford.

Sherrington's election to the Royal Society in 1893 (he became president in 1920) was the first of many honors which marked his distinguished career: he was knighted in 1922, accorded the rare distinction of the Order of Merit, and in 1932 shared a Nobel Prize with E. D. Adrian for "discoveries regarding the function of the neurons." The creative energy of Sherrington, who probably did more to influence thought in modern medicine than any other Englishman since William Harvey, has been attributed to his broad humanism. He was a book collector, a poet, and a polished writer with a wide knowledge of classical languages and literature, of general history, and especially of the history of art.

From Sherrington's comprehensive studies, and particularly those carried out on monkeys and the higher apes, there emerged the vast sweep of present-day knowledge of neurophysiology—the nature of the knee-jerk, reciprocal innervation of motor areas, focal epilepsy, the proprioceptive system, and finally the broad concepts of "the final common pathway" and the "integrative action of the nervous system."

The concept of the integrative function of the nervous system was first set forth in 1906 under the auspices of the Silliman Lectureship at Yale University.[17] The first quotation is taken from the *British Association Report* in which the principle of the common path was initially described. In the second selection the original definition of the proprioceptive system is given. The third concerns the discovery of the stretch reflex, one of the most important single contributions from Sherrington's laboratory made early in a long and fruitful collaboration with Edward George Tandy Liddell (1895-), F.R.S., M.D., M.A. Oxon., who succeeded him as Waynflete Professor of Physiology (1940-1960). They found that the long-debated problem of muscle tonus resolved itself into an analysis of the response of muscles to stretch, and that postural contraction is maintained chiefly through stretch imposed upon antigravity muscles.

CORRELATION OF REFLEXES AND THE PRINCIPLE OF THE COMMON PATH

The principle I have tried to outline to you has many and wide applications; it seems fruitful for problems of Pathology and Psychology, as well as for those of Physiology. But I keep you too long. Let me sum up. The reflex arcs (of the synaptic system) converge in their course so as to impinge upon links possessed by whole varied groups

---

[17] Sherrington, C. S. *The integrative action of the nervous system.* New Haven, Yale University Press, 1906. xviii, 411 pp.; 2d ed., 1947; paperbound ed., 1961.

in common—*common paths*. This arrangement culminates in the convergence of many separately arising arcs upon the efferent-root neurone. This neurone thus forms a final common path for many different reflex arcs and acts. It is responsive in various rhythm and intensity, and is relatively unfatigable. Of the different arcs which use it in common, each can do so exclusively in due succession, but *different* arcs cannot use it simultaneously. There is, therefore, interference between the actions of the arcs possessing the common path, some reflexes excluding others and producing inhibitory phenomena, some reflexes reinforcing others and producing phenomena of 'bahnung.' Intensity of stimulation, species of reflex, fatigue, and freshness, all these are physiological factors influencing this interaction of the arcs—and under pathological conditions there are many others, e.g. 'shock' toxins, &c. Hence follows successive interchange of the arcs that dominate one and the same final common path. We commonly hear a muscle—or other effector organ—spoken of as innervated by a certain nerve; it would be more correct as well as more luminous to speak of it as innervated by certain receptors; thus, the hip flexor, now by this piece of skin, now by that, by its own foot, by the opposite fore-foot, by the labyrinth, by its own muscle-spindles, by the eye, by the 'motor' cortex, &c. This temporal variability, wanting to the nerve-net system of medusoid and lower visceral life, in the *synaptic* system provides the organism with a mechanism for higher integration. It fits that system to synthesise from a mere collection of tissues and organs an individual animal. The animal mechanism is thus given solidarity by this principle which for each effector organ allows and regulates interchange of the arcs playing upon it, a principle which I would briefly term that of 'the interaction of reflexes about their common path.' (Sherrington, C. S. "Correlation of reflexes and the principle of the common path." *Rept. Brit. Ass.*, 1904, pp. 728-741 [pp. 740-741].)

THE PROPRIOCEPTIVE SYSTEM

The receptor organs, if one regards their distribution from a broad point of view, fall naturally into two great groups, as judged by their locus in the body. They are distributed in two great separate fields, each field circumstanced fundamentally differently from the other. Multicellular animals, regarded broadly throughout a vast range of animal forms, are cellular masses which present to the environment a surface sheet of cells and, underneath that surface sheet, a bulk made up of cells more or less screened from the environment by the surface sheet overlying them. The surface sheet is directly exposed to the environment, and is adapted to react to many of the factors composing that environment, these factors constituting stimuli. Bedded in the surface sheet are numbers of receptor cells, developed in adaptation to the stimuli delivered by environmental agencies. Many of the agencies by which the environment acts on the organism do not, however, penetrate to the mass of cells forming the organism's deeper parts. Thus various stimuli in the forms of light and heat, and localised pressures, and chemical substances expend themselves as stimuli at the surface sheet, and do not penetrate into the depth of the organism. But the deep tissues, although devoid of receptors adapted to these surface-reaching stimuli, are, nevertheless, not unprovided with receptors. They have receptors of other kinds apparently specific to them. Some agencies act not only at the surface of the organism, but also through its mass. For some of these agencies no receptors appear to be adapted; for instance, there seem to be none adapted for the Röntgen rays. For others of more common occurrence, receptors in the deep tissues seem to have been evolved. The deep receptors appear to be very usually adapted to mechanical stimuli of certain kinds. Thus they seem adapted to react to the compressions and strains produced by muscles, and an important adequate agent for them seems to be mass acting in the modes of weight and inertia, involving mechanical pressures and mechanical stresses.

The main fields of distribution of the receptor organs fundamentally distinguishable seem, therefore, to be two, namely, a *surface* field constituted by the surface layer of the organism and a *deep* field constituted by the tissues of the organism beneath the surface sheet.

But the surface field is further broadly subdivisible. Its subdivisions are two. Of these one lies freely open to the numberless vicissitudes and agencies of the environment; it is co-extensive with the so-called external surface of the animal. It is cutaneous in the widest sense of that term. It possesses as receptive organs not only those of touch, &c., in the skin proper, but also the eye, nose, and organ of hearing. This subdivision of the surface field contrasts with a second subdivision of it, constituted by what is commonly termed the internal surface of the animal, the alimentary or intestinal surface. This latter surface is, it is true, in contact with the environment; but the environment with which it is in contact is a portion of the environment greatly modified from the general environment outside by lying almost completely surrounded by the animal itself. This part of the receptive field of the animal's surface, which is turned inward upon the alimentary contents, may be termed the *intero-ceptive,* in contradistinction to that larger part of the surface field which looks outward upon the free environment in general, and the latter may from that circumstance be termed the animal's *extero-ceptive* surface. . . .

Returning to the receptor organs bedded in the deep tissues, and to the study of the reactions which they subserve, two characters attract attention as differentiating them from those of the surface field, whether extero-ceptive or intero-ceptive. Of these features, one is that the *stimuli* effective on the receptors of the deep field differ fundamentally from those operative on the receptors of either subdivision of the surface field. Most of the stimuli by which the external world commonly acts on the surface of the animal are excluded from the deep field. But the organism itself, like the external world surrounding it, is a field of ceaseless change where internal energy is continually being liberated, whence chemical, thermal, mechanical, and electrical effects appear. It is a microcosm in which forces which can act as stimuli are at work, as in the macrocosm around. The receptors which lie in the deep tissues appear adapted for excitation by changes going forward in the organism itself. These changes work, it appears, largely through the agency of mass with its mechanical consequences of weight and inertia, and also largely through mechanical strains and alterations of pressure resulting from contractions and relaxations of muscles. *Therefore, a character of the stimulations occurring in this deep field is that the stimuli are traceable to actions of the organisms itself,* and are so in much greater measure than are the stimulations of the surface field of the organism. Since in the deep field the stimuli to the receptors are delivered by the organism *itself* the deep receptors may be termed, *proprio-ceptors,* and the deep field a field of proprioception. (Sherrington, C. S. "On the proprioceptive system, especially in its reflex aspect." *Brain,* 1906, *29,* 467-482 [pp. 468-469, 471-472].)

REFLEXES IN RESPONSE TO STRETCH
(MYOTATIC REFLEXES)

Familiar to those who work with the decerebrate preparation must be the observation that passive flexion of the characteristically extended knee is felt to evoke some development or resistance of it against that passive movement. Examination by the myograph of this resistance formed the point of departure of the following observations.

In this same muscle the "knee jerk" is doubtless a reflex in response to a stretch; but it is a reaction whose brevity makes it perhaps the most twitch-like of all reflexes, whereas the reflex under consideration here is tetanic and prolonged. Patellar-clonus, likewise a reaction to stretch, resembles a spaced series of knee jerks and, wanting tetanic character, likewise differs from the reflex under consideration here. . . .

SUMMARY OF CONCLUSIONS

In the knee-extensor (decerebrate preparation) a stretch applied to the muscles evokes contraction in it. This is reflex and purely proprioceptive, its receptors lying in the fleshy region of the muscle. A stretch less in extent than .8 per cent. of the total muscle-length suffices to evoke the reflex. Slow stretches, *e.g.,* of 5 mm. performed in 6 sec., evoke the reflex as well as do quick. The latency of the reflex is short, *e.g.,* less than 20σ, but the lower limit of latency we have not determined.

Within limits, so long as the stretch increases, the reflex continues to increase. When augmentation of the stretch ceases, augmentation of the reflex contraction also ceases and the reflex usually declines, merging into long-lasting plateau-like contraction, which is maintained by the stretched-posture, consequent from the precurrent stretch-movement. Withdrawal of the stretch causes immediate cessation of this postural stretch contraction. The stretch-reflex unlike the ordinary contralateral extensor reflexes, therefore, exhibits little or no after-discharge, *i.e.,* the reflex is relatively dead-beat.

When the application of the stretch is confined to a portion only of the muscle, the reflex contraction is also confined to that portion.

The reflex is readily diminished and annulled by reflex inhibition provoked from the sources recognized as regularly inhibitory for the knee-extensor. Under this inhibition, the muscle's reaction to stretch resembles indistinguishably in our records that yielded by the muscle after complete paralysis from severance of its motor nerve. Similarly, after severance of the afferent nerve-fibres of the muscle the reaction of the muscle to stretch becomes indistinguishable from that of the inhibited or paralysed muscle, and no trace of reflex con-

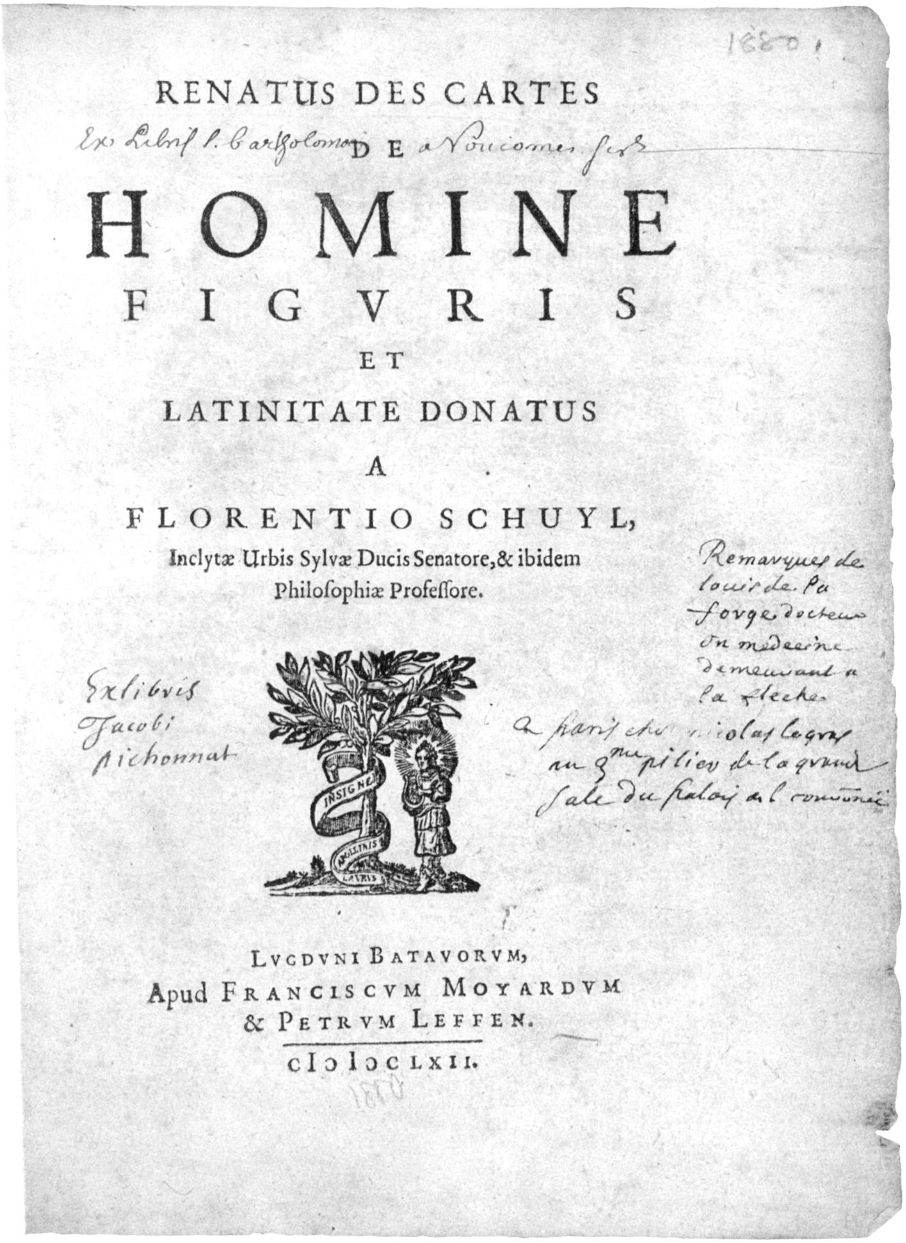

RENATUS DES CARTES

Ex Libris P. Bartholomæi DE *à Nouicomen fer?*

HOMINE

FIGVRIS

ET

LATINITATE DONATUS

A

FLORENTIO SCHUYL,

Inclytæ Urbis Sylvæ Ducis Senatore, & ibidem
Philofophiæ Profeffore.

Remarques de
louis de. Pa
forge docteur
en medecine
demeurant a
la flecke.

a paris chez niclas legras
au m.me pilier de la grand
Sale du palay a l' commuñe.

LVGDVNI BATAVORVM,
Apud FRANCISCVM MOYARDVM
& PETRVM LEFFEN.
CIↃIↃCLXII.

PLATE 56. The title-page of the first edition of Descartes' *De homine,* 1662, which contains the passages on reflex action, reciprocal innervation, and the pineal gland as the seat of the soul.

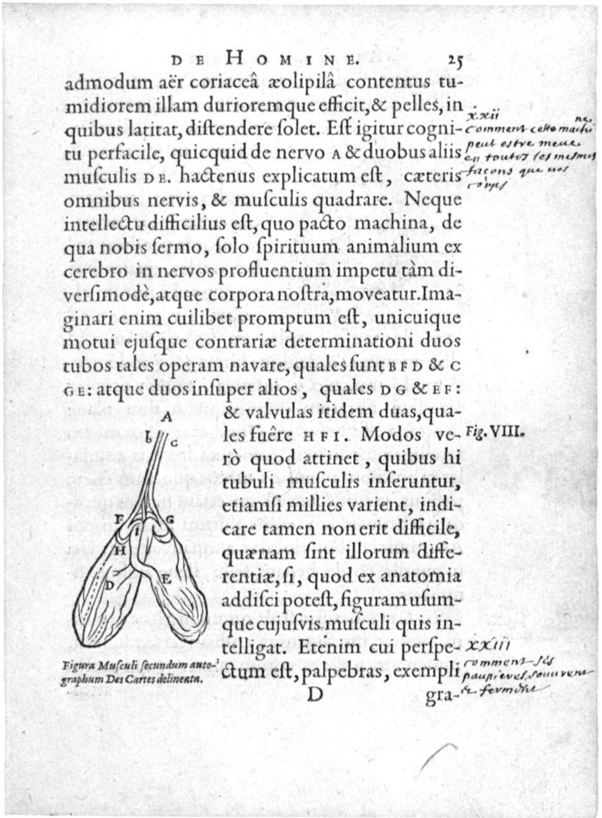

admodum aër coriacâ xolipilâ contentus tu-
midiorem illam durioremque efficit, & pelles, in
quibus latitat, diftendere folet. Eft igitur cogni-
tu perfacile, quicquid de nervo A & duobus aliis
mufculis D B. hactenus explicatum eft, cæteris
omnibus nervis, & mufculis quadrare. Neque
intellectu difficilius eft, quo pacto machina, de
qua nobis fermo, folo fpirituum animalium ex
cerebro in nervos profluentium impetu tâm di-
verfimode, atque corpora noftra, moveatur. Ima-
ginari enim cuilibet promptum eft, unicuique
motui ejufque contrariæ determinationi duos
tubos tales operam navare, quales funt B F D & C
G E: atque duos infuper alios, quales D G & E F:
& valvulas itidem duas, qua-
les fuére H F I. Modos ve-
rò quod attinet, quibus hi
tubuli mufculis inferuntur,
etiamfi millies varient, indi-
care tamen non erit difficile,
quænam fint illorum diffe-
rentiæ, fi, quod ex anatomia
addici poteft, figuram fum-
que cujufvis mufculi quis in-
telligat. Etenim cui perfpe-
ctum eft, palpebras, exempli
gra-

Fig. VII.

Fig. VIII.

Figura Mufculi fecundum auto-
graphum DesCartefii. definit.

D

PLATE 57A. One of Descartes' diagrams illustrating the effect of light upon the rational soul lying within the pineal.

dant in tubulum 2, ex puncto b in tubum 4, & ex
puncto c in tubum 6. Confiderandum quoque,

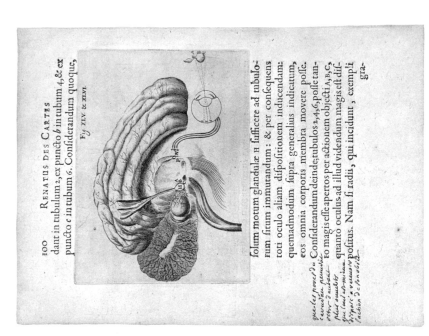

Fig XLV. & XLVI.

folum motum glandulæ H fufficere ad tubulo-
rum fitum immutandum: & per confequens
toti oculo aliam difpofitionem inducendam:
quemadmodum fupra generalius indicatum,
eos omnia corporis membra movere poffe.
Confiderandum deinde; tubulos 2, 4, 6, poffe tan-
to magis effe apertos per actionem objecti A, B, C,
quanto oculus ad illud videndum magis eft dif-
pofitus. Nam fi radii, qui incidunt, exempli
gra-

PLATE 57B. Descartes' original diagram illustrating reciprocal innervation of the eye muscles.

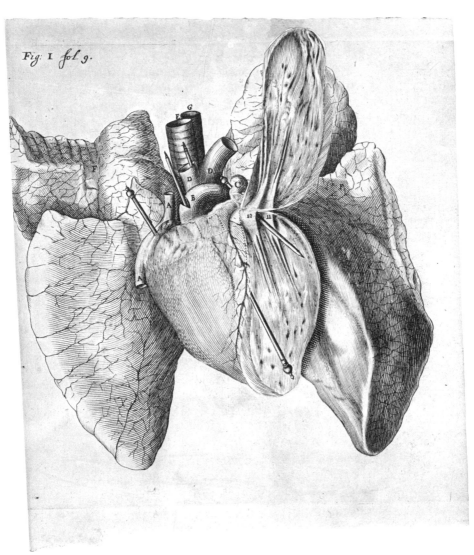

PLATE 58. Descartes' excellent figure of the heart with one of the flaps up showing the corda tendinae. This is an early instance of the use of superimposed drawings to illustrate successive anatomical layers.

PLATE 59. The portrait of Whytt which hangs in the Royal College of Physicians, Edinburgh. Reproduced by their kind permission.

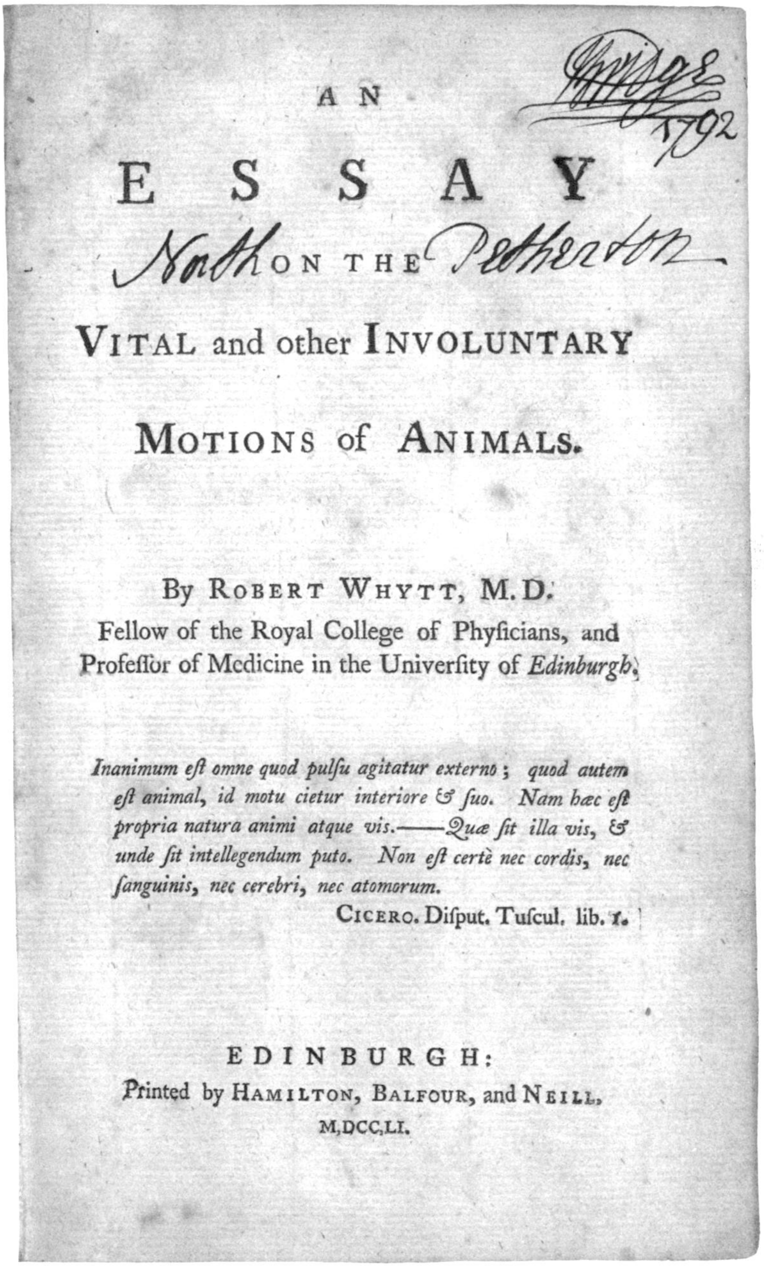

AN

ESSAY

 ON THE

VITAL and other INVOLUNTARY

MOTIONS of ANIMALS.

By ROBERT WHYTT, M.D.
Fellow of the Royal College of Phyſicians, and
Profeſſor of Medicine in the Univerſity of *Edinburgh.*

*Inanimum eſt omne quod pulſu agitatur externo; quod autem
eſt animal, id motu cietur interiore & ſuo. Nam hæc eſt
propria natura animi atque vis.———Quæ ſit illa vis, &
unde ſit intellegendum puto. Non eſt certè nec cordis, nec
ſanguinis, nec cerebri, nec atomorum.*
CICERO. Diſput. Tuſcul. lib. I.

EDINBURGH:
Printed by HAMILTON, BALFOUR, and NEILL,
M,DCC,LI.

PLATE 60. The title-page of Robert Whytt's book in which the theory
of reflex action was set forth, 1751.

PLATE 61. François Magendie (1783-1855).

PLATE 62. Marshall Hall (1790-1857).

PLATE 63. Charles Edouard Brown-Séquard (1817-1894).

PLATE 64. John Hughlings Jackson (1835-1911). (By permission of the Treasurer of the Royal College of Physicians, London.)

PLATE 65. Sir David Ferrier (1843-1928). (Courtesy of the Royal College of Physicians, London.)

PLATE 66. Sir Charles Sherrington, O.M. (1857-1952), *c.* 1913.

PLATE 67. Harvey Cushing (1869-1939), taken in his Baltimore laboratory, *c.* 1912.

traction in response to the stretch has been discoverable. Direct stimulation, electrical or mechanical, of the afferent nerve of a part of the muscle produces inhibitory relaxation of the stretch contraction in the other parts of the muscle, *i.e.* among receptors in the muscle, there are in addition to those excitable by stretch and provoking reflex contraction in the muscle, others which provoke reflex inhibition of the muscle.

Post-inhibitory rebound is facilitated and augmented by stretch of the muscle; this is so even when the stretched-posture has been maintained for many minutes at the time when the post-inhibitory period occurs. Knee-jerk and patellar clonus seem to be fractional examples of the stretch-reflex.

Some application of the experimental results to the reflex co-ordination of standing and of locomotor acts is attempted. (Liddell, E. G. T. and Sherrington, C. S. "Reflexes in response to stretch (myotatic reflexes)." *Proc. roy. Soc.*, 1924, *96B*, 212-242; 1925; 267-283 [pp. 212, 241].)

Harvey Cushing
1869-1939

Harvey Cushing, Moseley Professor of Surgery at Harvard Medical School and Surgeon-in-Chief of the Peter Bent Brigham Hospital for two decades (1912-1932), was born in Cleveland, Ohio, and educated at Yale and Harvard Medical School. Before settling in Boston, he spent sixteen years at Johns Hopkins (Pl. 67), the first three (before a year in clinics and laboratories abroad) as assistant to the great surgeon, William Halsted. The first to devote himself entirely to surgery of the brain, Cushing, after his return from Europe in 1901, began to take advantage of the exceptional opportunities which operations on the human brain offered for analysis of function, especially when carried out under local anesthesia (a procedure he was initially to introduce in brain surgery). As a pupil in Sherrington's laboratory at Liverpool, he assisted in experiments on stimulation of the motor area of the higher apes and soon afterwards he made corresponding observations on human beings under surgical anesthesia. The story of his first experience in stimulating the motor and sensory areas of a conscious patient is told in the following passage. The appeal of the human experiment is always great and it is particularly so in this instance, for it established convincingly that the reactions studied in higher apes were applicable to human beings, and it provided for the first time direct evidence that irritation of the postcentral gyrus gives rise to sensation, a fact which could not be established by experiments on animals.

THE HUMAN MOTOR CORTEX

A year ago I reported, with Dr. H. M. Thomas, a surgical experience* in which at a second-stage operation an osteoplastic flap, previously made, was re-elevated, the dura reflected, the cortex incised, and a subcortical cystic tumour removed from the postcentral field of an unanaesthetized patient. The procedure, with the exception of accidental dragging upon the dura, and the final reclosure of the scalp, not only occasioned no discomfort, but was attended on the part of the patient by a lively and helpful interest in the performance. He even informed us of a focal sensory attack which occurred early in the proceedings, evidently incited by the preliminary palpation of the exposed brain. . . .

In the past year, however, the exigencies of two surgical cases have given us the looked-for opportunity of making further observations upon the sensory field. . . .

Operation (second stage, July 6, 1908).—After a preliminary injection of ⅛ gr. of morphia, and under primary anæsthesia by chloroform, the edges of the former incision were newly separated and the original bone-flap quickly re-elevated. The patient promptly regained complete consciousness, and while in this state, without occasioning discomfort, the dura was divided in the line of the previous closure, and the membrane was again reflected.

Cortical stimulation.—The following electrical observations were then made. The same movements as before were easily elicited with a mild faradic current from the precentral strip. These motor responses in detail and in the order in which they were obtained from the areas shown in the accompanying sketch (fig. 60) [Fig. 8] consisted of:—

(1) An opposing movement of thumb and fingers from points opposite to the unmistakable genu.

(2) Somewhat higher up, extension of the index finger.

(3) Still higher flexion of the fingers, which carried over to flexion of the wrist.

(4) At the upper margin of the exposed field, flexion of the elbow.

(5) Below the evident middle genu the movements, which required a somewhat stronger current, consisted of contraction of the side of the face.

* "Removal of a subcortical, cystic tumour at a second-stage operation without anaesthesia." *J. Amer. med. Ass.* 1908, vol. 1, p. 847.

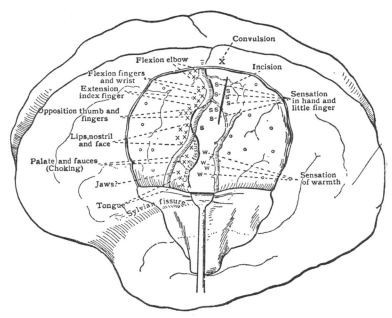

Figure 8. The motor and sensory areas as first delineated experimentally by Cushing in a conscious human being.

(6) Movements of palate and fauces, a curious choking sensation being occasioned whenever they were obtained; and

(7) From the very lowest exposed part of the strip movements of the tongue occurred, and the patient experienced a sensation of movement in the lower jaw, though this was not certified by the observers.

It is to be noted that the subject was perfectly aware of these movements, and in the attempt to express the sense of feeling which was occasioned by them he said that it was the same sort of a drawing sensation appreciated when the muscles are "pulled" by peripheral stimulation—a familiar experience for him, owing to a long course of electrical treatment before his admission to the hospital. The movements, in other words, gave him the sensation of active muscular contraction alone.

Posterior to the central fissure, over an area roughly corresponding with the upper two-thirds of the exposed postcentral convolution [Fig. 8], stimulation, with the same strength of current used to elicit the motor responses from the precentral gyrus, led to a sensation in the hand, arm and little finger—chiefly in the little finger—

which was said to be exactly akin to the sensation that inaugurated his attacks. Stimulation lower down on the postcentral gyrus occasioned a sensation of warmth in the arm, but this was rather vague and indescribable.

It is to be noted that there were no painful sensations whatsoever, and further, that stimulation of the field in front of the motor strip and back of the postcentral convolution elicited no movements or sensations whatsoever, and the patient seemed to be unaware of the application of the electrode.

On elevating the upper edge of the dura at the point X [Fig. 8] and placing the electrode there, an attack precisely similar to his usual attacks, inaugurated by the same sensory disturbances and followed by the customary abduction of the arm and arching of the body to the side, was produced. This lasted but a few moments, and was not followed by a general convulsion nor by loss of consciousness. . . .

COMMENT

These observations seemingly add confirmation to the view which ascribes a sensory function to the gyrus centralis posterior, but beyond this I shall make no endeavour to interpret their significance. Just what relation the afferent impulse bears to a motor response; just how stimulation of this supposedly sensory field is interpreted by the subject as sensory; why the motor response from stimulation of the gyrus centralis anterior occurs without any primary afferent impression, but only with the secondary consciousness of the movement—these and many other questions that arise are matters rather for the psychologist.

It is, perhaps, noteworthy that the sensations which were obtained were limited entirely to the hand and arm; and whether this means that there is an especially wide cortical representation for afferent impulses from this region, or whether these patients, owing to the characteristics of their seizures, possessed sensory centres from hand and arm which were unduly excitable, is difficult to tell, and will need further elucidation. (Cushing, H. "A note upon the faradic stimulation of the postcentral gyrus in conscious patients." *Brain,* 1909, *32,* 44-54 [(pp. 45, 46, 47-49, 52].)

Rudolf Magnus
1872-1927

Rudolf Magnus, for many years the professor of pharmacology at Utrecht, set himself the problem of turning anatomical facts concerning the nervous system into physiological language. His investigations in this field of work were commenced in 1908 after spending a winter in Sherrington's laboratory at Liverpool and they culminated in 1924 in a now classical monograph on animal posture.[18] During that interval nearly 150 papers on the physiology of posture had come from his laboratory. Magnus had the happy faculty of being able to describe with astonishing clearness, even in a tongue that was not his own, reactions occurring in three dimensions of space. This is nowhere better illustrated than in his Croonian Lecture from which the following passage is taken.

ANIMAL POSTURE

Every movement starts from and ends in some posture, so that I think a discussion of "Animal Posture" falls well within the scope of the intention of Dr. William Croone, when he founded these annual Lectures to promote the study of "Muscular Motion." Before beginning I wish to emphasise how greatly I appreciate the honour of delivering before you this Lecture, and how I especially enjoy the pleasure of doing so with Sir Charles Sherrington in the Chair, who long ago took the trouble to introduce me to his beautiful methods of investigating the central nervous system, and to allow me an insight into his fruitful views on the function of nervous centres.

As it is impossible to consider the whole problem of posture in one short lecture, I propose to speak to you to-day on four partial problems, which are closely connected with each other, and which provided the starting points for investigations which have been carried out in my laboratory at Utrecht, with the aid of a great number of able collaborators. These partial problems are:—

1. *Reflex standing.*—In order to carry the weight of the body against the action of gravity, it is necessary that a certain set of muscles, the "standing muscles," should have by reflex action a certain degree of enduring tone, to prevent the body from falling down on the ground.

2. *Normal distribution of tone.*—In the living animal not only do

[18] Magnus, R. *Körperstellung.* Berlin, Springer, 1924. xiii, 740 pp.

these standing muscles possess tone, but also the other muscles of the body, especially their antagonists, *i.e.* the flexors. Between these two sets of muscles a certain balance of tone exists, so that neither set of muscles gets too much or too little tone.

3. *Attitude.*—The position of the different parts of the body must harmonise with each other; if one part of the body be displaced, the other parts also change in posture, so that different well-adapted attitudes, evoked by the first displacement, will result.

4. *Righting function.*—If by its own active movements or by some outside force the body of an animal is brought out of the normal resting posture, then a series of reflexes are evoked, by which the normal position is reached again.

The main *centres* for all these four functions are situated in close neighbourhood subcortically in the brain-stem. Their function is to compound the activity of the whole body musculature to what we call *"posture."* The lower centres for the muscles of the different parts of the body are arranged segmentally in the spinal cord; the higher centres in the brain-stem put them into combined action, and in this way govern the posture of the animal as a whole. We have here a very good example of what Sherrington has called the "integrative action of the nervous system." And integration is especially necessary in the case of posture, because nervous excitations arising from very different sense organs are flowing towards the postural centres in the brain-stem, and must be combined so that a harmonising effect will result.

Nervous impulses, which can influence posture, arise: (1) From the labyrinths, a double sense-organ: the otoliths reacting to changes in position, the ampullae of the semicircular canals to accelerations; (2) from the proprioceptive sense-organs in muscles, joints and tendons; (3) from exteroceptive nerve endings of the body surface, chiefly from the pressure sense-organs, which are stimulated, if the body touches the ground; (4) from teleceptors [*sic*], reacting to distance stimuli, such as the eye, the ear, the nose. In fact a very finely elaborated central apparatus is needed to combine and distribute all these afferent impulses, depending on and adapted to the always changing circumstances of environment. . . .

Suppose a cat is standing in the middle of the room, and a mouse is running on its right side along the wall. The optic and acoustic stimuli act on the telereceptors of the cat's head, and make it turn the heavy head to the right. By this the centre of gravity of the fore part of the body is displaced to the right. At the same time tonic neck reflexes are evoked, by which the vertebral column is curved and the right fore-limb strongly extended, so that it carries the weight of the body alone and prevents it from falling. The left fore-limb has nothing to carry, and in harmony therewith this limb relaxes under the influence of the tonic neck reflex. At the same time the distribution of excitability in the motor centres of the spinal cord is rearranged by the turning of the neck, so that, if for some reason running movements begin, the limb which has no static function will always make the first step. In this way the moving mouse impresses on the cat through the mediation of tonic neck reflexes an attitude, by which the cat is focussed towards the mouse and made ready for movement. The only thing the cat has to do is to decide: to jump or not to jump; all other things have been prepared beforehand reflexly under the influence of the mouse, which will be the object of the resulting jump.

These examples may give an impression of the different ways in which the tonic labyrinthine and neck reflexes are used during the normal life of intact animals. They can easily be extended by watching various kinds of animals. Only in the monkey they cannot easily be detected, because with the higher development of the fore-brain and the greater complication of movements these lower postural reflexes are partly suppressed. It is necessary to decerebrate or narcotise a monkey in order to show that he has the same attitudinal reflexes, obeying the same laws, as are shown by other animals.

Also, in man during ordinary life the attitudinal reflexes cannot easily be detected. In the infant child several of them are present. In adults instantaneous photographs show sometimes postures in agreement with the laws of attitudinal activity of the brain-stem centres. I owe to Dr. Wolf the acquaintance with fast cinema photos of golf players, showing that at the top of the swing the shoulders are turned by 180° in relation to the head, which is kept fixed in space as firmly as possible. In this way a tendency is evoked to extend the left arm and to twist the body to the left—movements which appear to be performed, indeed, by the subsequent photographs, and which seem to be facilitated and strengthened by the preliminary starting posture of the head and body. It is this fixing of the head in the line of sight of the ball which is insisted upon as essential to the performance of a correct shot. (Magnus, R. "Animal posture." Croonian Lecture. *Proc. roy. Soc.*, 1925, *98B*, 339-353 [pp. 339-340, 345-346].)

Wilder G. Penfield
1891-

Wilder Graves Penfield, O.M., M.D., was born at Spokane, Washington, was graduated B.Litt. from Princeton University in 1913, and was a Rhodes Scholar at Merton College, Oxford (1914, 1918-1920), in between times having two tours of duty in France and graduating M.D. from Johns Hopkins Medical School in 1918. After 1921 Penfield was engaged in research at the Presbyterian Hospital, New York City, and in 1928 he moved to Montreal where in 1934 he became director of the newly formed Montreal Neurological Institute of McGill University.

Dr. Penfield pioneered in electrical stimulation of the cerebral cortex of human subjects during brain operations and thus utilizing the opportunities for observation offered by his surgical experience, he discovered that such stimulation could evoke complex thought patterns including the vivid recall of past experience. Here he describes some of the conclusions drawn from these observations and their relation to earlier work.

PSYCHICAL RESPONSES

The positive psychical responses which have been produced by electrical stimulation of the superior and lateral surfaces of the temporal lobes are clearly of a different physiological order from those produced by stimulation elsewhere in the brain. Perhaps most of the results, of stimulation of sensory and motor areas of conscious patients, which we have just described might have been predicted and expected from the previous observations made by physiologists in the laboratory and neurologists in the ward.

But psychical responses came to us as a complete surprise. Perhaps they too should have been expected because of the nature of certain seizures long recognized as being associated with abnormalities of the temporal lobe. Hughlings Jackson, long ago (see his *Writings*, 1931), surmised that an epileptic fit was a symptom or group of symptoms produced occasionally by local spontaneous discharges in some area of grey matter of the brain. Whether there was local or general convulsion or whether consciousness was preserved or lost depended upon the site and degree of discharge, not upon any essential causal difference. Studies of epilepsy during the past 90 years have only served to confirm his thinking.

He referred to "Psychical states during the onset of certain epileptic seizures, states which are much more elaborate than crude sensations." And he left us the following descriptions: "The state is often like that occasionally experienced by healthy people as a feeling of 'reminiscence.'—It is sometimes called 'dreamy feelings' or is described as 'dreams mixing up with present thoughts,' 'double consciousness,' 'feeling of being somewhere else,' 'as if I went back to all that occurred in my childhood'—'silly thoughts.' "

INTERPRETIVE CORTEX

Such illusions are interpretations of present experience and it seems likely that the area of cortex in which they may be produced plays some role in normal interpretation. Present interpretation must depend upon comparison of the present with similar or related experience from the past. Thus it is consistent that these two types of response occur in the same general area of the cerebral cortex—the superior and lateral surfaces of the temporal lobes.

Interpretation, as I am using the term, is part of the process that converts sensation into perception. It represents a further stage in the total integrative action of the brain. This area of cortex seems to have a relationship to the process of interpretation. This relationship is analogous to that which the sensory areas of the cortex bear to various types of sensation and the motor areas bear to the control of movement. They are links, important and essential links, in the chains of three different neurone circuits which make possible sensation, perception and voluntary action. To speak of "motor cortex" and "sensory cortex" is no more than physiological slang. But it has proved to be useful slang and it might serve a similarly useful purpose to refer to the superior and lateral surfaces of the temporal lobes as perceptional cortex. (Penfield, W. *The excitable cortex in conscious man.* Sherrington Lecture Series V. Liverpool, Liverpool University Press, 1958. 42 pp. [pp. 20-21, 24].)

Horace Winchell Magoun

1907-

Horace W. Magoun, American neuro-anatomist and physiologist, has become widely known for his studies on the functions of a hitherto largely unexplored region of the brainstem known in classical neurology as the "reticular forma-tion." He was originally led to investigate this part of the brain through work carried out in collaboration with his preceptor Stephen W. Ranson of Chicago, using the Horsley-Clarke stereotaxic instrument in exploring the excitable properties of the hypothalamic region.[19] This was followed by anatomical studies on the centers and central pathways of the masticatory and pupillary reflexes and later, with J. R. Brobeck *et al.*, by a brilliant analysis of the mechanisms involved in heat regulation.[20] Magoun and his pupils then devoted themselves to study of the postural reflexes and to the phenomena of spasticity and the augmented stretch-reflexes evoked by lesions of certain cortical motor areas and subcortical structures such as the reticulum.[21] Magoun's first paper on the reticular formation, published in 1946 with Ruth Rhines,[22] marked the be-ginning of the series of classic studies summarized in 1958 in the Thomas Wil-liam Salmon Memorial Lecture from which the following résumé has been taken.

FUNCTIONS OF RETICULAR FORMATION

When one attempts to formulate generalizations concerning the neurophysiological developments discussed above, and to character-ize their additions to the rich contributions of the Edwardian peri-od, the introduction of a more operational point of view in both neuronal and brain functions seems to form the most obtrusive fea-ture.

Within the individual neuron, graded response mechanisms have been identified at either end of the classically conducting nerve fiber. These have greatly increased the scope of comprehension of neuronal function over that provided by the concept of all-or-none activity, now confined to the conducting portion of the axon.

Within the brain, a central transactional core has been identified between the strictly sensory or motor systems of classical neurology. This central reticular mechanism has been found capable of grading the activity of most other parts of the brain. It does this as a reflexion of its own internal excitability, in turn a consequence of both afferent and corticifugal neural influences, as well as of the

[19] Magoun, H. W., Barris, R. W., and Ranson, S. W. "Stimulation of the hypo-thalamus with the Horsley-Clarke stereotaxic instrument." *Anat. Rec.*, 1932, *52*, 24, Suppl.

[20] Magoun, H. W., Harrison, F., Brobeck, J. R., and Ranson, S. W. "Activation of heat loss mechanisms by local heating of the brain." *J. Neurophysiol.*, 1938, *1*, 101-114.

[21] Magoun, H. W. *Spasticity, the stretch-reflex and extrapyramidal systems.* Spring-field, Ill., Charles C Thomas, Publisher, 1948. vi, 59 pp.

[22] Magoun, H. W. and Rhines, R. "An inhibitory mechanism in the bulbar reticular formation." *J. Neurophysiol.*, 1946, *9*, 165-171.

titer of circulating humors and hormones which affect and modify reticular activity.

While the activities of this reticular system tend generally to be more widespread than those of the specific systems of the brain, it is proposed to be subdivided into a grosser and more tonically operating component in the lower brain stem, subserving global alterations in excitability, as distinguished from a more cephalic, thalamic component with greater capacities for fractionated, shifting influence upon focal regions of the brain.

Influences of this reticular system which are directed spinalward modify central afferent transmission, as well as the activities of motor outflows from the cord, in particular those subserving posture. Recticular influences which are directed forward to the cephalic brain stem and rhinencephalon affect visceral and endocrine regulating systems and basal forebrain mechanisms for reward, punishment and emotion. Ascending reticular influences which are exerted upward upon the cerebral neocortex contribute to the initiation and maintenance of wakefulness and to the focus of attention.

These manifold and varied capacities of the reticular system suggest that it serves importantly, and in the closest conjunction with the cortex, in the central integrative processes of the brain. In no area do the findings seem more intriguing than in the new developments exploring its involvement in conditioned learning. (Magoun, H. W. *The waking brain.* Salmon Memorial Lecture, 1958. Springfield, Ill., Charles C Thomas, Publisher, 1958. viii, 138 pp., 55 illus. [pp. 115-116].) (2d ed. 1963.)

VIII

Homeostasis and the Regulation of Body Temperatures

From about 1854 Claude Bernard was accustomed to include in his lectures a discussion of the principle of the constancy of the *milieu intérieur* or internal environment and in 1865 he published his thoughts upon this principle in his *Introduction à l'étude de la médecine expérimentale* although he does not there express it so clearly and concretely as he did later. This principle was a corollary to Bernard's doctrine of determinism, namely, that vital phenomena were determined by physicochemical conditions. However, the physicochemical conditions to which he referred were, he pointed out, those of the *milieu intérieur,* not those of the external world. Bernard was guided in the development of this concept by the recently enunciated cell theory which was being vigorously applied to pathology by Rudolf Virchow. In the light of the cell theory Bernard saw the fundamental problems of physiology in the relation between the cells and their immediate surrounding environment.[1] Subsequently, the progress of physiology has revealed the far-reaching significance of Bernard's concept. As more—and more varied and elaborate—physiological mechanisms have been studied, each is seen to contribute, directly or indirectly, to the maintenance of constant internal conditions.

In 1926 Macallum gave historical and phylogenetic meaning to the constancy of the *milieu intérieur* when he demonstrated the startling resemblance between the ionic composition of blood sera and that of sea water and suggested that tissue cells could only live within a relatively narrow range of physicochemical conditions—conditions which represented those of the ancient ocean in which the cells of ancestral organisms had taken their origin. In the same year

[1] Holmes, F. L. "The *milieu intérieur* and the cell theory." *Bull. Hist. Med.,* 1963, *37,* 315-335.

Cannon coined his famous term "homeostasis" to describe the condition of constancy of the *milieu intérieur*.

The subsequent chapters of this book, dealing as they do with kidney function, sexual generation, endocrines, and vitamins, will each reveal particular aspects of homeostasis. Together they show how many-sided and how delicate a balance homeostasis is. However, the history of the study of body temperature, the recognition of its constancy and limits, and the later development of the concept that it is a regulated phenomenon (at least in the higher animal forms) provide a particularly clear example of the historical development of this one aspect of homeostasis. Moreover, it is a uniquely important example because the control of body temperature is fundamental to the activity of all body functions. Without a uniform internal temperature the body could not be free, and its activity would be utterly dependent on the temperature of its environment. The recognition of body warmth or "animal heat" (see Ch. IV, Respiration) was made in ancient times. However, it may be fairly stated, from one point of view, that until the thermometer had been invented there could not be a "temperature" of the body. The provision of such a device for scaled measurement by Galileo, and its development by Santorio and Duke Ferdinand II of Tuscany, made possible a series of observations by Blagden, John Hunter, James Currie, Carl Wunderlich, and many others which demonstrated the constancy of body temperature and some of the mechanisms for maintaining such constancy within limits which prevent the freezing of cellular water on one side and denaturation of proteins on the other. A clear definition of homeothermy (marked constancy of body temperature) and poikilothermy (body temperature which more nearly follows the ambient environment) was provided in the eighteenth century by John Hunter who also recognized that, in the cold, animals increase their heat production in order to maintain their body temperature.

The clinical importance of body temperature, particularly of hyperthermia or fever, was recognized by others before Wunderlich, but his monumental text is the definitive summation of his observations of patients which "amounts to nearly 25,000, and the number of single observations to some millions." All these observations were available to Claude Bernard when he used the demonstrated constancy of body temperature as another illustration of his thesis of the constancy and limit ranges of the *milieu intérieur*.

Further understanding of the mechanisms of control and regulation of body temperature did not occur until two new methods of research were available—at approximately the same time. The study of the body by the technique of calorimetry was developed by Max Rubner,[2] who demonstrated that living bodies obey the law of the conservation of energy—defined only a few years earlier by Helmholtz (1847). His research provided the first clear understanding of the way body temperature is controlled by submission to Newton's laws of cooling, and how the heat generated in the body is dissipated by radiation, conduction, convection, and evaporation. This approach culminated in the long series of detailed contributions made by Eugene F. DuBois[3] and his co-workers, principally James D. Hardy.

At about this time, neurophysiological technique began to be systematically applied to the study of nervous control of the body temperature. The experiments of Ott and Richet, performed almost simultaneously, demonstrated that there are areas in the brain which exert considerable control over the body temperature. From this pioneering work have come a multitude of studies, some of the most precise observations being those in the work of S. W. Ranson and his co-workers.[4]

Finally, there is evidence that the body maintains constancy of temperature by making adjustments in other physiological mechanisms which appear to make regulation of temperature an easier task by increasing or decreasing heat loss or increasing heat production. Acclimatization to heat and cold are equally well-established phenomena.[5]

Modern research in this field is directed toward the biochemical aspects of maintenance of body temperature[6] and toward combining

[2] Rubner, Max. *Die Gesetze des Energieverbrauchs bei der Ernährung*. Leipzig and Vienna, Franz Deuticke, 1902. iv, 426 pp.

[3] DuBois, E. F. *The mechanism of heat loss and temperature regulation. Lane medical lectures*. Stanford, Calif., Stanford University Press, 1937. 95 pp.

[4] Clark, G., Magoun, H. W., and Ranson, S. W. "Hypothalamic regulation of body temperature." *J. Neurophysiol.*, 1939, *2*, 61-80.

[5] For a full discussion see the excellent monographs by Alan C. Burton and Otto G. Edholm (*Man in a cold environment, physiological and pathological effects of exposure to low temperatures*. London, Edward Arnold, 1955. xiv, 273 pp.) and by E. F. Adolph and associates (*Physiology of man in the desert*. New York, Interscience, 1947. xiii, 357 pp.).

[6] Smith, R. E. and Hoijer, Dorothy J. "Metabolism and cellular function in cold acclimation." *Physiol. Rev.*, 1962, *42*, 60-142.

neurophysiological and calorimetric techniques with the methodology of systems-engineering and computer analysis.[7]

Claude Bernard
1813-1878

Claude Bernard, one of the greatest names in the history of physiology (Pl. 68), has left his mark on so many branches of the subject that it is impossible to say which of his many discoveries was the most significant: vasomotor nerves, glycogen and carbohydrate metabolism, curare and muscle; perhaps greater than all these was his teaching of the internal environment of the organism. It is expressed more fully in Bernard's last published work, and represents the outcome of a life of profound thought. Little appreciated at the time, this far-reaching concept has now come into its own, and as it will continue to exert a great influence on the physiology of the future. Bernard's simple description of the *milieu intérieur* is here given, together with his application of the concept to temperature regulation and his experimental production of hypothermia.

THE *MILIEU INTÉRIEUR*

The various ways in which living organisms are related to their cosmic environment enable us to study life in three forms according as existence is entirely dependent upon external conditions, less dependent, or relatively independent. These three forms of life are as follows:

1. *Vie latente,* where life is not evident.

2. *Vie oscillante,* where evidences of life are variable and dependent upon external environment (milieu extérieur).

3. *Vie constante,* where life manifests itself independently of the external environment.

III. The third form of existence, characterised by freedom and independence is found in the more highly organised animals. Here life is never suspended, but flows steadily on apparently indifferent to alterations in its cosmic environment or changes in its material surroundings. Organs, structural mechanisms and tissues all function uniformly and their operations show no sign of the considerable variations present in organisms where conditions are inconstant. This is due to the fact that the *milieu intérieur* surrounding the or-

[7] Hardy, J. D. "Physiology of temperature regulation." *Physiol. Rev.,* 1961, *41,* 521-606.

gans, the tissues and their elements never varies; atmospheric changes cannot penetrate beyond it and it is therefore true to say that the physical conditions of environment are unchanging in a higher animal: each one is surrounded by this invariable *milieu* which is, as it were, an atmosphere proper to itself in an ever-changing cosmic environment. Here we have an organism which has enclosed itself in a kind of hot-house. The perpetual changes of external conditions cannot reach it; it is not subject to them, but is free and independent.

I think I was the first to urge the belief that animals have really two environments: a *milieu extérieur* in which the organism is situated, and a *milieu intérieur* in which the tissue elements live. The living organism does not really exist in the *milieu extérieur* (the atmosphere if it breathes, salt or fresh water if that is its element) but in the liquid *milieu intérieur* formed by the circulating organic liquid which surrounds and bathes all the tissue elements; this is the lymph or plasma, the liquid part of the blood which, in the higher animals, is diffused through the tissues and forms the ensemble of the intercellular liquids and is the basis of all local nutrition and the common factor of all elementary exchanges. A complex organism should be looked upon as an assemblage of simple organisms which are the anatomical elements that live in the liquid *milieu intérieur*.

The stability of the *milieu intérieur* is the primary condition for freedom and independence of existence; the mechanism which allows of this is that which ensures in the *milieu intérieur* the maintenance of all the conditions necessary to the life of the elements. From this we know that there can be no freedom or independence of existence for simple organisms whose constituent parts are in direct contact with their cosmic environment, and that this form of life is, in fact, the exclusive possession of organisms which have attained the highest state of complexity or organic differentiation.

Stability of environment implies an organism so perfect that it can continually compensate for and counterbalance external variations. Consequently, far from the higher animals being indifferent to their surroundings, they are on the contrary in close and intimate relation to it, so that their equilibrium is the result of compensation established as continually and as exactly as if by a very sensitive balance.

The necessary conditions for the life of the elements which must be brought together and kept up constantly in the *milieu intérieur* if freedom and independence of existence are to be maintained are already known to us: water, oxygen, heat, and reserve chemical substances.

These are the same conditions as are necessary for life in simple organisms; but in the perfected animal, whose existence is independent, the nervous system is called upon to regulate the harmony which exists between all these conditions. (Bernard, C. *Leçons sur les phénomènes de la vie communs aux animaux et aux végétaux.* Paris, J. B. Baillière et Fils,) 1878-79. 2 vols. xxxii, 564 pp. [vol. 1, pp. 67, 111-114, 123-124.)

THE *MILIEU INTÉRIEUR* AND TEMPERATURE REGULATION

The first fact which strikes us in the study of animal heat is that it is an essential vital condition of the *milieu intérieur,* an important attribute of the blood plasma in which all the anatomical elements are immersed. . . .

HYPOTHERMIA

I place here in front of you a rabbit in which we sectioned the medulla about five hours ago. Its temperature which was 40 degrees in the rectum before sectioning of the medulla has been lowered to 24 degrees. It is only 6 degrees above that of the environment which is 18 degrees. In an hour's time the animal will be in a condition favorable for experiment.

You ascertain that breathing is rare; the amplitude of the movements of the chest is almost imperceptible. The nervous reactions are obliterated; the animal no longer reacts to excitation. (Bernard, Claude. *"Leçons sur la chaleur animale, sur les effets de la chaleur et sur la fièvre."* Paris, J. B. Baillière et Fils, 1876, 471 pp. [pp. 10, 161. Translated by L. G. W.].)

Archibald Byron Macallum
1858-1934

Archibald Byron Macallum was born at London, Ontario, and was educated at the University of Toronto (B.A. 1880) and Johns Hopkins (Ph.D. 1888). From

1887 he taught physiology and later biochemistry at the University of Toronto but in 1920 he became professor of biochemistry at McGill University where he remained until his retirement in 1930. Over a long period of his career Macallum interested himself in the ionic composition of body fluids and made many determinations of such ionic compositions for the first time.

THE PALEOCHEMISTRY OF BODY FLUIDS

When, however, the ratios of the elements sodium, potassium, calcium and magnesium in the sera of these forms, as given in table 3, are examined there is revealed a degree of parallelism between the series from each of the forms which points unmistakeably to a com-

TABLE 3

	Na	K	Ca	Mg	Cl	SO₂
Ocean water (Dittmar)..	100	3.613	3.911	12.10	180.9	20.9
Homarus americanus	100	3.73	4.85	1.72	171.2	6.67
Acanthias vulgaris	100	4.61	2.71	2.46	165.7	
Carcharias littoralis	100	5.75	2.98	2.76	168.8	
Gadus callarias	100	9.50	3.93	1.41	149.7	
Pollachius virens	100	4.33	3.10	1.46	137.8	
Rana virescens	100	11.8	3.17	0.79	135.6	
Dog	100	6.62	2.8	0.758	139.5	
Man: serum	100	6.75	3.10	0.695	128.8	
Pleuritic fluid	100	7.08	2.83	0.71	115.8	
Hydrocele fluid . . .	100	4.95	2.78	0.666	123.6	
Ascitic fluid	100	5.58	3.10	0.626	132.4	

mon origin for all. Summarily these sera are, so far as their inorganic composition is concerned, but sea waters of different concentrations, sea waters, not of to-day, but as an attempt will be made to show, sea waters each derived from a particular period in the remote past history of the ocean and, in the marine forms, affected in each case by the change in composition and increase in concentration of the salts which have taken place in ocean water during the long time intervening between the age of origin in each case and the present period. (Macallum, A. B. "The paleochemistry of the body fluids and tissues." *Physiol. Rev.*, 1926, *6*, 316-357 [p. 330].)

Walter Bradford Cannon

1871-1945

In 1926 *Walter Bradford Cannon* outlined for the first time his classic concept of homeostasis which he was later to develop so successfully in *The Wisdom of the Body* (1931). This concept has had such a profound influence upon the recent development of physiology that its first enunciation is of both historic and scientific interest. Yet this important paper was buried in a Jubilee Volume in honor of Charles Richet—a book which was never widely circulated and is now decidedly obscure. We print it here in full. We have amplified Dr. Cannon's brief references because they represent the background of research which led him to formulate the concept of homeostasis and for that reason are of unusual historical importance.

PHYSIOLOGICAL REGULATION OF NORMAL STATES: SOME TENTATIVE POSTULATES CONCERNING BIOLOGICAL HOMEOSTATICS

"The living being is stable. It must be so in order not to be destroyed, dissolved, or disintegrated by the colossal forces, often adverse, which surround it. . . . In a sense it is stable because it is modifiable—the slight instability is the necessary condition for the true stability of the organism." Thus wrote Richet (1) in 1900. This stability is maintained by numerous regulatory agencies which are called into action when the normal state is disturbed. As Bernard expressed it, "All the vital mechanisms, however varied they may be, have only one object, that of preserving constant the conditions of life in the internal environment" (2).

The steady states of the fluid matrix of the body are commonly preserved by physiological reactions, i.e., by more complicated processes than are involved in simple physico-chemical equilibria. Special designations, therefore, are appropriate:—"homeostasis" to designate stability of the organism; "homeostatic conditions," to indicate details of the stability; and "homeostatic reactions," to signify means for maintaining stability.

I suggest the following postulates as pertinent to homeostasis:—

1. In an open system, such as our bodies represent, composed of

unstable structure and subjected continually to disturbance, constancy is in itself evidence that agencies are acting or are ready to act to maintain this constancy. This has not been proved for all homeostatic conditions. But there are known cases which illustrate the postulate, e.g., homeothermia; and the abolition of relatively constant temperature when the homeostatic reactions are abolished, e.g., as in the effect of ether on body temperature. The homeostasis may be maintained by antagonistic agents, e.g., the cardiac nerves; or by overflow, e.g., by the kidney; or by disturbing stimuli, e.g., thirst; or by magnification of a constant process, e.g., excess of CO_2; by structural adjustments, e.g., more erythrocytes at high altitudes; and probably by other types of function.

2. If a homeostatic condition continues, it does so because any tendency towards a change is automatically met by increased effectiveness of a factor or factors which lessen the change. This postulate resembles the principle of Le Chatelier, but differs in being conditional; in biology the organism may not become more, but less, resistant to a disturbing agent, e.g., anaphylaxis. As illustrating the postulate, there is thirst, which becomes progressively more intolerable as deprivation of water continues, and which promptly disappears when water is drunk (3); and the mechanism for releasing sugar from the liver, which works more and more vigorously as hypoglycemia increases, and which stops at once when glucose is injected into a vein (4).

3. A homeostatic agent does not act in opposite directions at the same point. It may seem to do so, e.g., as when insulin is said to lessen the sugar storage in the liver in normal animals (5), and to increase the sugar storage in diabetic animals (6). But in the experiments cited as proving hepatic glycogenolysis, insulin was given until convulsions occurred, i.e., until the opposing homeostatic agent was evoked (7).

4. Homeostatic agents, antagonistic in one region of the body, may be cooperative in another region. For example, a sympathico-adrenal factor and insulin, or possibly a vagal insulin factor (8), are opposed in action on the liver, but they appear to be collaborators in the muscles, i.e., each causes acceleration of metabolism and increased utilization of sugar by active organs (9, 10). In discussing homeostatic states, therefore, the field of action of the regulating factors must be closely defined.

5. The regulating system which determines a homeostatic state may comprise a number of cooperating factors brought into action at the same time or successively. For example, when the body temperature tends to fall, vasoconstriction checks heat loss, increased adrenal secretion accelerates metabolism (11), shivering further increases heat production, and a more abundant growth of hair offers further protection; and when the temperature tends to rise, vasodilation, sweating and faster breathing oppose the change. If the oxygen delivery to the tissues is inadequate, deeper ventilation of the lungs and a faster circulation are the first reactions of the organism, and later the increased production of red corpuscles. Appetite is the first defense against a lowering of the food and when that does not meet the need, hunger (12) and thirst (3) become insistent.

6. When a factor is known which can shift a homeostatic state in one direction, it is reasonable to look for automatic control of that factor or for a factor or factors having an opposing effect.

This last postulate follows from the examples illustrating earlier postulates. It is clear that an examination of homeostatic conditions in the body and the agencies controlling them is of very great biological and medical interest and importance. It is a field which has been too little cultivated. The postulates presented above are not exhaustive and are tentative, but they may be suggestive for further investigation into the physiology of the organism.

BIBLIOGRAPHY

1. Richet, Charles. *Dictionnaire de physiologie*. Paris, Baillière et Cie, 10 vols., 1895-1923 [1900, vol. IV, p. 721].
2. Bernard, Claude. *Leçons sur les phénomènes de la vie communs aux animaux et aux végétaux*. Paris, J. B. Baillière et Fils, 1878-79, 2 vols. [vol. I, p. 121].
3. Cannon, W. B. "Croonian Lecture. The physiological basis of thirst." *Proc. roy. Soc. B*, 1917-1919, *90*, 283-301.
4. Cannon, W. B., McIver, M. A., and Bliss, S. W. "Studies on the conditions of activity in endocrine glands. XIII. A sympathetic and adrenal mechanism for mobilizing sugar in hypoglycemia." *Amer. J. Physiol.*, 1924, *69*, 46-66.
5. McCormick, N. A. and Macleod, J. J. R. "The influence of insulin on glycogen formation in normal animals." *Trans. roy. Soc. Can.*, *Sect. V*, 1923, 3d ser., *17*, 63-73.
6. Banting, F. G., Best, C. H., Collip, J. B., Macleod, J. J. R., and Noble,

E. C. "The effect of insulin on the percentage amounts of fat and glycogen in the liver and other organs of diabetic animals." *Trans. roy. Soc. Can., Sect. V,* 1922, 3d ser., *16,* 39-41.

7. Cannon, W. B. "Some general features of endocrine influence on metabolism." *Amer. J. med. Sci.,* 1926, *171,* 1-20.

8. Britton, S. W. "Studies on the conditions of activity in endocrine glands. XVII. The nervous control on insulin secretion." *Amer. J. Physiol.,* 1925, *74,* 291-308.

9. Hepburn, J. and Latchford, J. K. "Effect of insulin (pancreatic extract) on the sugar consumption of the isolated surviving rabbit heart." *Amer. J. Physiol.,* 1922, *62,* 177-184.

10. Burn, J. H. and Dale, H. H. "On the location and nature of the action of insulin." *J. Physiol. (Lond.),* 1924, *59,* 164-192.

11. Cannon, W. B. and Querido, A. "The rôle of adrenal secretion in the chemical control of body temperature." *Proc. nat. Acad. Sci. (Wash.),* 1924, *10,* 245-246.

12. Cannon, W. B. and Washburn, A. L. "An explanation of hunger." *Amer. J. Physiol.,* 1912, *29,* 441-454.

(Cannon, Walter B. "Physiological regulation of normal states: some tentative postulates concerning biological homeostatics." In *A Charles Richet: ses amis, ses collègues, ses élèves, 22 Mai 1926.* Auguste Pettit, Ed. Paris, Les Éditions Médicales, 1926. 102 pp. [pp. 91-93].)

Charles Blagden

1748-1820

Sir Charles Blagden, physician, originally of Edinburgh (M.D. 1768), was made a Fellow of the Royal Society in 1772 when he was only twenty-four. Three years later his spectacular and well-conceived experiments[s] upon the ability of the human body to withstand extremes of dry heat—studies seldom referred to in modern literature on heat-regulation—were published in its *Philosophical Transactions.* His account is noteworthy for stressing the importance of *perspiration* in maintaining constancy of body temperature (see Ch. V, Santorio Santorio). The cooling effect of evaporation was proved by covering a vessel of water with a layer of oil which caused it to boil when placed in a warm atmosphere; otherwise the temperature of the water did not rise above 140° even though the atmosphere was raised to 260° (Fahrenheit).

[s] A reprint of these two papers formerly belonging to Sir Joseph Banks, bound together and paged continuously from 1-24, is now in the Historical Library of the Yale Medical Library; it bears Bank's autograph "J:J: Banks 1775." and his library stamp; both appear on the first page.

The incidental observation of the effect of salt in raising the boiling point of water undoubtedly led Blagden several years later (1788) to the memorable discovery that the depression of the freezing point of water by inorganic salts was in proportion to the amount dissolved. Sir Joseph Banks, his close friend for fifty years, acted as a subject for several of his experiments. Blagden served as Secretary to the Royal Society for a long period (beginning in 1784) during Banks's forty-one-year presidency (1778-1820).

EXPERIMENTS & OBSERVATIONS IN HEATED ROOM

Paper I

About the middle of January, several gentlemen and myself received an invitation from Dr. George Fordyce, to observe the effects of air heated to a much higher degree than it was formerly thought any living creature could bear. We all rejoiced at the opportunity of being convinced, by our own experience, of the wonderful power with which the animal body is endued, of resisting an heat vastly greater than its own temperature; and our curiosity was not a little excited to observe the circumstances attending this remarkable power. . . .

January 23 (1774). The honourable Captain Phipps, Mr. Banks, Dr. Solander, and myself, attended Dr. Fordyce to the heated chamber, which had served for many of his experiments with dry air. We went in without taking off any of our cloaths. It was an oblong-square room, fourteen feet by twelve in length and width, and eleven in height, heated by a round stove, or *cockle,* of cast iron, which stood in the middle, with a tube for the smoke carried from it through one of the side walls. When we first entered the room, about 2 o'clock in the afternoon, the quicksilver in a thermometer which had been suspended there stood above the 150th degree. . . .

The air heated to these high degrees felt unpleasantly hot, but could be born very well. Our most uneasy feeling was a sense of scorching on the face and legs; our legs particularly suffered extremely, by being exposed more fully than any other part to the body of the stove, heated red-hot by the fire within. Our respiration was not at all affected; it became neither quick nor laborious; the only difference was a want of that refreshing sensation which accompanies a full inspiration of cool air. . . . . .

But the most striking effects proceeded from our power of preserving our natural temperature. Being now in a situation in which our bodies bore a very different relation to the surrounding atmosphere from that to which we had been accustomed, every moment presented a new phænomenon. Whenever we breathed on a thermometer the quicksilver sunk several degrees. Every expiration, particularly if made with any degree of violence, gave a very pleasant impression of coolness to our nostrils scorched just before by the hot air rushing against them when we inspired. In the same manner our now cold breath agreeably cooled our fingers whenever it reached them. Upon touching my side, it felt cold like a corpse; and yet the actual heat of my body, tried under my tongue and by applying closely the thermometer to my skin, was 89°, about a degree higher than its ordinary temperature. . . . .

[At 260°] The air felt very hot, but still by no means to such a degree as to give pain: on the contrary, I had no doubt of being able to support a much greater heat; and all the gentlemen present, who went into the room, were of the same opinion. I sweated, but not very profusely. For seven minutes my breathing continued perfectly good; but after that time I began to feel an oppression in my lungs, attended with a sense of anxiety; which gradually increasing for the space of a minute, I thought it most prudent to put an end to the experiment, and immediately left the room. My pulse, counted as soon as I came into the cool air, for the uneasy feeling rendered me incapable of examining it in the room, was found to beat at the rate of 144 pulsations in a minute, which is more than double its ordinary quickness. . . .

About the middle of the day two similar earthen vessels; one containing pure water, and the other an equal quantity of the same water with a bit of wax, were put upon a piece of wood in the heated room. In one hour and a half the pure water was heated to 140° of the thermometer, whilst that with the wax had acquired an heat of 152°, part of the wax having melted and formed a film on the surface of the water, which prevented the evaporation. The pure water never came near the boiling point, but continued stationary above an hour at a much lower degree; a small quantity of oil was then dropped into it, as had before been done to that with the wax; in consequence of which, the water in both the vessels came at length to boil very briskly. A saturated solution of salt in water put into the room, was found to heat more quickly, and to an higher degree, than pure water, probably because it evaporated less; but it could not be brought to boil till oil was added, by means of which it came

toward evening into brisk ebullition, and consequently had acquired
an heat of 230° . . . . . Perhaps no experiments hitherto made furnish
more remarkable instances of the cooling effect of evaporation than
these last facts; a power which appears to be much greater than hath
commonly been suspected. The evaporation itself, however, was
more considerable in our experiments than it can be in almost any
other situation, because the air applied to the evaporating surface
was uncommonly hot, and at the same time not more charged with
moisture than in its ordinary state. (Blagden, *Sir* Charles. "Experiments and observations in an heated room." *Phil. Trans.*, 1775, *65*,
Pt. I, 111-123; 484-494 [pp. 116, 117, 118, 485-486, 491-492].

John Hunter

1728-1793

Born at Long Calderwood in the parish of East Kilbride, Lanarkshire, Scotland, *John Hunter* went in 1748 to London where he studied anatomy with his
elder brother William Hunter and where he was soon both teaching anatomy
and practising medicine. In 1760 he became a military surgeon and served
abroad but in 1763 settled again at London in private practice. He also taught
students and collected anatomical specimens for the private museum which in
1764 he established in his house at Earl's Court, London. In 1767 he was elected
a Fellow of the Royal Society.

John Hunter was throughout his life an assiduous investigator and made
many original contributions to both anatomy and physiology. In his studies on
animal heat he took precise observations of body temperatures at various sites
in the body and under different conditions.

THERMOMETERS FOR PHYSIOLOGICAL USE

Having found variations in the degree of heat and cold in the
same experiment, for which I could not account; I suspected that
this might arise from some imperfection in the construction of the
thermometer. I mentioned to Mr. RAMSDEN my objection to the
common construction of that instrument, and my ideas of one more
perfect in its nature, and better adapted to the experiments in which
I was engaged. He accordingly made me some very small thermometers, six or seven inches long, not above 2/12ths of an inch thick in
the stem; having the external diameter of the ball very little larger
than that of the stem, on which was marked the freezing point. The
stem was embraced by a small ivory scale so as to slide upon it easily,

and retain any position. Upon the hollow surface of this scale were marked the degrees which were seen through the stem. By these means the size of the thermometer was very much reduced, and it could be applied to soft bodies with much more ease and certainty, and in many cases in which the former ones could not be conveniently applied: . . .

THE CONSTANCY OF BODY TEMPERATURE

EXP. XII. I took a healthy dormouse, which had been asleep in a room in which there was a fire (the atmosphere at 64°); I put the thermometer into its belly, nearly at the middle, between the thorax and pubis, and the quicksilver rose to 74° or 75°; when I turned the ball towards the diaphragm, it rose to 80°; and when I applied it to the liver, it rose to 81° 1/2.

EXP. XIII. The mouse was put into an atmosphere at 20°, and left there half an hour; when taken out, it was very lively, much more so than when put in. I introduced the thermometer into the lower part of the belly, and it rose to 91°; and upon turning it up to the liver, to 93°.

EXP. XIV. The animal was put back into the cold atmosphere at 30° for an hour, when the thermometer was again introduced into the belly; at the liver it rose to 93°; in the pelvis, to 92°: it was still lively. . . .

From these experiments we have actual heat increased and decreased by the application of external cold; and likewise the heat varied according to the powers of life, as well in the same parts, as also in the different parts, of the same animal: for at first the natural heat of the animal was much below the common standard, and, by the application of cold, and the powers of resistance to the cold being thus increased, the heat was considerably augmented; but when the animal was weakened by those exertions, it fell off with respect to the power of producing heat, and this in proportion to the distance from the heart. . . .

VARIABLE BODY TEMPERATURE

The frog being, in its structure, more similar to the viper than to either fowl or fish, I made the following experiments on that animal.

EXP. XXX. I introduced the ball of the thermometer into its stomach, and the quicksilver stood at 44°. I then put it into a cold mixture, and the quicksilver sunk to 31°; the animal appeared almost dead, but recovered very soon: beyond this point it was not possible to lessen the heat, without destroying the animal. But its decrease of heat was quicker than in the viper, although the mixture was nearly the same. . . . (Hunter, John. "Of the heat of animals and vegetables." *Phil. Trans.*, 1778, *68*, 7-49 [pp. 7-8, 18-20, 26].)

Isaac Ott

1847-1916

A native of Pennsylvania, *Isaac Ott* (Pl. 69) was educated at Lafayette College and the University of Pennsylvania Medical School where he was graduated M.D. in 1869. He practised medicine at Easton and was one of the early teachers of physiology at the University of Pennsylvania and the Medico-Chirurgical College of Philadelphia. Among his extensive researches in neurophysiology Ott showed that the centre for temperature regulation lay in the region of the corpora striata.

THE HEAT CENTRE IN THE BRAIN

These experiments prove that at the anterior inner end of the optic thalami a puncture causes an increase of temperature due to increased heat-production. Fig. A [Fig. 9]—1 shows about the point

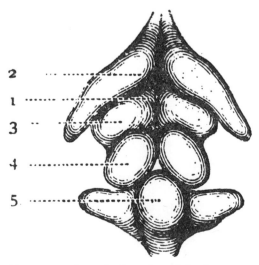

Figure 9. Ott's diagram to show the location of the heat center in the brain.

that the puncture should be made to cause the greatest increase of temperature; 2, is the corpus striatum; 3, optic thalamus; 4, corpora quadrigemina; 5, cerebellum. The cut was drawn by my student, Mr. Carter, from the brain of a rabbit.

Experiments made during last summer show that the tissues between the optic thalami and corpora striata along the median line also cause an increase of temperature, especially at the point which Schiff has pointed out as causing upon injury in rabbits a peculiar cry.

We have here an artificial fever due entirely to nervous disturbance, and not to any poisons circulating in the blood. The rise of 7°F. in an hour shows that the nervous system plays a very extended part in the phenomena of fever. As to the nature of these centres, all opinions are more or less conjectural. With our present information on other functions of the brain, the inference is that they are inhibitory in their nature. (Ott, Isaac. "The heat-centre in the brain." *J. nerv. ment. Dis.*, 1887, *14*, 152-162. [p. 154].)

Henry Gray Barbour
1886-1943

Henry Gray Barbour, in his lifetime a leading authority on temperature regulation, showed at the beginning of his career that the temperature of the body was determined by the temperature of the heat-regulating centre in the brain.

Born at Hartford, Connecticut, Henry Barbour was educated at Trinity College (Hartford) and at Johns Hopkins where he was graduated M.D. in 1910. After three years of study at Freiburg, Vienna, and London he returned to teach pharmacology at the Yale University School of Medicine. In 1921 he left Yale to go to McGill and later to the University of Louisville, but in 1931 returned again to Yale where he remained until his premature death.

THE INFLUENCE OF DIRECT HEATING AND COOLING OF THE HEAT CENTRE ON BODY TEMPERATURE

(p. 4) After one has evoked a satisfactory puncture-induced fever one may try to quiet the irritated centre with heat. The results are very striking. The water in the vessel was generally heated to 48-51° C. In its passage to the puncture tube in the brain it loses about 2° C. The temperature of the rabbits fell within an hour from the beginning of the flow of hot water by almost 1.5° C. When the circulating hot water was replaced by cold, the body temperature reacted with a rapid rise. These two constrasting experiments could be repeated at will with constant results. . . .

That the heat of the brain centre subsides in the presence of the irritating probe emerges clearly from the above experiment. Whether cold may be an active stimulating agent for the elevation of temperature was still not proven. The production of fever remission by itself undoubtedly already permits the reappearance of the puncture effect. One sees nevertheless in Curve 4 a distinction between the simple stimulus of the warm inflow and its interruption by the cold inflow. In the first there results a greater fall (while the brain is still not cooled to the body temperature) and then a rise (puncture effect) while the latter, as was also shown in the other curve, always evoked an immediate rise.

In Curve 6 one sees an interesting variation of the phenomenon. The operation was carried out in the same manner as before with the exception of the insertion of the puncture tube. The puncture was carried out after partial recovery from shock and made with a tube which was heated by a current of water at 49 degrees. The current flowed continuously for 3 hours without the body temperature's rising higher than 37.9 degrees that is always 0.65 degrees below the pre-operative temperature—a quite unusual state. Under the influence of cold the temperature rose in the next hour by 2.15 degrees. The simultaneous application of heat to the centre is thus capable of preventing the effect of puncture.

4. Cooling of the temperature centre heats the body. None of the facts brought forward above was sufficient to determine whether cold is an active means of stimulation. Two methods by which I tackled this question gave satisfactory results. The first is that by which Aronson and Sachs showed that the electrical stimulation of the centre is an adequate cause of fever. As already mentioned they persisted until the puncture fever was past. After the temperature was again normal, they stimulated electrically and produced a new onset of fever. In one of our cases the temperature on the first day after the operation returned to or almost to its original level. Curves 7 and 8 illustrate the fact the fever could be freshly evoked simply by cold as a stimulating agent. (Barbour, H. G. "Die Wirkung unmittelbarer Erwärmung und Abkühlung der Wärmezentra auf die Körpertemperatur." *Arch. exp. Path. Pharm.,* (Springer-Verlag) 1912, *70,* 1-16 [pp. 4-9. Translated by L. G. W.].)

Joseph Barcroft
1872-1947

There is evidence that the body maintains constancy of temperature by making adjustments in other physiological mechanisms, which appear to make regulation of temperature an easier task by increasing or decreasing heat loss or increasing heat production. One of the modes of acclimatization to heat, discovered by Barcroft and his co-workers in 1922, is an increase in blood volume.

Dill and his co-workers were later to show that adaptation to high temperature also involves an increased capacity for perspiration combined with the production of a more dilute sweat so as to maintain an economy of salt in the body subjected to great heat.[9] Thus a whole series of adaptations may combine to maintain homeostatic conditions under circumstances of unusual stress.

THE RELATION OF EXTERNAL TEMPERATURE TO BLOOD VOLUME

During the voyage from Liverpool to Callao, and again on the return journey from Callao to New York, a number of determinations were made for the purpose of measuring the blood volume of various members of the Expedition which went to Peru in the winter of 1921-22. The first set of these observations was intended merely to establish the blood-volumes at sea-level for the purpose of comparison with those found at high altitudes. It very soon transpired that the blood volumes, as estimated, were not constant, and that the only factor with which they appeared to be correlated was the temperature of the environment, the blood volume increasing as the temperature rose and decreasing as it fell.

This result was in many ways so surprising, and in any case so difficult to explain, that it seemed desirable to test it by subjecting one or two individuals to high temperatures in an artificially heated atmosphere and making observations of the "blood volume." . . .

The deduction is, that there is a more or less gradual rise in the volume of circulating blood in the two days spent in the warm chamber, followed by a fall immediately on coming out. . . .

The comparison of the various curves in fig. 2 [Fig. 10] is instructive. During the night of the 23rd to the 24th there was a considerable rise in blood volume. This initial rise was accompanied by a con-

[9] Dill, D. B. *Life, heat and altitude: physiological effects of hot climates and great heights.* Cambridge, Mass., Harvard University Press, 1938. xiv, 211 pp. [p. 49].

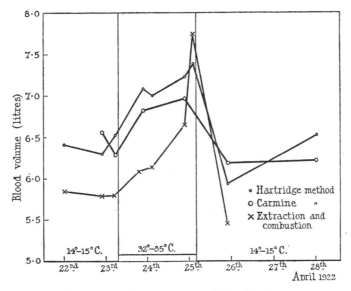

Figure 10. Barcroft's graph of the relation of blood volume to temperature.

siderable fall in the haemoglobinometric reading, suggesting that the increased blood volume was caused mainly by dilution. This suggestion is borne out by the fact that there was no appreciable change in the total oxygen capacity. Between the morning and evening determinations on the 24th a considerable amount of exercise was taken in the warm chamber on the bicycle ergometer. There was a marked rise in the haemoglobinometer reading; this rise was reflected in the measurement of total oxygen capacity. It would appear, therefore, that from some store or stores within the body enough corpuscles could be produced in a few hours to make an appreciable rise in the total oxygen capacity of the circulating blood. . . . (Barcroft, J., Meakins, J. C., Davies, H. W., Duncan Scott, J. M., and Fetter, W. J. "On the relation of external temperature to blood volume." *Phil. Trans.*, 1923, *211B*, 455-464 [pp. 455, 459-460, 461].)

Walter Bradford Cannon

1871-1945

In addition to neural and physical regulation of body temperature there is an important hormonal control mediated by the sympathetic nervous system. In 1927 it was demonstrated by Cannon and his co-workers that the adrenal glands were necessary for temperature regulation and that an increase of adrenin would occur in the cold-exposed animal and would cause an increase in heat production before shivering occurred.

ADRENAL CONTROL OF HEAT PRODUCTION

Our previous observations have shown that when an animal has to develop heat to prevent lowering of body temperature it may rely both on the calorigenic effect of increased adrenal secretion and on the extra heat accompanying reflex muscular contractions. The results just detailed indicate that the primary protection against a heat deficit is found in activities of the sympathetic system (bristling of hairs, probably vasoconstriction and hyperglycemia, and surely by increased medulliadrenal secretion), for these responses occur before the onset of shivering, and may be the only manifestations of a heat debt. If animals have been deprived of the calorigenic service of the adrenal medulla, however, greater demands are made on muscular activity as a means of maintaining the normal temperature— then, in the presence of a given need for heat shivering occurs more frequently and lasts longer. The non-use of the shivering mechanism, or the relatively slight reliance on it when the adrenals are present, implies that the secretion poured out by them when the organism is in danger of cooling is an efficient means of increasing heat production. (Cannon, W. B., Querido, A., Britton, S. W., and Bright, E. M. "Studies on the conditions of activity in endocrine glands. XXI. The rôle of adrenal secretion in the chemical control of body temperature." *Amer. J. Physiol.*, 1926-1927, *79*, 466-507 [pp. 486-487].)

Allen Dudley Keller

1901-

and

William Kendrick Hare

1908-

In 1932 Keller and Hare were able to give the heat-regulating centre of the brain a more specific location in the hypothalamus.

Born at Minkcreek, Idaho, *Allen Dudley Keller* was educated at Utah State Agricultural College (B.S. 1924) and Cornell where he was graduated Ph.D. in

PLATE 68. Claude Bernard (1813-1878) aged 53. (Courtesy of the Bibliothèque de l'Académie Nationale de Médecine, Paris.)

Arnold C. L. Hsieh
1922-
and
Loren Daniel Carlson
1915-

One of the most remarkable features of body temperature regulation is the ability of both animals and man to adapt themselves to cold as well as heat. That adaptation to cold involves changes in endocrine secretions has been revealed by the discovery of Cottle and Carlson[10] that cold-adapted rats are capable of increased heat production by chemical regulation. Carlson and his co-workers have found that the hormone chiefly responsible for this heat production is noradrenaline.

A native of Shanghai, China, *Arnold Hsieh* was educated at St. John's University, Shanghai (B.Sc. 1943; M.D. 1946). Later he went to Seattle to the University of Washington School of Medicine where he worked with Carlson and his group. At present he is at the Department of Physiology of the University of Hong Kong.

Loren Daniel Carlson, originally of Davenport, Iowa, was educated at Saint Ambrose College (B.Sc. 1937) and the University of Iowa where he took his Ph.D. in zoology in 1941. In 1946 he went to the University of Washington and from 1955 until 1962 he was professor of physiology there. At present he is professor of physiology at the University of Kentucky Medical Center.

THE ROLE OF NORADRENALINE IN THE CHEMICAL REGULATION OF HEAT PRODUCTION

After injection of adrenaline the oxygen consumption of all the rats increased. . .This increase reached a maximum about 15 minutes after the injection, and consumption returned to initial levels about 100 minutes later. The intact, cold-adapted rats showed the greatest increase in oxygen consumption. In the thyroidectomized groups, the increase was about the same regardless of previous cold exposure, and less than that in the intact cold-adapted rats.

The initial glucose levels of the four groups of spinal rats. . . were not significantly different. Forty minutes after adrenaline, blood glucose concentration of all the rats increased similarly, and there was no significant difference between groups.

[10] Cottle, W. H. and Carlson, L. D. "Regulation of heat production in cold-adapted rats." *Proc. Soc. exp. Biol. Med.,* 1956, *92,* 845-849.

The initial glucose concentrations of the curarized rats. . . were considerably higher than those found in the spinal rats. This difference may have resulted from a greater initial release of adrenaline in the curarized rats. On exposure to cold, the curarized rats increased their oxygen consumption, but there was no significant change in blood glucose levels. Adrenaline was followed by a some-

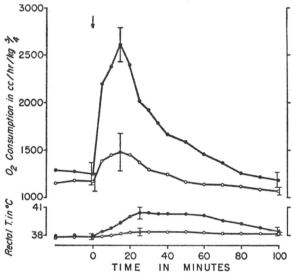

FIG. 1. Effects of *l*-noradrenaline, 0.2 mg/kg, on the oxygen consumption and rectal temperature of cold-adapted rats (*solid dots*) and warm-adapted rats (*open circles*). Experiments were conducted at 30°C ± 1°. *L*-noradrenaline was injected intramuscularly at the point indicated by the *arrow*. *Vertical bars* indicate the standard deviation. Each point represents the mean of 4 experiments.

Figure 11. Graph of the effect of noradrenaline on O_2-consumption.

what smaller rise in oxygen consumption and a 50% rise in blood glucose concentration. After injection of *l*-noradrenaline the increase in oxygen consumption was much greater than that following either adrenaline or cold exposure; the blood glucose levels, however, did not change significantly.

The time course of the response in oxygen consumption following single injection of *l*-noradrenaline is given in figure 1 [Fig. 11]. The oxygen consumption of the warm-adapted group increased very little. The possibility that the results were affected by an interaction between *l*-noradrenaline and the *d*-tubocurarine used in these experiments was ruled out by the finding that noncurarized, cold-adapted rats increased oxygen consumption from 1040 50 cc/hr/kg$^{3/4}$ a maximum of 2103 200 cc/hr/kg$^{3/4}$ after *l*-noradrenaline (Hsieh and Carlson, unpublished data). . . .

Adrenaline has been suggested as a possible mediator in chemical regulation. If release of adrenaline, either by the adrenal medulla or by the sympathetic nervous system, was the sole cause of the increase in metabolism on exposure to cold, then adrenaline given alone should simulate cold exposure. This is not the case. The two main discrepancies are: a) the persistence of a metabolic response to cold with a reduction in response to adrenaline on blood glucose levels. . . .

The results with *l*-noradrenaline . . . indicate that the main change in cold-adapted rats may be an alteration in the response of the tissues to this substance. The close similarity between the metabolic effects of *l*-noradrenaline and of cold exposure and the small amounts of *l*-noradrenaline required to produce these effects, strongly suggest that noradrenaline may be the mediator in chemical regulation of heat production.

The metabolic actions of adrenaline in normal animals, such as increased oxygen uptake and hyperglycemia, have been repeatedly observed to be greater than those of noradrenaline, pointing to a functional differentiation between the two substances. The surprising observation in this study is that *l*-noradrenaline exerts a strong calorigenic effect in cold-adapted rats without producing a hyperglycemia and no such effect is produced in nonadapted rats. (Hsieh, A. C. L. and Carlson, L. D. "Role of adrenaline and noradrenaline in chemical regulation of heat production." *Amer. J. Physiol.,* 1957, *190*, 243-246 [pp. 244-245].)

IX

Kidney:
Concepts of Renal Function

Although writers in antiquity often speculated about how fluid taken by mouth passed from the gut to the bladder, it was Galen who demonstrated that the urine was in fact formed in the kidneys and transmitted from them to the bladder by the ureters. He tied the ureters experimentally and made this observation: "Now the method of demonstration is as follows. One has to divide the peritoneum in front of the ureters, then secure these with ligatures, and next, having bandaged up the animal, let him go (for he will not continue to urinate). After this one loosens the external bandages and shows the bladder empty and the ureters quite full and distended—in fact almost on the point of rupturing; on removing the ligature from them, one then plainly sees the bladder becoming filled with urine."[1]

Galen goes on to say that if the ureters are cut within the body, the abdomen then becomes filled with urine as with a person suffering from dropsy. He was thus the first to connect the kidneys with urine formation.

Theories concerning kidney function date from the thirteenth century when William of Salicet (1210-1280) propounded his ideas of urine formation and gave his classical account of renal "dropsy."[2] However, four hundred years were to elapse before the Dutchman Frederik Dekkers (M.D., Leyden, 1668)[3] observed albumin in the urine of "diabetics" (acetic acid test), recording that the urines of such patients "have the savor of sweet milk."

Other early writers on the kidney may be mentioned briefly. Eu-

[1] Galen. *On the natural faculties.* A. J. Brock, Tr. London, William Heinemann, 1916, p. 59.

[2] Salicet, W. For English translation see Ralph H. Major, *Classic descriptions of disease.* 3d ed. Springfield, Ill., Charles C Thomas, Publisher, 1945. xxxiii, 679 pp. [pp. 525-527].

[3] Dekkers, Frederik. *Ibid.,* pp. 527-528.

stachius (1520-1574) in his *Opuscula anatomica* (Venice, 1564) published several admirable plates dealing with the structure of the kidney. He was followed a century later by two of the great north Italian microscopists, Lorenzo Bellini (1643-1704), who described the renal tubules for the first time ("Bellini's ducts") and propounded a physical hypothesis concerning urine formation, and Marcello Malpighi (1628-1694) who, in his *De viscerum structura* (see essay "De renibus"), elaborated on Bellini's account of the uriniferous tubules and described the glomeruli, still known as Malpighian bodies, attached to the tips of the arterial branches. Again a long interval passed until William Bowman described the capsule surrounding the Malpighian body and showed that the cavity of this capsule is continuous with that of a uriniferous tubule.

Historically, the physiological developments in knowledge of kidney function illustrate the way in which close clinical study of disease in human beings often supplements, and now and again leads to, a signal advance or even a major discovery in this area of pure physiology. Thus Domenico Cotugno (1736-1822), distinguished Neapolitan physician, in his well-known book, *De ischiade nervosa commentarius* published in 1764 (which includes a classical account of sciatica, arthritic and nervous, as well as of the cerebrospinal fluid), describes a memorable case of acute nephritis in which he confirmed Dekker's conclusion that in such patients the urine coagulates on heating.[4]

The case was that of a twenty-eight-year-old soldier who following an attack of "quotidian fever" became dropsical with large "watery swellings" of the whole body; his urine was scant and he became mentally depressed ("wholly cast-down in mind"). Cotugno provoked flow of urine by using cream of tartar which caused the patient to pass 10 to 12 pints of concentrated urine in a single night. There follows an almost perfect modern textbook description of an acute nephritis with swelling of the ankles and other parts of the body, virtual anuria, and profuse diuresis following ingestion of the tartaric acid, a preparation still used in rural districts as a diuretic. His urine, though scant, contained enormous quantities of albumin.

Another colorful clinical observer who contributed useful information on kidney function was William C. Wells, born of Scottish

[4] Viets, H. R. "Domenico Cotugno: His description of the cerebrospinal fluid with a translation of part of his *De ischiade nervosa commentarius*." *Bull. Hist. Med.*, 1935, *3*, 701-738.

parentage in South Carolina, who obtained his M.D. from Edinburgh in 1780. He returned briefly to the Colonies but in 1785 took up practice in London where he published many original papers, the best known being his *Essay on Dew* (1814). One of his contributions was a provocative paper on the occurrence of hematuria in dropsical patients. In this Wells mentions the presence of blood and albumin in dropsical urine, thus confirming Cotugno's observations; he also established that dropsy in such cases occurs in the upper parts of the body as well as in the lower extremities and he gave a vivid description of the uremic seizures which often develop in these patients. Two years later similar observations were reported by the Exeter physician John Blackall (1771-1860) in a small monograph, *Observations on the Nature and Cure of Dropsies* (London, 1813).

We now turn to the work of one of the greatest clinical observers in the annals of medicine, Richard Bright (1789-1858). The reports just described of Salicet, Dekkers, Cotugno, Wells, and Blackall served merely as backdrop for the epic studies of Bright. An account of his work will follow below as introduction to the quoted passage describing the disease which still bears his name.

The modern history of the study of kidney function is one of peculiar drama. It was the scene of conflict of two opposed theories which represented not merely different interpretations of the evidence, but opposite philosophies of research. When, in 1842, William Bowman discovered the capsule surrounding the Malpighian body and showed that this capsule was continuous with the urinary tubule, he established for the first time the anatomical framework within which any theory of kidney function must be placed. At the same time he suggested that the watery portion of the urine was secreted by the glomerulus, while the urea was secreted by the epithelium lining the tubules. Bowman's own attitude was not perhaps vitalistic, but when later in the century his theory was taken up and espoused by Rudolf Heidenhain, Heidenhain stressed that the secretion of urea by the tubule epithelium was a *vital* activity of these cells—by which he meant an activity not readily susceptible of investigation. The trend of the cell theory and of cell research at this period was distinctly vitalistic. Physiologists attempted to explain function in terms of the cell and its activities, instead of in terms of physical and chemical relationships. Intracellular phenomena were thought to be far too complex for simple explanation.

This whole current of thought was strongly resisted by Carl Ludwig and his pupils. In 1844 Ludwig propounded a purely physical theory of urine formation. He suggested that from the arterial blood entering the glomerulus there was separated a filtrate which was the serum of the blood without the plasma proteins. As this filtrate passed along the tubule it was reabsorbed by diffusion except for the urea and other waste products to which the epithelium was presumably impermeable.

Eclipsed for a long time by the Bowman-Heidenhain hypothesis, Ludwig's theory was revived with modifications in 1917 by Arthur Cushny, a scientific grandson of Ludwig for he had studied with one of Ludwig's pupils. Whereas the Bowman-Heidenhain hypothesis had brought kidney research to a standstill, Cushny claimed for the new theory not only that it was more consistent with experimental results but that it offered a plan for further work. The later development of kidney research has borne him out. Most recent research on the kidney has consisted of further exploration of particular aspects of the Cushny theory.

Lorenzo Bellini

1643-1704

Lorenzo Bellini, Italian anatomist and pupil of Giovanni Alfonso Borelli (1608-1679), is important for his classical description of the gross anatomy of the kidney in which he announced the discovery of the renal secretory ducts, known from then onward as "Bellini's ducts." Bellini's book is remarkable in itself and especially so when it is realized that the first edition of *Exercitatio anatomica de structura et usu renum* was published in 1662 when the author was but nineteen years of age (Pl. 70a).

Bellini, who so well illustrates "the vision and daring of youth," attacked the then prevalent belief that urinary secretion was brought about, as those of the chemical school had taught, through the action of ferments. For their fanciful notions, Bellini substituted a mechanical concept. He showed that the kidneys are not mere flesh, as his contemporaries believed, similar to liver, spleen, or muscle, but consist of minute ducts, and he elaborated a mechanical theory for the formation of urine which was very much in the spirit of the iatromechanical doctrines of his teacher Borelli.

ON THE STRUCTURE AND FUNCTION OF THE KIDNEY

The common opinion is that the kidneys are made up of a hard, solid, fleshy substance with no fibres or with only a few interwoven.

However, the state of affairs is otherwise, for the substance of the kidneys is nothing else than an aggregate of an infinite number of vessels of a kind peculiar to itself. Having cut through any part of the kidney, certain fibres or filaments extending from the outer surface to the hollow or pelvis are quite plainly visible. In order that you may see them more clearly you may separate a particular slender portion of them with your fingers . . . and then it will appear more distinctly that these fibres are continuous from the outermost surface even to the hollow of the pelvis. . . .

These renal fibers which were tinged reddish in colour towards the outer part of the kidney become whitish where they descend toward the pelvis and, interwoven and enfolded together, . . . they terminate in the cavity of the pelvis, not divided into many little papillae but passing out in one body, not only in animals but also in man (fig. VIII BBB) [Pl. 70b], a fact which has hitherto been overlooked by everyone for they admit as many distinct papillae, each the size of a pea and pointed like a wart, as there are tubes in the pelvis. But these are arranged in a different way for when the pelvis has been removed, the fibrous flesh of the kidney comes into view, not forming one united body as in many other animals nor divided into several small fleshy masses as a number of persons assert, but as an irregular, twisted, and enfolded mass everywhere surrounding the pelvis. . . .

If therefore you compress these filaments from their further end, that is, with respect to the pelvis, and examine them, you will find water welling up everywhere. If you are not afraid to present this to your tongue, you will discover a certain saltiness and in some the taste of urine. You can test this also if you cut across the body of the kidney, for then you may also see this same juice arise from the renal ducts severed in this way and you may clearly observe its quality and nature. You may observe this much more easily if you apply a glass lens to your eye for then, when the tubules are compressed, the urine is very clearly seen welling out as if gushing forth from so many little water pipes.

From these things we can confidently infer that the substance of the kidney, even though they have called it parenchyma, is nothing else than . . . a mass of canaliculae and capillary spaces through which the urine flows into the pelvis. . . .

The blood flowing through the trunk of the descending aorta enters the renal artery from which it passes through very fine arterioles, penetrating the kidney even to its outermost surface. But since they terminate in open mouths and are not joined by mutual anastomoses with the veins (for when liquids are injected through the renal artery, they are seen to exude by capillary openings on the surface of the kidney if its tunic has been stripped away), the blood must necessarily flow out of a vessel into a little space which although it could not be perceived by sense yet reason persuades and the glass clearly confirms that it occurs. Thus the capillaries of the renal veins and that which we have called the renal duct terminate in the same space for it has been demonstrated that both these vessels terminate at the outermost surface. When, therefore, the blood emerges from the arteries, it comes in contact with two classes of vessels, namely, on the one hand venous vessels, on the other, renal vessels. Therefore, the serum enters the renal ducts, separated from the blood, and the blood enters the veins, separated from the serous humor.

But this secretion occurs neither by attraction nor by familiarity, nor by sympathy, but is accomplished solely by the configuration of the vessels producing it. (Bellini, Lorenzo. *Exercitatio anatomica de structura et usu renum.* 2d ed. Padua, Matthaeus Cadorinus, 1663. 48 pp. [pp. 28-34. Translated by L.G.W.].)

Marcello Malpighi
1628-1694

The facts of Malpighi's life have been stated earlier. When in the 1660's he took up the study of the microscopic structure of the kidney along with that of the liver, spleen, pancreas, and other viscera, he was a more mature scientist than Bellini and also had the benefit of the latter's discovery. This discovery was important for Malpighi because it showed him that the kidney had a minute structure analogous to that of the secreting gland. He therefore sought for the glandular unit in which the urine might be formed from the arterial blood. (Pl. 71).

THE STRUCTURE OF THE KIDNEYS

It must be added, however, that the idea that this whole portion of the kidney is completely fibrous and that nothing is present in addition to this except blood vessels has much difficulty in it. For in every kidney which I have so far been able to obtain I have detected an abundance of very minute glandules and it was my good fortune to observe these invariably in quadrupeds, tortoises, and man himself. But in order to see these to best advantage a black liquor mixed with spirit of wine must be injected through the renal artery so that the whole kidney swells and becomes blackened outwardly, for then, when the covering membrane of the kidney has been removed, glandules dyed with the same dark colour appear even to the naked eyes, attached to the arteries branching hither and thither. When the same kidney has been cut through its length, then you will observe, between the fascicles of urine vessels and also arising in the interspaces, almost countless numbers of these bodies which are attached like apples to the blood vessels swollen with black liquid and spread out in the form of a beautiful tree. . . .

Chapter III

Since in the previous section we have demonstrated that glandules are found in the kidneys and, as will be shown below, they perform the chief function in the excretion of the urine, it is now proper to consider briefly their relationships. Thus, these bodies located in the outermost part of the kidney are almost innumerable and so I think they probably correspond [in number] to the urinary vessels which form the mass of the kidney. The number of such vessels in any individual fasciculus, from which arise those small divisions described in all kidneys, exceeds forty.

As for their shape—on account of their smallness and translucency they shine very much and they do not have a distinct outline. Yet they seem round like the eggs of fishes and when a black fluid is impelled through the arteries, they are blackened and you would say that they have surrounded the uttermost offshoots of the vessels proceeding like creeping tendrils so that they appear as if haloed, but with this reservation that the part which is attached to the arterial branch blackens especially while the remainder retains its own colour. The glandules have the following connection with the branches of the arteries. They spring from their interior branches and sometimes from the outer branches which are reflected inward and proliferated into many offshoots. That they are attached to these vessels may be clearly demonstrated by injecting a coloured liquid through the renal artery, for the glandules and connected arteries will be dyed the same colour so that the eye very easily perceives the clear connection between them.

The glandules also have an association with the veins which follow upon the distribution of the arteries for when the veins are swollen by having been injected with a black liquid, although the adjacent glandules do not swell with the same liquid, yet the colour seems to be diffused so that nothing intervenes between the glandules and the tips of the dyed veins. For it is probable that a liquid injected through the veins by force, having overcome their valves, sticks at the mouths of the glandules and is shut out by their dissimilar cavities. . . .

Still another question can be asked, namely, whether a portion of the ureter extends into these sanguineous glandules, for the pelvis, as will be shown below, holds veins and arteries and even their capillary offshoots within its arc. Consequently, we can also suspect that it is connected to the glandules by its own fibrils.

There remains another urine-excreting vessel of whose branches, as we have hinted above, the outer mass of the kidney is chiefly composed. I worked for a long time in order that I might render visible this continuity, which reason sufficiently demonstrates, to my eyes. For when liquids have been infused through the arteries, although they fill the glandules, yet I could never observe them penetrating the urinary vessels. The same thing occurred also with the veins and when liquor was injected through the ureters by the standard method, it stained only some extensions of the pelvis with its colour, but never that urine-excreting vessel which some call fibres and hence it was not able to blacken the glandules. Thus many devices having been tried for this purpose (but in vain), I could not demonstrate the connection of the glandules with the urinary vessels. (Malpighi, Marcello. *De viscerum structura exercitatio anatomica.* Bologna, 1666. 100 pp. [pp. 80-84. Translated by L.G.W.].)

William Charles Wells

1757-1817

Although most of his life was spent in Great Britain, *William Charles Wells* was an American born at Charleston, South Carolina. In 1780, he received the M.D. degree from Edinburgh. He was never very successful as a practitioner, but he nonetheless had distinguished friends who included David Hume and Matthew Baillie. In 1793, he was elected F.R.S. and published a number of scientific books and papers. In one, "An Account of a Female of the White Race of Mankind Part of Whose Skin Resembles that of a Negro. . . .," he offers a discussion which foreshadows Charles Darwin's theory of natural selection. Wells clearly was a man of remarkable scientific insight. His medical observations which follow are little known and reveal that he had studied closely the appearance of albumin in the urine of certain dropsical patients.

THE PRESENCE OF BLOOD SERUM IN THE URINE OF DROPSY

I have hitherto seen only one case of dropsy, not occurring after scarlet fever, in which the red matter of blood was found in considerable quantity in the urine. On this account, and as the case was in other respects remarkable, I shall relate it at some length. . . .

The heat of boiling water, and the nitrous acid, were the means which I chiefly employed for the purpose of ascertaining, whether urine contained serum. For reasons which I do not comprehend, very small portions of serum in urine will sometimes be detected by one of these tests, and not by the other. Heat, however, more frequently shews its presence than the acid, on which account, and as it adds nothing to the bulk of the fluid which is the subject of experiment, and seldom occasions any alteration in its colour, I formerly often employed it singly. But having found of late, that the external appearance of urine, containing even a considerable quantity of serum, will now and then be little changed by heat, I have since always used both tests. . . .

I have examined by means of one, or other, or both, of the tests which have been mentioned, the urine of one hundred and thirty persons affected with dropsy from other causes than scarlet fever, of whom ninety-five were males, and thirty-five females; and have found serum in that of seventy-eight, sixty of whom were males and eighteen females.* . . .

Urine in dropsy, when it contains serum, is often more abundant than in health. It is sometimes discharged, though not for any long time, in the quantity of six pints daily; in one person the daily quantity was for a short time ten pints. . . . (Wells, W. C. "On the presence of the red matter and serum of blood in the urine of dropsy, which has not originated from scarlet fever." *Trans. Soc. Improve. med. chir. Knowl.*, 1812, *3*, 194-240 [pp. 194, 203-204, 205-206, 207].)

* No conclusion is to be drawn from these numbers, in regard to the comparative frequency of dropsy in the different sexes; for the whole number of male patients admitted into St. Thomas Hospital, where by far the greater part of the cases were seen by me, is much greater than that of the female.

Richard Bright
1789-1858

Born at Queen Square, Bristol, *Richard Bright* attended school at Bristol and Exeter and in 1808 began to study medicine at Edinburgh. In 1810, he went with Sir George Mackenzie and Sir Henry Holland to Iceland and later wrote the botanical and zoological parts of Mackenzie's *Travels in Iceland*. On his return he studied medicine for two years at Guy's Hospital, but in 1812 went back to Edinburgh to take his M.D. degree. After a prolonged period of travel on the continent, described in his *Travels from Vienna through Lower Hungary*. . . . (London, 1818), Bright began to practise medicine at London where in 1820 he was appointed Assistant Physician to Guy's Hospital, an institution with which he remained associated until his death and where he performed his greatest work.

Extraordinary in many respects, Richard Bright possessed unusual powers of observation coupled with an incisive intellect. He correlated the appearance of certain kinds of dropsy with albuminous urine and with a diseased state of the kidneys. By thus revealing the role of the kidney in disease, he also threw light upon its normal function.

THE SEAT OF DISEASE IN DROPSY WITH ALBUMINOUS URINE

. . . Where those conditions of the kidney to which I allude have occurred, I have often found the dropsy connected with the secretion of albuminous urine, more or less coagulable on the application of heat. I have in general found that the liver has not in these cases betrayed any considerable marks of disease, either during life or on examination after death, though occasionally incipient disorganization of a peculiar kind has been traced in that organ. On the other hand, I have found that where the dropsy has depended on organic change in the liver, even in the most aggravated state of such change no diseased structure has generally been discovered in the kidneys, and the urine has not coagulated by heat. I have never yet examined the body of a patient dying with dropsy attended with coagulable urine, in whom some obvious derangement was not discovered in the kidneys. (Bright, Richard. *Reports of medical cases selected with a view of illustrating the symptoms and cure of diseases by a reference to morbid anatomy*. London, Longman, Rees, Orme, Brown, Green, 1827-1831. 2 vols. [vol. 2 in 2 parts]. [Vol. 1, p. 2].)

William Bowman
1816-1892

Sir William Bowman, who appears first in Chapter VI with his description of striated muscle, published his theory of urinary secretion and his discovery of the capsule surrounding the Malpighian body, which he showed to be continuous with the urinary tubule, in 1842 when he was twenty-six (Pl. 72). As pointed out in the Introduction to this chapter, he thus established for the first time the anatomical framework within which any theory of kidney function must be placed.

ON THE STRUCTURE AND USE OF THE MALPIGHIAN BODIES OF THE KIDNEY, WITH OBSERVATIONS ON THE CIRCULATION THROUGH THAT GLAND

I was led to the examination of these bodies in the course of an inquiry into the ultimate structure of the true glands, in which I have been engaged for the last two years. I had frequently injected them from the artery, but had never inspected them under high powers of the microscope, until they arrested my attention while examining the structure of the uriniferous tubes. These tubes consist of an external tunic of transparent homogeneous tissue (which I have termed the *basement membrane*), lined by epithelium. The Malpighian bodies I saw to be a rounded mass of minute vessels invested by a cyst or capsule of precisely similar appearance to the basement membrane of the tubes. Seeing these similar tissues in such close proximity, it was not easy to resist the conviction that the capsule was the basement membrane of the tubes expanded over the vessels, but, after many trials, I could not at that time succeed in gaining an unequivocal view of their continuity. All that I could accomplish was to perceive here and there an ambiguous approach to such an arrangement, sufficient to make it appear probable.

I should perhaps have relinquished the idea thus presented to my mind, had not accident again drawn me to it. Having, during last summer, been made acquainted, through the kindness of Dr. Milne Edwards, with a new method of injection employed with great success by M. Doyère of Paris, I injected some kidneys through the artery, by this method, in order to notice the nature of the vascular ramifications in the Malpighian bodies. I not only found what I sought but the clearest evidence that the capsule which invests them is, in truth, the basement membrane of the uriniferous tube expanded over the tuft of vessels. The injected material had, in many instances, burst through the tuft, and, being extravasated into the capsule, had passed off along the tube. I have since made numerous injections of the human kidney, and of that of many of the lower animals, and in all, without exception, have met with the same disposition. I have also repeated, with better success than before, the examination of thin slices of the recent organ with high powers of the microscope, and in this manner have fully corroborated the evidence furnished by injections. This mode of examination has likewise led to the interesting discovery of ciliary motion within the orifice of the tube.

According to my own observations, the circulation through the kidney may be stated to be as follows:—All the blood of the renal artery (with the exception of a small quantity distributed to the capsule, surrounding fat, and the coats of the larger vessels) enters the capillary tufts of the Malpighian bodies; thence it passes into the capillary plexus surrounding the uriniferous tubes, and it finally leaves the organ through the branches of the renal vein. . . .

The basement membrane of the uriniferous tube, expanded over the Malpighian tuft to form its capsule, is a simple, homogeneous, and perfectly transparent membrane, in which no structure can be discovered. It is perforated, as before stated, by the afferent and efferent vessels, and is certainly not reflected over them. They are united to it at their point of transit, but in what precise manner I have not been able to determine. Opposite to this point is the orifice of the tube, the cavity of which is continuous with that of the capsule, generally by a constricted neck. I have specimens prepared with the double injection showing this continuity in Mammalia, Birds, Reptiles and Fish; and, in Mammalia and Reptile, I have obtained the still more satisfactory proof afforded by a clear view of the whole of the textures magnified 300 diameters. As the Malpighian bodies are placed in every possible direction, it often happens that a third section, parallel to the neck of the tube, cannot at once be obtained: but with perseverance this may always be done. The capsule is then seen to pass off into the basement membrane of the tube, as the body of a Florence flask into its neck. The basement membrane of the tube is lined by a nucleated epithelium of a finely-granular opake aspect, while the neck of the tube and its orifice become abruptly covered with a layer of cells much more transparent, and clothed with vibratile cilia. The epithelium is continued in many cases over the whole inner surface of the capsule; in other instances I have found it impossible to detect the slightest appearance of it over more than a third of the capsule. When fairly within the capsule, the cilia cease, and the epithelium beyond is of excessive delicacy and translucence. Its particles are seldom nucleated, and appear liable to swell by the addition of the water added to the specimen. They frequently fill up the space between the capsule and tuft, and touching the latter, may seem to be united to it. The lines of their mutual contact may then wear the aspect of a highly delicate areolar tissue, connecting the capsule with the tuft. The cavity existing in the natural state between this epithelium and the tuft, is filled by fluid, in which the vessels are bathed, and which is continually being impelled along the tube by the lashing movement of the cilia. In the Frog, where alone I have as yet been able to see these wonderful organs in motion, they were longer than those from other parts of that animal, and extremely active. . . .

Reflecting on this remarkable structure of the Malpighian bodies, and on their singular connection with the tubes, I was led to speculate on their use. It occurred to me that as the tubes and their plexus of capillaries were probably, for reasons presently to be stated, the parts concerned in the secretion of that portion of the urine to which its characteristic properties are due (the urea, lithic acid, &c.), the Malpighian bodies might be an apparatus destined to separate from the blood the watery portion. . . .

It would indeed be difficult to conceive a disposition of parts more calculated to favour the escape of water from the blood, than that of the Malpighian body. A large artery breaks up in a very direct manner into a number of minute branches, each of which suddenly opens into an assemblage of vessels of far greater aggregate capacity than itself, and from which there is but one narrow exit. Hence must arise a very abrupt retardation in the velocity of the current of blood. The vessels in which this delay occurs are uncovered by any structure. They lie bare in a cell from which there is but one outlet, the orifice of the tube. This orifice is encircled by cilia, in active motion, directing a current towards the tube. These exquisite organs must not only serve to carry forward the fluid already in the cell, and in which the vascular tuft is bathed, but must tend to remove pressure from the free surface of the vessels, and so to encourage the escape of their more fluid contents. Why is so wonderful an apparatus placed at the extremity of each uriniferous tube, if not to furnish water, to aid in the separation and solution of the urinous products from the epithelium of the tube? (Bowman, William. "On the structure and use of the Malpighian bodies of the kidney, with observations on the circulation through that gland." *Phil. Trans.*, 1842, *132*, 57-80, 1 pl. [pp. 58-59, 60-61, 73, 75].)

Carl Friedrich Wilhelm Ludwig
1816-1895

One of the greatest physiologists of the nineteenth century, *Carl Ludwig* was perhaps especially important for his influence on students who included John Scott Burdon-Sanderson (1828-1905) and Henry Pickering Bowditch (1840-1911), to mention only one representative from each of the important groups from Britain and America. His influence upon the development of physiology in America in this way was especially profound. After brief periods at Zurich and Vienna he became professor of physiology at Leipzig where he established an institute for physiology.

Throughout his life a vigorous opponent of vitalism, Ludwig (Pl. 73) became interested in the problem of kidney function while still a student and devoted his M.D. thesis to the elaboration of a purely physical theory of urine formation.[5] This essay, which appeared in 1842, the same year that Bowman published his work, was written in ignorance of the latter's discoveries. In 1844, Ludwig published a new version of his theory, modified to take Bowman's work into account, in Wagner's *Handwörterbuch der Physiologie*. From this time forward until 1917 there were two opposed theories of renal function current in the literature: that of Bowman, later modified by Heidenhain, and that of Ludwig. Bowman had suggested that water alone was separated at the Malpighian body while the dissolved constituents of the urine were secreted by the epithelium of the urinary tubules. Ludwig on the other hand argued that a filtrate containing all the water-soluble constituents of the blood was separated at the glomerulus and that a process of selective reabsorption occurred in the urinary tubule. He thereby hoped to remove all need to invoke the vital properties of the tubule epithelium to account for urine formation. Ludwig's interest in this problem led him to study further the properties of membranes and osmotic phenomena.

THE PHYSICAL THEORY OF URINE SECRETION

According to this hypothesis the glomeruli are, above all, the place at which the urine is separated from the blood. At this point,

[5] Ludwig, Carl. *De viribus physicis secretionem urinae adjuvantibus*. Marburg, 1842. 23 pp.

namely, where the circulating blood flows from a narrower cavity (that of the afferent vessel of the glomerulus) into a wider one (the glomerulus itself) and then again into a narrower (the efferent vessel) it must, according to the laws of hydraulics, exert a greater pressure on the walls of the vessel. By this pressure a significant amount of liquid must be squeezed out through the thin vascular membrane; this part of our theory can scarcely even be called hypothetical. However, hypothetically, we may suppose further that these vessel walls possess the characteristic power that, of the fluid and dissolved constituents of the blood, they allow only water (i.e., part of the substance to be excreted) and the salts freely soluble in water to pass through, while none of the protein substances (fat and the mineral constituents occurring in combination with them) are allowed through. This, at first glance somewhat daring, hypothesis loses its recklessness when one considers the most interesting experiment of Brücke in which the eggshell membrane, in its endosmotic flow, is independent of the albumen and will call to mind the remarkable experiments of Matteuci and Cima on endosmosis through animal membranes. If one only grants this theory so far, then one would have in the beginning of urine formation a fluid which would contain all the constituents of the urine, and furthermore all of these constituents in the same amounts proportional to one another as in the urine, but dissolved in much more water than in the latter. This fluid, by the continued squeezing of additional fluid into the capsule, is driven from there into the urinary vessels and thereby comes in contact with the blood which is flowing in the narrow vessels described above and which has originated from the glomerulus. There flows in these vessels, according to our hypothesis, blood which has become very concentrated through the removal of much of its water. Between the very dilute fluid occurring in the urinary canals and the very concentrated fluid contained in the blood vessels there would again set in an endosmotic flow which from known experience would include especially the exchange of water, that is, it would draw water from the urinary canals into the blood vessels whereby the urine would become concentrated. . . . (Ludwig, Carl. "Nieren und Harnbereitung" in Rudolph Wagner's *Handwörterbuch der Physiologie.* Braunschweig, 1842-1853. 4 vols. in 5; vol. 2, 1844, pp. 628-640 [pp. 637-638. Translated by L.G.W.].)

Charles Edward Isaacs

1811-1860

Charles E. Isaacs, New York anatomist, physiologist, pathologist, and practising physician, was the first American to make detailed studies on the anatomy and pathological physiology of the kidney, as studied experimentally in animals through the use of dyes, and also the first author of consequence to take issue with William Bowman's conclusions concerning the functional activity of the Malpighian glomeruli. In a previous paper Isaacs had sought to discover whether the Malpighian tuft or glomerulus lay actually naked in Bowman's capsule or was covered by epithelium and found that it was enclosed by a thin layer of pavement epithelium. He also confirmed Bowman's discovery of the continuity of the capsule with the urinary tubule (Pl. 74), a fact which had been questioned by some.[6] In a second paper he reported that by means of special injection techniques he was able to visualize the vascular tufts that constitute the glomeruli. This led him to propose a relatively new and ingenious theory concerning the secretion of urine.

MALPIGHIAN BODIES OF KIDNEY

. . . 4. According to Mr. Bowman, the Malpighian coil or tuft lies naked in the capsule of the uriniferous tube; which is a proof that it does not separate the complex proximate elements of the urine from the blood, but merely water, the coil or tuft being, as he says, "a bare or naked system of capillaries." Now I have conclusively demonstrated, by various processes, that the Malpighian tuft or coil is covered by oval, nucleated cells, which are differently affected by chemical reagents from those which line the capsule, and consequently have a different organization. The Malpighian tuft is evidently, then, a glandular structure, every way adapted for the separation of the proximate elements of the urine. . . .

Let us now review the facts and arguments which thus far throw light upon the function of the Malpighian tuft:

1. That it is not for the purpose of merely separating water from the blood is proved by its distribution throughout the substance of the kidney in some animals whose urine is semi-solid.

2. The proximate elements of the urine exist ready formed in the blood.

3. These elements can only reach the kidney through the renal ar-

---

[6] Isaacs, C. E. "Researches into the structure and physiology of the kidney." *Trans. N. Y. Acad. Med.*, 1857, *1*, 377-435.

tery, upon whose minute terminal branches are placed the Malpighian bodies.

4. It has been shown that the Malpighian tuft is covered by peculiar oval nucleated cells. This glandular structure seems to be, in every respect, well fitted for the separation of these substances.

5. The action of diuretics upon the Malpighian tuft.

6. The actual separation by it of coloring substances, as demonstrated by these experiments.

7. The existence of the coloring matter of the bile in the Malpighian tuft and capsule.

8. The facts here adduced relative to the presence of lithic acid in the Malpighian tuft, and its detection by chemical tests.

9. From all these considerations, it seems that we are justified in concluding that the Malpighian tuft separates from the blood most of the proximate elements of the urine.

10. Any element of the urine which is not secreted by the Malpighian tuft is then probably separated by the epithelial lining of the tubes, as is generally believed. . . . All the facts, however, adduced in this paper, lead to the conclusion that it is to the Malpighian body that we are to attribute the principal agency in the secretion of the urine. . . . (Isaacs, C. E. "On the function of the Malpighian bodies of the kidney." *Trans. N. Y. Acad. Med.*, 1857, *1*, pt. IX, 437-456 [pp. 438, 451-452].)

Rudolf Peter Heinrich Heidenhain
1834-1897

Member of a Prussian family of physicians, *Rudolf Heidenhain* was born at Marienwerder and educated at Königsberg, Halle, and finally at Berlin where he worked with Emil Du Bois-Reymond (1818-1896). In 1859 he was appointed professor of physiology and histology at Breslau where he continued for the remainder of his career. Heidenhain made important contributions to histology, a subject he pursued because it established the structural matrix within which physiological processes had to occur. His prime interest was physiology, as is evident from his long essay on secretion and kidney function which he published in Hermann's *Handbuch der Physiologie*. Some of his conclusions are given here. Heidenhain reasserted Bowman's doctrine of kidney function in opposition to that of Ludwig and thereby gave it a place in the literature which it held until Cushny's work in 1917.

SUMMARY OF THE SECRETION THEORY IN RELATION TO THE FACTS

In the confusion of previous discussions it appears appropriate to summarize in brief the difficulties which the filtration theory encounters. . . .

The filtration hypothesis leads to the consequence that in the kidneys in order to accomplish the removal of the actual daily amount of urine from the blood it would be necessary to filter and again resorb an amount of fluid (in human beings about 70 kg.) which far exceeds every conceivable limit.

Insofar as the filtration hypothesis will avoid this conclusion it will require, to be sure, for any actual case its express subsidiary hypothesis that the glomerular filtrate already possesses a urine content of high percentage. Quite irrespective of the improbability of this assumption it is incompatible with the idea of a simple mechanical filtration process.

In consequence of the filtration hypothesis the amount of urine must increase invariably with the [blood] pressure which according to experience is not the case (venous obstruction).

The presupposition of the filtration hypothesis—that the urine in its passage through the canaliculi becomes concentrated as a result of diffusion—is not true because its concentration can be greater than that of the blood serum, moreover than that of the lymph which flows around immediately adjacent to the urinary canaliculi. . . .

These numerous considerations can, it appears, be circumvented if one is allowed to make for the kidneys, in conjunction with knowledge acquired in all other glands, the following assumptions:

1. As in all other glands, so it remains also in the kidneys that secretion is an active function of special secretion cells.

2. As such there function first those in the simple layer of cells enveloping the vascular loops of the Malpighian tuft which has the task of secreting water and those salts of urine which everywhere in the organism are the attendants of water, as for example, common salt.

3. Another system of secretion cells, which covers the walls of the tubule and of the broad loop (Henle's loop), serves for the secretion of the specific constituents of the urine; in certain cases there would also be secreted at the same time a certain amount of water.

4. The degree of activity of both sorts of secretion cells is deter-

mined: (a) by the composition of the blood with respect to water and the solid constituents; (b) by the velocity of the blood in the kidney capillaries inasmuch as the cells in question depend upon it partly for their specific secretion material and partly for their oxygen.

5. The great variability in the composition of the urine is to be explained by the variations in the secretion activity of the two kinds of cells whose relative proportions may fluctuate within broad limits. (Heidenhain, Rudolf. "Physiologie der Absonderungsvorgange" in Hermann, *Handbuch der Physiologie*, 1879-1883. 6 vols.: 5, part I, 1883, pp. 1-420 [pp. 360-362. Translated by L.G.W.].)

Arthur Robertson Cushny
1866-1926

Arthur R. Cushny, Scottish pharmacologist, was born at Fochabers, Morayshire, son of a clergyman, on 6 March 1866. He entered the University of Aberdeen and obtained an M.A. (1886), M.B. and C.M. (1889) with highest honors. He then went to Oswald Schmiedeberg's laboratory at Strasbourg and from there to Bern to Hugo Kronecker who, like Schmiedeberg, was a pupil of Carl Ludwig. In 1893, Cushny was induced by John Jacob Abel, who had just resigned from the University of Michigan chair of pharmacology to go to Johns Hopkins, to take his post, although Cushny was only twenty-seven years of age at the time; he remained at the University of Michigan for twelve years and then went back to Scotland to become professor of pharmacology at the University of Edinburgh.

The three major interests with which his name is identified are: (i) digitalis, (ii) contrasted actions of optical isomers, (iii) urinary secretion. Cushny (Pl. 75) outlined his theory of kidney function in 1917 in *The Secretion of the Urine*, a book written at the request of E. H. Starling to whom he addressed a prefatory letter. He modestly designates his own theory simply as the "modern theory." One of his most important contributions was to introduce the concept of "threshold bodies" which is fundamental to all modern renal theory and to renal function tests.

CUSHNY'S 'MODERN VIEW' ON KIDNEY FUNCTION AS OUTLINED IN A LETTER OF TRANSMITTAL TO COL. E. H. STARLING, EDITOR OF MONOGRAPHS ON PHYSIOLOGY

It is often complained that the physiology of the kidney given in the textbooks is made up of a wrangle between the two great views of its activity; on the other hand, it may be argued that the many isolated observations need to be correlated with each other, and this can only be done by welding them with some definite view of renal function. I have not avoided the controversy, but I have at any rate given the ascertained facts apart from the discussion, so that they at least may remain, whatever theory of kidney activity may survive. The different views are presented, and one is advocated which differs in some respects from any that has been accepted hitherto, and which embraces some of the features of each of its precursors. Since it has been developed gradually from the work of many, it would not be fair to attach to it the name of any one investigator, and I have therefore called it "the modern view"; it has not been treated in detail previously. It is based largely on physical chemistry as well as on the direct observations of physiologists, and it appears to conflict with no ascertained fact in physiology, while it gives an intelligible connection between almost all those that have been established; above all, it is capable of expansion. It has been a special pleasure in working out this view to find that many observations which have been held to be opposed to any such physical correlation really fall into place easily when looked at from the proper angle. I do not flatter myself that this treatise attains finality in regard to the secretion of the urine; that is impossible at the present time. If it serves as an advanced post from which others may issue against the remaining ramparts of vitalism, its purpose will be attained.

You will probably complain that instead of presenting the facts and following them to the theoretical principle to which they point, I have first stated the theory and then discussed how far each set of observations can be brought into accord with it. I acknowledge the superiority of the first method, but I feared that it was impossible to follow it. For the facts are so multitudinous that unless the student were first given some general scheme on which he could arrange them, he would be lost in detail and might fail to appreciate where the path was leading. (Cushny, A. R. *The secretion of urine.* London and New York, Longmans, Green and Co., 1917. xi, 241 pp. [pp. viii-ix].)

GENERAL CONSIDERATION OF THE BOWMAN-HEIDENHAIN AND THE MODERN THEORIES

The two leading theories of renal secretion agree in locating the secretion of water in the glomerular capsule at any rate for the most part. And, in fact, they do not differ fundamentally in their conceptions of the function of the capsule. The one regards mechanical filtration as sufficient to explain the glomerular fluid, while Heidenhain held it to be insufficient and therefore contended for further unknown, or vital, activities. But both schools agree fairly satisfactorily that the fluid is of the nature of a deproteinized plasma as a general rule. A more marked divergence exists as to the quantity of the glomerular fluid, for while Heidenhain supposes this to be approximately that of the urine, the modern view requires a vastly greater amount of fluid, since it has to supply not only the water of the urine, but the whole of the solids also.

In regard to the tubular epithelium the two views are diametrically opposed, the later ascribing to it merely the function of absorption, while Heidenhain held that it is primarily secretory, though he conceded that under exceptional conditions it may absorb fluid from the tubules to some extent. The problem here is therefore to determine the direction of the current in the epithelium. Does it set towards the lumen of the tubule, as Heidenhain supposed, or away from the lumen, as Ludwig suggested? . . .

The chief attraction of the original Ludwig theory lay in its eliminating altogether the unknown vital activity of the cell. The modern theory accepts this activity as necessary, and it may be asked wherein it can claim preference over the Bowman-Heidenhain view. It is true that in essential features it is fairly simple, but in detail it bristles with complications and difficulties, which are at any rate not so obvious in the straightforward statement that the urine is secreted like the saliva. The chief advantage of the modern view is that it reduces the kidney to a machine instead of postulating for it the capacity of a highly trained analytical chemist. One part of the kidney filters off the plasma colloids, another part absorbs a fluid of unchanging composition. The kidney exercises no discrimination, but continues these activities through life, just as a muscle exercises no discrimination. The kidney loses somewhat in dignity and romance when it is thus represented as merely a hard-working organ, which is admirably fitted to remove the waste products of the blood, but which is so devoid of judgment that in some conditions it acts to the prejudice of the organism by removing the diluent instead of the poison. And the complications and difficulties of the modern view arise from its attempt to take cognizance of the intricate conditions under which the organ functions. . . .

In short, the modern theory holds that the constituents of the plasma which I have termed Threshold Bodies . . . are taken up by the cells of the tubules and return to the blood, while the No-threshold substances, such as urea, are rejected and can only escape by the ureter. Further, the threshold bodies are not absorbed indiscriminately but in definite proportions, which are determined by their normal values in the plasma; otherwise the kidney would eliminate waste products, but would fail to regulate the concentration of the threshold bodies in the plasma. The cells lining the tubules thus absorb from the glomerular filtrate a slightly alkaline fluid containing sugar, amino-acids and other similar food substances, and chloride, sodium, and potassium in approximately the proportions in which they are present in normal plasma, or in the artificial mixtures which have been introduced for the perfusion of surviving organs. (Cushny, A. R. *The secretion of the urine.* London and New York, Longmans, Green and Co., 1917. xi, 241 pp. [pp. 51, 55-56, 47].)

Alfred Newton Richards
1876-
and
Carl Frederic Schmidt
1893-

Born at Stamford, New York, *Alfred Newton Richards* attended Yale College (B.A. 1897; M.A. 1899) and then did graduate work in physiological chemistry at Columbia University where he took his Ph.D. in 1901. In 1910 Richards went to the University of Pennsylvania School of Medicine as professor of pharmacology, a post he continued to hold until his retirement in 1946 when he was appointed emeritus professor.

Carl Frederic Schmidt was born at Lebanon, Pennsylvania, and after graduating from Lebanon Valley College in 1914 went to the University of Pennsylvania Medical School (M.D. 1919) where he then spent three years as an instructor in pharmacology. It was during this period under Richards from 1919 to 1922 that the work here described was carried out. Their success permitted the study of the specific effects of adrenalin and other substances on the glomeruli.

GLOMERULAR CIRCULATION IN FROG KIDNEY

Intermittence of glomerular circulation can frequently be observed. It can be produced by reflex constriction of the renal vessels, by electrical stimulation of sympathetic fibers to the kidney and by slow intravenous injection of adrenalin. It is thought to be due to the antagonism between nervous or chemical constrictor influences and the dilator influence of oxygen deficiency which begins to be manifest as soon as circulation ceases in the small arterioles. It is regarded an essential factor in the capacity of the kidney to utilize a fraction of its glomerular equipment without damage to the rest.

No conclusive evidence has been collected to show that the described variations in the glomerular circulation are due primarily to contraction or relaxation of the glomerular capillary wall. They appear to be the result of changes in the arterioles.

Phenomena have been encountered which lead to the conclusion that structures situated at the origin of the glomerular capillary from the afferent arteriole may not only exhibit spontaneous contractility, but may be more susceptible to constrictor influences than is the rest of the muscle of the wall of the arteriole. Observations of arterioles in striated muscle and in the kidney have been made which suggest that in general the small arterioles constrict more readily at their points of branching from parent vessels than at other points [Fig. 76]. Such a view is in harmony with observations of Cohnstein and Zuntz, of Krogh and with our own finding concerning apparent dilutions of blood of varying degrees which can be seen in small arterioles and in glomerular capillaries. . . .

These observations provide evidence upon which to re-introduce into considerations of renal physiology the conception held by Hermann and doubtless by Ludwig that the extent of filtration surface in the kidney is variable and a factor which must be of major importance in the adjustment of renal function to excretory requirement. (Richards, A. N. and Schmidt, C. F. "A description of the glomerular circulation in the frog's kidney and observations concerning the action of adrenalin and various other substances upon it." *Amer. J. Physiol.*, 1924, *71*, 178-208 [pp. 206-207].)

Joseph Trebar Wearn
1893-
and
Alfred Newton Richards
1876-

A native of North Carolina, *Joseph Wearn* was educated at Davidson College (B.S. 1913) and the Harvard Medical School (M.D. 1917). In 1923 he joined the faculty of Harvard where he collaborated with A. N. Richards in the work presented here. In 1929 he moved to the Western Reserve Medical School where he has since remained.

EXPERIMENTAL PROOF OF REABSORPTION FROM THE TUBULE

The essential part of the apparatus used for drawing fluid from Bowman's capsule is a sharp pointed capillary pipette. A small piece of quartz tubing, 1 mm. in diameter, was drawn out in a flame and broken at the narrow part. The point (10 to 20 μ inner diameter) was either sharpened on a stone or broken in such a way that a sharp edge or spicule projected from the tip. This quartz pipette was sealed into the end of one arm of a 3-way glass stop-cock tube by means of wax. A piece of thick walled rubber tubing, 3 to 4 inches long, closed at one end by a bit of glass rod was attached to the opposite arm. The third arm, projecting at right angles to the other two, was connected with a glass levelling bulb by 2½ feet of rubber tubing. By means of the levelling bulb the whole apparatus including the quartz tip was filled with mercury.

The pipette was firmly held in a stage of Barbour's pattern capable of giving micrometric adjustment in three planes. The stage in turn was firmly clamped to a Zimmerman stativ, well adapted to coarse adjustments. . . .

Insertion of the pipette into the glomerular space was carried out with the aid of the binocular microscope in the following manner. The point of the pipette was brought into the microscopic field directly over the capsule to be punctured, so that it was poised about one millimeter above the surface of the kidney. A very fine stream of air, issuing from a small hypodermic needle attached to the microscope stand, was allowed to play upon the surface of the kidney until the thin layer of fluid on the surface was removed and the field of operation dried. This procedure made it possible to introduce the pipette through the capsule of Bowman without contamination. This drying of the surface helped to overcome to some extent the difficulty encountered in puncturing the capsule because of its elasticity and toughness; it prevented accidental trauma of the capillary tuft or of the inner surface of the capsule opposite the point of puncture. The point of the pipette was directed at the clear space visible between the capillary tuft and the capsule of Bowman. The point of puncture was so chosen that the tip of the pipette after insertion could not exert pressure by contact upon the glomerular vessels. . . .

After insertion of the pipette the three-way stop-cock was turned so that the connection between the levelling bulb and the pipette was opened. The bulb was then lowered to a point two or three centimeters below the level of the kidney, thus creating negative pressure sufficient to draw the glomerular fluid into the pipette. To discontinue collection of the glomerular urine the three-way cock was turned so that connection between the collecting tip and the rest of the system was closed. Contamination during withdrawal of the pipette was avoided by again drying the surface of the kidney. The tip of the pipette was carefully rinsed with distilled water immediately after its withdrawal.

Transfer of fluid from the pipette to tubes adapted to chemical testing was carried out as follows: A long glass capillary tube with an inner diameter from three to six times that of the quartz pipette was mounted obliquely upon the microscope stage so that its upper opening was within the field of vision. Using the Barbour stage the tip of the pipette was inserted into the opening and the contents expelled into it by pressure.

After transfer of the glomerular fluid to the glass capillary, division into portions sufficient for single tests was made by drawing it further into the capillary and cutting the tube at the midpoint of the column of fluid. This process was repeated as many times as the volume of the original sample justified.

To add a reagent to any portion of the glomerular urine it was sufficient to touch the end of the capillary to the surface of the reagent and thus permit capillarity to force it into the tube. Mixture of urine with reagent was accomplished by moving the fluids back and forth in the tubes by gentle suction and pressure. In tests which required heat, the ends of the capillary were sealed in a flame, and the tube immersed in boiling water.

During the collection of glomerular fluid, urine accumulated in the bladder which had been emptied at the beginning of the experiment. This bladder urine was taken at the end of the experiment and subjected to tests identical in method with those applied to the glomerular urine.

Results. *Protein.* The acetic acid-potassium ferrocyanide test was used. Samples of glomerular fluid and of bladder urine from eleven different frogs were tested and in none was a precipitate formed. This result is important not only from the standpoint of the physiology of the kidney, but also because it indicates that the methods used to avoid contamination with tissue fluid were successful. As a control, a small portion of the fluid which normally covers the surface of the kidney was collected, diluted one hundred times with water, and subjected to test in a capillary tube. An easily distinguishable, flocculent precipitate was obtained. Frog's plasma, diluted 1:100, yielded a similar result. These control tests indicate the delicacy of the method employed and proved that there was neither significant contamination of the pipette during its insertion or withdrawal and that there was no leakage of tissue fluid into the capsule of Bowman during collection. . . . Direct testing of the fluid eliminated by the frog's glomerulus proves the assumption which was made by the earliest of the modern students of renal physiology, that a protein-free, watery fluid is separated from the blood stream as it passes through the glomerular capillaries. Absence of protein from the glomerular fluid constitutes serious objection to de Haan's hypothesis of the normal permeability of the glomerular membranes to colloids.[7]

The discovery that two substances, sodium chloride and glucose, both of which are normal constituents of blood plasma, are not to be found in bladder urine under the conditions of these experiments, but are to be found in considerable concentration in the fluid taken directly from the glomerulus, proves beyond doubt that reabsorption of these substances must take place in the renal tubules. Proof is also at hand in these experiments that the threshold of reabsorption

[7] de Haan, J. "The renal function as judged by the excretion of vital dye-stuffs." *J. Physiol. (Lond.),* 1922, *56,* 444-450.

of these two substances is not the same. The conception of differential reabsorption in the tubules therefore receives support of the most direct character. (Wearn, J. T. and Richards, A. N. "Observations on the composition of glomerular urine, with particular reference to the problem of reabsorption in the renal tubules." *Amer. J. Physiol.*, 1924, *71*, 209-227 [pp. 216-219, 225].)

Ernest Henry Starling
1866-1927

and

Ernest Basil Verney
1894-

After receiving his early education at King's College School, *Ernest Starling* studied medicine at Guy's Hospital and on graduating in 1886 went for a few months to Kühne's laboratory at Heidelberg, but returned to London to complete his medical training. With the help of scholarships he was able to begin research in physiology and in 1893 went to Heidenhain's laboratory at Breslau, followed by a brief period at the Pasteur Institute. By 1897 Starling had obtained his own well-equipped physiological laboratory at Guy's, but in 1899 accepted the chair of physiology at University College, London where he continued for the remainder of his life.

In 1921 *Ernest Basil Verney,* after two years in the Royal Army Medical Corps, went to University College to begin his research career in physiology; later he became professor of pharmacology. Verney had attended Cambridge University and studied medicine at St. Bartholomew's Hospital, London.

Early in his career Starling had studied the formation of lymph which he had shown to be a physical process governed by two factors—permeability of the capillary wall and intracapillary blood pressure—which, when in excess of the osmotic pressure of the serum proteins, permitted the formation of lymph by filtration. These studies prepared him to appreciate Cushny's theory of kidney function, based as it was on filtration and reabsorption. With the aid of a heart-lung preparation, Starling and Verney were able to supply an isolated kidney with oxygenated blood of controlled composition at controlled pressures, rates of flow and temperature, and could thereby produce a regular flow of normal urine. They thus demonstrated that the glomeruli generate a protein-free filtrate and, by blocking tubular activity with hydrocyanic acid, it was possible to collect this filtrate from the ureter. This inhibition was reversible and they showed that water, chloride, bicarbonate, and glucose are normally reabsorbed by the tubule cells from the glomerular filtrate. Their experiments revealed, too, the remarkable influence on the kidney of pituitrin discussed here.

ON ISOLATED KIDNEY

It is clear, then, that this action in the normal animal is quite different from that obtaining in the diuresis resulting from water administration, from diabetes insipidus, and from complete isolation of the kidney. Here we have a true specific action of the tubule cells regulating the absorption of both water and possibly of chloride, an action that we should expect to be accompanied by changes in the oxygen consumption of the organ. It is interesting to note that in one of our experiments we found that the kidney was markedly fibrosed. The bladder urine from the dog was alkaline and loaded with protein. In this case pituitrin had very little, if any, effect on the percentage of chloride, whilst definitely lowering the absolute amount eliminated, probably as a secondary result of the vascular changes and the diminished glomerular filtration thereby induced. A similar result was obtained by von den Velden (loc. cit.) in cases of chronic nephritis in man. Molitor and Pick (loc. cit.) have shown that in cantharidin and uranium nephritis on dogs, water diuresis fails to be inhibited by pituitrin. These results obtained on the pathological kidney strengthen our belief in the localisation of the action of pituitrin to the re-absorptive mechanism of the tubule.

We suggest, therefore, that some substance or substances with an action similar to that of pituitrin are normally present in the intact mammal and serve as the means whereby the kidney is controlled in its important function of regulating the output of water and of chloride. The isolated kidney is divorced from this regulating mechanism—a mechanism which has presumably been produced during phylogenetic development in response to the request for an increasing control over salt-and-water metabolism. It is not surprising, then, that without this aid the kidney functionally reverts to the type of gland characteristic of the fish and amphibian classes of the vertebrate phylum. In these classes, so far as we have been able to find urinary analyses in the literature, the chloride percentage in the urine is always below that in the blood plasma.

The puzzling rapid reaction of the kidney to the ingestion of large amounts of water by the alimentary tract, in which large quantities of urine of very low molecular concentration are secreted, must be ascribed to an inhibition of the normal process or processes of water re-absorption with concentration of the chlorides, i.e., to

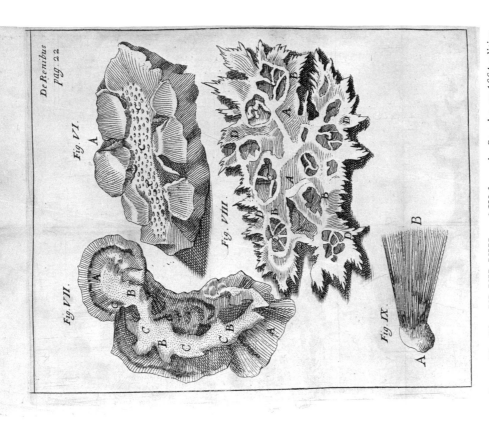

De Renibus
pag. 22

Fig. VI.

Fig. VII.

Fig. VIII.

Fig. IX.

PLATE 70B. Figs. VI, VII, VIII, and IX from the Strasbourg 1664 edition.

EXERCITATIO
ANATOMICA

LAVRENTII BELLINI
FLORENTINI

DE STRVCTVRA,
ET VSV RENVM.

PATAVII, Apud Matthæum Cadorinum.
Superiorum permiſſu 1666.

PLATE 70A. Title-page of Bellini's *Exercitatio anatomica de structura et usu renum* (Pavia, 1663 [date
changed in ink to 1666].)

DE VISCERVM
STRVCTVRA
EXERCITATIO
ANATOMICA
MARCELLI MALPIGHII

Philof. & Med. Bononien. in Meſſa-
nenſi Academia Medicinę
Primarij.

BONONIÆ,

Ex Typographia Iacobi Montij. MDCLXVI.
Superiorum pèrmiſſu.

PLATE 71. Title-page of one of two rare issues of Malpighi's treatise of 1666.

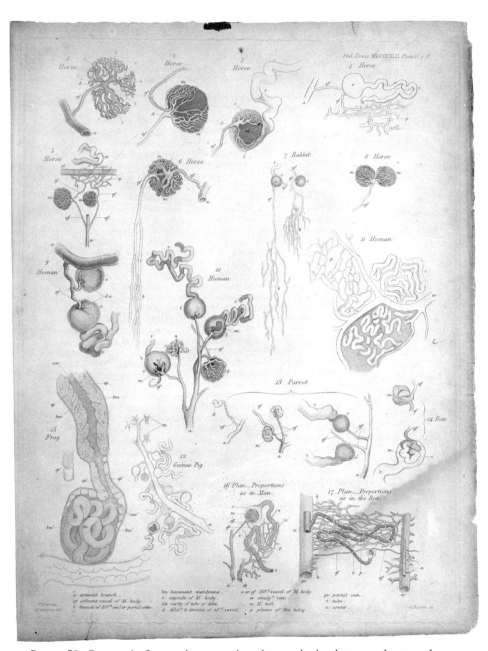

PLATE 72. Bowman's figures demonstrating the continuity between the capsule surrounding the glomerulus and the urinary tubule from his paper "On the structure and use of the Malpighian bodies of the kidney," 1842.

PLATE 73. Carl Ludwig (1816-1895). Drawing by L. Knaus, 27 August 1867. (Courtesy of the National Library of Medicine.)

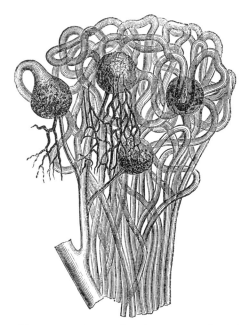

PLATE 74. Bowman's capsule of the sheep, from Isaac's paper, "Researches into the structure and physiology of the kidney," 1857.

PLATE 75. Arthur R. Cushny (1866-1926). (Courtesy of the National Library of Medicine.)

Fig. 6. R. pipiens. Variations in capillary pathway within a single glomerulus. *a*, 5 minutes before an intravenous injection of 0.1 cc. of 10 per cent glucose: blood flow very slow. *b*, 10 minutes after glucose: blood flow still slow. *c* and *d*, 25 and 30 minutes after glucose; blood flow more rapid and cells less closely packed. *e*, 45 minutes after glucose: blood flow slow, cells densely packed. *f*, 9 minutes after intravenous injection of 0.5 cc. 0.7 per cent NaCl: flow more rapid and cells less dense. *g*, immediately after injection of 0.1 cc. adrenalin 1/100,000: blood flow very slow. *h*, 5 minutes after a *g*, blood flow rapid.

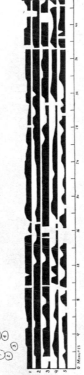

Fig. 7. Chart representing spontaneous variations in the flow of blood through five closely adjacent glomeruli, the relative positions of which are indicated by the sketch at the upper left hand corner. A broad line represents rapid flow, a narrow line slow flow and interruption of the line represents discontinuance of flow.

PLATE 76. Figs. 6 and 7 from Richards and Schmidt's paper, "A description of the glomerular circulation in the frog's kidney," 1924.

PLATE 77. Homer Smith (1895-1962). Photograph taken in 1958 by Fabian Bachrach. (Courtesy of the New York University Medical Center.)

neutralisation of the effect of the hormonic influence we have just imagined. It may be that the passage of the hypotonic fluid through the intestinal wall or through the liver is responsible for the production of another chemical messenger inhibiting those with a pituitrin action, or there may be some slight blood change which inhibits the formation of the pituitrin like hormones. These are problems which only further research can solve. (Starling, E. H. and Verney, E. B. "The secretion of urine as studied on the isolated kidney." *Proc. roy. Soc. B.*, 1925, *97*, 321-361 [pp. 360-361].)

Donald Dexter Van Slyke
1883-

Donald Dexter Van Slyke was born at Pike, New York, and educated at the University of Michigan where he took his A.B. in 1905 and his Ph.D. in 1907. In the same year he went as a fellow in physiological chemistry to the Rockefeller Institute where he was to remain throughout his active life. In 1921 he became a member of the Institute and since 1948 he has been an Emeritus member. He now works at the National Science Laboratory at Brookhaven on Long Island. His work has comprehended many aspects of physiology and physiological chemistry besides that of kidney function to which he made the most important contribution of the concept of renal clearance.

Homer Smith gives an enlightening account of the origin of this concept:

"In 1926 Van Slyke had been on his way to Baltimore to give an address on kidney function, and on the train his courage failed him when he thought of facing an audience again with a mathematical equation. He had learned what every lecturer must ultimately learn that . . . the simplest equation has the fearsome power of completely dispelling the comprehension of an audience, at least in the fields of medicine. As Van Slyke sat on the train seeking a solution of how to dispense with mathematics for the benefit of the medical profession, it occurred to him that all that the equation for high urine flows said was that in effect some constant volume of blood was being 'cleared' of urea in each minute's time."[8]

In an earlier investigation Van Slyke and his co-workers had shown that when the urine volume is above a certain limit, there is a direct ratio between the blood urea content and the urea excretion rate. To this limit they gave the name "Augmentation limit."[9]

[8] Smith, Homer W. *Lectures on the kidney.* Lawrence, Kansas, 1943. 134 pp. [p. 77].
[9] Austin, J. H., Stilman, E., and Van Slyke, D. D. "Factors governing the excretion rate of urea." *J. biol. Chem.*, 1921, *46*, 91-112.

DEFINITION AND CALCULATION OF THE MAXIMUM AND STANDARD BLOOD UREA CLEARANCES

When the urine volume output is at any point *above the augmentation limit,* urea excretion proceeds at maximum speed, and the output per minute represents the urea content of a maximum blood volume. This blood volume, averaging in normal men about 75 cc. per minute, we shall for convenience term the *maximum blood urea clearance, or simply the maximum clearance.* It represents the volume of blood which one minute's excretion suffices to clear of urea when the urine volume is large enough to permit a maximum urea output. The value of the maximum clearance, C_m, is calculated from the observed urea concentrations of the blood and urine, B and U, and the urine volume, V, in cubic centimeters per minute, by the formula,

$$\text{Maximum clearance} = C_m = \frac{UV}{B}$$

The concentration ratio, U/B, indicates the number of cubic centimeters of blood the urea content of which is represented in 1 cc. of urine. $U/B \times V$ therefore indicates the number of cubic centimeters of blood represented in the urea content of the V cubic centimeters of urine excreted in 1 minute. (Möller, E., McIntosh, J. F., and Van Slyke, D.D. "Studies of urea excretion. II. Relationship between urine volume and the rate of urea excretion by normal adults." *J. clin. Invest.*, 1928, *6*, 427-465 [pp. 427-428].)

Homer William Smith

1895-1962

Born at Denver, Colorado, *Homer Smith* was educated first at the University, graduating in 1917, and then at Johns Hopkins, where he obtained his doctorate in physiology in 1921. After a period of time spent in research, he taught at the University of Virginia until 1928 when he moved to the New York University School of Medicine, remaining there until his death. Homer Smith (Pl. 77) studied the physiology of the kidney in the broadest possible way, for he endeavored to relate the development of its complex functional pattern to its evolution as an organ. Moreover, he wrote about both his own work and that of others in a remarkably trenchant style.

THE INULIN CLEARANCE AS A MEASURE
OF GLOMERULAR FILTRATION

. . . A substance suitable for measuring the glomerular clearance must fulfil certain specifications. It must be *completely filterable at the glomerulus* (i.e., its molecular size must not be so great as to prevent its passing through the glomerular membranes, and it must not combine with the plasma proteins, which are themselves unfilterable), and *it must not be reabsorbed, excreted or synthesized by the tubules.* . . .

Since it has been shown that the tubules of the aglomerular kidney can excrete magnesium, sulphate, chloride, creatinine, uric acid, phenol red, etc., one had to assume, in the absence of evidence to the contrary, that the tubules of other animals might also be able to excrete these, and perhaps related, substances. On the other hand, the fact that the aglomerular tubules cannot excrete glucose, although it does not prove that this substance cannot be excreted by glomerular tubules, offered a promising line of investigation. On broad principles it may be supposed that, being a food and not a waste product, glucose has been conserved by the vertebrates throughout their evolution, and at no time continuously excreted from the body. Consequently the tubules have never been called upon to excrete it, and remain incapable of doing so. . . . Inasmuch as glucose is normally reabsorbed by the tubules it can furnish no evidence itself on the rate of glomerular filtration, unless the reabsorptive process is blocked by phlorizin; and since this drug may have other and perhaps deleterious effects upon the kidney, its use is of dubious value. It seemed, however, that if glucose were not excreted by the renal tubules, other sugars might not be excreted by them, and that among the metabolically inert carbohydrates one or more might be found which were not reabsorbed as was this physiologically important foodstuff. With this thought we began our examination of the excretion of non-metabolized carbohydrates, xylose, sucrose and raffinose, in normal and phlorizinized animals, in relation to the simultaneous excretion of urea, creatinine, etc. . . .

The evidence is now fairly convincing that the polysaccharide, inulin, fulfils the specifications for measuring glomerular filtration in all vertebrates. . . . . (Smith, H. W. *The physiology of the kidney.* New York, Oxford University Press, 1937. 305 pp. [pp. 58-61].)

Heinrich Wirz, Bartholomew Hargitay,
(*1914-*) (*1924-*)
and Werner Kuhn
(*1899-1963*)

In 1951 the setting forth of a simple but ingenious scheme for water-reabsorption in the kidney by Wirz, Hargitay, and Kuhn at Basle solved a multitude of difficult problems and in a sense completed Ludwig's dream of seeing the physiology of the kidney explained in physicochemical terms. They showed that there was a decreasing gradient of osmotic pressure from the medulla of the kidney outward toward the cortex and argued that the concentration of the urine occurred primarily in the medulla while the re-absorption of water occurred in the cortex in both the proximal and distal convoluted tubules. The loop of Henle together with the canaliculus operated as an osmotic counter-current system. At the time of this work and until his death Werner Kuhn was professor of physical chemistry at the University of Basle. Heinrich Wirz is now professor of physiology at Basle while Bartholomew Hargitay is Senior Scientist at the Union Carbide Research Institute, Tarrytown, New York.

COUNTER-CURRENT MECHANISMS IN THE KIDNEY

The osmotic pressure of the renal tubular content has been determined. Frozen sections of rat kidneys are mounted between cover glasses in a bath whose temperature is gradually raised. The disappearance of the ice cristals, as observed in a polarising microscope, yields the freezing point depression of the tubular content.

The contents of all tubuli throughout the cortex are isotonic with blood. From the cortico-medullar boundary onwards to the tip of the papilla the osmotic pressure rises steadily in *all* of the tubuli. The points of equal osmotic pressure form shells which are concentric about the tip of the papilla, and which run parallel to the interzonal boundary. This means that the tubular content is blood-isotonic within the proximal as well as within the distal convolutions. It is concentrated while descending the loop of Henle, being diluted again in the ascending limb of the loop before reaching its final concentration in the collecting ducts.

These findings indicate that the concentration of the urine occurs without steep osmotic gradients. The loops of Henle are an example of a hair-pin counter-current system. They prepare a hypertonic surrounding for the collecting ducts so that the contents of the collecting ducts are being concentrated by loosing water in this hypertonic milieu. (Wirz, H., Hargitay, B., and Kuhn, W. "Lokalisation des Konzentrierungsprozesses in der Niere durch direkte Kryoskopie." *Helv. physiol. pharmacol. Acta*, 1951, *9*, 196-207 [p. 207].)

X

Sexual Generation

This chapter on reproduction has been added to the second edition of these *Readings* in recognition of the widespread interest in the subject and the signal importance now attaching to this rapidly expanding field of physiology.

One of the great landmarks in the field is William Harvey's monograph, *Exercitationes de generatione animalium* (1651), a book not as well known as it deserves. It contains, among many other important things, a description of the changes undergone by the uterine endometrium in pregnancy based on original research and challenging the ancient Aristotelian theory of conception. In modern times a comprehensive treatise on the subject was published in 1910 by Francis H. A. Marshall (1878-1949) of Christ's College, Cambridge, who has received very little credit for his great synthesis of the physiology of reproduction and for his many original observations on the breeding season, the human and primate menstrual cycle of fertilization, or for his biochemical studies which helped to usher in our knowledge of the sexual hormones. Marshall's *Physiology of Reproduction*[1] perhaps did more to stimulate younger workers in the field than any other general study in the period immediately following the end of World War I.

In this same period the discovery by Stockard and Papanicolaou in 1917 that the process of ovulation could be followed by changes in the cellular characteristics of a vaginal smear provided a powerful

[1] Marshall, F. H. A. *The physiology of reproduction* (with contributions by William Cramer, James Lochhead, and Cresswell Shearer). 2d ed. London, Longmans, Green and Co., 1922. xvi, 770 pp. The first edition of this monograph appeared in 1910 and the first volume of a third edition, which had been prepared in part by Marshall prior to his death on 1 February 1949, appeared in 1956 under the editorship of Marshall's onetime pupil and colleague, Professor A. S. Parkes. As an introduction Parkes included a useful biographical sketch of the author; other details concerning Marshall's life are to be found in the official obituary of The Royal Society (*Obituary Notices of Fellows of the Royal Society*, No. 19, November 1950, vol. 7, pp. 239-251).

investigative tool. By means of it they traced the oestrous cycle in the guinea pig, and in the next few years the oestrous cycles of the rat (Long and Evans, 1920), the mouse (Allen, 1922), and the longer 28-day menstrual cycle of the monkey (Corner, 1923) were revealed in rapid succession. The monograph by Long and Evans in 1922 on *The Oestrous Cycle in the Rat and its Associated Phenomena* was a monumental work which not only gave the four-day "clock-like" oestrous cycle for this animal but also included a detailed study of the effects of pregnancy and lactation upon the whole reproductive system. They distinguished the different types of corpora lutea and demonstrated that ovulation was suppressed in both pregnancy and lactation. The thoroughness of their work established the basis for the widespread use of the rat in the further study of reproductive physiology.

Evans and Long went on to investigate the effect which other endocrine secretions might have upon the oestrous cycle. They injected an aqueous extract of beef anterior pituitary into immature rats and found that their growth was so greatly stimulated as to produce gigantism, while ovulation was delayed or completely suppressed.[2] This result was surprising because it suggested that while the secretions of the anterior pituitary stimulated growth, they were antagonistic to sexual development. In 1910 Cushing and his co-workers, on the other hand, had shown that one of the effects of hypophysectomy in immature dogs was to produce an atrophy of the gonads and genital system.[3] It had been generally assumed that the secretion of the anterior pituitary was necessary for normal sexual development.

The difficulty presented by Long and Evans's striking results was in some measure defined, if not resolved, when in 1926 P. E. Smith succeeded in perfecting the operation of hypophysectomy in the rat. He found that transplants of anterior pituitary were capable of restoring all of the normal functions to his hypophysectomized rats. However, extracts identical with those used by Evans were capable of restoring growth, but were completely unable to repair ovaries or testes atrophied by hypophysectomy.[4] Smith next administered an-

[2] Evans, H. M., and Long, Joseph A. "The effect of the anterior lobe administered intraperitoneally upon growth, maturity and oestrous cycles of the rat." *Anat. Rec.*, 1921, *21*, 62-63.

[3] Crowe, S. J., Cushing, Harvey, and Homans, John. "Experimental hypophysectomy." *Johns Hopk. Hosp. Bull.*, 1910, *21*, 126-169.

[4] Smith, P. E. "The disabilities caused by hypophysectomy and their repair." *J. Amer. med. Ass.*, 1927, *88*, 158-161.

terior pituitary transplants to immature normal mice and rats and found that they produced precocious sexual development. He was also able to show that his transplants acted directly on the gonads and through them on the other organs of the genital system.[5] From these experiments it was necessary to assume that there must be *at least two* hormones secreted by the anterior pituitary: (i) the growth hormone present in Evans' extract, and (ii) a gonadotrophic hormone destroyed in the production of the Evans extract. In 1928 Zondek and Aschheim in Germany and Evans and Simpson in California independently obtained crude extract of anterior pituitary which were gonadotrophic in action.[6,7] This was the state of knowledge when in 1931 Fevold, Hisaw, *et al.* made the startling announcement that there were not one but two gonadotrophic hormones secreted by the anterior pituitary, each with a specific action. One stimulated the development of the follicle in the ovary while the other stimulated the development of the corpus luteum. Then in 1932 a fourth anterior pituitary hormone was discovered by Riddle and his co-workers when they obtained an extract which was principally lactogenic in action.

The problem of the control of the pituitary over sexual reproduction now became primarily a biochemical one. With the apparent existence of at least three anterior pituitary hormones influencing different aspects of reproduction, not to mention the growth hormone, the adrenotrophic hormone, and the thyrotrophic hormone, it became extremely difficult for physiologists to tell whether one substance might be exerting different effects under different conditions or whether effects might be attributable to impurities or to the combined action of two or more substances. Only when a hormone had been isolated as a pure substance could its physiological effects be clearly distinguished. Since the anterior pituitary hormones were all proteins, and since in 1931 protein chemistry was still in its infancy, purification offered no easy task.

In 1937 the discovery of electrophoresis by Tiselius placed a powerful tool in the hands of protein chemists, and the first purification

[5] Smith, P. E. and Engle, Earl T. "Experimental evidence regarding the rôle of the anterior pituitary in the development and regulation of the genital system." *Amer. J. Anat.*, 1927, *40*, 159-217.

[6] Zondek, Bernard and Aschheim, Selmar. "Das Hormon des Hypophysenvorderlappens." *Klin. Wschr.*, 1928, *71*, 831-835.

[7] Evans, H. M. and Simpson, Miriam E. "Antagonism of growth and sex hormones of the anterior hypophysis." *J. Amer. med. Ass.*, 1928, *91*, 1337-1338.

of a pituitary hormone, that of the interstitial cell-stimulating hormone or luteinizing hormone by Li, Simpson, and Evans at Berkeley, occurred just three years later. The isolation of prolactin by White and his group at Yale followed in 1942, and the remaining three hormones were isolated by Li, Simpson, and Evans: the adrenocorticotrophic hormone in 1943 (isolated independently by White *et al.*), the growth hormone in 1945, and the follicle-stimulating hormone in 1949.

In 1949 oxytocin, the hormone of the posterior pituitary, was also purified by Livermore and du Vigneaud.[8] As early as 1909 Dale had shown that extracts of posterior pituitary stimulate the contraction of smooth muscle.[9] In 1915 Gaines, in a series of classical experiments, demonstrated the role played by this hormone in milk letdown and showed that its secretion was determined by a nervous reflex.

Parallel with the investigation of the over-all control by the pituitary of sexual reproduction, many physiologists vigorously pursued the problems posed by the gonadal and placental hormones and their actions and interactions both in the oestrous cycle and in pregnancy, parturition, and lactation. Their contributions are far too numerous to mention in detail and we must allow the discovery of an ovarian hormone by Allen and Doisy in 1923 and of progesterone by Corner and Allen in 1929 to suggest the others.

Gabriele Falloppio
1523-1562

Gabriele Falloppio—or Fallopius—, anatomist of Modena and Venice, was one of the favorite pupils of Andreas Vesalius (1514-1564) whose great "Anatomy of the human body" (*De humani corporis fabrica*) had appeared in 1543 at about the time young Falloppio joined Vesalius as student and prosector. It is not known how long he remained with him, but there can be no doubt that the author of the *Fabrica* gave him inspiration and returned his pupil's devotion and affection.

Falloppio was the author of two important books, the first being the more

[8] Livermore, A. H. and du Vigneaud, Vincent. "Preparation of high potency oxytocic material by the use of counter-current distribution." *J. biol. Chem.*, 1949, *180*, 365-373.

[9] Dale, H. H. "The action of extracts of the pituitary body." *Biochem. J.*, 1909, *4*, 427-447.

important, *Observationes anatomicae* (Pl. 78). In this one finds his principal contribution, namely, the discovery of the ovarian-uterine tubes still known in English as the Falloppian tubes. In the "Observationes" he likewise gave first-rate accounts of the human ovaries, virginal hymen, clitoris, and round ligaments, and he introduced the modern scientific names for vagina and placenta. He established the presence of seminal vescicles in the human male.

Falloppio's second book, *De morbo gallico* (Padua, C. Gryphius), published in 1563, a year after his death, is less widely known. The book is of interest because he was one of the first to oppose the use of mercury for syphilis and other forms of venereal infections (incidentally, he was one of the first to distinguish between venereal and non-venereal condylomas). Falloppio died in his thirty-eighth year, two years prior to Vesalius.

THE FALLOPPIAN TUBES

That slender and narrow seminal passage arises from the horn of the uterus very white and sinewy but after it has passed outward a little way it becomes gradually broader and curls like the tendrils of a vine until it comes near the end when the tendril-like curls spread out and it terminates in a very broad ending which appears membranous and fleshy on account of its reddish colour. This ending is much shredded and worn as if it were the fringe of a worn piece of cloth and it has a broad opening which always lies closed by the coming together of those fringed ends. However if they be opened carefully and spread apart they form, as it were, the bell-like mouth of a bronze trumpet. Consequently since, whether the tendril-like curls be removed from this classical instrument or even added to, the seminal passage will extend from its head even to its uttermost ending and so it has been designated by me the trumpet of the uterus. They are arranged in this way in all animals not only in man, but also in fowls and cattle and in the corpses of all the other animals which I have studied. . . . (Falloppio, Gabriele. *Observationes anatomicae*. Venice, Marco Antonio Ulmo, 1561. 221 pp. [pp. 196 verso-197 verso. Translated by L.G.W.].)

William Harvey
1578-1657

William Harvey's great distinction was his discovery of the circulation but his work on generation, by far the most extensive of his writings, reveals vividly the range of his investigations and the quality of his mind (Pl. 79). Moreover, it contains many remarkable observations and acute insights. As a result of his observations on deer Harvey criticized the ancient doctrine of Aristotle that the male semen imparted form to matter contained within the uterus.

THE UTERUS OF THE DEER IN PREGNANCY

. . . In the month of September, then, when the female deer first comes in season, her cornua uteri, uterus, or place of conception, grows somewhat more fleshy and thick, softer also, and more tender. In the interior of either cornu, at that part, namely, which looks drawn together by a band, and is turned towards the spine, we observe, protruding in regular succession, five caruncles, soft warts, or papillae. The first of these is larger than any of the others, and each in succession is smaller than the one before it, just as the cornua themselves become smaller and smaller towards their termination. Some of the caruncles grow to the thickness of the largest finger, and look like proud flesh; some are white, others of a deeper red.

From the 26th to the 28th of September, and also subsequently, in the month of October, the uterus becomes thicker, and the carunculae mentioned come to resemble the nipples of the woman's breast: you might fancy them ready to pour out milk. Having removed their apex that I might examine their internal structure, I found them made up of innumerable white points compacted together, like so many bristles erect, and connected by means of a certain mucous viscidity; compressed between the fore finger and thumb, from the base upwards, a minute drop of blood oozed out from each point, a fact which led me, after farther investigation, to conclude that they were entirely made up of the capillary branches of arteries. . . .

Towards the end of October and beginning of November, the rutting season being now ended, and the females separating themselves from the males, the uterus begins (in some sooner, in others later) to shrink in size, and the walls of its internal cavity, inflated in appearance, to bulge out; for where the cells existed formerly there are now certain globular masses projecting internally, which nearly fill the whole cavity, by which the sides are brought into mutual contact, and almost agglutinated, as it seems, so that there is no interval between them. Even as we have seen the lips of boys who, in robbing a hive, had been stung in the mouth, swollen and enlarged, so that the oral aperture was much contracted, even so does the internal surface of the uterus in the doe enlarge, and become filled with a soft and pulpy substance, like the matter of the brain, that fills its cavity and involves the caruncles, which, though not larger than before, look whiter, and as if they had been steeped in hot water, much as the nurse's nipple appears immediately after the infant has quitted it. And now I have not found it possible by any compression to force blood out of the caruncles as before. Nothing can be softer, smoother, more delicate, than the inner aspect of the uterus thus raised into tubers. It rivals the ventricles of the brain in softness, so that without the information of the eye we should scarcely perceive by the finger that we were touching anything. When the abdomen is laid open immediately after the death of the animal, I have frequently seen the uterus affected with a wavy and creeping motion, such as is perceived in the lower part of a slug or snail whilst it is moving, as if the uterus were an animal within an animal, and possessed a proper and independent motion. . . .

Shortly afterwards, the tubercular elevations of the inner surface of the uterus that have been mentioned begin to shrink; it is as if, losing a quantity of moisture, they became less plump. . . .

Having frequently shown this alteration in the uterus to his majesty the king as the first indication of pregnancy, and satisfied him at the same time that there was nothing in the shape of semen or conception to be found in the cavity of the organ, and he had spoken of this as an extraordinary fact to several about him, a discussion at length arose: the keepers and huntsmen asserted at first that it was but an argument of a tardy conception occasioned by the want of rain. But by and by, when they saw the rutting season pass away, I still continuing to maintain that things were in the same state, they began to say that I was both deceived myself and had misled the king, and that there must of necessity be something of the conception to be found in the uterus. These men, however, when I got them to bring their own eyes to the inquiry, soon gave up the point. . . .

In the dog, rabbit, and several other animals, I have found nothing in the uterus for several days after intercourse. I therefore regard it as demonstrated that after fertile intercourse among viviparous as well as oviparous animals, there are no remains in the uterus either of the semen of the male or female emitted in the act, nothing produced by any mixture of these two fluids, as medical writers maintain, nothing of the menstrual blood present as 'matter' in the way Aristotle will have it; in a word, that there is not necessarily even a trace of the conception to be seen immediately after fruitful union of the sexes. It is not true, consequently, that in a prolific connexion there must be any prepared matter in the uterus which the semen masculinum, acting as a coagulating agent, should congeal, concoct, and fashion, or bring into a positive generative act, or by drying its outer surface, include in membranes. Nothing certainly is to be seen within the uterus of the doe for a great number of days, namely, from the middle of September up to the 12th of November. . . . (Harvey, William. "Anatomical exercises on the generation of animals, 1651." Pages 143-586 in: *The works of William Harvey,* translated by Robert Willis. London, Sydenham Society, 1847. xcvi, 624 pp. [pp. 235-238].)

Regner de Graaf
1641-1673

Regner de Graaf, whose earlier work on pancreatic juice (1664) has already been described, is even more celebrated for his later studies on the organs of reproduction of the human male (1668) and female (1672, Pl. 80). Several paragraphs from Dr. George W. Corner's translation of de Graaf's account of the human ovary and its follicles—"Graafian follicles"—follow (Pls. 81 & 82).

ON THE FEMALE TESTES OR OVARIES

[171] The testes of women differ much from those of the male as to position, form, size, substance, integuments, and function, as we are about to describe.

Thus, they have not an external position as in men, but are located in the lowest portion of the abdominal cavity about two finger breadths from each side of the fundus of the uterus, to which they are attached by a strong ligament which is called "Vas Deferens" by many anatomists, because they believed that semen was transferred through it from the testes to the uterus; on the other sides they are firmly attached to the peritoneum about the region of the iliac bone by the spermatic vessels, which supply them, and by the membranes with which the spermatic vessels are involved; so that the testes, fixed [172] on each side, as if suspended, reach about the same level as the fundus of the uterus in the non-pregnant; in the pregnant, however, although they follow the fundus of the uterus to some extent, they do not rise to an equal degree, and thus, the more the fundus of the uterus rises, the farther they are from it, always keeping a lower position.

The testicles are not suspended by any cremaster muscle, although some state this opinion, following Soranus. . . .

[181] We may assert confidently that eggs are found in all kinds of animals, since they may be observed not only in birds, in fishes, both oviparous and viviparous, but very clearly also in quadrupeds and even in man himself. Since it is known to everyone that eggs are found in birds and fishes, this needs no investigation; but also in rabbits, hares, dogs, swine, sheep, cows, and other animals which we have dissected, those structures similar to vesicles exhibit themselves to the eyes of the dissectors like the germs of eggs in birds. Occurring in the superficial part of the testicles, they push up the common tunic, [182] and sometimes shine through it, as if their exit from the testis is impending.

These ova differ much in animals of various kinds, for we have observed that in rabbits and hares they scarcely exceed the size of rape seeds; in swine and sheep they reach the size of a pea or larger; in cows they often exceed the size of a cherry. . . .

[186] Thus, the general function of the female testicles is to generate the ova, to nourish them, and to bring them to maturity, so that they serve the same purpose in women as the ovaries of birds. Hence, they should rather be called ovaries than testes because they show no similarity, either in form or contents, with the male testes properly so called. On this account, many have considered these bodies useless, but this is incorrect, because they are indispensable for reproduction. This is proved by the remarkable convolutions of the nutritive vessels about them, and is confirmed by the castration of females, which is invariably accompanied by sterility. . . . (De Graaf, Regner. *De mulierum organis generationi inservientibus tractatus novus demonstrans tam homines et animalia caetera omnia, quae vivipara dicuntur, haud minus quam ovipara ab ova originem ducere,* Leyden, 1672. Translated by George W. Corner, pp. 125-137 in *Essays in biology in honor of Herbert M. Evans.* Berkeley and Los Angeles, University of California Press, 1943. xxxi, 684 pp. [pp. 125, 128, 129-130].)

John Hunter
1728-1793

John Hunter, experimental physiologist and surgeon, is perhaps even better known as an anatomist, but while his elder brother William (1718-1783) gave to the world much new knowledge in the field of reproductive physiology through his incomparable monograph on the human gravid uterus (1774), John Hunter's work on the physiology of reproduction has been much less widely recognized. Forbes[10] draws attention to the fact that whereas Berthold's fundamental experiment demonstrating the endocrine function of the testes in birds (1849) is recognized as a classic, the fact that John Hunter successfully transplanted the testicles of a rooster is virtually unknown. This is probably for the good reason that his original notes on the subject were undoubtedly among those consigned to a bonfire by his jealous brother-in-law, Everard Home (1756-1832) after Hunter's death. In the first volume of Hunter's book, *The Natural History of the Human Teeth* . . , there occurs the following brief passage.

TRANSPLANTING TESTES

Taking off the young spur of a cock, and fixing it to his comb, is an old and well known experiment.

I have also frequently taken out the TESTIS of a cock and replaced it in his belly, where it had adhered, and has been nourished; nay, I have put the TESTIS of a cock into the belly of a hen with the same effect. (Hunter, J. *The natural history of the human teeth: Explaining their structure, use, formation, growth and diseases.* London, J. Johnson, 1771, 4 *ll.,* 128 pp., 8 *ll.,* 16 pl. [pp. 127-128].)

[10] Forbes, T. R. "Testis transplantations performed by John Hunter." *Endocrinology,* 1947, *11,* 329-331. The Historical Library, Yale University School of Medicine, has a volume of manuscript notes taken by William Tempest Mercer at the "Anatomical and Chirurgical Lectures read by Dr. William Hunter and Mr. William Cruikshank at their Anatomy Theatre in Windmill Street, Haymarket, London" in which it is stated (see page 249, lines 20-22): "John Hunter has cut yᵉ Testicles out of a Cock, & placed them in yᵉ belly of a Hen so as to grow there to yᵉ Liver, & by injecting yᵉ Vessels of yᵉ Liver he also injected the Testicles growing to it by its Vessels." Once again, therefore, we see Hunter's conviction that there might be sexual transformation as a result of male transplant into the avian female. See also H. Burrows' *Biological actions of sex hormones.* Cambridge University Press, 1945, pp. 106-107.

William Cumberland Cruikshank
1745-1800

The problem posed by Harvey's observations in deer that, for a period of time after mating there was no sign of any conceptus in the uterus, was solved by Cruikshank who showed in rabbits that there was an interval following mating when the fertilized ova were to be found in the Falloppian tubes. Later they would be moved into the uterus and there implanted.

EXPERIMENTS TO DISCOVER THE OVA OF RABBITS

In the beginning of summer 1778, I was conversing with Dr. HUNTER on this subject, and said, "I should like to repeat those experiments, now that lectures are over, and that I have the summer to myself." "You shall make the experiments," said he, "and I shall be at all the expence." Accordingly he carried me to Chelsea, introduced me to a man who kept a rabbit warren, and desired him to let me have as many rabbits as I pleased. I made the experiments; and shall now lay a copy of my journal, then made, before this Society. . . .

Opened another rabbit at the end of the third day: same appearance as in Exp. XX.: searched in vain for the ova on the right side; at last, by drawing a probe gently over the fallopian tube on the left side, before it was opened, more than an inch on the side next the uterus, I pressed out several ova, which seemed to come from about its middle, as I began the pressure there, and the ova did not appear till the very last; the amnion made a centre spot, and appeared small compared to the chorion; no ova in the uterus. . . .

Opened one the third day all but two hours: found six ova in one fallopian tube, and seven in the other, which corresponded exactly to the number of *corpora lutea* in each ovarium; the ova had three membranes as before. The circles in the cicatricula of the hen's egg are perhaps similar to these. The ova seem to enlarge in their way down the tube, as a pea swells in the ground before it begins to take root; even in the uterus, for two days, the ova of rabbits were found in the fallopian tubes; and in the fourth day after impregnation they are either loose and unconnected by vessels, or the vessels are so small as not to be discovered by the microscope. The *corpora lutea* were flatter on the head than I had ever seen them before. . . .

1st. The ovum is formed in, and comes out of the ovarium after conception.

2dly. It passes down the fallopian tube, and is some days in coming through it.

3dly. It is sometimes detained in the fallopian tube, and prevented from getting into the uterus.

4thly. DE GRAAF saw one ovum only in the fallopian tube, "in oviductus dextri medio *unum!*" I saw thirteen in one instance, five in another, seven in another, and three in another, in all twenty-eight.

5thly. The ovum comes into the uterus on the fourth day. (Cruikshank, William. "Experiments in which on the third day after impregnation, the ova of rabbits were found in the fallopian tubes; and on the fourth day after impregnation in the uterus itself; with the first appearances of the foetus." *Phil. Trans.*, 1797, *87*, 197-214 [pp. 199, 208, 209-210, 211].)

Arnold Adolph Berthold
1803-1861

Arnold Adolph Berthold, earliest among the German investigators of sex hormones, is responsible for establishing that transplantation of the rooster's testicles to another part of the body prevented atrophy of the cock's comb which ordinarily follows castration. In having done this, he may be regarded as the earliest to establish the existence of a gonadal internal secretion.

THE TRANSPLANTATION OF TESTES

These experiments provide the following general conclusions for physiology:

1. The testes may be termed transplantable organs for they were found to heal again after they were removed from the abdomen. The testes may even be transplanted from one individual into another and healing will occur both at the place from which the testes have been removed and also at the quite unusual place [where they have been implanted] at the walls of the intestines.

2. The transplanted testis developed even at a quite different place into its characteristic form as a seminal organ; the seminal canal became broadened and enlarged to fulfill its normal function

while it secreted a quite normal semen characterized by sperma-
tozoans. We find here exactly the same relationship as in plants
where the graft scion develops into its specific character upon
the wild stock and bears fruit corresponding not to the wild
stock but to itself.

3. It is a known fact that severed nerves again grow together and
that in the parts whose nerves have been cut through, sensation
and movement again return following healing. However, the fact
that in such healing the individual nerve fibres cannot always
grow together often arises from the circumstance that a piece of
skin is shifted from one position in the body to another. From
the growth of the excised testis at an entirely different place in
the body, namely to the gut where the testis develops vigorously
as a semen-producing organ and actually prepares semen, it also
follows that there are no specific semen nerves, and this is a
strong argument against the assumption of certain trophic nerves
among which the sympathetic nervous system has been considered in very recent times.

4. The remarkable interdependent and antagonistic relationship
between the life of the individual and that of the species which
manifests itself especially at the time of puberty and continues
through more advanced years is also not lacking when the testes
are separated from their original position and from their nerves
and allowed to heal on at a quite different place in the body. In
the sound of the voice, the sexual instinct, the desire for territory, the growth of the comb, and the neck flaps such an animal
remains a genuine rooster. Since, however, when the testes are
transplanted to a strange place they can no longer remain in
connection with their original nerves, it is therefore clear from
this fact that the nerves give no specific secretion, so it follows
that the interaction in question is exerted through the productive relationship of the testes, that is, through their action on the
blood and next through a consequent action of the blood on the
organism as a whole of which, to be sure, the nervous system
forms a very substantial part. (Berthold, A. A. "Transplantation
der Hoden." *Arch. Anat. Physiol. wiss. Med.*, 1849, 42-46 [pp. 44-
46. Translated by L.G.W.].)

Charles Edouard Brown-Séquard
1817-1894

Charles E. Brown-Séquard, the French-American neurophysiologist, endocrinologist, and clinician, looms large in the history of medicine during the nineteenth century. A picturesque figure who found himself as much at home in the United States as he did in his native island of Mauritius and in France, or wherever his restless nature took him, he always proved a stimulating teacher. He was a man of omnivorous curiosity whose mind, at times uncritical and never fully disciplined, was ever seaching for new truths. In 1856 he proved that excision of both adrenal glands invariably proved fatal, which led to the obvious conclusion that they were indispensable for life. And there is no question but that he was responsible for drawing fresh attention to the importance of the internal secretions.

Less creditable, perhaps, was Brown-Séquard's enthusiastic espousal of the notion that sexual powers of the aging human male could be restored and a man "rejuvenated" through injection of testicular extract. His obviously sincere and abiding conviction concerning the alleged favorable effect of such injections stemmed from having tried it on himself in 1889 when he had reached the age of seventy-two, five years prior to his death. The phrase "male sex hormone" came to be introduced as a result of these studies. It was to be expected that his extravagant claims would evoke a skeptical reaction. The controversy which followed did much to stimulate serious research in the field of sex hormones, and when the male hormone was obtained in more pure state by Carl R. Moore *et al.* in 1929, many of Brown-Séquard's original claims were, in fact, vindicated. It was Moore and his colleagues who introduced the term "testosterone." Adolph F. J. Butenandt must be given credit for having been the first (1931) to isolate the male sex hormone in crystalline form. For this he was awarded the Nobel Prize in chemistry in 1939.

Brown-Séquard also conducted early studies of the vasomotor system in which on many points he anticipated the work of Claude Bernard. Thus, in 1852, he noted that stimulation of the cervical sympathetic chain evoked contractions of the small vessels of the rabbit's ear accompanied by a fall of temperature where a simple section of the sympathetic trunk led to vasomotor paralysis, dilatation, and increased temperature of the ear. Although known to endocrinologists for his studies on testicular extract, students of experimental neurology hold as classic a series of detailed studies on the effects of circumscribed lesions of the spinal cord on sensation and motor power. He observed that when a lateral hemi-section of the cord is performed, there follows the so-called "Brown-Séquard paralysis" characterized by loss of motor power and position sense on the side of the lesion, with loss of pain and thermal sensibility on the side opposite to the lesion. This work, which led to publication of many preliminary notes, culminated in a monographic report published in 1863 in three installments to be found in the Paris *Journal de Physiologie*. See also his first report on this subject, "De la transmission croisée des impressions sensitives par la moelle épinière" *(C.R. Soc. Biol. (Paris), 1850, 2, 33-34).*

EXPERIMENT DEMONSTRATING THE DYNAMOGENIC POWER IN MAN OF AN EXTRACT OF THE TESTICLES OF ANIMALS

Last first of June I sent to the Society of Biology a communication, which was followed by several others, showing the remarkable effects produced on myself by the subcutaneous injection of a liquid obtained by the maceration on a mortar of the testicle of a dog or of a guinea pig to which one has added a little water.

. . . V. I wrote what follows during last June: "I hope that other physiologists of advanced age will repeat these experiments and will show whether the effects which I have obtained on myself depend on my personal idiosyncrasy or not. As for the question of knowing whether it is a kind of auto-suggestion without hypnotism to which must be attributed entirely the very considerable changes which have been produced in my body, I do not wish to discuss that today. The very interesting work of Dr. Hack Tuke *(Illustrations of the influence of the mind upon the body* 2nd edit., London, 1884, 2 vol.) is full of facts showing that most of the changes which I observed myself, after the injections which I made, can be produced by the mere influence of an idea on the human body. In the account which I shall give now (in this number) of a considerable number of cases in which injections similar to mine have been given, without the individuals concerned knowing that we were seeking to learn whether they would increase in strength, this result has been obtained. It is therefore clear that it is not as the result of a kind of auto-suggestion that the vigour of the nerve centres is increased and that it is in fact to a particular action of the injected liquid that this effect is due." (Brown-Séquard, C. E.: "Expérience démontrant la puissance dynamogénique chez l'homme d'un liquide extrait de testicules d'animaux. *Arch. Physiol. norm. path.,* 1889, 5 sér.-*1*, 651-658 [pp. 651, 658. Translation by L.G.W.].)

Walter Lee Gaines

1881-

Walter Lee Gaines was born at Crete, Illinois, and was educated at the University of Illinois (B.S. 1908) and the University of Chicago where he received his Ph.D. in 1915. From 1918 until his retirement he was professor of milk production at the University of Illinois.

THE OXYTOCIC FUNCTION OF THE PITUITARY

The flow of milk from an active mammary gland, which has not been drained for a few hours, upon injection of pituitrin is a very striking reaction. In the goat I have never failed to secure some flow of milk from its use even immediately after milking "dry." The amount obtained, however, varies considerably. . . .

The intravenous injection of pituitrin immediately following a regular milking produces a further flow varying in amount inversely with the yield secured by the hand milking which preceded it. That is, injection of pituitrin following a relatively high yield of milk produces a small flow; and following a relatively low yield it produces a large flow. A second, third or fourth dose produces only a very slight flow, 2-4 cc. in the goat.

I have followed the yield of milk in the nursing dog very satisfactorily by keeping the pups separated from the mother and allowing them to nurse at 8-hour intervals (Fig. 12). The pups were balanced on a smooth-working balance, with shot, then allowed to nurse, and again balanced with the standard weights. The increase in weight represents approximately the yield of milk by the mother.

Under the above conditions, after the pups have nursed fully (6 or 7 minutes), I have never succeeded in producing any further flow of milk by the intravenous injection of pituitrin. But if the mother be placed under ether at the regular nursing hour and the pups then allowed to nurse the yield of milk is greatly depressed, although the pups do their part of the act in the usual vigorous manner. Often, in fact usually, the yield is so low as not to be detectable by the method used (that is, it appears, well under 5 gms., considering errors in loss of saliva, etc.). If, now, pituitrin be injected intravenously, with the mother still under ether, the pups immediately secure the normal

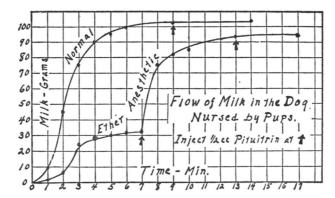

Fig. 2. Showing failure of pituitrin to cause a flow of milk following normal nursing in the dog; and, its restoral of the flow normal to the stimulus of nursing when the normal flow is inhibited by anesthesia; and, the failure of a second dose to cause any further flow. Also, showing under the stimulus of normal nursing the latent period in the flow of milk during the first minute, followed by the very rapid flow for the next two minutes, and then the gradual decline to zero (cf. figs. 4–8).

Figure 12. Yield of milk in the nursing dog.

yield, or the balance of it which they had failed to get in the first nursing, and this, in rather less time than is required in nursing under normal conditions. A second dose following the first in 10 minutes, produces no further flow. . . .

The form of the curves showing the effect of pituitrin on an active, air-inflated mammary gland shows a muscular response. The relatively rapid rise of pressure as expressive of a contraction of the milk passages, followed by the slow decline as expressive of a relaxation is characteristic of the response of smooth muscle. . . . (Gaines, W. L. "A contribution to the physiology of lactation." *Amer. J. Physiol.*, 1915, *38*, 285-312 [pp. 293, 306-307].)

Charles Rupert Stockard
1879-1939
and
George Nicholas Papanicolaou
1883-1962

Charles Rupert Stockard of Washington County, Mississippi, was educated at the Mississippi Agricultural and Mechanical College at State College (B.S.

1899) and at Columbia University (Ph.D. 1907). In 1906 he joined the faculty of the Cornell University Medical College at New York where from 1911 until his death he was professor of anatomy.

George Nicholas Papanicolaou was born at Coumi, Greece, and educated at the Universities of Athens (M.D. 1904) and Munich (Ph.D. 1910). In 1913 he came to the United States and a year later joined the Department of Anatomy of Cornell University Medical College. He was appointed professor of clinical anatomy in 1924 and Emeritus professor in 1950. Papanicolaou is today best known for his development of the "Pap" smear test for uterine cancer which is based on the cytological examination of cells exfoliated from the uterus. The widespread use of this test since 1947 has saved the lives of thousands of women because it has permitted detection of their cancers at an early stage when treatment is most effective.

In 1917 Stockard and Papanicolaou applied similar cytological methods in their pioneer study of the oestrous cycle in the guinea pig. They thereby established criteria for the determination of the various phases of this cycle in animals whose sexual rhythm was otherwise obscure. They were also to determine the precise time of ovulation in the guinea pig from the cellular picture given by a vaginal smear. Thus, whereas Marshall in 1910 had considered it impossible to determine the prooestrous condition in rodents, the application of the vaginal smear method developed by Stockard and Papanicolaou resulted in the working out of the oestrous cycle in the rat by Long and Evans in 1920, in the mouse by Allen in 1922, and in the monkey by Corner in 1923. We have here, therefore, an example of the impact of cytological methods upon both physiology and medicine.

THE OESTROUS CYCLE IN THE GUINEA PIG

. . . Recognizing, on the other hand, that no thorough investigation of the uterus and vagina in the living female had been made, it occurred to us that possible oestrous changes might take place even though they are so feebly expressed as not to be noticeable on casual observation. The absence of an apparent oestrous or prooestrous flow from the vagina of the guinea-pig has, as before mentioned, no doubt been the chief reason for the general lack of knowledge of the oestrous cycle. It was therefore determined to make a minute examination of the contents of the vaginae of a number of females every day for a long period of time, to ascertain whether a feeble flow might exist although insufficient in quantity to be noticed at the vaginal orifice or vulva.

The observations were made by using a small nasal speculum which was introduced into the vagina and the arms opened apart by means of the thumb screw. The speculum permits an examination of the entire surface of the vaginal canal. In this way the vaginae of a number of virgin females have been examined daily and smears made from the substances that happened to be present in the lumen.

By use of such a simple method, it was readily determined after examining the first lot of animals for a few months that a definite sexual period occurs lasting for about twenty-four hours and returning with a striking regularity every fifteen or sixteen days. During this twenty-four hour period the vagina contains an abundant fluid which is for about the first half of the time of a mucous consistency. The vaginal fluid then changes into a thick and cheese-like substance which finally becomes slowly liquified and serous. This thin fluid exists for a few hours and then disappears. Occasionally toward the end of the process a slight trace of blood may be present giving the fluid a bloody red appearance, otherwise it is milk-white or cream-color.

According to the changes in appearance and consistency of the vaginal fluid, one may distinguish four different stages. The first stage having a mucous secretion, a second stage the cheese-like secretion, a third stage with the fluid becoming serous and a fourth stage, not always recognized, during which a bloody discharge is present. The duration of these several stages is subject in the different animals to individual variations. The first stage, however, is generally longest and lasts from six to twelve hours or even more and during this time there is a gradually increasing quantity of the mucous secretion which at its height is very abundant and fills the entire lumen of the vagina. The second stage is shorter, lasting from two to four hours, and passes gradually over into the third stage which lasts from four to six hours. The fourth stage is the shortest, only about one to two hours long, and for this reason it is often missed in examining the animals during the periods. It is also possible, as mentioned above, that the fourth stage may not typically exist in all individuals and the quantity of blood present is very different in the different specimens. The succession in which these stages follow one another is remarkably definite. We have never observed any change in the typical sequence of the stages and the time consumed by the entire process is generally as stated about twenty-four hours. . . .

A microscopical examination of the smears prepared from the vaginal fluid taken at the several stages separated above shows decidedly typical differences. The cellular character of a smear made at a given stage differs from the cellular make-up of all other stages. The relative numbers of various cell types in the fluid at different stages

are so definite that one with a little experience may diagnose the
exact sexual stage of the animal concerned solely by an examination
of the smear. . . .

A study of the ovaries fixed during different stages of the oestrous
cycle has shown that every change taking place in the uterus and the
vagina has its corresponding stage of change in the ovary. At the beginning of the first stage the ovaries possess large, ripe follicles. . . .
The nuclei of the eggs contained in the follicles are in a resting condition. The theca folliculi shows the beginning of a slight congestion. As the first stage advances this congestion becomes more and
more pronounced and by the beginning of the second stage it is
highly developed. . . . This extreme congestion of the theca folliculi,
which exist at about the same time as the congestion stage in the uterus . . indicates that the follicle is ready for rupture. Heape has
pointed out that the rupture of the follicle is due to this congestion
and if the ovarian blood supply be tied off follicles do not rupture.
During this time the nucleus of the egg is still in a resting condition.

The ripe follicles break at about the end of the second or the beginning of the third stage. . . . (Stockard, Charles R. and Papanicolaou, George N. "The existence of a typical oestrous cycle in the guinea pig—with a study of its histological and physiological changes."
Amer. J. Anat., 1917, 22, 225-265 [pp. 236-237, 238, 249-250].

Edgar Allen
1892-1943
and
Edward Adelbert Doisy
1893-

Edgar Allen was born at Canon City, Colorado, and attended Brown University where he was graduated Ph.B. in 1915 and Ph.D. in 1921. From 1923
to 1933 he was professor of anatomy at the University of Missouri, but in the
latter year he moved to the Yale University School of Medicine where he remained as professor of anatomy until his premature death.

Edward Adelbert Doisy of Hume, Illinois, was educated at the University
of Illinois (A.B. 1914) and Harvard University (Ph.D. 1920). In 1923 he was
appointed professor of biochemistry at the St. Louis University School of
Medicine where he has since remained. In 1943 Doisy shared the Nobel Prize
with Henrik Dam for his isolation of vitamin K from alfalfa.

In 1923 Allen and Doisy demonstrated that the ovarian follicles exerted their influence upon oestrus through the production of a hormone and thereby initiated the long series of investigations which was ultimately to reveal the complex pattern of hormonal control in the oestral cycle and pregnancy. In 1927 Allen showed that the onset of menstruation in the monkey resulted from a deficiency of follicular hormone and that in the spayed monkey oestrus could be induced by injections of this same hormone.

AN OVARIAN HORMONE

Our first experiments were carried out with liquor folliculi from hog ovaries, which are a readily available source for the isolation of the contents of the follicles. Since the estrual cycle in the sow is of three weeks' duration, and large follicles are present in the ovaries during only a part of this time, only one in every three or four ovaries is a profitable source of liquor folliculi. A selection is made of ovaries containing follicles larger than 5 mm. in diameter. The follicular contents (liquor folliculi, follicle cells and occasional ova are aspirated through a hypodermic needle into a suction bottle. At least 100 c.c. of readily workable material can be obtained from one pound of carefully selected ovaries.

In the first series of experiments, nine mice and rats were prepared for use as test animals by double ovariectomy. A week later they were given three injections at intervals of five hours of liquor folliculi aspirated from large follicles. These injections were made subcutaneously with the expectation that slow absorption from this region would be more closely comparable to the secretion of the hormone in normal animals. From forty to forty-eight hours after the first injection, all of the animals receiving liquor folliculi were in full estrus, as determined by microscopic examination of the smears. As a check on these results, the animals were killed and the uterus and vagina of each studied histologically. They were in a typical estrual condition as described for these rodents. . . .(Allen, Edgar and Doisy, E. A. "An ovarian hormone: preliminary report on its localization, extraction and partial purification, and action in test animals." *J. Amer. med. Ass.*, 1923, *81*, 819-821 [p.820.]

Philip Edward Smith
1884-

One of the most widely used tools of investigation in endocrinology and reproductive physiology today is the hypophysectomized rat, and this animal we owe to P. E. Smith (Pl. 83). But Smith did more than perfect an immensely useful though difficult technique; at the same time he showed that transplants of the anterior pituitary were capable of restoring the functions which had been atrophied by hypophysectomy. Smith and Engle also showed that anterior pituitary transplants into immature female rats and mice produced a very rapid and precocious development of the genital system.

Philip Edward Smith was born at DeSmet, South Dakota, and educated at Pomona College, Pomona, California (B.S. 1908) and at Cornell where he received his Ph.D. in anatomy in 1912. From 1912 until 1926 he taught anatomy at the University of California. Then, after a year at Stanford University, he was appointed professor of anatomy in the College of Physicians and Surgeons, Columbia University, where he remained until his retirement in 1952 when he became Emeritus professor. Since 1956 he has been a research associate at Stanford University.

THE PITUITARY SYNDROME

Hypophysectomy in the rat gives an invariable syndrome, the main features of which are: an almost complete inhibition in growth in the young animal, and a progressive loss of weight (cachexia) in the adult; an atrophy of the genital system with loss of libido sexualis, and in the female an immediate cessation of the sex cycles; an atrophy of the thyroids, parathyroids and suprarenal cortex; and a general physical impairment characterized by a lowered resistance to operative procedures, loss of appetite, weakness and a flabbiness that readily distinguishes the hypophysectomized from the normal animal [Pl. 84]. It seems unlikely that they can live an average life span.

Attempts carried on for the last three years to secure a successful replacement therapy have proved successful as regards all the disabilities arising from hypophysectomy only when the fresh living hypophyseal tissue was administered. The gland material, secured from adult rats, was transplanted intramuscularly. Cushing and his co-workers have reported that pituitary transplantation prolonged the life of their hypophysectomized dogs.

The response to daily transplants is immediate and striking. Within two or three days the treated dwarf assumes a normal rate of growth. In the female, estrus occurs invariably in from five to seven days, the uterus changing from its atrophic, threadlike, pale appearance to the estrua type, and examinations of this organ at later periods reveal a normal organ in either the estrous or the diestrous stage. The ovaries become usually as large as or larger than normal and show many follicles and corpora lutea. In the male the testes, which invariably become much atrophied following hypophysectomy, weighing only 0.15 Gm. or even less, will after treatment for a few weeks increase in weight to a normal size, and be not distinguishable from the gland in the unoperated control. . . . These males will mate and normal litters result, though previous to the treatment they displayed no interest in an estrous female. The same repair is effected in mature as in the younger animals.

These transplants also induce reparative phenomena in the thyroid and suprarenal cortex, so that they appear structurally normal. However, they usually remain somewhat underweight, though in several animals they have become normal in size. Parabiosis assists their repair. . . . (Smith, Philip E. "The disabilities caused by hypophysectomy and their repair." *J. Amer. med. Ass.*, 1927, *88*, 158-161 [pp. 158-159].)

George Washington Corner
1889-
and
Willard Myron Allen
1904-

George Washington Corner was born at Baltimore, Maryland, and took both his A.B. and M.D. degrees at Johns Hopkins University in 1909 and 1913 respectively. His particular interest lay in anatomy and embryology, and in 1923 he became professor of anatomy at the University of Rochester where he remained until 1940 when he was appointed director of the department of embryology of the Carnegie Institution of Washington. In 1956 he retired from the Carnegie Institution. From 1956 to 1960 he was historian at the Rockefeller Institute and since 1959 has been Executive Officer of the American Philosophical Society. He is the author of many books and, as the following extract will illustrate, an important contributor to our knowledge of the physiology of reproduction.

Willard Myron Allen was born at Macedon, New York, and educated at Hobart College and the University of Rochester where he took his M.D. in 1932. After graduation he continued as a research fellow and member of the faculty at the University of Rochester School of Medicine until 1940 when he moved to the Washington University School of Medicine at St. Louis as professor of obstetrics and gynecology. While he was still a medical student, Dr. Allen collaborated with Dr. Corner in the work described below.

EXTRACTS OF CORPUS LUTEUM

[p. 338] The experiments described in this paper show that alcoholic extracts of the corpus luteum, freed from phospholipids, contain a substance which when injected into castrated adult female rabbits induces a characteristic alteration of the endometrium identical with the progestational proliferation previously shown to be due to the presence of corpora lutea in the ovaries. A similar effect is sometimes but not always produced in immature rabbits 8 to 12 weeks old. Extracts of follicular fluid containing large amounts of oestrin do not produce progestational proliferation, nor have extracts of human placenta given positive results. It appears, therefore, that the extracts of corpus luteum contain a special hormone which has for one of its functions the preparation of the uterus for reception of the embryos by inducing progestational proliferation of the endometrium.

[p. 326] Among the numerous functions attributed to the corpus luteum, the best attested is that based upon the work of Fraenkel, Loeb, Ancel and Bouin, and others. The results of this work indicate that following ovulation and formation of the corpus luteum the endometrium undergoes histological changes leading to the production of a special state, which may be called progestational proliferation. In this state the uterus becomes enlarged and hyperemic; its epithelium, both superficial and glandular, undergoes mitotic proliferation, and the crypts and glands increase their complexity of ramification until in cross-section a very characteristic picture is produced. This condition occurs only in the presence of recent corpora lutea in the ovaries and can be prevented if both ovaries or all the corpora lutea are removed soon after ovulation (Bouin and Ancel). At the same period of the reproductive cycle the endometrium of certain mammals is known to be in a special condition by which placentation is facilitated, since it responds even to traumatic injury by producing decidual tissue at the site of stimulation; this reaction is prevented by removal of the corpora lutea soon after ovulation (Loeb). Finally, if both ovaries or all the corpora lutea of pregnant rabbits are removed at any time during the first week of pregnancy, implantation does not occur, and the embryos are lost (Fraenkel). (Corner, G. W. and Allen, W. M. "Physiology of the corpus luteum. II. Production of a special uterine reaction [progestational proliferation] by extracts of the corpus luteum." *Amer. J. Physiol.*, 1929, *88*, 321-339 [pp. 338, 326].)

Harry Leonard Fevold,

1902-

Frederick Lee Hisaw

1891-

and

Samuel Leeson Leonard

1905-

A native of Iowa, *Harry Leonard Fevold* was educated at St. Olaf College, Northfield, Minnesota, and the University of Wisconsin where he took his Ph.D. in chemistry in 1928. He remained at Wisconsin as a research associate until he went to Harvard University in 1935. Later he became a research chemist with the United States Department of Agriculture and ultimately with the Baxter Laboratories.

Frederick Lee Hisaw was born at Newtonia, Missouri, and attended both the University of Missouri and the University of Wisconsin, where he received a Ph.D. in zoology in 1924. He stayed at Wisconsin to teach, but in 1935 was appointed Fisher Professor of Natural History at Harvard University and remained there until retirement.

Samuel Leeson Leonard of Elizabeth, New Jersey, was educated at Rutgers University and the University of Wisconsin (Ph.D. 1931) where as a graduate student he assisted Hisaw.

The work of Fevold, Hisaw, and Leonard began from the fact that P. E. Smith had demonstrated a direct influence of the anterior pituitary upon the ovaries. The hormones, whose individual existence they demonstrated, were only to be isolated much later and after great progress had been made in the techniques of protein chemistry. The electrophoresis technique announced by Tiselius in 1937 proved especially valuable in their isolation. The luteinizing hormone (LH), also known as the interstitial-cell-stimulating hormone (ICSH), was isolated in 1940 by Li, Simpson, and Evans and the follicle-stimulating hormone was not isolated until 1949 by the same team of workers. It is of course important to remember that the reality of these hormones as individual entities was subject to question until they were isolated as pure substances.

THE DISCOVERY OF THE FOLLICLE-STIMULATING HORMONE (FSH) AND THE INTERSTITIAL-CELL-STIMULATING HORMONE (ICSH)

The evidence for the secretion of two distinct hormones by the anterior lobe of the hypophysis, namely, a growth hormone and a hormone functioning as a gonad stimulator, seems to be rather definite. On the other hand, while various authors have put forth the idea that there are two different hormones secreted by this gland, which act on the ovary, still no very definite evidence is at hand proving this contention. . . .

In this paper we wish to present definite evidence for the presence of two distinct anterior lobe hormones which promote follicular and lutein development in the ovary. One of these is the gonad stimulating hormone which causes precocious sexual maturity when injected into immature rats. Its primary function seems to be the stimulation of follicular activity in the ovary. The second is the luteinizing hormone which alone cannot affect the ovaries of an immature animal. It does, however, cause luteinization of the follicles which are produced by the gonad stimulator. These two hormones have been extracted quantitatively from dried pituitary glands and have been separated from each other in two fractions. Each of the two preparations produces a different effect from the original whole extract, but when they are again united a preparation is obtained which is entirely similar to the original. . . .

The physiological activities of the anterior lobe fractions were determined by their effects on the reproductive tract of immature female rats, twenty to twenty-five days of age. The chief criteria used were the ability of the extracts to produce follicular and lutein development in the ovaries and opening of the vaginal orifice. . . .

If the gonad stimulating hormone is injected for two days and the animals are killed on the fifth day the animal comes to sexual maturity on the third day as usual, but at autopsy the increase in the weight of the ovary is very slight, and the anatomical changes in the ovary are likewise much less pronounced than if the injections are continued for five days. If, however, the injections of the gonad stimulating hormone are followed by the luteinizing hormone for two days and the animals are killed at the end of five days, the ovary shows a marked change. Corpora lutea are present but the most noticeable change is the presence of numerous "blutpunkte." In some cases these are so numerous that the entire ovary is entirely red. The production of the "blutpunkte" described by Zondek evidently is caused by the action of the luteinizing hormone on the developing follicles. . . .

The experimental results which have been presented would seem to lead to only one conclusion, namely, that there are two separate hormones, elaborated by the anterior lobe of the hypophysis, which affect the ovary, one of which promotes follicular development and the other growth of the corpora lutea. The aqueous pyridine removes these hormones from the gland quantitatively since the residue after extraction is inactive while the extract is equally as active as the emulsified pituitary powder before extraction. We have, therefore, removed the active principles without injuring them in any way. The water soluble preparation contains all of the gonad stimulating hormone and is equally as potent in bringing about sexual maturity as is the whole pyridine extract. It contains at the most only small amounts of the luteinizing hormone. The luteinizing principle is present in the water insoluble, but alkali soluble, part of the pyridine extract associated with very little or none of the gonad stimulating hormone.

As a rule the luteinizing hormone cannot act on the ovaries of immature rats as is evidenced by the fact that no change occurs when such animals are treated with this fraction. However, a small corpus luteum or two may occasionally form in the ovaries of rats so treated, but the vaginas do not open, the uterus remains infantile and there is no increase in the weight of ovaries over those of the control animals. If the ovaries are first stimulated to follicular growth by means of the gonad stimulating hormone, and then treated with the luteinizing hormone, the follicles become luteinized and a typical mulberry ovary is produced. It is, therefore, a one-two reaction which must take place in the order which has been designated. . . .

The gonad stimulating hormone which we have obtained from the pituitary gland would seem to be identical with Zondek and Ascheim's Prolan A. which they have prepared from urine. The physiological and chemical properties which have been determined for the active material are the same in every respect. Prolan A. produces only follicular growth with no luteinization when injected into immature rats or mice for two days and the animals are killed on the fifth day. This is also true when our preparation is used. . . .(Fevold, H. L., Hisaw, F. L., and Leonard, S. L. "The gonad stimulating and the luteinizing hormones of the anterior lobe of the hypophysis." *Amer. J. Physiol.*, 1931, 97, 291-301 [pp. 291-292, 294, 297-299].)

Oscar Riddle,
1877-
Robert Wesley Bates
1904-
and
Simon William Dykshorn
1903-1932

Oscar Riddle was born and educated in Indiana and at the University of Chicago, receiving his Ph.D. in zoology in 1907. In 1912 he joined the Carnegie Institution where he remained until his retirement in 1945. Much of his work was carried out at their Station for Experimental Evolution at Cold Spring Harbor, Long Island.

A native of Iowa, *Robert Wesley Bates* attended Simpson College, Indianola, Iowa, and the University of Chicago where he took his Ph.D. in physiological chemistry in 1931. The same year he went to Cold Spring Harbor where he collaborated with Riddle in the work presented here.

Also from Iowa, *Simon William Dykshorn* was graduated from Hope College, Holland, Michigan, in 1927 and as a graduate student under Riddle had shared in the exciting discovery of the lactogenic hormone just before his tragic death in a hunting accident.

The discovery in 1928 by Stricker and Grueter that extracts of the anterior pituitary were capable of stimulating the formation of milk in the mammary gland was followed quickly by the work of Riddle and Braucher in 1931 who showed that extracts of the anterior pituitary also could cause the enlargement and functioning of the crop-glands of pigeons. Riddle and his co-workers went on to prepare an extract which would be free of the growth- and gonad-stimulating principles then known to be present in the anterior pituitary. In 1932 they succeeded and concluded that they had found a third anterior pituitary hormone to which, since it was responsible for lactation in mammals, they gave the name "prolactin." In a second paper they reported their results more fully, and we have chosen our selection from this paper. Since prolactin or lactogenic hormone is, like the other pituitary hormones, a protein, its purification raised many difficulties and it was obtained as a crystalline protein only in

GABRIELIS FALLOPPII

MEDICI MVTINENSIS

OBSERVATIONES
Anatomicæ.

AD PETRVM MANNAM
medicum Cremonenſem.

Cum Priuilegio Summi Pontificis,
Regis Philippi, Senatusq́ue
Veneti.

VENETIIS.

Apud Marcum Antonium Vlmum
M D LXI.

PLATE 78. Title-page of Falloppio's *Observationes anatomicae* (Venice, 1561.)

Gulielmus Harveus
de
Generatione Animalium.

PLATE 79. The engraved and the printed title-pages of Harvey's work on generation, 1651.

EXERCITATIONES
DE
Generatione Animalium.

Quibus accedunt quædam
De Partu : de Membranis ac humoribus Uteri :
& de Conceptione.

AUTORE
GVILIELMO HARVEO
Anglo, in Collegio Medicorum *Londi-*
nensium Anatomes & Chirurgiæ Professore.

LONDINI,
Typis Du-Gardianis ; impensis *Octaviani*
Pulleyn in Cœmeterio *Paulino.*
M. DC. LI.

REGNERI DE GRAAF

DE

MULIERUM
ORGANIS

GENERATIONI
INSERVIENTIBUS

TRACTATUS NOVUS:

DEMONSTRANS

Tam Homines & Animalia cætera omnia,
quæ Vivipara dicuntur, haud minus quàm
Ovipara ab Ovo originem ducere.

AD

COSMUM III.

MAGNUM ETRURIÆ DUCEM.

LVGDVNI BATAV.
Ex Officinâ **HACKIANA,** 1672.

PLATE 80. Title-page of de Graaf's treatise on the organs of
generation in woman (Leyden, 1672.)

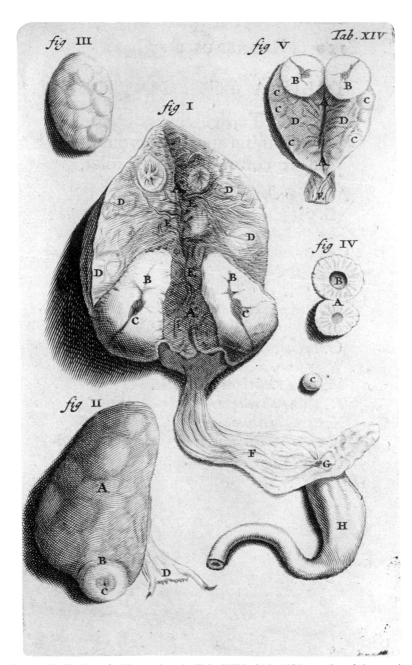

PLATE 81. De Graaf's illustrations in Tab. XIV of his 1672 treatise of the ovaries of the cow and sheep, designed to indicate what takes place in them after coitus. Fig. 1. The ovaries of a cow. Fig. 2. Unopened ovary. Fig. 3. Ovary of a sheep with transparent follicles. Fig. 4. An intact follicle removed from the ovary of a sheep. Fig. 5. Ovary of sheep with a burst follicle.

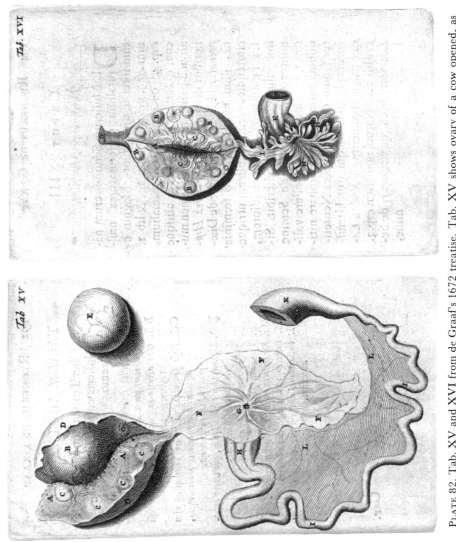

PLATE 82. Tab. XV and XVI from de Graaf's 1672 treatise. Tab. XV shows ovary of a cow opened, as observed before coitus. Tab. XVI depicts the ovary of a woman, with the end of the tube attached.

PLATE 83. Philip E. Smith, photographed in his laboratory in 1930. (Kindness of Dr. Smith.)

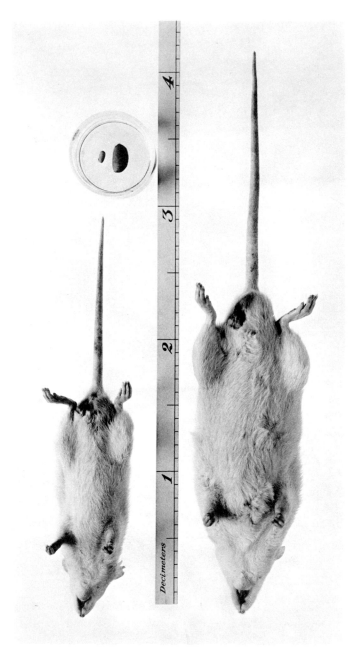

PLATE 84. Smith's demonstration of control by the anterior pituitary of growth and sexual development. Littermate brothers
showing comparative size of testes of control and dwarf three
months after hypophysectomy. Reported by Harvey Cushing
(*Brit. med. J.*, 2 and 9 July 1927.)

1942 by White, Bonsnes and Long, although Lyons had earlier obtained an amorphous product of essentially the same degree of purity and biological activity.

THE DISCOVERY OF LACTOGENIC HORMONE

The effective stimulus to milk secretion in the prepared mammary gland is neither the growth nor the gonad-stimulating (maturity) pituitary principle. This stimulus is provided by a hitherto unidentified anterior pituitary hormone for which the name "prolactin" is proposed.

The effective stimulus to a specific enlargement and functioning ("crop-milk" formation) of the crop-gland in doves and pigeons is neither the growth nor the gonad-stimulating (and thyroid-stimulating) pituitary principle; neither is it obtained in detectable quantity from other tissues or fluids than the anterior pituitary. This stimulus is provided by the same anterior pituitary hormone which excites lactation in mammals.

Other specific actions of the hormone are at present unknown. The hormone is shown to be effective after castration or hypophysectomy. Prolactin has no specific power to enlarge thyroids in doves and pigeons.

Prolactin can be prepared from beef, sheep and hog anterior lobes by either acid or alkaline extraction followed by procedures described in this paper. It can be made quite free of gonad-stimulating and thyroid-stimulating action, and probably largely free of active growth hormone. Other apparently inert substance is doubtless present with the hormone as now prepared since 0.2 mgm. is the minimal quantity capable of giving a definite response. (Riddle, Oscar, Bates, Robert W., and Dykshorn, Simon W. "The preparation, identification and assay of prolactin—a hormone of the anterior pituitary." *Amer. J. Physiol.*, 1933, *105*, 191-216 [p. 215].)

Bernhard Zondek

1891-

Bernhard Zondek, German gynecologist and obstetrician, was born near Berlin and received his medical training at the University of Berlin where in 1925 he became professor extraordinary. Since 1935 he has been professor of obstetrics and gynecology at the Hebrew University at Jerusalem.

Zondek entered the field of the sex hormones in 1925 when he and Brahn isolated an estrogenic hormone from the ovarian follicle,[11] confirming the disclosure the following year. In 1927, Selmar Aschheim (1878-   ) and Zondek extracted estrogenic hormone from the urine of pregnant women in amounts averaging 12,000 mouse units per liter, Zondek confirming and extending this discovery the following year. Also in 1928 Zondek and Aschheim succeeded in isolating the gonadotropic hormone of the anterior lobe of the pituitary, naming the extract "Prolan." Their celebrated test for pregnancy was likewise reported in 1928 under the title "Schwangerschaftsdiagnose aus dem Harn (durch Hormonnachweis)" and in greater detail in 1930 in a monograph by Aschheim alone with the same title but with the subtitle, "Aschheim-Zondek-Reaktion."[12]

HORMONAL REGULATION OF MENSTRUAL CYCLE

1. Administration of estrogenic hormone is able to influence the course of the menstrual cycle in women, i.e., it is possible to postpone the time of menstruation, thereby producing a limited amenorrhea.

2. In order to postpone menstruation at least 70,000 i.u. of estrogenic hormone must be administered but 200,000 to 300,000 i.u. are more likely to produce the desired effect. We need, therefore, at least one-third of the amount which is necessary to bring about proliferation of the uterine mucosa. The earlier the administration of hormone is begun (the best time is the postmenstrual stage) the more certain are we to achieve the effect.

3. The duration of the amenorrhea which can be achieved in this way is not in proportion to the dosage of hormone administered. Menstruation can be delayed by 6 to 70 days.

[11] Zondek, B. and Brahn, B. "Über Darstellung des Ovarialhormons in wässriger Lösung." *Klin Wschr.*, 1925, *4²*, 2445-2446. Succeeding articles appeared in the same journal as follows: Zondek, B. "Das Ovarialhormon und seine klinische Anwendung." *Ibid.*, 1925, *5²*, 1218-1224; "Darstellung des weiblichen Sexualhormons aus dem Harn, insbesondere dem Harn von Schwangeren." *Ibid.*, 1928, *7¹*, 485-486; Zondek, B. and Aschheim, S. "Das Hormon des Hypophysenvorderlappens." *Ibid.*, 1927, *6¹*, 248-252; 1928, *7¹*, 831-835; Aschheim, S. and Zondek, B. "Schwangerschaftsdiagnose aus dem Harn (durch Hormonnachweis)." *Ibid.*, 1928, *7¹*, 8-9; "Die Schwangerschaftsdiagnose aus dem Harn durch Nachweis des Hypophysenvorderlappenhormons." *Ibid.*, *7²*, 1404-1411; *7²*, 1453-1457.

[12] Berlin, S. Karger (1930) 62 pp., 4 pls.; belongs to series *Bibliotheca gynecologica*, vol. 3.

The first edition of Bernhard Zondek's monograph was published in 1931 under the title, *Die Hormone des Ovariums und des Hypophysenvorderlappens* (Berlin, J. Springer); the second edition under the same title came out in 1935 and was translated by Dr. Zondek's associates, Drs. Gertrude Kallner, Helen Gluech, and Miriam Roskin-Levy of Jerusalem. The Introduction by Zondek on pp. vii-xvii comprises "A short survey of the historical development of sex endocrinology," and is a valuable and fully documented outline.

4. If the estrogenic hormone (at least 200,000 i.u.) is given before the premenstrual phase, the further development of the uterine mucosa is checked.

5. The administration of estrogenic hormone interferes with or prevents the formation of the corpus luteum.

6. Estrogenic hormone acts primarily on the gonadotropic mechanism of the anterior pituitary which assumption is supported by the increased excretion of prolan A in cases of amenorrhea, which are produced by means of estrogens.

7. Estrogenic hormone provides us with a means of postponing the time of menstruation, i.e., producing artificial amenorrhea, a point of clinical significance. (Zondek, B. *Clinical and experimental investigations on the genital functions and their hormonal regulation.* Baltimore, Williams & Wilkins, 1941. xxiv, 264 pp. [pp. 184-185].)

XI

Endocrinology:
Glands of Internal Secretion

It is sometimes stated that study of the glands of internal secretion began between 1848 and 1855 when Claude Bernard was pursuing his analysis of the glycogenic functions of the liver.[1] In the years that followed, Bernard and others analyzed extracts of other ductless glands such as the thyroid and the adrenal, and he was responsible in 1855 for introducing the term "internal secretion." A century prior to Bernard, however, the Frenchman Joseph Lieutaud had studied the ductless glands anatomically (1742), and his contemporary Théophile de Bordeu (1775) had speculated concerning the functional activity of various organs of the body, suggesting that each gland and organ produced a specific secretion that passed into the blood stream and in this way maintained bodily functions in a state of equilibrium.

The first practical endocrinologist, one who sought to use the internal secretions, as Bernard had named them, as remedial agents, was also a picturesque Frenchman, Charles Edouard Brown-Séquard (1817-1894). In 1889 this French-American investigator attracted widespread attention when he suggested that testicular extracts might possibly be used to rejuvenate the elderly human male whose sexual potentialities had waned. He is sometimes referred to by admiring contemporaries as "the father of endocrinology." Unfortunately for him, some of his principal advocates—those who fancied themselves rejuvenated by his glandular extracts—gave fantastically exaggerated reports of the extent to which they had been benefitted. Harvey Cushing, who himself never appreciated being referred to as

[1] Bernard, C. "De l'origine du sucre dans l'économie animale." *Arch. gén Méd.,* 1848, 4 sér. *18,* 303-319; also "De suc pancréatique et de son rôle dans le phénomènes de la digestion." *C. R. Soc. Biol. (Mémoires),* (1849), Paris, 1850, *1,* 99-115, and "Sur la mécanisme de la formation du sucre dans le foie." *C. R. Acad. Sci. (Paris),* 1855, *41,* 461-469.

an "endocrinologist," once christened Brown-Séquard as the "Ponce de León of endocrinology," and his uncritical followers as "endocriminologists." However this may be, no one can deny that it was Brown-Séquard who gave the first great impetus to scientific study of the glands of internal secretion.

A few years prior to Brown-Séquard's death, George R. Murray established the value of thyroid extract in the treatment of myxoedema (1891); in 1894 Oliver and Schäfer disclosed that extract of the suprarenal glands contained an agent that caused abrupt elevation of the systolic blood pressure, this to be followed in 1897 by John J. Abel's brilliant demonstration that this active principle could be isolated in crystalline form. To this extract he gave the name "epinephrin" which pharmaceutical firms promptly made available for clinical use under the term "adrenaline" (now adrenalin). Five years later, Bayliss and Starling discovered "secretin," an extract of the mucosa of duodenum and ileum that stimulated the flow of pancreatic juice from the pancreas (the *external* secretion of that important gland); it was Ernest Henry Starling who gave the term "hormone" not only to secretin, but to the other internal secretions of the endocrine glands.

Thereafter advances in this field came in even more rapid succession; thus in 1909 MacCallum and Voegtlin established that parathyroid extract governs calcium metabolism, disclosing that parathyroidectomy is followed by tetany which is the result of calcium loss—a pathological state promptly relieved by administration of any soluble calcium ion. Three years later Alfred E. Frank isolated the antidiuretic hormone from the posterior lobe of the hypophysis ("pituitary"), and also disclosed that ablation of the posterior lobe led to rapid water loss—a condition now referred to as "diabetes insipidus" as opposed to "diabetes mellitus" resulting from destruction of the islet tissue of the pancreas islets. Edward C. Kendall in 1915 (Christmas Day 1914) succeeded in isolating and crystallizing the active principle of the thyroid to which the name "thyroxin" was given and by which it is still known. In 1921 Herbert M. Evans and Joseph A. Long disclosed that extracts of the anterior lobe of the pituitary gland yielded a growth hormone essential to the normal growth and development of human beings and that absence of this secretion, as first pointed out by Cushing, is associated with dwarfism, while its excess causes gigantism (if occurring prior to epiphyseal closure) or acromegaly in the adult.

Of even greater portent was the isolation in the year 1921 of insulin from the islet tissue of the pancreas by Frederick Banting and his co-workers at Toronto, Canada, a powerful agent made available during the following year for the treatment of human diabetes mellitus. The sex hormones followed in rapid sequence. In 1922 Edgar Allen and E. A. Doisy isolated the ovarian hormone, the hormone responsible for inducing oestrus in warmblooded animals, designating it "oestrin"; this agent was successfully crystallized in 1930 by Doisy, Veler, and Thayer. In 1925 James B. Collip, who had been largely responsible for the purification of insulin, crystallized "parathormone," the active principle of the parathyroid, but it was not until 1927 that Rogoff and Stewart distinguished the hormone of the adrenal cortex from that of the adrenal medulla, the cortical extract being employed two years later in the treatment of Addison's disease. Pfiffner and Swingle crystallized the extract from the adrenal cortex. Finally, Zondek and Aschheim isolated the gonadotropic hormone of the anterior pituitary lobe, the agent responsible for growth of the reproductive system, and it was this that led to their well-known test for pregnancy and the isolation of other pituitary tropic hormone fractions.

In 1933, Collip, Anderson, and Thomson obtained an extract from the anterior pituitary which, they showed, contained an adrenotropic hormone, and a year later this hormone was isolated in crystalline form by Kendall and his co-workers. Thus ACTH was discovered, and with its discovery there emerged the concept of the pituitary as a master gland which not only controls growth but also regulates the activity of a whole group of endocrine glands. Just prior to this period the studies of Walter Cannon and his co-workers on the manner in which the secretions of the adrenal medulla opposed the action of insulin led him to enunciate the principle of homeostasis—an outgrowth of Claude Bernard's concept of the constancy of the *milieu intérieur*. Further discoveries in endocrinology have added numerous facets to the significance of homeostasis and have shown that there is a delicate balance to be maintained between the interactions of many different endocrine secretions. As a matter of methodology the physiologist attempts to determine the function of any given hormone by his observations of how this balance is disturbed by either excess or deficiency of the hormone. At the same time it has become apparent in clinical medicine that whenever the delicate balance of homeostasis is disturbed, a diseased state results. The discovery of every new hormone has produced in its train the recognition of new diseases resulting from an imbalance in the body's production of that hormone. The rapid development of endocrinology in recent years has therefore repeatedly had exciting consequences in medicine. Perhaps its most striking triumph was the discovery by Hench, Kendall, *et al.* in 1949 that cortisone could relieve the symptoms of rheumatoid arthritis—an affliction as common as it is crippling and painful.

Cortisone is but one of a series of hormones which have been extracted from the adrenal cortex and whose chemical structure has been revealed by a long series of brilliant and painstaking researches carried on especially by Reichstein and his co-workers. It was early apparent that the adrenal cortical hormones were essential to life, but their precise actions were slow to reveal themselves. In 1950 Deming and Luetscher showed that extracts of urine from edematous patients showed unusually high sodium-retaining activity when administered to experimental animals. By chromatographic fractionation they obtained an extract which was very highly active in causing retention of sodium, and in 1954 this extract was proven by Wettstein and Neher to contain aldosterone, the 18-aldehyde derivative of corticosterone, as its active element. Thus aldosterone was shown to be concerned with accumulations of fluid in the body in direct response to the body's need for salt and water. It was also shown to be identical with electrocortin, so called because of its action on electrolytes. As is typical of the discovery of a new hormone, the discovery of aldosterone resulted in the recognition of a new metabolic disease for the first time. Thus Dr. Jerome Conn identified the muscular weakness of a patient with periodic paralysis as the result of an excess of aldosterone resulting from adrenal tumor.

While study of chemical structure and synthesis of the steroid hormones such as those of the adrenal cortex has proven to be a prolonged and arduous endeavour, the synthesis of protein hormones such as insulin and ACTH has been even more exacting. It was therefore a great triumph when in 1953 Vincent du Vigneaud and his co-workers succeeded in synthesizing the pituitary hormone oxytocin which is a peptide protein. For this discovery du Vigneaud received the Nobel prize in 1955.

Endocrine research is now in full flood. Recent discoveries are both too numerous to mention in detail and too new for their implications yet to be clear. The elaborate and delicately balanced endocrine pattern for the maintenance of homeostasis is gradually emerging and with it many exciting prospects for the treatment of metabolic diseases.

Joseph Lieutaud
1703-1780

Joseph Lieutaud, anatomist and physiologist, served for many years as professor of medicine at the University of Aix en Provence in the south of France. His work as an anatomist was highly regarded by his contemporaries; thus in 1739 he was made a Fellow of the Royal Society (along with his eminent countryman the Comte de Buffon and another great anatomist of the time, Albrecht von Haller). In addition, King Louis XIV made him *Conseiller du Roi.* As an anatomist, Lieutaud is best known for his detailed studies on the heart and its cavities and for his description of the anatomical relations of the bladder, its *trigonum vesicae* being still known as "Lieutaud's trigone."

As a physiologist, Lieutaud's studies on the endocrines, to which attention has recently been drawn by Sir Solly Zuckerman in his Thomas Addison Memorial Lecture on "The Secretions of the Brain," are of prime importance.[2] The structure of each ductless gland is described in detail, and Lieutaud's account of the pituitary is particularly noteworthy for his recognition of the pituitary-portal system of veins passing between the hypothalamus and the hypophysis. This occurs in Part V of his *Essais Anatomiques* first published in 1742; here one also finds an excellent account of the peripheral and central nervous systems with the classic description of the third ventricle in which attention is drawn to a deep midline fossa passing anteriorly toward the base of the pituitary stalk. Lieutaud states that the stalk itself is not a hollow tube but is formed rather of solid grey substance covered by pia mater. Running along the outside of this solid cylinder are small longitudinal vessels which communicate with those of the pituitary gland below. Incidentally, Lieutaud is responsible for the term *tige pituitaire,* i.e., pituitary stalk.

THE THIRD VENTRICLE, PITUITARY STALK AND GLAND

When one has separated the layers of the optical nerves, one sees beneath their juncture a small space elongated like a canal. This is the third ventricle into which lead the two openings which we have just mentioned. The anterior pillar of the vault and the anterior commissure of the brain do not appear even when one has opened

---

[2] Zuckerman, *Sir* Solly. "The secretions of the brain. Relation of hypothalamus to pituitary gland." (Seventh Thomas Addison Memorial Lecture, delivered at Guy's Hospital, London, 16 December 1953.) *Lancet,* 1954, *1,* 739-743, 789-796.

this cavity. It is essential to note in this anterior part a rather deep groove whose broad opening narrows imperceptibly. Until now, it has been believed that it terminated in a membranous canal which ends in the pituitary gland at the point where it breaks through the dura mater which covers it, and the term funnel has been applied to this cavity. The stalk which arises from the pituitary gland corresponds accurately to the deepest part of this gland but it has no cavity as has been assumed. It is a kind of cylinder two or three lines [*lignes*] high formed of grey matter and covered by the pia mater. One may note minute vessels which pass along its axis communicating with those of the gland which receives this column or which generates it. I have given the name pituitary stalk to this part because I believe that the term funnel would not be suitable for it. It is not difficult to demonstrate the solidity of the pituitary stalk and I shall describe the mode of procedure for doing so.

The pituitary gland which receives the tip of the aforementioned stalk is a spongy body located on the sphenoid bone (selle turcique) and fitting its cavity exactly. It is enclosed between the two layers of the dura mater; the lower being attached to it by very strong fastenings; the upper is pierced to allow the tip of the stalk to escape. The pituitary gland also is endowed with an envelope of pia mater which is only a continuation of that which encloses the stalk. It receives arterioles which come from the first curvature of the carotids; the nerves of the sixth pair send it several branches; its veins empty into the cavernous sinus.

At the posterior end of the third ventricle one may note the opening of a canal which, passing beneath the corpora quadragemini, communicates with the fourth ventricle. It is called the aqueduct of Sylvius (*sic*). (Lieutaud, J. *Essais anatomiques, contenant l'histoire exacte de toutes les parties qui composent le corps de l'homme, avec la manière de dissequer.* Paris, P.-M. Huart, 1742. xxiv, 724 pp., 8 *ll.*, 6 pl. [pp. 395-396. Translated by L.G.W.].)

Théophile de Bordeu

1722-1776

Théophile de Bordeu, French anatomist and endocrine physiologist, was professor of anatomy at Pau (Dept. Basses Pyrennes) and, like his contemporary and adversary, Joseph Lieutaud, had been named *Conseiller du Roi*. He also served as inspector of the mineral water springs in the vicinity of Auch (Dept. Gers) and Pau. Lieutaud had published his *Essais Anatomiques* in 1742 and before de Bordeu published his work in 1751 he had had nine years to ponder upon Lieutaud's findings. Although the latter had made some excellent new anatomical observations, he was still at heart a Galenist, and he might have asked himself why it was not still sufficient to regard the nerves as microscopical tubes along which subtle spirits passed from the brain to all parts of the body, including glands such as the pineal, pituitary, adrenals, etc. For de Bordeu this was not enough, for each gland and tissue of the body must have a specific function. He therefore formulated the challenging hypothesis that every gland, and probably every tissue and cell, discharges products into the blood stream which influence *other* glands and tissues. This idea was set forth at some length in a small octavo volume of some 520 text pages bound with 88 pages at the end made up of two Appendices, both in Latin, the first entitled *Chilificationis historia* (pp. 1-52), the second *Dissertatio phisiologica de sensu genericè considerato* (pp. 53-88), previously published at Montpellier in 1742. In developing his argument, de Bordeu assures his readers at some length that he does not subscribe to the Galenic concept of vital spirits. He concludes somewhat disparagingly that the blind disciples of the ancient concept of vital spirits are fanciful and wishful in their thinking—if indeed they do "think."

In 1775 de Bordeu returned to this theme in the sixth part of his large monograph, *Recherches sur des maladies chroniques*. Here he uses, again with an air of some disparagement, the term "humours" to describe the substances such as testicular and ovarian secretions which affect other parts of the body, and he suggests that these gonadal glands may in fact be responsible for secondary sexual characters and behavior.

THE CONCEPT OF HUMORAL ACTION

[p. 379]. What I believe with certainty is that each organ—holding its own position, as I have just said, and living its own life (taken up and renewed within the mass [of the body] as each animal takes up and renews its life in the air)—does not fail to discharge around itself into its atmosphere, into its immediate surroundings, exhalations—aroma—emanations which have taken on its tone and its ways,—which are ultimately true parts of itself. XXIV°. I do not regard these emissions as useless and purely the result of physical necessity; I think them useful and necessary for the existence of the individual as a whole.

[p. 382] . . . I conclude from this that the blood circulates with, always in its bosom, extracts from all the organic parts, which no one will ever make me consider useless for the harmony of the life of the whole, and which have particular qualities and properties which the experiments of Chemists cannot yet detect. I shall tell, as the opportunity may present itself, how Physicians try to trace these corpuscles in the blood and to measure the effects which they produce there. Let us conclude that each organ of the body has, in consequence of the emanations resulting from its vital activity, some resemblance to flowers which scatter a seminal emanation in the air,—which gives an idea of [the distribution in the body of] the semen of animals and of all the other exhalations to which their parts are subject. (Bordeu, Antoine de, Bordeu, Théophile de, and Bordeu, François de. *Recherches sur les maladies chroniques.* Paris, Ruault, 1775. 592 pp. [pp. 379, 382. Translated by L.G.W.].)

George Redmayne Murray
1865-1939

George Redmayne Murray was born at Newcastle-on-Tyne, England, and educated at Trinity College, Cambridge, where he was graduated B.A. in 1886 and M.B. in 1889. From 1893 to 1908 he was professor of comparative pathology at Durham University. In the latter year he moved to Manchester University where he was professor of systematic medicine until 1925.

While still a very young house physician at University College Hospital, London, Murray decided to attempt the treatment of myxoedema by thyroid extract. In 1884 Victor Horsley had shown that experimental removal of the thyroid in a monkey could produce all the symptoms of myxoedema.

THYROID EXTRACT IN MYXOEDEMA

Since suggesting this treatment at the February meeting of the Northumberland and Durham Medical Society, I have been able to carry it out in a well-marked case of myxoedema. Such decided improvement has resulted that the details of the method of treatment employed and the results obtained are worth recording. After trying one or two slightly different methods, the following has been found to be the most convenient, but is probably capable of considerable improvement:

The lobe of the thyroid gland of a sheep is removed as soon as possible after the animal has been killed. The surrounding fat and connective tissue are removed from it. All the instruments and glass vessels used in the further preparation of the extract should be either sterilised by heat or thoroughly cleansed with a 1 in 20 solution of carbolic acid. The gland is cut up on a glass dish into small pieces, and then placed in a test tube with 1 cubic centimetre of pure glycerine and 1 cubic centimetre of a 0.5 per cent solution of carbolic acid. The mouth of the tube is closed with a plug of cotton-wool, and the mixture allowed to stand in a cool place for twenty-four hours. The mixture is then placed in a fine handkerchief which has previously been placed for a few minutes in boiling water. It is then firmly squeezed by screwing up the handkerchief so as to express as much liquid as possible through the handkerchief. By this means 3 cubic centimetres (50 minims) of a turbid pink liquid are obtained. This preparation, which will keep quite fresh for at least a week, should be kept in a small bottle with a glass stopper. It is best to make the extract fresh each week, so as to avoid any risk of putrefaction taking place. This extract may be given in two equal injections of 1.5 cubic centimetre (25 minims) each during the week, so that at first the patient receives the extract of one lobe of a sheep's thyroid in the course of each week. After a time the injections need not be made so frequently. The injections are made with an ordinary hypodermic syringe, which is carefully washed out with a 1 in 20 solution of carbolic acid both before and after the injection is made. The surface of the skin is also carefully cleansed with the same carbolic solution at the point where the injection is made. The loose skin of the back, between the shoulder-blades, is a convenient situation in which to make the injection.

The following note gives the history and condition of the patient before the commencement of the treatment.

April 13th. Mrs. S., aged 46. Four or five years ago it was first noticed by her friends that her speech and actions were becoming very slow. She herself began to feel soon after that it required a great effort to do her ordinary housework. Her features gradually became enlarged and thickened. The hands and feet increased in size and became altered in shape. She has not perspired at all during the last four years. Six years ago she had a miscarriage; since then she has only menstruated once, four years ago. At the present time she presents most of the characteristic symptoms of myxoedema. She complains of languor, a disinclination to see strangers, and great sensitiveness to cold. The temperature is subnormal, and varies between 95.6 and 97.2 in the mouth. The pulse varies between 60 and 70. The face is blank and expressionless, and the features are notably thickened. This change is well seen in the alae nasi and lips. The subcutaneous connective tissue of the eyelids is so swollen that she finds it difficult to look upwards. There is also considerable swelling beneath the eyes and of the cheeks. The hands and feet are both enlarged; the former have that peculiar shape which has been described as "spade-like." The skin is very dry, there is no perspiration, and the superficial layers of the epidermis are continually being shed as a fine white powder. The hair is very fine in texture, and a considerable quantity of it has been lost. She is slow in answering questions; all her actions are slow, and are performed with difficulty. The speech is remarkably slow and drawling, and the memory is bad. No thyroid gland can be felt in the neck. The urine contains no albumen or sugar.

July 13th. It is now three months since the treatment was commenced; it has not, however, been carried out continuously all the time, and at first a weaker preparation than that described was used. Extracts of five lobes of sheep's thyroid have been injected, that is altogether equal to the extract of two and a half thyroid glands. The patient has steadily improved since the treatment commenced, and, though three weeks were allowed to elapse between the injection of the last two extracts, she did not lose any of the ground she had previously gained. The swelling has gradually diminished, and has practically disappeared from the backs of the hands, the skin over them being now loose and freely movable. The lips are much smaller. The swelling of the upper eyelids has diminished so much that she can look upwards quite easily. The swelling beneath the eyes and of the cheeks has also much diminished. The face consequently, as a whole, has greatly improved in appearance, and has much more expression, as many of the natural wrinkles, especially about the forehead, have returned. The speech has become more rapid and fluent, the drawl being scarcely noticeable at the present time. She answers questions much more readily, the mind has become more active, and the memory has improved. She is more active in all her movements, and finds that it requires much less effort than formerly to do her housework. She now walks about the streets without any hesitation without a companion.

She has menstruated normally during the last six weeks at the regular interval. For the last four weeks the skin has been much less dry and she perspires when walking. The hair remains as before. She is no longer so sensitive to cold. Unfortunately owing to circumstances a daily record of the temperature has not been kept, but out of four observations that have been made lately, about 11 A.M., three times the temperature has been 98.2°F. and once 97.4°. (Murray, G. R.

"Note on the treatment of myxoedema by hypodermic injections of an extract of the thyroid gland of a sheep." *Brit. med. J.*, 1891, 2, 796-797 [p. 797].)

George Oliver
1841-1915
and
Edward Albert Sharpey-Schafer
1850-1935

George Oliver and Sir *Edward Sharpey-Schafer* were the first to isolate the active principle of a ductless gland and to investigate its physiological effects. It is difficult to realize that the enormous growth of knowledge concerning the endocrines has taken place almost entirely since 1894, when Oliver and Schäfer discovered the potency of an extract of the suprarenals (Pl. 85). The thyroid was soon studied, and cretinism had proved curable by feeding of the whole gland. Then came pituitrin, and, after an interval, insulin and parathormone. The following passage on the isolation of adrenal secretion is taken from the original announcement of Oliver and Schäfer.

ON THE PHYSIOLOGICAL ACTION OF EXTRACT OF THE SUPRARENAL CAPSULES

The suprarenal capsules yield to water (cold or hot), to alcohol or to glycerine a substance which exerts a most powerful action upon the blood vessels, upon the heart, and upon the skeletal muscles. These effects have been investigated upon the dog, cat, rabbit and frog. In the frog the solutions were injected into the dorsal lymph-sac, in the rabbit subcutaneously and into a vein, in the other animals into a vein. The alcohol extracts were first dried and the residue extracted with normal saline; the watery decoctions were made with normal saline, and the glycerine extracts were largely diluted with the same previous to injection. The doses employed have varied from a mere trace up to an amount of extract equivalent to 3 grains (0.2 gramme) of the fresh gland; in one or two instances we have given larger doses with the object of obtaining if possible a lethal result. The extracts used have been made from the suprarenals of the calf, sheep and dog. Exactly similar effects have been obtained in each case. Except in the case of the frog we have not obtained any marked effect from subcutaneous injections of comparatively small doses. . . .

The effect upon the blood vessels is to cause extreme contraction of the arteries, so that the blood-pressure is enormously raised. This is most evident when the vagi are cut in order to obviate the inhibitory action upon the heart which otherwise occurs; it is also seen after section of the cervical cord. The blood-pressure may rise from 2 to 4 times above normal. This extreme contraction of the vessels is evidenced by the plethysmograph; section of the nerves going to the limb produces no difference in the result. The effect is therefore peripheral. This can also be shown in the frog with its nerve-centres destroyed, and through the blood vessels of which normal saline is allowed to circulate; if only a small quantity of suprarenal extract is added to the saline the flow almost entirely ceases.

The time which elapses between the injection into a vein and the first effect upon the blood vessels is in the dog from 25 to 30 seconds. But if an experiment has been conducted for some three hours or more, the animal during the whole of this time having been under the influence of morphia and curare, the contraction of the vessels of a limb is preceded by a preliminary expansion, the cause of which is as yet not clear. It is however a constant phenomenon. . . .

The effect upon the skeletal muscles has been investigated in the frog. The movements of a frog to which a hypodermic injection of extract of suprarenal capsule (equal to 1 or 2 grains of the fresh gland) have been given soon become slow, and after about half-an-hour the reflexes are very faint and almost abolished; the animal soon appears completely paralysed. The muscles however still contract on being stimulated, either directly or through the motor nerves, but the contractions are modified, the relaxation period being greatly prolonged, as with veratria poisoning. The period of latent stimulation is not greatly, if at all, lengthened. The fatigue curves were rapidly developed. The effect is not at all comparable to that produced by curare.

We have noticed a slight effect to be produced upon the respiration, which may become shallower; but in the doses we have used the result was very slight when compared with the prodigious effects upon the heart and blood vessels which were obtained. . . . Oliver, G. and Schäfer, E. A. "On the physiological action of extract of the suprarenal capsules." *J. Physiol. (Lond.), Proc.*, 1894, *16*, i-iv [pp. i-iii].)

ON SUPRARENAL EXTRACTS

It appears to be established as the result of these investigations that, like the thyroid gland, the suprarenal capsules are to be regarded although ductless, as strictly secreting glands. The material which they form and which is found, at least in its fully active condition, only in the medulla of the gland, produces striking physiological effects upon the muscular tissue generally and especially upon that of the heart and arteries. Its action is to increase the tone of all muscular tissue, and this result is produced mainly if not entirely by direct action. On the other hand the removal of the suprarenal capsules produces extreme weakness of the heart and muscular system generally, and great want of tone in the vascular system. A similar result is known to be characteristic of advanced disease of these organs (Addison's disease). It may fairly be concluded therefore that one of the main functions, if not the main function, of the suprarenal capsules is to produce a material which is added in some way or another to the blood, and the effect of which is to assist by its direct action upon the various kinds of muscular tissue in maintaining that amount of tonic contraction which appears to be essential to the physiological activity of the tissue. Any further conclusion than this we cannot legitimately draw from our experiments, and we do not propose at this time to discuss such other conclusions as it may be possible to arrive at from the results of ablation experiments. . . . (Oliver, George and Schäfer, E.A. "The physiological effects of extracts of the suprarenal capsules." *J. Physiol. (Lond.)*, 1895, *18*, 230-276 [pp. 273-274].)

John Jacob Abel
1857-1938
and
Albert Cornelius Crawford
1869-1920

John Jacob Abel was one of the great pioneers in the development of physiology and experimental medicine in America. A native of Ohio, he was educated at the University of Michigan. He had to interrupt his college course to spend three years in the teaching of Latin, mathematics, physics, and chemistry in a high school at La Porte, Indiana, in order to earn his way but graduated in pharmacy in 1883. At this point Abel decided to make scientific medicine his lifework and therefore with characteristic thoroughness entered upon a broad program of training. After a year at Johns Hopkins, he spent nearly seven years in the study of chemistry and medicine at European universities. He learned anatomy under His, Braune, and Schwalbe; physiology from Carl Ludwig; pharmacology from Oswald Schmiedeberg; biochemistry with Drechsel, Hoppe Seyler, and von Nencki; and chemistry with Wislicenus. In 1888 Abel was graduated M.D. at the University of Strasbourg and then interned at Vienna.

His return to America in 1891 was thus an event of considerable significance for the development of medicine here. In the preceding decades physiology and chemistry had been deeply cultivated in Germany. Of particular importance were the new methods and techniques which German scientists had developed. Abel had an intimate acquaintance with this new knowledge, and what he brought was the more important for the kind of man he was. All he had learned with care and industry he was prepared to teach with imagination and sympathy. The influence of Abel upon his students and upon his students' students has left a deep imprint upon scientific medicine in America.

After two years as professor of pharmacology at the University of Michigan, he went in 1893 to Johns Hopkins University where he remained for the rest of his long and productive life (Pl. 86). He carried out research in many fields but among his most important contributions must be mentioned his crystallization of insulin in 1926 and his early studies on the adrenal medullary hormone presented here.

Albert Cornelius Crawford was born at Baltimore, Maryland, 10 June 1869 and received his M.D. degree at the College of Physicians and Surgeons, Baltimore, in 1893. From 1894 to 1900 he was assistant in pharmacology at Johns Hopkins, and it was during this period that he collaborated with Abel in the investigation of the adrenal. In 1910, after several years as a research pharmacologist, he was appointed professor of pharmacology at Stanford University at Palo Alto, California. He died there on 14 March 1921.

In this work, which occupied several years, Abel and Crawford obtained the active principle of the adrenal gland as a monobenzoyl derivative to which Abel gave the name *epinephrine*. This was the first isolation of an endocrine secretion as a chemically pure substance.

BLOOD-PRESSURE-RAISING ACTION OF SUPRARENAL EXTRACT

Physiologists have proved that a very small quantity of an aqueous extract of the medullary substance raises the blood pressure to a great height above the normal. It has also unequaled power in reviving a poisoned heart. Gottlieb, for example, has shown that it will revive the heart of a rabbit which has practically stopped beating in consequence of an intravenous injection of chloral hydrate. . . .

... There is therefore at present great diversity of opinion as to the chemical character of the blood-pressure-raising constituent of the gland.

Whatever the probability may be of the correctness of this or that view, it is to be noted that all of the above-named investigators have based their conclusions on reactions made with aqueous, alcoholic or acetonic extracts; none of them have even roughly isolated a definite chemical compound. The subject is one of great difficulty, and our own work is at present merely preliminary, but we have arrived at the following conclusions which we believe to be borne out by our experiments.

First, we have found by isolating the blood-pressure-raising constituent in the form of a benzoyl compound and decomposing it, that the active principle is a substance with basic characteristics and that it must in all probability be classed with the pyrrol compounds or with the pyridine bases or alkaloids. ...

We have used sheep's glands in large quantity. The medullary substance of the fresh glands was scraped out, dried on the water-bath at 60°C., ground up finely, and extracted with ether for several days until the fats and the substance known as Manasse's jecorin were removed. In this way a fine dry powder of a grayish white appearance is obtained, the aqueous extract of which is very active in raising the blood pressure.

With 100 grammes or more of this powder, representing one kg. in weight or about 1000 fresh glands, we proceeded. ...

The blood-pressure-raising constituent of the suprarenal capsule may be completely precipitated from an aqueous extract by treatment with benzoyl chloride and sodium hydrate, according to the Schotten-Baumann method.

On decomposing the resulting benzoyl products, a residue is obtained which possesses great physiological activity. It gives the color reactions of Vulpian, reduces silver nitrate and possesses the other specific qualities of suprarenal extracts.

With the help of alkalies a carmine-red pigment may also be separated from these decomposition products. We take this pigment to be that one of the chromogenic substances of Vulpian which gives the rose-carmine color when suprarenal extracts are treated with oxidizing agents or alkalies.

A volatile, basic substance of a coniine-like odor is always found to accompany the crude benzoate. When these substances are removed the active principle is left as a highly active sulphate or hydrochlorate, as the case may be. It is therefore a basic substance. Its salts give a color reaction with ferric chloride; they also reduce silver nitrate, but not Fehling's solution. . . .

(Abel, J. J. and Crawford, A. C. "On the blood-pressure-raising constituent of the suprarenal capsule." *Johns Hopk. Hosp. Bull.,* 1897, *8,* 151-157 [pp. 151, 152, 156].)

Ernest Henry Starling
1866-1927

In his series of four Croonian lectures delivered in 1905 E. H. Starling (Pl. 87) brilliantly summarized the knowledge of the endocrines up to that time and made prophetic suggestions as to the future course of research. He also added to the language of physiology a new and immensely useful term.

THE CHEMICAL CORRELATION OF THE FUNCTIONS OF THE BODY (THE COINING OF THE TERM *HORMONE*)

To which of these two groups of bodies must we assign the chemical messengers which, speeding from cell to cell along the blood stream, may coördinate the activities and growth of different parts of the body? The specific character of the greater part of the toxins which are known to us (I need only instance such toxins as those of tetanus and diphtheria) would suggest that the substances produced for effecting the correlation of organs within the body, through the intermediation of the blood stream, might also belong to this class, since here also specificity of action must be a distinguishing characteristic. These chemical messengers, however, or "hormones" (from ὁρμάω, I excite or arouse), as we might call them, have to be carried from the organ where they are produced to the organ which they affect by means of the blood stream and the continually recurring physiological needs of the organism must determine their repeated production and circulation through the body. . . .

. . . I have already mentioned that excision of the suprarenal bodies causes a profound fall of blood pressure, which continues until the death of the animal, and it has been stated that when this fall is well established it is impossible to raise the blood pressure by stimulation of the splanchnic nerve or, indeed, to produce any effect at all on stimulation of the sympathetic nerve. Thus not only does adrenalin excite the whole sympathetic system in its ultimate terminations but its presence in the body as a specific secretion of the suprarenal bodies seems to be a necessary condition for the normal functioning, by ordinary reflex means, of the whole sympathetic system. We are dealing here with a problem which betraying, as it does, an intimate relationship between nerve excitation and excitation by chemical means, promises by its solution to throw a most interesting light on the nature of the nerve process and of excitatory processes in general. . . . (Starling, E. H. "The Croonian lectures on the chemical correlation of the functions of the body." *Lancet*, 1905, 2, 339-341, 423-425, 501-503, 579-583 [pp. 340, 341].)

Henry Hallett Dale
1875-

Born at London, *Henry Hallett Dale* was educated at Trinity College, Cambridge. After graduating in 1898 he continued to work in physiology at Cambridge under John Newport Langley (1852-1925) until 1900 when he went to St. Bartholomew's to study clinical medicine. In 1903 he was graduated B.Ch. from Cambridge and then worked for a time with E. H. Starling at University College, London, and in Paul Ehrlich's laboratory at Frankfort. In 1904 he was appointed a pharmacologist at the Wellcome Physiological Research Laboratories where he remained until 1914 when he became head of the Department of Biochemistry and Physiology in the National Institute for Medical Research of which he was appointed director in 1928 (Pl. 88).

In 1936 Sir Henry (he had been knighted in 1932) shared with Otto Loewi (1873-1961) the Nobel Prize in Medicine for their discoveries relating to the chemical transmission of nerve impulses. Loewi, who had studied medicine at Strasbourg and received his pharmacological training under Hans Meyer, had occupied the chair of pharmacology at Graz since 1909. In an active experimental career he had touched on many phases of physiology and experimental medicine—nuclein metabolism, diabetes, renal function, and digitalis as well as the autonomic nervous system.

Dale had demonstrated the production of acetylcholine at the end plates of the motor nerves in skeletal muscle. Loewi showed that acetylcholine was also identical with the *Vagusstoff* which he had found to be produced at the nerve endings of the vagus.

OXYTOCIC ACTION OF PITUITARY EXTRACTS

Though the activity of pituitary extracts was discovered by Oliver and Schäfer almost simultaneously with that of suprarenal extracts, the conceptions of the nature of the action of the former are as yet far less precise. A comparison of the two was inevitable, and it has more than once been suggested that their action, at least as regards vaso-constriction, is of the same kind and produced by stimulation of the same structures. Herring advanced this view as regards the arteries: a more recent observation by Cramer, of the action of pituitary extract on the pupil of the frog's eye (enucleated), lends support to the same idea: still more recently an account given by Bell and Hick of the action on the uterus emphasised the similarity between the action of extracts from the two organs. I thought it worth while, therefore, to bring together a number of observations, made at different times and in different connections, which appear to me to indicate that such correspondence as exists is wholly superficial and illusory. In the first place it must be admitted that the actions of pituitary and suprarenal extracts have superficially several points of suggestive similarity. Both raise the blood-pressure, peripheral vaso-constriction being a principal factor in the effect (Oliver and Schäfer): in both cases the active principle is limited to a small, morphologically independent portion of the gland, developmentally related to the central nervous system in the one case, as to the sympathetic system in the other. Attention is drawn to these points of similarity by Schäfer and Herring, who state that 'here the parallelism ends'· but the divergence of which they make specific mention is that the pituitary extract has an additional effect on the kidney. Since they attribute this to a separate active principle, no true divergence is indicated between the *pressor* principles of the two organs. It has been shown (Langley, Brodie and Dixon, Elliott) that the action of adrenaline reproduces with striking accuracy the effects of stimulating nerves of the true sympathetic or thoracico-lumbar division of the autonomic system. An examination of the action of pituitary extract on various organs and systems containing plain muscle and gland-cells will indicate whether its action has more than a superficial resemblance to that of adrenaline by showing whether its effects, or any group of them, can be similarly summarised by relating them to a particular element of the visceral nervous system. Incidentally evidence will be discussed which throws light on the contention of Schäfer and Herring that two active principles exist in the extract, one acting on the circulatory system, the other specifically on the kidney. . . .

It is clear from the foregoing that the characteristic action of extracts of the posterior lobe of the pituitary body is stimulation of plain muscle fibres. Different organs containing plain muscle show a varying sensitiveness of response to the extract, the arteries, the uterus and the spleen being conspicuously affected. This unequal distribution of effect cannot, however, in any way be related to inequalities of innervation by nerves of the true sympathetic or of the autonomic system as a whole. Ergotoxine, which excludes motor effects of true sympathetic nerves, and of drugs acting through those nerves or like them, leaves the action of pituitary extract intact. Neither atropine nor curare affects its direct action in any degree. The muscle of the mammalian heart is possibly affected to some extent by the extract, apart from effects secondary to constriction of the coronary arterioles: Herring's observations on the frog's heart render this most probable. No effect could be detected on the response of voluntary muscles, either to direct or indirect stimulation. The active principle is then essentially a stimulant of involuntary, and especially of plain muscle. (Dale, H. H. "The action of extracts of the pituitary body." *Biochem. J.*, 1909, *4*, 427-447 [pp. 427-428, 443].)

Alfred Erich Frank
1884-

Alfred Erich Frank was born in Berlin and educated at Breslau and at Strassburg where in 1908 he was graduated in medicine. After a period of study at the State Hospital, Wiesbaden, and at the University Medical School Clinic at Breslau, in 1913 he became a resident in internal medicine, also at Breslau, where he was appointed professor in 1918.

In pursuit of the new ideas then developing concerning internal secretions, Frank showed in 1912 that diabetes insipidus was associated with a disturbance of the pituitary.

THE INFLUENCE OF THE POSTERIOR LOBE OF THE PITUITARY UPON *DIABETES INSIPIDUS*

From a general standpoint it also appears that the idea that the permanent state of excitation of a nerve centre is the cause of diabetes insipidus is today no longer to be considered tenable. Among other human diseases—diabetes mellitus and Basedow's disease, for example—in which likewise experimental data originally pointed to the nervous system as a causal factor, successive developments have shown that disturbance of the internal secretion of certain organs is incomparably more significant for their pathogenesis. Should the same thing not also hold for diabetes insipidus? In fact, it now appears to me that there is sufficient experimental and clinical material at hand to make worth mentioning the organ which today comes into question. I wish to show you experimentally that it is the hypophysis and still more particularly, a specific independent organ within this organ—the pars intermedia. . . .

The pars intermedia appears strictly distinguished, both structurally and functionally from the anterior lobe, as a gland which produces a colloidal secretion probably discharged into the ventricle fluid. While to the cells of the anterior lobe is assigned the influence of the hypophysis on the growth process in the organism, the cells of the intermediary portion yield the active substance of the aqueous extract, especially therefore the hypophyseal diuretic. This was demonstrated to a certain degree directly by the results of the microscopic investigation of the hypophysis in those dogs in which Schäfer had slightly injured this organ. The anterior lobes were in these cases intact but in contrast blood was found extravasated in the cavity of the hypophysis and there was a significant increase in the colloids of the intervening layer. . . .

From the experimental and clinical facts adduced, it may be concluded that a gland occupying the pars intermedia of the hypophysis has by means of its internal secretion an influence on the activity of the kidneys and that true diabetes insipidus can be traced to a pathological hyperfunction of this gland. It remains to determine whether all forms of the disease hitherto observed can be explained from this single point of view. In order to deal with the objection that in the human disease one never observes the excessive activity of pituitrin (increase in blood pressure and the resultant appearance of the smooth muscle organs), I eliminated from the experimental facts that the smooth musculature very rapidly falls into a state refractory against pituitrin, while the diuretic action remains unhindered. (Frank, A. E. "Ueber Beziehungen der Hypophyse zum Diabetes insipidus." *Berl. klin. Wschr.*, 1912, *49*, 393-397 [pp. 394-396, Translated by L.G.W.].)

Herbert McLean Evans
1882-

and

Joseph Abraham Long
1879-

One of the most imaginative and persevering contributors to the subject of endocrinology, *Herbert McLean Evans,* was born at Modesto, California, and educated at the University of California at Berkeley where he received the B.S. degree in 1904. He then went to Johns Hopkins and after he acquired his M.D. degree in 1908 joined the department of anatomy first as assistant and later as associate professor. In 1915 he was appointed professor of biology at the University of California (Pl. 89) where he remained until his retirement in 1953 as Emeritus professor. In 1930 Evans was instrumental in the establishment at Berkeley of the Institute for Experimental Biology of which he became director.

In collaboration with *Katherine Bishop* (1889-   ), Evans in 1923 discovered a new dietary factor essential for reproduction which in 1936 he and his co-workers isolated as vitamin E. Two years earlier Evans and his group also had demonstrated the dietary need for certain unsaturated fatty acids, one of which they isolated as vitamin F or linolenic acid. However, these important nutritional discoveries grew out of the main line of his researches on the internal secretions concerned with reproduction and growth.

Joseph Abraham Long was born at Lebanon, Pennsylvania, and educated at Harvard University (B.S. 1904, Ph.D. 1908). Immediately after receiving his degree he began teaching embryology at the University of California where he has remained ever since.

In 1920 and 1921 Evans and Long collaborated in a series of investigations on the endocrinology of reproduction which culminated in the discovery of the influence of the anterior pituitary upon growth here described.

ANTERIOR PITUITARY AND GROWTH

The anterior lobes were dissected from fresh glands, were immersed five minutes in 30 percent alcohol, rinsed thoroughly in sterile Locke's solution, triturated with a small amount of sand, and centrifuged for about half an hour, care being taken to carry out all manipulations aseptically. The supernatant fluid from centrifuging was injected into the peritoneal cavity in amounts from 1/8 to 1 cc., according to the age of the rat, the first dose being given at an age of about fourteen days. At the beginning a similarly obtained fluid substance from liver was given some controls, but soon discontinued because of its toxic effect. Every animal was weighed at intervals of five days, beginning with the twentieth day of age. To date daily observations have been carried to the eightieth day. The subjoined table shows a greater rate of growth of the experimental animals as compared with their controls, a disparity which is increasing.

At the same time the effect of the anterior lobe has been to repress sexual development by delaying sexual maturity and lengthening the oestrous cycles, in some cases oestrus being entirely inhibited.

In the case of five adult rats with previously regular four-day cycles, doses of 1 to 2 cc. of the anterior lobe fluid substance caused an immediate cessation of the four-day rhythm, the smaller doses permitting oestrus to recur at longer intervals, the larger inhibiting it altogether. These results are in marked contrast to the lack of effect produced by oral administration of the anterior hypophysis. As far as the influence on sex function is concerned, they are in marked contrast to prevalent opinion. (Evans, H. M. and Long, J. A. "The effect of the anterior lobe administered intraperitoneally upon growth, maturity and oestrous cycles of the rat." *Anat. Rec.*, 1921, *21*, 62-63.)

Frederick Grant Banting
1891-1941
and
Charles Herbert Best
1899-

Frederick Grant Banting was born near Alliston, Ontario, and educated at the University of Toronto, where he completed the medical course at the end of 1916 in a wartime accelerated program and immediately joined the Canadian Army Medical Corps. He served overseas as a medical officer from 1917 to 1919. Upon his return to Canada he spent a year in the study of orthopedic surgery at the Sick Children's Hospital in Toronto before going to London, Ontario, to enter practice. While at London he undertook part-time teaching duties at the University of Western Ontario and became interested in diabetes.

In the spring of 1921 he returned to Toronto to begin research on this disease in Professor J. J. R. Macleod's Department of Physiology at the University. This work, in which he was assisted by C. H. Best and later by J. B. Collip, resulted in the isolation of insulin by the end of 1921 (Pl. 90). The first diabetic patients were treated successfully in 1922. By the following year insulin was being produced on a large scale, and Banting was awarded, jointly with J. J. R. Macleod, the Nobel Prize in medicine for 1923. In 1923 also Banting was appointed professor of medical research at the University of Toronto and awarded an annuity for life by the Parliament of Canada. At the University of Toronto a Banting Institute was established for medical research in 1930 and in 1934 Banting was knighted. In February, 1941, while on a wartime mission to Great Britain, he died of injuries and exposure following an aircrash in Newfoundland.

Charles Herbert Best was born at West Pembroke, Maine, and was educated at the University of Toronto where he was graduated B.A. in 1921 and M.D. in 1925. He assisted Banting in his work on insulin in 1921 and from that time forward was active in research directed toward the development and production of insulin for general clinical use. From 1924 to 1941 he was assistant professor and research associate in the Department of Medical Research of the University of Toronto and since 1941 he has been professor of physiology and head of the department. More recently the University has established the Best Institute.

THE RELIEF OF EXPERIMENTAL DIABETES IN DOGS

Chart 2 (Fig. 13) is the record of dog 92, weight 11.9 kg. A complete pancreatectomy was performed on this animal at three P.M. August 11. The first injection of extract was given six hours after the operation and subsequently an injection every four hours. This extract was freshly prepared from a ten kg. dog whose pancreatic ducts had been ligated for ten weeks. One hundred and twenty-five c.c. of extract were prepared from the gland residue but this supply was exhausted by two P.M., August 13, after which other extracts were used. Blood samples were always taken before the injections of extract.

On August 12, the blood sugar curve shows that neither five nor eight c.c. of this extract every four hours were sufficient to counterbalance the upward trend of the percentage of sugar of the blood. At 10 P.M. the dose was increased to twelve c.c. and a marked fall is noted. The chart at 10 A.M. August 14 records the reduction of the percentage of sugar in the blood below its normal level, as a result of extract from another degenerated gland. (The exceptionally higher values for the volume of urine and the urinary nitrogen for August 15 and 16 may be due to the adulteration of the urine with vomit.) On August 15 at 10 A.M. the chart shows the effect produced by ten c.c. of the same gland extract made 0.1 per cent acid with HCl. This

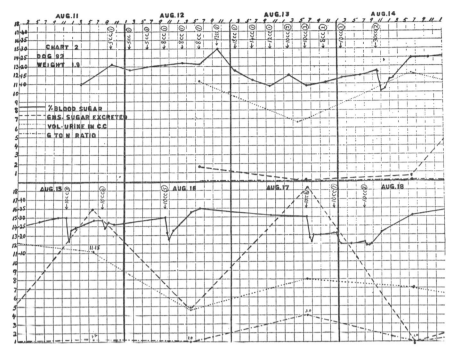

Figure 13. Chart 2.—(1) Regenerated pancreas, dog 394. (2) Degenerated pancreas, dog 390. (3) Degenerated pancreas, + .1% HCl. (4) Degenerated pancreas + 0.10% NaOH. (5) Degenerated pancreas + .1% HCl. (6) Whole gland extract, fresh, cold. (7) Whole gland extract, + .1% HCl. (8) Whole gland extract + .1% NaOH.

extract made 0.1 per cent alkaline with NaOH causes a slight reduction (August 15, 8 P.M.). The effect may be due to the alkali.

The extract administered at 10 A.M. August 16 was neutral and made from the same degenerated gland.

On August 16 and 17 effects of extracts from normal glands were tested. A normal pancreas from a ten kg. animal was divided into three equal parts. One third was extracted with neutral saline, the second portion with 0.1 per cent HCl and the third with 0.1 per cent NaOH. On August 17 at four P.M. the neutral whole gland extract was administered. A marked fall in blood sugar resulted. The acid and alkaline extracts were injected at 12 P.M. August 17, and 7 A.M. August 18. The last two injections were perhaps not given a fair opportunity to develop their effects. We do not take colorimeter readings by artificial light and therefore did not have an accurate knowledge of height of blood sugar at these times.

The conclusion from this experiment is that freshly prepared neutral or acid extracts of the whole pancreas do have a reducing effect on blood sugar, thus confirming Kleiner. It may be stated here that repeated injections of whole gland extracts cause marked thrombosis of the veins where the injections are made and a noticeable interference with kidney function. It is obvious from the chart that the whole gland extract is much weaker than that from the degenerated gland. . . . (Banting, F. G. and Best, C. H. "The internal secretion of the pancreas." *J. Lab. clin. Med.,* 1922, *7,* 251-266 [p. 256].)

THE SUCCESSFUL TREATMENT OF HUMAN DIABETES

Seven cases of diabetes mellitus have so far been treated with the extract under the personal supervision of two of us (W. R. C. and A. A. F.), and the preliminary results have been published elsewhere. These have shown that subcutaneous injection of insulin causes the blood sugar to become markedly reduced even to the normal level, with disappearance of both sugar and ketone bodies from the urine. Evidence that these effects depend on an improved utilization of carbohydrate in the body was obtained by observing the respiratory quotient. In two severe cases this value rose decidedly within a few hours after giving the extract, a result which confirms that of similar observations on a diabetic patient and on depancreated dogs in the laboratory, the details of which will be published shortly. Not only were the objective symptoms of diabetes practically removed but a definite improvement was observed in the general condition of the patients, who also reported a subjective sense of well-being and of increased vigor for a period following each injection. . . . (Banting, F. G., Best, C. H., Collip, J. B., Campbell, W. R., Fletcher, A. A., Macleod, J. J. R., and Noble, E. C. "The effect produced on diabetes by extracts of pancreas." *Trans. Ass. Amer. Phys.,* 1922, *37,* 337-347 [pp. 340-341].)

Julius Moses Rogoff
1883-
and
George Neil Stewart
1860-1930

Born in Russia in 1883, *Julius Moses Rogoff* came with his parents to the United States during his boyhood and was educated first at Ohio Northern University where he became qualified in pharmacy in 1900. Later he studied medicine at Ohio Wesleyan University where he received the M.D. degree in 1908. After periods of teaching and research at various medical schools, Rogoff became in 1939 professor of endocrinology at the University of Pittsburgh Medical School and in 1950 Emeritus professor.

The work described here was done while Rogoff was at the Western Reserve University Medical School at Cleveland, Ohio, where Stewart was then professor of experimental medicine. *George Neil Stewart* was born at London, Ontario, and was educated at the University of Edinburgh where he was graduated D.Sc. in 1887 and M.D. in 1891. In 1894 he went to Western Reserve, remaining there until his death in 1930.

In 1926 Rogoff and Stewart began their experiments on adrenalectomized dogs to determine the physiological changes which had taken place and to determine the normal survival period after the operation. The following year they began to administer adrenal extracts to adrenalectomized dogs. These extracts proved so effective in prolonging life and in relieving symptoms resulting from adrenalectomy that they were excited by the prospect that their observations in the physiology laboratory might offer a treatment for Addison's disease. They proceeded immediately to a clinical trial.

DISCOVERY OF THE NECESSITY OF THE SECRETIONS OF THE ADRENAL CORTEX FOR SURVIVAL

Among about 30 dogs treated with extracts, one lived into the 18th day, one into the 20th day, one into the 22nd day, one into the 23rd day, one into the 28th day, and one survived 78 days after removal of the second adrenal. Nothing like those results were seen among the much larger number of control dogs. It is impossible to draw any other conclusion than that the extracts in some way prolonged the life of the animals in the absence of the adrenals. The rest of the treated animals compared favorably with the controls as regards duration of survival. As the extracts injected into the different animals were often obtained from different adrenals, it is easily understood that their potency would vary.

There is no reason to suppose that the epinephrine, present in larger or smaller amount in the extracts, could have had any appreciable influence in prolonging life. No effect of this kind was observed when epinephrine equal to the maximum amount which could have been contained in the dose, given on the assumption that none of it had been destroyed, was injected. Much of the epinephrine was destroyed in making the extract. (Rogoff, J. M. and Stewart, G. N. "The influence of adrenal extracts on the survival period of adrenalectomized dogs." *Science*, 1927, *66*, 327-328.)

THE USE OF ADRENAL CORTICAL EXTRACT IN ADDISON'S DISEASE

Although, as has been indicated, Addison's disease and the condition seen in suprarenalectomized animals are not to be considered identical, there are present in both cases certain symptoms which, though varying in severity, are qualitatively the same and are to be considered as a part of the manifestations of suprarenal insufficiency. One symptom commonly observed in suprarenalectomized dogs and very frequently reported by patients with Addison's disease is an aversion to food rich in fat. Anorexia and gastric disturbances (including bilious vomiting) are common in the two conditions. Frequently, symptoms referable to the nervous system develop, especially in acute conditions. The low blood pressure associated with Addison's disease, which heretofore has been interpreted as an indication of interference with epinephrine secretion, is more probably a manifestation of the intoxication that develops as a result of deficient cortical function.

In cases in which the clinical diagnosis of Addison's disease seems fully justified, treatment with interrenalin has yielded results that may be considered promising. Even during acute exacerbations we have sometimes seen evidence of improvement in the symptoms referable to the suprarenal deficiency. The possibility of temporary spontaneous improvement or of psychologic effects simulating benefit due to the treatment cannot always be eliminated, but it is significant that when improvement is seen it generally occurs about two to four weeks after the beginning of treatment. . . . (Rogoff,

J. M. and Stewart, G. N. "Suprarenal cortical extracts in suprarenal insufficiency [Addison's disease]." *J. Amer. med. Ass.,* 1929, *92,* 1569-1571 [p. 1570].)

Bernardo Alberto Houssay
1887-

Bernardo Alberto Houssay was born at Buenos Aires where he also was educated. When he was graduated from the School of Pharmacy of the University of Buenos Aires in 1904 he had already entered upon the study of medicine there. In 1911 he received his M.D. for a thesis on the pituitary body. Before this (in 1910) he had been appointed professor of physiology at the School of Veterinary Medicine of the University, and he remained there until 1919 when he was appointed professor of physiology in the Medical School and Director of the Institute of Physiology. In 1944 Professor Houssay moved to a new and privately endowed Institute of Experimental Biology and Medicine where he has since carried on his research. Since the time of his first investigations as a student he has continued to study the functions of the hypophysis and in 1947 shared with C. F. and G. T. Cori the Nobel Prize in medicine for his demonstration, together with Biasotti in 1931, of the rôle of the anterior pituitary in sugar metabolism.

THE HYPOPHYSIS AND SUGAR DIABETES

. . . The principal arguments in favor of a predominant if not exclusive rôle played by the anterior lobe of the pituitary in carbohydrate metabolism are two: (1) Frequent occurrence of diabetes in acromegaly, in which disease there is an acidophile adenoma of the anterior lobe. (2) Implantation of the anterior lobe in the hypophysectomized toad protects against hypersensitiveness to insulin and reestablishes diabetes after pancreatectomy. The fact that in mammals implantation or injection of extracts have been unsuccessful prevents stating definite conclusions.

The fact that extracts of the posterior lobe produce hyperglycemia, and have an antagonistic action to insulin, indicates the possibility that this part of the gland plays a certain rôle. Implantation of posterior lobe in toads is less active than anterior lobe implantation in this respect.

The importance of the pituitary on carbohydrate metabolism is made clear by consideration of the following facts that have been discussed: (1) In hypophysectomized animals hypoglycemia occurs more readily and is less well tolerated, therefore there is greater sensitiveness to insulin, phlorhizin and fasting. (2) Pancreatic diabetes (dog and toad) and phlorhizin diabetes (dog) are much less severe. (3) Glycosuria is less marked after pancreatectomy or phlorhizin injection. (4) Sugar may be metabolized after pancreatectomy (increase in R.Q. and partial retention after sugar ingestion).

It is not yet possible to conclude whether in these cases there is greater consumption or less production of sugar. In favor of the first hypothesis it can be said that the R.Q. increases on sugar ingestion, a certain tolerance to sugar exists and the D:N ratio is low. On the other hand, against a high consumption of sugar we have the fact that the basal metabolism remains low, or increases only slightly, the basal R.Q. is 0.70, the elimination of nitrogen is also low, and the small amount of sugar eliminated by the urine, reasons all for supposing a smaller production of sugar. Perhaps both circumstances occur, lower production being the principal factor and also the cause of greater consumption.

The action of the pituitary may be direct on the tissues or indirect through the pancreas, liver or nervous system. An indirect action might be carried out by the regulation of the insulin secretion or the neutralization of its effects. The remarkable action of fasting on glycosuria and the attacks of hypoglycemia observed in hypophysectomized pancreatectomized dogs are not explained by this hypothesis. These observations can be understood if it is supposed that the anterior lobe hormone acts directly on the tissues, stimulating the production of sugar and perhaps retarding its consumption when insulin is lacking. It is interesting to correlate this hypothesis with the reduced endogenous protein metabolism observed in hypophysectomized dogs. It seems that the transformation of endogenous (or tissue) protein into sugar is reduced in hypopituitarism. . . . (Houssay, B. A. and Biasotti, A. "The hypophysis, carbohydrate metabolism and diabetes." *Endocrinology*, 1931, *15*, 511-523 [pp. 519, 522].)

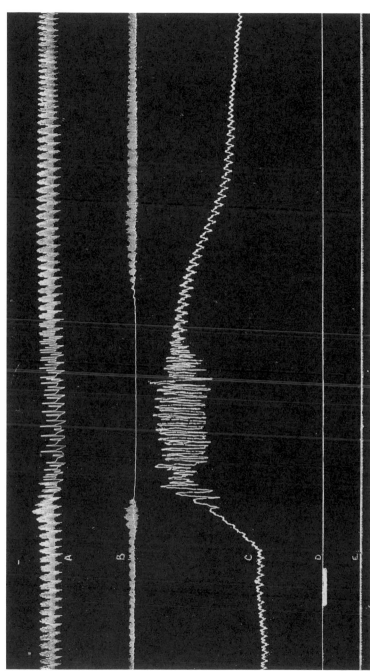

PLATE 85. Oliver and Schafer's graph showing the effect of suprarenal extract on the heart beat and blood pressure. "Dog of 9 kilos. Morphia. Artificial respiration. One vagus cut. A, ventricle; B, auricle; C, femoral; D, abscissa of blood-pressure; E, time 0.5″. To the left of D, intravenous injection of decoction of 0.2 gramme dog-suprarenal." (*J. Physiol.*, 1895, *18*, 258.)

PLATE 86. John J. Abel (1857-1938) in his laboratory at Baltimore, *c.* 1905.

PLATE 87. Ernest Henry Starling (1866-1927). (Courtesy of the National Library of Medicine.)

PLATE 88. Sir Henry Hallett Dale, from a photograph of *c.* 1918. (Kindness of Sir Henry Dale.)

PLATE 89. Herbert M. Evans (1882-   ) *c.* 1921. (Kindness of Dr. Evans.)

PLATE 90. Charles H. Best and Sir Frederick Banting with dog no. 394 — the first to be kept alive by insulin (1921). (Reproduced with kind permission of Dr. Best.)

PLATE 91. J. B. Collip (1892-1965).

PLATE 92. Edward C. Kendall (1886-   ). (Kindness of Dr. Kendall.)

James Bertram Collip,
1892-1965
Evelyn Mary Anderson
1899-
and
David Landsborough Thomson
1901-

James Bertram Collip was born at Belleville, Ontario, and educated at the University of Toronto (B.A. 1912; Ph.D. in biochemistry 1916) (Pl. 91). In 1928 he became professor of biochemistry at McGill University and in 1947 Dean of the Medical Faculty of the University of Western Ontario, a position which he held until 1961. His important work on adrenotropic hormones from which an excerpt is given here was carried on at McGill with two collaborators, *Evelyn Mary Anderson* and *David Landsborough Thomson*.

A native of Minnesota, Evelyn Anderson was born at Willmar and educated at Carleton College (A.B. 1921). From Carleton she went first to the University of California Medical School, where she received the M.D. in 1928, and next to McGill, studying biochemistry under Collip and receiving her Ph.D. in 1934. She returned to the University of California Medical School the following year remaining until 1947 when she joined the National Institutes of Health of the United States Public Health Service as an endocrinologist.

Both born and educated at Aberdeen, Scotland, where he was graduated M.A. in 1921 and B.Sc. in 1924, David Thomson proceeded next to Cambridge University. He received a Ph.D. in biochemistry in 1928 and in the same year went to the department of biochemistry at McGill, arriving there just after J. B. Collip. In 1936 he became Gilman Cheney Professor of Biochemistry.

ADRENOTROPIC HORMONE

. . . Out of 40 different extracts of the anterior pituitary lobe which have been tested, 34 were found to contain the adrenotropic hormone. Eight of these extracts show a fairly high degree of potency, causing an increase of 50-300 per cent in the weight of the right adrenal over that of the left adrenal which had been removed previously as a control. Furthermore, two of the extracts which have been assayed bring about repair of the adrenal in the hypophysectomised rat when 0.025 c.cm. (1/8mg. total solids) is administered twice a day for one week.

Four of the extracts having a high degree of potency show no trace of the thyrotropic hormone by the following tests: (1) failure to raise the low metabolic rate of the hypophysectomised rat; (2) failure to prevent the atrophy of the thyroid which occurs after hypophysectomy; and (3) lack of effect upon the thyroid of the immature guinea-pig. These extracts also have no effect upon body growth.

Extracts boiled for 30 minutes still show adrenotropic activity. Active extracts were found to be ineffective when administered orally. (Collip, J. B., Anderson, Evelyn M., and Thomson, D. L., "The adrenotropic hormone of the anterior pituitary lobe." *Lancet*, 1933, 2, 347-348.)

Edward Calvin Kendall

1886-

Edward Calvin Kendall was born at South Norwalk, Connecticut, and educated at Columbia University (B.S. 1908; M.S. 1909; Ph.D. 1910). In 1914 he was appointed professor of physiological chemistry at the Mayo Foundation, Rochester, Minnesota, where he has been Emeritus professor since his retirement in 1951 (Pl. 92).

Soon after his arrival at the Mayo Clinic Kendall succeeded in isolating from extracts of thyroid the pure crystalline substance now known as thyroxine. This was the second instance of the isolation of a hormone as a pure substance, the first being the isolation of adrenalin by Abel and Crawford in 1897. Then, in 1934, Kendall and his co-workers succeeded in isolating in crystalline form physiologically active hormone of the suprarenal cortex. This signal advance was announced on 13 April at a meeting of the Research Club of the Mayo Foundation, and on 25 April at a clinic staff meeting; on the same day Kendall's paper was published in the *Proceedings of the Staff Meetings*.

In 1950 Kendall, Philip S. Hench (1896-1965), and Tadeus Reichstein (1897-) were jointly awarded the Nobel Prize for their work on the adrenal cortical hormones. After the first isolation of an adrenal cortical hormone substance in 1934, described here, further investigations were carried out by Wintersteiner and Pfiffner, by Reichstein and his co-workers, and by Kendall and his associates. This massive effort resulted in the isolation of some 28 crystalline substances from the adrenal cortex, but of these at first only four were found to have biological activity.

By his observations of the effects of pregnancy and jaundice on rheumatoid arthritis, Philip Hench had become convinced that the latter was a metabolic disease rather than the result of infection. In 1949, Hench, Kendall, and their co-workers administered one of the biologically active compounds, compound E (cortisone) to a number of rheumatoid arthritic patients with dramatic results.

ADRENAL CORTICAL HORMONE CRYSTALS-1934

After solutions of the hormone had been prepared free from epinephrine, attempts to purify the preparation were made by extraction of the solution with ether. . . . The ether solution contains the hormone in relatively pure condition. It may be crystallized in several ways; one of the best methods is from a water solution which contains sodium bisulphite and is saturated with sulphur dioxide. . . .

The isolation of a new compound in pure crystalline form is of interest to the chemist but is not of significance in medicine unless it possesses the essential physiologic activity. In this instance, it may be said that administration of the crystalline product will maintain a dog in a normal condition after double suprarenalectomy. (Kendall, E. C., Mason, H. L., McKenzie, B. F., Myers, C. S., and Koelsche, G. A. "Isolation in crystalline form of the hormone essential to life from the suprarenal cortex: its chemical nature and physiologic properties." *Proc. Mayo Clin.,* 1934, *9,* 245-250 [pp. 247, 248].)

THE EFFECT OF CORTISONE AND ACTH ON ARTHRITIS-1949

. . . In each of the 14 patients the initial results were as follows. Within a few days there was marked reduction of stiffness of muscles and joints, lessening of articular aching or pain on motion and tenderness, and significant improvement of articular and muscular function.

A pattern of improvement was evident. Usually, the fibrositic component (muscular and articular stiffness) began to diminish first, often within the first forty-eight hours after use of the hormone was begun, and often was markedly or completely relieved within a few days. Second, articular tenderness and pain on motion were lessened. Then articular swellings generally diminished, sometimes fairly rapidly and completely, occasionally tardily and incompletely (perhaps a matter of dosage). In 3 cases mild flexion deformities of knees or elbows disappeared within seven to ten days. In another patient (case 6) a knee, flexed at 165 degrees, straightened to 175 degrees after the use of compound E for ten days, flexed again to 150 degrees when the control injections of cholesterol were being given, and

later straightened to 180 degrees when adrenocorticotropic hormone
was employed.

Those who had found the following maneuvers difficult or impossible often were able within a few days to do them much more easily
or even "normally": getting in or out of bed unassisted, rising from
chairs or toilets, shaving, washing the hair or back of the neck, opening doors with one hand, wringing a wash cloth, lifting a cup or
book with one hand, and climbing stairs. . . .

Two female patients with severe rheumatoid arthritis received 100
mg. of adrenocorticotropic hormone intramuscularly for twelve
days. . . . Marked clinical improvement essentially similar to that resulting from the use of compound E occurred promptly. Within a
few days there was striking reduction of stiffness, pain on motion
and articular tenderness. Sedimentation rates decreased even more
promptly and steadily than when compound E was employed: from
93 to 18 mm. within nine days in 1 case; from 78 to 5 mm. within
twelve days in the second case. . . . (Hench, P. S., Kendall, E. C., Slo-
cumb, C. H., and Polley, H. F. "The effect of a hormone of the adrenal cortex (17-hydroxy-11-dehydrocorticosterone: compound E) and
of pituitary adrenocorticotropic hormone on rheumatoid arthritis."
Proc. Mayo Clin., 1949, *24*, 181-197 [pp. 190, 195].)

Choh Hao Li, et al.

and

George Sayers, et al.

The simultaneous isolation in 1943 by two different groups of workers of
the adrenocorticotropic hormone from the pituitaries of different kinds of animals provides a dramatic instance both of parallel discovery and of the chemical identity of a protein hormone regardless of the animal species from which
it was derived. Li, Simpson, and Evans at Berkeley, California, isolated the
hormone from sheep pituitary while Sayers, White, and Long at Yale isolated
it from the pituitaries of hogs, and the chemical and biological properties were
in both cases identical.

The fundamental anatomical studies which revealed the probable existence
of a pituitary hormone controlling the growth and secretion of the adrenal
cortex had been carried out in 1930 by Philip Smith.[3] Smith showed that re-

[3] Smith, P. E. "Hypophysectomy and replacement therapy in the rat." *Amer. J.
Anat.*, 1930, *45*, 205-274.

moval of the anterior lobe of the pituitary not only prevented further development of the adrenal gland but also produced actual regression, and that this regression occurred primarily in the cortex. There was a similar atrophy of the thyroid gland and the reproductive organs. By transplantations of living pituitary gland, Smith was able to cancel these effects and to restore and maintain the organs atrophied in hypophysectomized animals. On the basis of Smith's findings, various teams of researchers attempted to isolate the adrenocorticotropic hormone, and success was finally achieved in 1943.

THE ISOLATION FROM SHEEP PITUITARY— BERKELEY, CALIFORNIA

. . . In order to establish the biological characteristic of a hormone from a complex source such as the pituitary, it must first be isolated in pure form judged both by *chemical* and *biological* data. The present paper presents a method for the isolation of the adrenocorticotropic hormone which is freed from other active contaminants, and behaves chemically as a single substance. . . .

The importance of a sensitive assay method for the isolation of a hormone hardly needs to be emphasized. Among the difficulties experienced by others in securing highly potent adrenocorticotropic extracts may be reckoned the lack of a satisfactory method of assay. . . . The use of hypophysectomized rats in assay of the hormone have allowed the reliable detection of small quantities of hormone. This test animal can be used satisfactorily either to maintain or repair the adrenal cortex after atrophy. A detailed account of these methods will be given in a separate paper but a brief description must be presented here.

Adrenal Repair—The method, based on repair of the adrenals of hypophysectomized rats, is as follows: Female rats are hypophysectomized at 26 to 28 days of age; 14 days later the rats are injected intraperitoneally once daily for 4 days, followed by autopsy examination 96 hours after the first injection. The minimum amount of the hormone which gives microscopically recognizable beginnings in the repair of the adrenals in such rats is about 0.02 mg.

Adrenal Maintenance—The maintenance test used is as follows: Male rats, 40 days of age, are hypophysectomized and injected daily (except Sunday) from the day of operation for 15 days (thirteen injections). The adrenal weight of uninjected hypophysectomized animals regresses during this period from about 26 mg. to a constant weight of 12 mg. The amount of hormone which maintains the adrenal at 26 mg. is about a 0.2 mg. daily dose. (Li, Choh Hao,

Evans, H., and Simpson, Miriam E. "Adrenocorticotropic hormone." *J. biol. Chem.*, 1943, *149*, 413-424 [pp. 413, 419-420].)

THE ISOLATION FROM HOG PITUITARY— NEW HAVEN, CONNECTICUT

Although the pure adrenotropic preparation which has been examined in some detail in the present study has been obtained from hog pituitary glands, highly purified fractions of adrenotropic hormone have also been obtained from bovine and sheep pituitaries. Preliminary studies of these preparations suggest that they are similar to, if not identical with, the product obtained from hog glands. This observation has been supported by personal conversations with Dr. C.H. Li who has stated that the pure adrenotropic hormone prepared from sheep glands has many properties identical with those reported here for the hormone obtained from hog pituitaries. These properties include biological activity, nitrogen content, isoelectric point, and sedimentation constant. It may be noted that the isoelectric point found for adrenotropic hormone is considerably different from that of pH 6.6 to 6.8, formerly assumed to be correct.

Although the assay data for adrenotropic hormone are based upon alterations in adrenal size, it has also been established in this laboratory that the hormone stimulates the functional activity of the adrenal cortex. This activity is manifested by changes in cholesterol concentration of the adrenals of rats injected with adrenotropic hormone and in the amount and distribution of lipid in the adrenal cortices of these animals. In fact, 25 γ of pure adrenotropic hormone administered daily to the hypophysectomized rat are sufficient to maintain not only normal adrenal size but also the normal concentration of cholesterol and lipid in the adrenals. . . . (Sayers, George, White, Abraham, and Long, C.N.H. "Preparation and properties of pituitary adrenotropic hormone." *J. biol. Chem.*, 1943, *149*, 425-436 [pp. 434-435].)

XII

VITAMINS

One of the great advances in physiology during the first decades of the twentieth century lies in the discovery, isolation, and chemical identification of those accessory food substances—vitamins—known to be essential to the life of higher animals. Since each of these substances has been found to play a fundamental role in cellular metabolism, their study has contributed significantly to our understanding of general physiology. However, a more immediate and profoundly human importance attaches to the history of the vitamins, for their discovery made possible for the first time the prevention of the deficiency diseases: scurvy, beriberi, rickets, pellagra, and pernicious anemia.

Scurvy had produced its greatest ravages among the crews and passengers of sailing ships, its victims numbering in the hundreds of thousands. Then in 1753 James Lind published *A Treatise of the Scurvy* advocating the juice of lemons and oranges as a preventative, and by the end of the century this treatment had been generally adopted. Scurvy continued to occur among infants and on some Arctic voyages, for control of the disease could not be entirely effective until the nature of the missing dietary factor was determined. By 1920 the existence of a distinct antiscorbutic substance was so well established that it was given the name vitamin C;[1] the antiscorbutic value of different foods could then be estimated accurately. Since the vitamin was both water-soluble and easily destroyed by heat and oxidation, it was especially important that it be isolated and its properties studied. This was accomplished simultaneously by two teams of workers in 1932, and the isolated vitamin was named ascorbic acid by Szent-Györgi and Haworth.[2] Its molecular structure and chemical properties were worked out by a number of different chemists in succeeding years and its metabolic role is under continuing study.

[1] Drummond, J. C. "The nomenclature of the so-called accessory food-factors (vitamins)." *Biochem. J.*, 1920, *14*, 660.

[2] Szent-Györgi, A. and Haworth, W. N. "'Hexuronic acid' (ascorbic acid) as the antiscorbutic factor." *Nature*, 1933, *131*, 24.

The history of vitamin C and scurvy illustrates a principle which is of general application in considering the history of vitamins —namely, that the only real protection against deficiency diseases is a thorough knowledge of the chemistry and metabolism of nutrition. This knowledge becomes more important with the prolonged storage, widespread distribution, and elaborate processing characteristic of modern food handling, factors which could result in loss of food values.

The modern study of vitamins which produced such a critically important series of discoveries really begins in 1890 when the Dutch physician Christiaan Eijkman went to Java for his government to study beriberi. By accident he observed a polyneuritis in chickens which was similar in its symptoms to beriberi. A diet of polished rice produced these conspicuous polyneuritic symptoms, whereas unpolished rice gave protection as did aqueous extracts of the polishings. Eijkman concluded that the polishings contained some essential food ingredient.

During the nineteenth century much work had been done on the food requirements of animals in terms of energy requirements and the substances needed to build tissues—protein, fat, and carbohydrate. When investigators began to study nutritional requirements by means of simplified diets made up of these substances in more or less purified form, they soon accumulated evidence that such diets were not adequate. In 1906 Frederick Gowland Hopkins suggested general biological reasons why they should not be. Since, in the course of evolution by natural selection, animals become adapted in a strict way to their specific environment, and since many animals had over a long period fed upon plants whose composition was not simple but included a wide range of substances in addition to proteins, fats, and carbohydrates, they must have become adapted to require certain of these "accessory substances" found in small quantities in plants.[3] In 1912 Casimir Funk, generalizing upon his own investigations on beriberi and on an extensive reading of the literature, stated his belief that the diseases beriberi, scurvy, pellagra, and possibly rickets were each caused by the deficiency in the diet of a specific substance. He believed that these substances were of the nature of organic bases or amines, and he therefore called them "vitamines." The coining of this word, by itself, probably did much to crystallize the thinking of workers in nutrition and to direct their attention to the iden-

[3] Hopkins, F. G. "The analyst and the medical man." *Analyst*, 1906, *31*, 385-404.

tification and isolation of these substances. In the same year Hopkins announced the dramatic effects which he had obtained from the feeding of small quantities of milk to rats fed on a purified diet which by itself did not sustain growth. In 1913 McCollum and Davis discovered a fat-soluble factor, present in butter and egg-yolk, which also maintained the growth of rats. This factor they later named vitamin A, the growth vitamin. In 1915 they found that there were at least two of these essential dietary factors. In addition to "fat-soluble A" they found a water-soluble factor which they named "water-soluble B."

The identification and isolation of the vitamins proved to be an arduous, time-consuming, and often bewildering and discouraging task. The first step in their study was to produce experimentally the disease resulting from a particular deficiency—then to strive to isolate the effective substance from the most promising corrective food. The early purified diets were probably deficient not in one but in several factors, and the effects they produced were correspondingly complicated. Similarly, when corrective foods were added to these diets, they would contribute more than one factor. Vitamin A fortunately existed in only one fraction, but B has been separated into at least twelve. The later members of the lettered vitamin series are C (ascorbic acid), D_1, D_2, E, F, K_1, K_2 and finally P (nicotinic acid). In this volume space cannot be given to the original descriptions of each vitamin; therefore, A, the growth vitamin; B_1, the antiberiberi factor; B_{12}, the preventative of pernicious anemia; D, the antirickettsial factor; E, the fertility vitamin; and P, the antipellagra factor, must suffice for representative examples.

James Lind

1716-1794

At the age of fifteen *James Lind* was apprenticed to a surgeon at Edinburgh, Scotland, his native town. Eight years later he entered the Royal Navy as a Surgeon's Mate and served in the Mediterranean, on the coast of Africa, in the West Indies, and in the English Channel. In 1746-1747 he cruised in *H.M.S. Salisbury* and while on board this ship performed the well-known critical experiment described here. Late in the year 1748 Lind left the navy and, after being graduated M.D. from the University of Edinburgh, settled in medical practice at Edinburgh. In 1750, he was elected a Fellow of the College of Physicians of Edinburgh. Three years later he published his classic book, *A Treatise of the Scurvy,* which he dedicated to Lord Anson. Lind said that it was in part the terrible mortality from scurvy on Anson's voyage round the world (1740-1744) which particularly attracted his attention to the problem of scurvy.

Lind remained at Edinburgh until 1758 when he was appointed physician to the new naval hospital at Haslar near Portsmouth. He continued in this post for the rest of his life and during this time was responsible for introducing measures to control typhus fever and other infectious diseases in the navy as well as measures for the improvement of living conditions among the sailors.

Lind's *Treatise of the Scurvy* is the document of an experienced, observant, educated, and humane man whose qualities stand out in contrast to the squalor, ignorance, and fumbling brutality of the times. He advocated procedures of diet, which, although not generally adopted until many years later, were ultimately responsible for the elimination of scurvy from the British navy.

OF THE PREVENTION OF THE SCURVY

On the 20th of May 1747, I took twelve patients in the scurvy, on board the *Salisbury* at sea. Their cases were as similar as I could have them. They all in general had putrid gums, the spots and lassitude, with weakness of their knees. They lay together in one place, being a proper apartment for the sick in the fore-hold; and had one diet common to all, viz, water-gruel sweetened with sugar in the morning; fresh mutton-broth often times for dinner; at other times puddings, boiled biscuit with sugar, &c; and for supper, barley and raisins, rice and currants, sago and wine, or the like. Two of these were ordered each a quart of cyder a-day. Two others took twenty-five gutts of *elixir vitriol* three times a-day, upon an empty stomach; using a gargle strongly acidulated with it for their mouths. Two others took two spoonfuls of vinegar three times a-day, upon an empty stomach; having their gruels and their other food well acidulated with it, as also the gargle for their mouth. Two of the worst patients, with the tendons in the ham rigid, (a symptom none of the rest had), were put under a course of sea-water. Of this they drank half a pint every day, and sometimes more or less as it operated, by way of gentle physic. Two others had each two oranges and one lemon given them every day. These they eat with greediness, at different times, upon an empty stomach. They continued but six days under this course, having consumed the quantity that could be spared. The two remaining patients, took the bigness of a nutmeg three times a-day, of an electuary recommended by an hospital-surgeon, made of garlic, mustard-seed, *rad. raphan.* balsam of Peru, and gum myrrh; using for common drink, barley-water well acidulated with tamarinds; by a decoction of which, with the addition of *cremor tartar,* they were gently purged three or four times during the course.

The consequence was, that the most sudden and visible good effects were perceived from the use of the oranges and lemons; one of those who had taken them, being at the end of six days fit for duty. The spots were not indeed at that time quite off his body, nor his gums sound; but without any other medicine, than a gargarism of *elixir vitriol,* he became quite healthy before we came into Plymouth, which was on the 16th of June. The other was the best recovered of any in his condition; and being now deemed pretty well, was appointed nurse to the rest of the sick.

Next to the oranges, I thought the cyder had the best effects. It was indeed not very sound, being inclinable to be aigre or pricked. However, those who had taken it, were in a fairer way of recovery than the others at the end of the fortnight, which was the length of time all these different courses were continued, except the oranges. The putrefaction of their gums, but especially their lassitude and weakness, were somewhat abated, and their appetite increased by it.

As to the *elixir* of *vitriol,* I observed that the mouths of those who had used it by way of gargarism, were in a much cleaner and better condition than many of the rest, especially those who used the vinegar; but perceived otherwise no good effects from its internal use upon the other symptoms. . . .

As I shall have occasion elsewhere to take notice of the effects of other medicines in this disease, I shall here only observe, that the result of all my experiments was, that oranges and lemons were the most effectual remedies for this distemper at sea. I am apt to think oranges preferable to lemons, though perhaps both given together will be found most serviceable. (Stewart, C. P. and Guthrie, Douglas. *Lind's Treatise on scurvy, A bicentenary volume containing a reprint of the first edition of* A TREATISE OF THE SCURVY *by James Lind, M.D. with additional notes.* Edinburgh, Edinburgh University Press, 1953. xi, 440 pp. [pp. 145-147, 148].)

Christiaan Eijkman
1858-1930

Christiaan Eijkman was born in Nijberk, a small town on the Zuyder Zee in Holland, and was educated at the University of Amsterdam where he studied physiology and later bacteriology. In 1886 he went to Java, then part of the Dutch East Indies, as a member of the Pekelharing-Winkler commission to study beriberi. Eijkman remained in Batavia as director of a new laboratory for bacteriology and pathology and of a medical school for native doctors. While he was there, he made observations on a disease resembling beriberi which occurred among fowl. In 1896 Eijkman returned to Holland as professor of hygiene at the University of Utrecht where he remained until his retirement in 1928.

A BERI-BERI-LIKE DISEASE OF CHICKENS

The first instances of disease occurred spontaneously among the small flock of chickens belonging to my laboratory.

As observations on newly provided chickens showed, the outbreak of the disease required an incubation period of 3 to 4 weeks during which the animals became considerably emaciated. Under certain circumstances, however, which we learned for the first time later, the incubation can also continue for a significantly longer time and the emaciation thereby entirely fails to appear.

The beginning of the disease characterizes itself by a restless movement which is especially noticeable when the animal is descending from the perch as if, lest its toes might not be solid enough to support it, it must often exert itself in order that it should not fall down. . . . The paralysis of the body musculature quickly progresses from below upwards. In a few days the animal has almost completely degenerated so that without help it would not be able even to eat nor to drink. . . . Its breathing is rare, its beak is open, the comb and skin become cyanotic, the neck is curved backwards, the head retracted. . . .

From the symptoms and the progress of the disease one already might have suspected what microscopical investigation confirmed in a whole series of cases, namely, that we are dealing with a form of polyneuritis. For not only in the peripheral nerves but here and there in the spinal cord (namely, in the ganglion cells of the posterior horns) degenerative and atrophic alterations had occurred. . . .

[p. 525] As to what was involved in the aetiology, our original suspicion that we had to deal with an infectious disease was not confirmed. Inoculation experiments with material derived from animals either sick or having just died of the disease gave no unambiguous results, for all the chickens without exception, including the uninfected controls, were overcome by the disease. No specific microbe was discovered nor any more highly organized parasite.

A chance circumstance at that point turned suspicion towards the diet, and correctly so, as presently became clear. It was those chickens, as I first realized later, which had for some time been fed principally on cooked rice—a left-over from the hospital kitchen—which recovered every time on the first day after [the administration of] the kitchen food ceased. The administration of this diet had been going on only from the 10th of June until the 20th of November. Thereupon the customary chicken food—raw unpolished rice—was again given. The epizootic, however, began on the 10th of July and ended on the last day of November. Thereafter no new battle victims fell, and those animals already ill recovered. After all these results were obtained, intentional feeding experiments were carried out to obtain a clearer proof of the apparent connection between the diet and the disease. From these it was established with certainty that the disease had its cause in the feeding with cooked rice, and this was also still the case when the rice was given quite fresh the first day after cooking. . . . (Eijkman, C. "Eine Beri Beri-ähnliche Krankheit der Hühner." *Virchows Arch.*, 1897, *148*, 523-532 [pp. 523-525. Translated by L.G.W.].)

Casimir Funk
1884-

Casimir Funk, formerly of the Department of Biochemistry in the School of Hygiene at Warsaw, is well known to physiologists for his pioneer contribution in the field of the vitamins. In a paper of seven pages he established the fact that beriberi is due to the lack of a specific chemical substance in rice polishings, and that a dose of the active extract containing only 4 mgr. of nitrogen promptly relieved symptoms of polyneuritis in pigeons. Funk received his Ph.D. from the University of Berne in 1904 and his D.Sc. in 1913 in London after several years' work at the biochemical department of the Lister Institute, where he carried out his investigations on vitamins. The following selections are taken from his first paper. In a second paper (1912), which also appeared in the *Journal of Physiology*, he introduced the term "vitamine" in the false belief that all accessory food factors were "amine" derivatives.

BERI-BERI AND RICE POLISHINGS

As a result of the work of a number of observers (Eykman,[*] Gryns,[**] and Fraser and Stanton[†]) it has been shown that the cor-

[*] Eykman. Virchow's Arch. 148, 523, 1892 [1897]; *Ibid.*, 149, 187, 1897. Arch. f. Hygiene, LVIII, 150 (1906).

[**] Gryns quoted by Schaumann. Arch. f. Schiffs-und Tropenhygiene, 1910.

[†] Fraser and Stanton. Studies from the Institute for Medical Research. Federated Malay States. No. 12. The etiology of beri-beri, 1911.

tical layers of rice contain a substance which cures beri-beri in man and the polyneuritis which is produced in birds by feeding them on polished rice.

The present inquiry is directed to determine the chemical nature of the curative substance.

The experiments were carried out on pigeons of which a large stock was kept. Polyneuritis was induced by feeding on ordinary polished rice. The average time before the onset of symptoms was three weeks. The presence or absence of the active principle in the different fractions, obtained during the investigation of rice-polishings, was determined by administering them to pigeons already severely affected with polyneuritis and observing the result. The condition of the birds at the time of the tests was such that untreated they succumbed within 12 hours.

It may be here mentioned that the extracts, if given in too large dose, were poisonous. This, as will be shown later, was due to the presence of choline which accompanied the active principle until the final stage of the separation. The poisonous action can be avoided by giving a dose calculated on the quantity of polishings used. With suitable doses passed into the crop by a tube, the pigeons recovered in 6-12 hours. Often, even after three hours the bird seemed quite well.

One symptom of polyneuritis in pigeons is paralysis of the crop and the birds being also generally paralysed the dose administered is very likely to run out again unless the head is supported. A further possible source of error occurs when the crop is not completely paralysed as the bird can vomit the material. . . .

Although the active substance has been definitely identified with the Ag salt obtained by precipitating with $AgNO_3$ in presence of baryta, the proof of activity of the nitrate obtained from this Ag salt and which was the salt submitted to analysis is less conclusive, as by this time the exhaustion of the material permitted of but four experiments, three of which were successful and one failed to cure the bird. For the same reason it was not possible to investigate further the chemical reaction of the substance but attempts to obtain by extraction of more raw material the active substance from other foodstuffs are in progress.

SUMMARY

(1) Polyneuritis of birds as shown by Eykman, Gryns, Fraser and Stanton, is due to the lack of an essential substance in the diet. The substance is only present in minute amount, probably not more than 1 grm. per kilo of rice.

(2) The substance which is absent in polished rice and is contained in rice-polishings is an organic base which is completely precipitated by phosphotungstic acid and by silver nitrate and baryta. It is partially precipitated by mercury chloride in alcoholic solution in the presence of choline and is not precipitated by platinum chloride in alcoholic solution.

Reasons for provisionally regarding the active substance as a body giving a crystalline nitrate which has the percentage composition of 55.63%C, 5.29%H and 7.68%N are adduced, but as by the time the search had approached the final stages the material became exhausted; duplicate analyses could not be made and but few animal experiments performed.

The chemical nature of the curative substance could not be further investigated immediately but larger quantities of raw material are being worked up.

(3) The curative dose of the active substance is small; a quantity of substance which contains 4 mgr. of nitrogen cured pigeons. (Funk, C. "On the chemical nature of the substance which cures polyneuritis in birds induced by a diet of polished rice." *J. Physiol.* [*Lond.*], 1911, *43*, 395-400 [pp. 395, 400].)

ETIOLOGY OF DEFICIENCY DISEASES

The deficiency diseases break out in countries where a certain unvarying diet is partaken of for long periods. When this food happens to be deficient in a substance which is necessary for the metabolism, we have the real conditions for the outbreak of this type of disease. From this point of view it is surprising to see peasants in Russia and in other countries, who live on potatoes, cabbage, and a little bacon nearly exempt from these diseases; it will be seen later, however, that this one-sided food contains apparently all the protective bodies which are necessary.

All these diseases present some general characters, which may be sketched here. The most prominent symptoms are a general cachexia with an enormous loss of weight; marked nervous symptoms are often present, which are due probably to the degeneration of the peripheral nervous system. It is now known that all these diseases, with the exception of pellagra, can be prevented and cured by the addition of certain preventive substances; the deficient substances, which are of the nature of organic bases, we will call "vitamines"; and we will speak of a beri-beri or scurvy vitamine, which means a substance preventing the special disease. As regards the classification two different groups present themselves: the beri-beri group and the scurvy group. The investigations made on pellagra, however, have not yet resulted in a sufficient elucidation of its etiology to establish it as a deficiency disease and it is included here provisionally owing to its similarity in some respects to the other diseases mentioned.

The Beri-Beri Group

To this group, which is characterized by more or less distinct neuritis symptoms, belong beri-beri, polyneuritis in birds and epidemic dropsy. Beri-beri occurs in countries such as Japan, Malay States, Philippine Islands, Indo-China, &c., where rice is used as a staple diet. This diet, however, must be eaten for long periods (six to seven months) to produce the disease. The symptoms which are described in most of the textbooks of tropical diseases present several distinct types, which can be shortly summarized as follows. In most cases the patients lose enormously in weight, and very often suffer from œdema, contractions, paralysis and anæthesia in the limbs. Pathological changes have been found such as degeneration in the nerves and heart. The disease, in most of the acute cases, terminates fatally.

Summarizing our knowledge till 1911 of the chemical nature of the protective substance from the rice-polishings, we find the following well-established facts:—

(1) The substance is soluble in water, in alcohol, and in acidulated alcohol.

(2) The substance is dialysable.

(3) It is destroyed by heating to 130° C.

(4) Is neither a salt nor a protein.

So far the few experiments performed have shown that this substance seems to be the curative agent, and for the purpose of simplicity I would propose to call it provisionally beri-beri vitamine. The method of fractionation is indicated in the following table:—

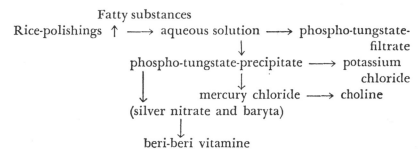

The yield of vitamine was extremely small. From 1 kg. polishings only ½ grm. of crystalline substance was obtained. This is the chief experimental difficulty in the research. It is hoped, however, that an extraction on a very large scale will give the opportunity of investigating this most interesting substance more closely.

The dose of the crystalline vitamine necessary for curing pigeons was very small. Such a minute dose as 40 mg. of the substance was not only sufficient to cure a pigeon in a very short time—often in three hours—but also maintained the cured animal in health for periods varying from seven to twelve days, when polished rice was used as food. After this time symptoms of the disease again manifested themselves. (Funk, C. "The etiology of the deficiency diseases: beri-beri, polyneuritis in birds, epidemic dropsy, scurvy, experimental scurvy in animals, infantile scurvy in animals, infantile scurvy, ship beri-beri, pellagra." *J. State Med.*, 1912, *20*, 341-368 [pp. 341-342, 345, 347-348].)

Frederick Gowland Hopkins

1861-1947

Sir Frederick Gowland Hopkins, professor of biochemistry at Cambridge, whose work is described elsewhere, initiated modern investigation of the vitamins. The following passage is taken from his first paper, now one of the classics of physiological literature.

FEEDING EXPERIMENTS ILLUSTRATING THE IMPORTANCE OF ACCESSORY FACTORS IN NORMAL DIETARIES

The experiments described in this paper confirm the work of others in showing that animals cannot grow when fed upon so-called "synthetic" dietaries consisting of mixtures of pure proteins, fats, carbohydrates, and salts. But they show further that a substance or substances present in normal foodstuffs (*e.g.* milk) can, when added to the dietary in astonishingly small amount, secure the utilization for growth of the protein and energy contained in such artificial mixtures.

The particular experiments, of which an account is now to be given, were undertaken to put upon a more quantitative basis results which I obtained as far back as 1906-1907.* Since that time, a fuller realization of the fact that (leaving on one side the influence of the inorganic constituents of dietaries) protein supply and energy supply do not alone secure normal nutrition, has arisen from the extremely interesting recent work upon the etiology of such diseases as beri-beri and scurvy.** It is not surprising that much work is now being done in connection with the subject; and since the experimental results given in this paper were obtained, the publications of others have covered part of the ground. In particular I may refer to the work of Stepp† upon mice, and to the extensive researches of Osborne and Mendel‡ upon rats. But the observations now to be described differ in some important details from those of the authors quoted. They bring out in particular the marked influence of minute additions of normal food constituents in promoting the nutritive power of synthetic dietaries. Stepp approached the subject on the lines of an attempt to estimate the importance of lipoids in nutrition. He found that food mixtures after extraction with lipoid solvents could not maintain life in mice. The total material extracted by the solvents when added to the diet made the food efficient once more; but Stepp was unable to obtain this result by adding any known lipoid. . . .

FINAL DISCUSSION

Convinced of the importance of accurate diet factors by my own earlier observations, I ventured, in an address delivered in November, 1906, to make the following remarks:

* The results of experiments made at this time were summarised in Lectures delivered at Guy's Hospital in June 1909. Owing to subsequent ill health these Lectures were never published. The results given in the present paper were communicated to the Biochemical Club in October 1911. See also *Analyst*, XXXI, p. 395. 1906.

** For references see Casimir Funk. This *Journal*, XLIII. p. 395. 1911; also *Journ. of State Medicine*, June, 1912; and Holst, *Journ. of Hygiene*, VII. p. 619. 1907.

† Stepp. *Bioch. Ztsch.* XXII. p. 452. 1909; and *Ztsch. Biol.* LVII. p. 135. 1911.

‡ Carnegie Institution, Publication No. 156, Parts I and II. 1911.

"But, further, no animal can live upon a mixture of pure protein, fat, and carbohydrate, and even when the necessary inorganic material is carefully supplied the animal still cannot flourish. The animal body is adjusted to live either upon plant tissues or the tissues of other animals, and these contain countless substances other than the proteins, carbohydrates, and fats. Physiological evolution, I believe, has made some of these well-nigh as essential as are the basal constituents of diet, lecithin, for instance, has been repeatedly shown to have a marked influence upon nutrition, and this just happens to be something already familiar, and a substance that happens to have been tried. The field is almost unexplored; only is it certain that there are many minor factors in all diets, of which the body takes account. In diseases such as rickets, and particularly in scurvy, we have had for long years knowledge of a dietetic factor; but though we know how to benefit these conditions empirically, the scale errors in the diet are to this day quite obscure. They are, however, certainly of the kind which comprises these minimal qualitative factors that I am considering. Scurvy and rickets are conditions so severe that they force themselves upon our attention; but many other nutritive errors affect the health of individuals to a degree most important to themselves, and some of them depend upon unsuspected dietetic factors."[*]

Evidence has now accumulated from various sides to justify these views. That a deficiency in quite other factors can induce disease is a fact which is now upon a firm experimental basis. That a deficiency, quite as little related to energy supply, may result in the failure of so fundamental a phenomenon as growth in young animals seems equally certain. To what extent bare maintenance of the body-weight is possible, in spite of such deficiencies, is perhaps less certain. Osborne and Mendel observed prolonged maintenance on artificial mixtures, but found that "sooner or later the animals declined; and, unless a change in the diet was now instituted, within a comparatively short period the animals died." I have myself seen quite young rats maintain their weight practically unaltered upon a casein mixture for three weeks, and then begin to lose weight, or on the other hand, if given the necessary small addendum, begin to grow briskly. Such observations give the impression that the factor missing from the artificial food is one concerned solely with growth. But it is certain, as Stepp also found, that the presence of a most extraordinarily small remainder of the substance or substances remova-

[*] *Analyst,* XXXI. p. 395. 1906.

ble by alcohol extraction, can affect the physiological value of artificial diets; and I am inclined to believe that apparent maintenance (which is usually very slow growth, or very slow decline) is only seen when the diet is not wholly free from them. If the food has been very thoroughly extracted, and if the fat subsequently added is wholly free from any tissue elements, I venture to think that only very short maintenance is possible. That "Denaturierung" plays no part here is shown by the fact that such food is clearly utilised when associated with a small addendum of the kind being discussed. . . .

It is possible that what is absent from artificial diets and supplied in such addenda as milk and tissue extracts is of the nature of an organic complex (or of complexes) which the animal body cannot synthesise. But the amount which seems sufficient to secure growth is so small that a catalytic or stimulative function seems more likely. It is probable that our conception of stimulating substances, "Reizstoffe," may have to be extended. The original vague conception of such substances as being condiments, chiefly affecting taste, gained in definiteness by the work of the Pawlov school. But the place of specific diet constituents which stimulate the gastric secretory mechanism can be taken by the products of digestion itself, and in this connection the stimulant in the diet is by no means indispensable. Most observers agree that the addition to normal dietaries of meat extracts capable of stimulating the gastric flow, does not increase the actual absorption of the food, though this point could only be properly tested by adding them to an artificial dietary known to be free from analogous substance. As was emphasized above, the milk did not affect absorption in my experiments. But such undoubted stimulating effects due to diet constituents as those discovered by Pawlov may quite possibly be paralleled elsewhere in the body on more specific and indispensable lines. Stimulation of the internal secretions of the thyroid and pituitary glands, which are believed, on very suggestive evidence, to play an important part in growth processes, can be legitimately thought of. On the other hand the influence upon growing tissues may be direct. If the attachment of such indispensable functions to specific accessory constituents of diets is foreign to current views upon nutrition, so also is the experimental fact that young animals may fail to grow when they are daily absorbing a sufficiency of formative material and energy for the purposes of growth. . . . [Fig. 14] (Hopkins, F. G. "Feeding experiments illus-

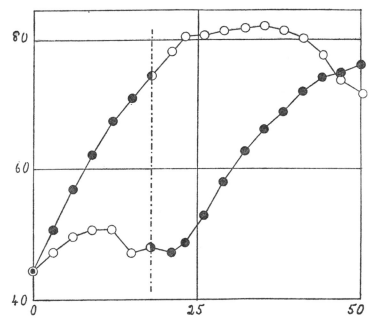

Fig. 2. Lower curve (up to 18th day) eight male rats upon pure dietary; upper curve eight similar rats taking 3 c.c. of milk each a day. On the 18th day, marked by vertical dotted line, the milk was transferred from one set to the other. Average weight in grms. vertical; time in days horizontal.

Figure 14. Hopkins' graph of the effect of milk on the growth of rats on a purified diet.

trating the importance of accessory factors in normal dietaries."
J. Physiol. [*Lond.*], 1912, *44*, 425-460 [pp. 425-426, 433 (linecut), 450, 452].)

Elmer Verner McCollum

1879-

and

Marguerite Davis

1887-

A native of Fort Scott, Kansas, *Elmer Verner McCollum* was educated at the University of Kansas (B.S. 1903, M.S. 1904) and at Yale where he received his Ph.D. in organic chemistry and biochemistry in 1906. The following year he went to the University of Wisconsin and there carried out the fundamental studies which ultimately resulted in the isolation of fat-soluble vitamin A and water-soluble B. In 1917 McCollum moved to Johns Hopkins University as professor of biochemistry (Pl. 93); he became Emeritus professor in 1946.

His collaborator in the paper from which quotations have been taken, *Marguerite Davis,* was a volunteer assistant at the University of Wisconsin.

THE DISCOVERY OF FAT-SOLUBLE A

During the past year we have been engaged in a study of the influence of the composition and quantity of the inorganic content of the ration on growth in the rat. In this work we have employed rations compounded of pure casein, carbohydrates, and salt mixtures made up of pure reagents, and the same rations in which a part of the carbohydrates was replaced by lard, with a considerable degree of success. Young rats have been found to be very sensitive to variations in the character of the salt mixtures supplied, but with certain mixtures we have been able to obtain practically normal growth for periods varying from 70 to 120 days. Beyond that time little or no increase in body weight can be induced with such rations. These rats may remain in an apparently good nutritive condition on these rations for many weeks after growth ceases. That they are still capable of growth has been repeatedly demonstrated by changing to naturally occurring food-stuffs. That our animals, during their period of growth or during the period of suspension of growth which always accompanies long continued feeding of purified food substances, are in a physiological state which is nearly normal is evident from the fact that we have had three female rats produce young after being fed only casein, carbohydrates, lard and salt mixtures, for periods of 108, 127 and 142 days, respectively. These rats had made approximately normal growth for about eighty days on this ration. In none of these cases did the mothers produce enough milk to properly nourish the young, so that they were found to be decidedly undersized when seven to eighteen days old.

The fact that a rat of 40 to 50 grams in weight can grow normally during three months or more on such rations, then cease to grow but maintain its weight and a well nourished appearance for weeks and then resume growth on a ration containing certain naturally occurring food-stuffs would lead one to the belief that on these mixtures of purified food substances the animals run out of some organic complex which is indispensable for further growth but without which maintenance in a fairly good nutritive state is possible.

After numerous attempts to prevent the occurrence of growth suspension by nice adjustments between the various ingredients of our diets, we have found that the failure of rats to make further growth, after being brought to this "critical" point on mixtures of isolated food substances, is due to a lack of certain ether-soluble substances in the diet. These can be supplied by the ether extract of egg or of butter. . . . [Fig. 15]

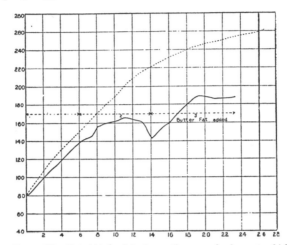

CHART II. *Rat 141* (male) shows the record of a rat which grew continuously although slightly under normal rate during eighty days on a ration of purified food substances. There was at this time a complete suspension of growth and a rapid decline in body weight. The addition of 10 per cent of ether-soluble butter fat to the diet led to a prompt resumption of growth during the following thirty-five days, when the rat gained 50 grams.

Figure 15. McCollum and Davis' graph of the effect of butter fat on the growth of a rat on a purified diet.

The extensive literature on the remarkable physiological properties of certain fresh food-stuffs as contrasted with the cooked or preserved materials, in preventing or curing scurvy and beriberi, diseases arising from unsatisfactory diets, has been recently summarized by Cooper.* From the experimental data available it seems apparent that very young animals cannot be made to complete their growth on rations supplying only purified proteins, carbohydrates, fats, and salts. Our observation that ether extracts from certain sources improve the condition of animals on such rations, strongly supports the belief that there are certain accessory articles in certain food-stuffs which are essential for normal growth for extended periods.

* Cooper: *British Med. Journ.*, No. 2727, p. 722, 1913.

It is interesting in this connection to correlate our observation on the physiological properties of ether extracts of butter or eggs, with those of Osborne and Mendel on the power of an animal to maintain itself on a ration containing gliadin as the only protein. While no growth is possible on this ration, notable increase in weight due to the building of young can take place and a milk supply capable of normally nourishing the young can be produced. Through the agency of the ovary in egg production, or the mammary glands in milk production, the necessary accessory bodies essential to the proper nourishment of the young are readily synthesized by the animal cell. The young themselves have not the power to produce these syntheses for their own preservation when these unknown substances are lacking in the diet. . . . (McCollum, E. V. and Davis, Marguerite. "The necessity of certain lipins in the diet during growth." *J. biol. Chem.*, 1913, *15*, 167-175 [pp. 167-168, 170 (linecut), 175].)

Edward Mellanby
1884-1955

Sir Edward Mellanby was born at West Hartlepool, Yorkshire, England and educated at Emmanuel College, Cambridge (B.A. 1905) and at St. Thomas's Hospital, London (M.B. 1910). While at Cambridge, Mellanby had come under the influence of Frederick Gowland Hopkins' ideas on nutrition so that when he began to teach physiology in 1913 at King's College for Women, he also began the series of nutritional experiments on dogs which ultimately showed that rickets was caused by the deficiency of a specific substance in the diet. It was Mellanby's announcement in 1918[4] of his experimental production of rickets which launched the series of studies, carried out by McCollum and his associates at Johns Hopkins, which resulted in the discovery of vitamin D.

In 1920 Mellanby became professor of pharmacology at the University of Sheffield where he remained until 1934 when he was appointed Secretary to the Medical Research Council of Great Britain (Pl. 94). In this post he played a primary role in the maintenance of the health and nutrition of the British people during the Second World War—with the paradoxical result that in a time of great adversity the children of Britain were on the whole better fed and healthier than they had been in the era of prosperity before 1914.

AN EXPERIMENTAL INVESTIGATION ON RICKETS

It is but little realised how great and how widespread is the part played by rickets in civilised communities. If the matter ended with

---

[4] Mellanby, Edward. "The part played by an 'accessory factor' in the production of experimental rickets." *J. Physiol. (Lond.)*, 1918, *52*, xi-xii.

bony deformities obvious to the eye it would be bad enough, but investigations have demonstrated that such deformities only represent a small part of the cases affected. Schmorl's histological investigations on children dying before the age of 4 years showed that 90 per cent had had rickets. Again, Lawson Dick's examination of the children in London County Council schools, and more particularly in the examination of their teeth, led him to state that 80 per cent of such children had had rickets. The relation between rickets and defective teeth has been placed on an experimental basis recently by the work of my wife,* and there can be little doubt that any remedy which would exclude the one would almost certainly improve and might eradicate the other. The rachitic child, in fact, carries the stigma of the disease throughout life in the form of defective teeth.

Nor is this the most serious part of the evil, for the reduced resistance to other diseases of the rachitic child and animal is so marked that the causative factor of rickets may be the secret of immunity and non-immunity to many of the children's diseases which result in the high death-rate associated with urban conditions. It is a striking fact to remember that in the West of Ireland, where the death-rate is only 30 per 1000, rickets is an unknown disease, whereas in poor urban districts of this country where rickets is rife the death-rate in children varies from 100 to 300 per 1000. It is at least suggestive that there may be some relation between rickets and the enormous death-rate of towns, even although the disease in itself does not kill.

The experimental work I wish to describe in these lectures has shown that the rachitic condition need not be at all advanced before the animal's whole behaviour is transformed. It becomes lethargic and is far more liable to be affected by distemper and broncho-pneumonia and is very susceptible to mange. The low resistance of animals which develops as the result of conditions which ultimately lead, under favourable circumstances, to rickets is impressive. . . .

A considerable number of experiments were first made in an attempt to see whether the aetiology of rickets was to be sought along non-dietetic lines and it was only after failure that the dietetic solution was resorted to. This type of work has continued and has clearly shown that, however, important other factors may be, and that there are other factors is not denied, the dietetic problem is the primary key to the situation. . . .

Having determined to see what part diet played as a causative factor in rickets, it was necessary to get a standard diet which would al-

* *The Lancet,* 1918, ii., 767.

ways produce this condition in the experimental animals. The first diet used consisted of whole milk (175 c. cm. per diem) and porridge made up of equal parts oatmeal and rice, together with 1-2 g. NaCl. The oatmeal and rice was later replaced by bread and found to be as effective and easier to use. This second diet was afterwards modified as the experimental results were obtained. . . .

The modifications of the diets were carried out in order to: (1) ensure a more rapid development of rickets; (2) to be compatible with better health and better rate of growth. As will be seen later, the better the animal grows on a rachitic diet the more easily is rickets produced or rather the more difficult it is to stop. In the close examination of foodstuffs from this point of view, this is eminently desirable. It is undesirable in such work to have animals in a semi-starved condition involving a high mortality due to broncho-pneumonia and marasmus. Puppies, like all young animals, tend to develop these diseases unless the diet is well chosen. . . .

A large number of experiments were now made in which the effect of different fats were analysed. . . . Many other fats and margarines, animal and vegetable, were tested, but almost uniformly they prevented rickets, the only undoubted exception being linseed oil. The results allowed the evolution of Diet III., in which separated milk was used in order to eliminate the milk fat, whose place was taken by linseed oil. Yeast was also added to the diet. Using this diet, a closer analysis of the effect of different fats was possible. Now we see from the calcium results, which are an accurate indication in this case of the rachitic picture, that the value of the oils is graded, cod-liver oil being the best and linseed oil the worst; the vegetable oils, olive and arachis, are not so good as butter. . . .

The above dietetic results indicate that diet plays an important part in the etiology of rickets. An examination of the results obtained suggests that rickets is a deficiency disease which develops in consequence of the absence of some accessory food factor or factors.

Of the three factors known, fat-soluble A, water-soluble B, and antiscorbutic, two of these can be at once excluded. Yeast has no preventive influence on the development of the disease, and in consequence water-soluble B cannot be considered as of importance. Again, orange juice, sufficient to exclude any possibility of scurvy when considered with the rest of the diet, did not inhibit the disease, and this therefore allows the exclusion of the antiscorbutic factor.

On the other hand, the anti-rachitic substances for the most part have been found, so far as the rickets experiments have gone, to be similar to those in which, according to the experiments on growth, of McCollum, Osborne, Mendel, and others, fat-soluble A is present. It therefore seems probable that the cause of rickets is a diminished intake of an anti-rachitic factor which is either fat-soluble A, or has a somewhat similar distribution to fat-soluble A. (Mellanby, Edward. "An experimental investigation on rickets." *Lancet,* 1919, *1*, 407-412 [pp. 407, 408-409].)

Elmer Verner McCollum
1879-
and Co-workers

Elmer V. McCollum, whose work on fat-soluble vitamin A and water-soluble B is mentioned earlier in this chapter (page 459), also discovered vitamin D in 1922. His co-workers in the paper from which the following quotation is taken were *Nina Simmonds, J. Ernestine Becker,* and *P. G. Shipley.*

THE DISCOVERY OF VITAMIN D

We have shown experimentally that cod liver oil oxidized for 12 to 20 hours does not cure xerophthalmia in rats. It does, however, cause the deposition of calcium in the bones of young rats which are suffering from rickets. This shows that oxidation destroys fat-soluble A without destroying another substance which plays an important role in bone growth.

Coconut oil is shown to be lacking in fat-soluble A, since it will neither prevent nor cure xerophthalmia. This oil, on the other hand, contains a substance which stimulates the deposition of calcium salts in rickets in a manner similar to cod liver oil. It is, like butter fat, far less effective from a quantitative standpoint.

Cod liver oil, shark liver oil, and burbot liver oil are highly effective for curing xerophthalmia, for protecting the body against the effects of a deficiency of calcium, and for the deposition of lime salts in rachitic bones. . . .

Our results are in harmony with those of Mellanby in that they show that coconut oil has an antirachitic effect. They prove conclusively, however, that this effect is not due to the presence of fat-soluble A in this fat. . . .

The evidence set forth in this paper demonstrates that the power of certain fats to initiate the healing of rickets depends on the presence in them of a substance which is distinct from fat-soluble A. These experiments clearly demonstrate the existence of a fourth vitamin whose specific property, as far as we can tell at present, is to regulate the metabolism of the bones. (McCollum, E. V., Simmonds, Nina, Becker, J. Ernestine, and Shipley, P. G. "Studies on experimental rickets. XXI. An experimental demonstration of the existence of a vitamin which promotes calcium deposition." *J. biol. Chem.*, 1922, *53*, 293-312 [pp. 303, 304].)

Herbert McLean Evans
1882-
and
Katherine Scott Bishop
1899-

One of the consequences of the intensive researches into the problems of reproductive physiology carried out in the laboratory of *Herbert Evans* at the University of California was his discovery, in collaboration with *Katherine Scott Bishop*, of a nutritional factor essential for fertility (vitamin E).

Dr. Bishop was born in New York City and educated at Wellesley College (A.B. 1910) and the Johns Hopkins Medical School, receiving her M.D. in 1915. She then went to Evans' laboratory where she remained until 1924. She spent the next six years at the Hooper Foundation, and now lives at Berkeley, California.

Although the factor was discovered in 1922, it was provisionally named vitamin X, the name vitamin E being assigned to it in 1925.[5] The first attempt to concentrate this vitamin was made by Evans and Burr in 1927[6] but it was not isolated as $\propto$-tocopherol until 1935.[7]

[5] Evans, H. M. and Burr, G. O. "The antisterility vitamin fat soluble E." *Proc. Nat. Acad. Sci.*, 1925, *11*, 334-341.

[6] Evans, H. M. and Burr, G. O. "The antisterility vitamin fat soluble E." *Mem. Univ. Calif.*, 1927, *8*, 1-176.

[7] Evans, H. M., Emerson, O. H., and Emerson, Gladys A. "The isolation from wheat germ oil of an alcohol, $\propto$-tocopherol, having the properties of vitamin E." *J. biol. Chem.*, 1936, *113*, 319-332.

THE DISCOVERY OF VITAMIN E

The fact has been abundantly demonstrated that rats may be reared on a dietary regime consisting of "purified" protein, fat and carbohydrate to which an appropriate salt mixture and adequate doses of the growth vitamines Fat Soluble A and Water Soluble B have been added. We have employed a ration of casein (18), cornstarch (54) and lard (15) to which butterfat (9) and salts (4) are added, the animals receiving separately and daily .4 gram each of dried whole yeast.

Such animals are sterile. They are chiefly so in the first generation and wholly so in the next succeeding one. The sterility of dietary origin yields a highly characteristic picture. Animals suffering from it do not differ so profoundly from normal ones in their ovarian function as they do in placental behavior. Approximately the same number of Graafian follicles mature and rupture per ovulation and the ova are fertilized and implanted. The placentae are abnormal. They may persist almost throughout gestation but show as early as the second day of their establishment beginning blood extravasations which increase in extent. Resorption invariably overtakes the products of conception.

Natural foodstuffs contain a substance, X, which prevents such a sterility or which cures the disorder occasioned by the purified dietary regime. We have thus been able to witness a comparatively sudden restoration of fertility to animals of proven sterility, and whose controls continued sterile, by the administration of fresh green leaves of lettuce. Even the dried leaves of alfalfa appear to possess a similar potency. . . . (Evans, H. M. and Bishop, Katherine S. "On the existence of a hitherto unrecognized dietary factor essential for reproduction." *Science,* 1922, *56,* 650-651 [p. 650].)

Joseph Goldberger
1874-1929
and
George Alexander Wheeler
1885-

About 1906 the frequent occurrence of the disease pellagra began to be noted in the southern United States although it had already been known in Europe since the eighteenth century as a disease particularly prevalent in Mediterranean countries. The disease was marked by a reddening of the skin similar to sunburn and was therefore known as *mal de la rosa,* but is referred to under the name of pellagra by Francesco Frapolli in 1771. The reddened patches develop into scaly eruptions which are followed by stomach upsets, diarrhea, and dizziness. Mental disturbance, even death, may ensue.

By 1911 the United States Public Health Service reported that over 25,000 cases of pellagra had occurred in the preceding four years and it was considered one of the most serious and widespread diseases in the South. In 1914 *Joseph Goldberger* was consulted by the Mississippi State Health Department about an outbreak of pellagra. Goldberger had come to the United States with his parents when he was six. After graduating from the College of the City of New York he received his M.D. from Bellevue Hospital Medical College in 1895. He began his career with work on the control of yellow fever and typhus as assistant surgeon in the United States Public Health Service, but in 1904 went to the Hygienic Laboratory at Washington, D.C., and remained there for the rest of his life. His preliminary observations of pellagra convinced him that the disease was not infectious but caused by a dietary deficiency. He proceeded to test this view and in 1915 succeeded in producing pellagra in human beings by means of a deficient diet. He then went on to try to determine the nature of the missing factor—a feat which was finally accomplished by Elvehjem and his associates at Wisconsin in 1937. However, Goldberger, before his untimely death in 1929, had laid the foundations for the nutritional study of pellagra. By his discovery of the presence of a pellagra-preventing factor in yeast he introduced a cheap and readily available food source for the treatment and prevention of the disease. His collaborator in the work reported here was *George Alexander Wheeler* (M.D., University of Virginia Medical School, 1913), who spent his entire career in the United States Public Health Service where he was active in research on pellagra and other nutritional diseases.

THE EXPERIMENTAL PRODUCTION OF PELLAGRA

The volunteers began the experimental diet with the midday meal of April 19, 1915, and continued it up to and including the midday meal of October 31, 1915. This is the second period of our study.

In planning the diet to be tested we followed, as closely as we could, the rather crude indications afforded by the institutional surveys previously referred to, and by other miscellaneous observations.

The ingredients of the diet were white wheat flour, corn (maize) meal, hominy grits, cornstarch, white rice, granulated cane sugar, cane sirup, sweet potatoes, pork fat, cabbage, collards, turnips, turnip greens, and coffee. In the preparation of biscuits and corn bread Royal baking powder was used. Table salt and pepper were freely allowed for seasoning. Up to July 28 buttermilk was used in making the wheat biscuit, this being the same biscuit as that provided the controls. During the week ended June 27, 3 pounds of beefsteak were served at one of the meals, thus giving each man approximately 4 ounces of lean beef on this occasion.

No fats other than those occurring naturally in the foods specified were used; the pork fat was extracted from salt pork by frying or boiling. The pork crackling or connective tissue remaining was not served. The sirup was home produced, made from "ribbon" sugar cane raised on the farm. . . .

During the period of study various minor ailments and a number of rather sharp attacks of malaria were observed among the controls, but in none was there observed any evidence justifying even a suspicion of pellagra. On the other hand, of the 11 volunteers who remained in the test to the end, not less than 6 developed evidence which experienced observers joined with us in recognizing as that of pellagra. . . .

In formulating the diagnosis, we followed the conventional rule of not considering any case pellagra in the absence of definite skin lesions having the characters usually considered distinctive of the pellagrous dermatitis, namely bilateral symmetry, sharpness of delimitation, and, when sufficiently advanced, pigmentation, keratosis, and desquamation. As already stated, our consultants and ourselves agreed in a diagnosis of pellagra in six of the subjects. We believe, however, that a definite diagnosis of pellagra was justified in at least one other of the men (A-E.S.), but in deference to the opinion of our consultants who, in this case, did not regard the skin manifestations (a mild erythema of the scrotum) as sufficiently marked, this case was not included as such in our preliminary report.

It is a not infrequent observation that, in a family of several members, although only one may show the distinctive cutaneous lesions, some, if not all, of the others may present subjective and other manifestations which leave little room for doubt that they also are suffering from the same disease. Now it seems to us that our squad of volunteers is strictly comparable to a family group or unit; the members of this squad lived together, worked together, ate at the same table, and, within much narrower limits than obtain in any family, ate the same diet. It would appear to follow that, having recognized the six or seven cases presenting the skin lesions as pellagra, this diagnosis may properly be extended to apply to the four or five without the cutaneous lesions but presenting the other manifestations. In other words, we are of the opinion that every one of the volunteers developed pellagra, six or seven with skin lesions and four or five without ("pellagra sine pellagra"). . . .

We now turn to the question as to what factor or factors in the diet are to be charged with bringing about the pellagra syndrome or syndromes. It has already been pointed out that with respect to the quantitative intake of energy, fat, carbohydrate, and protein the experimental diet differed from the diet of the controls significantly only in that the intake of protein was low though within the limits of recognized standards. These features of the diet do not, therefore, come up for consideration in this connection. With respect to the more intimate make-up of the diet, it has previously been noted that the protein was almost exclusively from products of highly milled cereals (wheat, maize, rice). In the light of recent studies, notably those of Osborne and Mendel and of McCollum and associates, this would suggest the probability of a deficiency in intake of some one or more of the amino acids, a probability that would be increased by the relatively low protein intake. This interpretation is strengthened by the indications afforded by the results of some feeding experiments in rats carried out by Sullivan at the United States Pellagra Hospital at Spartanburg, S.C., pointing to the protein as one of the limiting factors of the diet, at least for this species.

The antineuritic vitamine content of the diet was planned to be low, and feeding experiments by Sullivan show that it was actually deficient in this factor for the common fowl and the pigeon. It is of great interest to note, however, that none of the subjects developed any distinctive clinical manifestations of beriberi; whether they would have done so eventually had they continued on the diet is an interesting speculation.

PLATE 93. Elmer V. McCollum (1879-   ). (Kindness of Dr. McCollum.)

PLATE 94. Sir Edward Mellanby (1884-1955). (Reproduced through the kindness of Lady Mellanby and with the permission of The British Council.)

Judging by the fact that none of the men showed the slightest recognizable indications of scurvy, the content of the diet in the antiscorbutic factor would seem to have been adequate for the period of the experiment at least.

With regard to the adequacy of supply of the fat soluble vitamine, it is difficult to judge by reason of the meagerness of the available fundamental data; none of the men developed the eye symptoms currently considered indicative of a deficiency in this dietary essential. . . .

In pellagra, as in beriberi and scurvy, however, no unequivocal evidence in support of the existence of an essential infective factor has yet been adduced. Nevertheless, if in spite of this fact and in spite of the evidence demonstrating the vital relation of diet to these diseases, one still considers it logical to hold that there is also a second essential factor, an infection, in beriberi and likewise one in scurvy, we recognize that it is equally logical to hold a like view with respect to pellagra. It is clear, however, that even in this event diet is necessarily recognized as the primary controlling etiological factor. This is of considerable practical importance, for, whichever view may happen to appeal to the minds of those charged with the duty of preventing or controlling the disease, the fundamental guiding principle will not be affected. (Goldberger, Joseph and Wheeler, G. A. "The experimental production of pellagra in human subjects by means of diet." *U.S. publ. Hlth Serv. Hyg. Lab. Bull.*, 1920, No. 120, 7-116 [pp. 21, 30, 31-32, 34-35, 45-46].)

THE EXPERIMENAL PRODUCTION OF BLACK-TONGUE IN DOGS

It seems necessary at this juncture to anticipate the publication of the results of our experimental study of black tongue of dogs. This study, begun over four years ago, is still in progress, but we may now state that we have experimentally induced this canine disease by feeding dogs certain diets previously found associated with the occurrence of pellagra, including the Rankin prison farm experimental diet.[8] Some modifications of certain of these diets have resulted in giving us our standard experimental black-tongue-producing diet. . . . In this study white and yellow maize meal, casein, cod liver oil, and butter have been found very poor, or lacking, in the black-tongue

---

[8] Goldberger, Joseph and Wheeler, G. A., *op. cit.*, p. 469.

preventive factor. Milk has been found to possess inferior preventive activity. A test of fresh lean beef, although not yet completed, is sufficiently far advanced to warrant the statement that this possesses considerable black-tongue-preventive potency. Dried yeast and the commercial yeast extract referred to above have been found very efficient preventives of black tongue. Seidell's activated solid* in a daily dose at the rate of 2 grams per kilo of body weight as a supplement to basic diet 123, . . . has black-tongue-prevention action. Thus the black-tongue-preventive factor is present in lean beef muscle, in yeast, and in the commercial dried watery extract of yeast, and it is adsorbed from a watery extract of yeast by English fullers' earth. Our data appear to indicate that this factor is a dietary essential, heretofore either not recognized or not appreciated as such, necessary for the nutrition of the dog.

From the foregoing it appears that the substances that have been found to possess black-tongue-preventive potency have, when tried in pellagra, been found efficient preventives of the human disease; those that had failed in pellagra or were of low pellagra-preventive potency (milk) when tried in black tongue have failed or were feeble as preventives of the canine syndrome. In view of this striking similarity, if not identity, of behavior we feel justified in adopting, and are planning our studies of pellagra on, the working hypothesis that black tongue of dogs is the analogue of pellagra in man. Accordingly, it may tentatively be assumed that factor P-P is the dietary essential primarily concerned in the prevention and causation of both black tongue and pellagra. The assumption of this identity seems all the more reasonable as otherwise it would (and it still may) be necessary to conclude that the "yeast vitamine" powder contains in addition to the pellagra-preventive essential, also a special black-tongue-preventive factor. (Goldberger, Joseph, Wheeler, G. A., Lillie, R. D., and Rogers, L. M. "A further study of butter, fresh beef and yeast as pellagra preventives with consideration of the relation of factor P-P of pellagra (and black tongue of dogs) to vitamin B." *Publ. Hlth. Rep. (Wash.)*, 1926, *41*, 297-318 [pp. 305-306].)

* Seidell: Pub. Health Rep., Wash., D.C., 1922, *37:* 801.

Conrad Arnold Elvehjem
1901-1962
and Co-workers

Conrad Arnold Elvehjem was born at McFarland, Wisconsin, and received his education at the University of Wisconsin (B.S. 1923, Ph.D. 1927). In 1930 he joined the Department of Agricultural Chemistry there and in 1946 was appointed Dean of the Graduate School. Twelve years later he became President of the University, an office he held at the time of his death.

His co-workers in the fundamental research which resulted in identification of the symptoms of vitamin B deficiency had all done their graduate work at Wisconsin—*Robert James Madden* (Ph.D. 1938), *Frank Morgan Strong* (Ph.D. 1932), and *Dilworth Wayne Woolley* (Ph.D. 1938).

THE ISOLATION AND IDENTIFICATION OF THE ANTI-BLACK TONGUE FACTOR

Dogs have been used exclusively for assay purposes. Several different breeds have been used but in each case the animals were brought to the laboratory shortly after weaning. They were given a complete diet for about 2 weeks, during which time they were kept under observation, and were then placed on the modified Goldberger diet* described previously. Of the entire group, two have been adult dogs, but the time required to produce black tongue in the older animals makes them rather unsatisfactory for this work. In order to reduce the loss of dogs to a minimum, the animals were used for the assays before severe symptoms developed. However, in every case, the supplement was not given until the dog showed drastic loss of weight and the early but definite symptoms of black tongue. Usually the animal refused its food for at least 2 days before the test material was administered. Many of the dogs were used for several assays. In each case the dog was continued on the basal ration until typical symptoms reappeared, at which time a new supplement was given. The extent of the growth response and the time required for the symptoms to reappear gave a fair indication of the quantitative potency of the material tested. . . .

While this work was in progress other studies in our laboratory

* The casein was purified by washing crude casein with water eight times and then dissolving in ammonia and precipitating with hydrochloric acid.

(Frost and Elvehjem) showed that nicotinic acid had some growth-stimulating effects in rats reared on certain purified diets. Upon comparison of the properties of nicotinic acid with those observed for the vitamin, we decided to test nicotinic acid itself on dogs. A dog showing all the symptoms of black tongue was given a single dose of 30 mg. of nicotinic acid (Eastman Kodak Company) and a phenomenal response was obtained. The appetite improved in a very short time, the mouth lesions disappeared in less than 2 days, and the growth response was very similar to that obtained with active concentrates. . . . Dog 57 was kept on the basal diet plus 30 mg. of nicotinic acid every other day for 2 months, during which time the dog grew well and appeared normal in every way. Of the five dogs, four received commercial nicotinic acid, which is prepared by the oxidation of nicotine. Dog 51 received nicotinic acid prepared from quinolinic acid merely to show that the commercial preparation did not carry impurities which might account for its activity. . . .

The results presented in this paper demonstrate conclusively that nicotinic acid and nicotinic acid amide are active in the cure and prevention of canine black tongue and that the activity of liver in the treatment of this disease is undoubtedly due to its content of nicotinic acid amide. Whether the majority of the nicotinic acid amide occurs in liver as such or in a more complex form cannot be answered at present. In any case the entire activity of liver may be correlated with its potential supply of nicotinic acid amide. . . . A single dose of liver extract equivalent to 200 gm. of fresh liver fed to a dog suffering from black tongue cures the symptoms and gives a continued growth response for about 1 week. A single dose of 50 mg. of nicotinic acid amide gives a very similar response. If there has been no appreciable loss during the preparation of liver extract from liver, we may conclude that 100 gm. of fresh liver contain about 25 mg. of potential nicotinic acid amide. . . .

It is impossible to conclude definitely from the activity of nicotinic acid in canine black tongue that it will prove useful in the treatment of human pellagra. However, Spies has used nicotinic acid in four cases of classical pellagra and reports (personal communication) that the fiery red color associated with pellagrous dermatitis, stomatitis, and vaginitis improved promptly. (Elvehjem, C. A., Madden, R. J., Strong, F. M., and Woolley, D. W. "The isolation and identification of the anti-black tongue factor." *J. biol. Chem.*, 1938, *123*, 137-149 [pp. 137-138, 142-143, 145, 146, 147].)

Mary Shaw Shorb
1907-
and
Edward Lawrence Rickes
1912-

Although as early as 1926 Minot and Murphy showed that the eating of liver was a specific treatment for pernicious anemia, the active principle present in liver proved difficult to isolate because the only means of testing the activity of different liver extracts was by administering them to patients suffering with pernicious anemia.[9] Thus when in 1947 *Mary Shaw Shorb* showed that there was a direct relationship between the power of liver extracts to stimulate the growth of a microorganism *Lactobacillus lactis* Dorner and their effectiveness in curing pernicious anemia, she provided a means of bioassay which permitted repeated testing of numerous chemical extracts from liver. As a result the isolation of vitamin B_{12} went rapidly forward.

A native of North Dakota, Mary Shaw Shorb was educated at the College of Idaho (B.S. 1928) and at Johns Hopkins where she received her Sc.D. in immunology in 1933. In 1947 she went to the Department of Poultry Husbandry of the University of Maryland where she has since remained.

The isolation of crystalline vitamin B_{12} was carried out by a team of chemists at the Research Laboratories of Merck and Co. Inc., Rahway, New Jersey, headed by *Edward Lawrence Rickes*. A native of New York City, Rickes was educated at City College, New York (B.S. 1937). Since his graduation he has been a chemist with Merck and Co.

DISCOVERY OF THE LLD FACTOR

SIRS:

In an attempt to find a microorganism that might require a rat growth factor found in liver extracts and certain caseins and in some foodstuffs, it was noted that *Lactobacillus lactis* Dorner, required the presence of two unidentified factors for growth in an amino acid basal medium containing all the synthetic B vitamins. One factor, present in clarified canned tomato juice (TJ), was also found in low amounts in casein and in many other substances, while the second heat-stable factor (LLD) was found in highest concentrations in the

---

[9] Minot, G. R. and Murphy, W. P. "Treatment of pernicious anaemia by a special diet." *J. Amer. med. Ass.*, 1926, *87*, 470-476.

liver extracts active for rat growth, but not in casein or casein hydrolysates.

Assays for the LLD factor in crude and refined liver extracts of the type used for intramuscular injection in the treatment of pernicious anemia show that the LLD factor is apparently concentrated in the refined extracts in almost linear relationship to the potency of the extracts for effecting remission of symptoms in pernicious anemia. This relationship . . . suggests that the LLD factor might be the active principle in pernicious anemia. It is known that synthetic folic acid is not the active principle in pernicious anemia concentrates. . . . (Shorb, Mary S. "Unidentified growth factors for *Lactobacillus lactis* in refined liver extracts." *J. biol. Chem.*, 1947, *169*, 455-456.)

ISOLATION OF CRYSTALLINE VITAMIN B_{12}

Research in these laboratories in 1942, together with collaborative clinical tests conducted by Randolph West, showed that further purification of the "antipernicious anemia" principle in commercial liver concentrates could be effected. Subsequently, these chemical and clinical studies were extended, and more recently Mary S. Shorb and George M. Briggs collaboratively tested certain clinically highly active fractions for growth activity for *Lactobacillus lactis* Dorner and found them to be microbiologically active. This microorganism was found by Dr. Shorb to require two unidentified growth factors; one of them (LLD factor) appeared to be related to the activity of commercial liver preparations used in the treatment of pernicious anemia. For convenience in the testing of the fractions, use was made of an arbitrarily selected standard liver concentrate which was assigned a potency of 1,000 LLD units/mg.

Further purification of clinically active liver fractions has led to the isolation, in minute amounts, of a crystalline compound which is highly active for the growth of *L. lactis*. This compound is being called vitamin B_{12}. Its potency is about 11,000,000 LLD units/mg, and 0.000013 µg/ml of culture medium is capable of supporting half-maximal growth under the conditions used. This potency value was found by Dr. Shorb, using a 23-hr growth period. The compound crystallizes in the form of small red needles which, after drying showed refractive indices of α, 1.616; β, 1.652; and γ, 1.664. On the microstage, the crystals darken to black at about 210-220° but do not liquefy below 300°.

Randolph West* has tested this crystalline compound for activity in the clinical treatment of pernicious anemia in relapse. In one patient a single intramuscular dose of 150 µg gave a very strong hematopoietic response; in two other patients doses of 3 and 6 µg, respectively, produced a prompt increase in the circulating reticulocytes, red cells, and hemoglobin. These results are supported by early tests conducted by Dr. West, in which three separate concentrates, containing by microbiological assay 2-5 µg of vitamin B_{12}, gave strongly positive responses in four patients.

The biological activity of the new vitamin is extremely high in terms of its activity in these tests on pernicious anemia. For example, using pteroyl-glutamic acid, hematopoietic responses have been obtained with doses of the order of 20,000-50,000 µg during the first 10 days of treatment. (Rickes, E. L., Brink, N. G., Koniuszy, F. R., Wood, T. R., and Folkers, Karl. "Crystalline vitamin B_{12}." *Science,* 1948, *107,* 396-397 [p. 396].)

* West, R. *Science,* 1948, *107,* 398.

ACKNOWLEDGMENTS

The number of selections in this volume makes it impractical to list individual acknowledgments. We wish, however, to record our gratitude for the kind permission of the following authors, editors, and publishers to quote from their works. A full citation of source will be found at the end of each selection.

Chapter I. Clarendon Press; Dover Publications; Her Majesty's Stationery Office; History of Science Society (*Isis*); Methuen and Co., Ltd.; Oliver and Boyd; William P. D. Wightman.

Chapter II. American Philosophical Society: E. Edward Bittar; Clarendon Press; Executors of the late Dr. R. T. Gunther; Johns Hopkins Press (*Bulletin of the History of Medicine*); *Journal of Anatomy and Physiology; Journal of the History of Medicine and Allied Sciences;* Longmans, Green and Co.; Mrs. Margaret T. May; Oxford University Press; Charles C Thomas, Publisher; University of California Press; Yale University School of Medicine.

Chapter III. American Journal of Physiology; Journal of Physiology (London); Eugene M. Landis: *Nederlandsch Tijdschrift voor Geneeskunde;* Johns R. Pappenheimer; T. Shaw and Sons; The Wistar Institute of Anatomy and Biology (*American Journal of Anatomy*); Yale University Press; Benjamin W. Zweifach.

Chapter IV. Alembic Club; *American Journal of Physiology;* Cambridge University Press; College Book Company; Executors of the late Dr. R. T. Gunther; Hoeber Medical Division, Harper and Row, Publishers, Inc.; Mrs. Barbara E. Holmes (for Sir Frederick G. Hopkins); *Journal of Physiology (London).*

Chapter V. American Journal of Physiology; Cambridge University Press; The Johns Hopkins Press (*Bulletin of the History of Medicine*); *Journal of Physiology (London).*

Chapter VI. Lord Adrian; *American Journal of Physiology;* Burndy Library; Cambridge University Press; Joseph Erlanger; Alexander Forbes; Archibald V. Hill; Allen L. Hodgkin; Andrew F. Huxley; *Journal of Physiology (London);* Genichi Kato; Mrs. Mitsuko T. Laforet (for Dr. Shiro Tashiro); *Nature;* Royal Society; Société de Biologie (Paris).

Chapter VII. Brain; British Association for the Advancement of Science; Liverpool University Press; H. W. Magoun; Wilder G. Penfield; Royal Society.

Chapter VIII. American Journal of Physiology; Masson et Cie.; *Physiological Reviews; Proceedings of the Royal Society for Experimental Biology;* Springer-Verlag (*Naunyn Schmiedebergs Archiv für experimentelle Pathologie und Pharmakologie*).

Chapter IX. American Journal of Physiology; Journal of Clinical Investigation; Longmans, Green and Co.; Oxford University Press; Alfred N. Richards; Royal Society; University of Kansas; Donald D. Van Slyke; Ernest B. Verney.

Chapter X. Willard M. Allen; *American Journal of Physiology;* George W. Corner; Edgar A. Doisy; Frederick L. Hisaw; *Journal of the American Medical Association;* Mrs. George N. Papanicolaou (for Dr. Papanicolaou); Oscar Riddle; University of California Press; Williams and Wilkins; The Wistar Institute of Anatomy and Biology (*American Journal of Anatomy*); Bernhard Zondek.

Chapter XI. Charles H. Best; *Biochemical Journal;* Choh Hao Li; James B. Collip; Sir Henry H. Dale; Herbert M. Evans; Bernardo A. Houssay; *Journal of the American Medical Association; Journal of Biological Chemistry; Journal of Physiology (London);* Edward C. Kendall; *Lancet;* J. B. Lippincott Co. (*Endocrinology*); Mayo Clinic; C. V. Mosby Company (*Journal of Laboratory and Clinical Medicine*); Julius M. Rogoff; George Sayers; *Science;* Springer-Verlag

(*Berliner Klinische Wochenschrift*); *Transactions of the Association of American Physicians;* The Wistar Institute of Anatomy and Biology (*Anatomical Record*).

Chapter XII. Edinburgh University; Mrs. Conrad E. Elvehjem (for Dr. Elvehjem); Casimir Funk; *Journal of Biological Chemistry; Journal of Physiology (London); Lancet;* Elmer V. McCollum; Edward L. Rickes; Royal Institute of Public Health and Hygiene (*Journal of State Medicine*); *Science;* Mary S. Shorb.

Index

[Entries in **boldface** type refer to biographical data.]

Gastric fistula, 187-8

Gastric juice
acidity of, 182
in buzzard, 169-70
nature of its acid, 185-6

Gastric secretion, nervous control of, 192-3

Gehuchten, Arthur van, 257

Geppert, J., 148

Gibbon, Edward, 175

Giddy, Davies, 11

Gilbert, Davies, see Giddy, Davies

Gilbert, William, 4, **5**, 6-7

Glisson, Francis, 202-3, **218**

Glisson's capsule, 218

Gluech, Helen, 408n

Glutathione, 156

Goldberger, Joseph, **468**

Goldberger diet, 473

Goltz, F. L., 306

Gordon-Taylor, Gordon, 272

Gotch, Francis, 233n, 236

Gottlieb, Rudolph, 423

Gouy, L. G., 16

Graaf, Regner de, 160, **166**, 386, 390

Graves, Robert, 227

Gregg, Alan, **235**

Gréhant, Nestor, 91n

Grueter, F., 406

Gryns, Gerrit, 451, 453

Guenther von Andernach, Johann, 44

Guerlac, Henry, 124

Gunther, R. T., 120

Guthrie, Douglas, 449

H

Haan, J. de, 372

Hagen, W., 99

Haldane, J. S., 113, 145

Hale-White, William, 5n

Hales, Stephen, **56**, 66, **74**, 79n, 131, 134, 198, 257

Hall, Marshall, 66, 85, 87, 148, 257, **291**

Haller, Albrecht von, 66, 81, 88, 180, 289, 414

Halsted, W. S., 311

Hardy, J. D., 324, 325n

Hardy, William, 230

Hare, W. K., 342

Hargitay, B., **378**

Harrison, F., 320n

Hartree, William, **249**

Harvey, Thomas, 49

Harvey, William, 5, 25, 31, 32, **48**, 66, 67, 68, 74, 161, 179, 306, 379, **383**, 389

Hastings, 90

Haworth, W. N., 445

Head, Henry, 245

Heape, W., 398

Heart
Aristotle's three chambers of, 26
as a unidirectional pump (Erasistratus), 27
description by Aristotle, 32-4
early account of valves, 35
full of blood (Galen), 29
Galen's vivisection of, 39-40
innate heat, 30
law of, 63-5
pacemaker of, 62-3
structure of (Lower), 54-6
vagal inhibition of, 296

Heat, mechanical equivalent of, 20-2

Heat production, chemical regulation by noradrenaline, 344-6

Heffter, K. W. A., 156, 158

Heidenhain, Rudolf, 192, 349, 360, **363**, 366-7, 373

Helmholtz, Anna von, 24n

Helmholtz, Hermann von, 22, 57, 203, 324

Helmont, J. B. van, 160

Hench, P. S., 413, **440**

Henderson, Yandell, 149

Henle, F. G. J., 58, 227, 378

Henry, Thomas, 127, 136

Hepburn, J., 332

Hering, Ewald, 63

Hermann, Ludimar, 363, 365, 369

Herophilus of Chalcedon, 27, 201

Herring, P. T., 427, 428

Hewson, William, 160, **171**, 173, 176, 178

Hick, 427

Hill, *Miss*, 175

Hill, A. V., 64, 230, **249**

Hill, John, 212

Hippocrates, 179

Hippocratic Corpus, *Peri Kardies*, 34

His, Wilhelm, *Jr.* (1863-1934), **60**

His, Wilhelm, *Sr.* (1831-1904), 423

Hisaw, F. L., 381, **403**

Hitchcock, F. A., 145

Hitchcock, Mary A., 145

Hitzig, Eduard, 258, 300, **303**

Hodgkin, A. L., **254**

Those who are altogether unaccustomed to research are at the first exercise of their intelligence befogged and blinded and quickly desist owing to fatigue and failure of intellectual power, like those who without training attempt a race. But one who is accustomed to investigation, worming his way and turning in all directions, does not give up the search, I will not say day or night, but his whole life long. He will not rest but will turn his attention to one thing after another which he considers relevant to the subject under investigation until he arrives at the solution of his problem. ERASISTRATUS*

* A. J. Brock. *Greek Medicine*. London, 1929 (corrected reprinting), p. 185.